BD Chaurasia's

Human
Anatomy

Regional and Applied Dissection and Clinical

Seventh Edition

Head and Neck

Dr BD Chaurasia (1937–1985)

was Reader in Anatomy at GR Medical College, Gwalior.
He received his MBBS in 1960, MS in 1965 and PhD in 1975.
He was elected fellow of National Academy of Medical Sciences (India) in 1982.
He was a member of the Advisory Board of the *Acta Anatomica* since 1981,
member of the editorial board of *Bionature*, and in addition
member of a number of scientific societies.
He had a large number of research papers to his credit.

Volume **3**

BD Chaurasia's
Human
Anatomy

Regional and Applied Dissection and Clinical

Seventh Edition

Head and Neck

Chief Editor

Krishna Garg

MBBS, MS, PhD, FAMS, FIAMS, FIMSA, FASI

Member and Fellow, Academy of Medical Sciences;
Fellow, Indian Academy of Medical Specialists;
Fellow, International Medical Science Academy;
Fellow, Anatomical Society of India;
Life Time Achievement Awardee;
DMA Distinguished Service Award;

Ex-Professor and Head, Department of Anatomy
Lady Hardinge Medical College
New Delhi

Editors

Pragati Sheel Mittal MBBS, MS

Associate Professor, Department of Anatomy
KD Medical College, Hospital and Research Centre
Mathura, UP

Mrudula Chandrupatla MBBS, MD

Associate Professor, Department of Anatomy
Apollo Institute of Medical Sciences
Hyderabad, AP

CBS

CBS Publishers & Distributors Pvt Ltd

New Delhi • Bengaluru • Chennai • Kochi • Kolkata • Mumbai
Hyderabad • Nagpur • Patna • Pune • Vijayawada

ISBN: 978-93-85915-48-2

Copyright © Publisher and author

Seventh Edition: 2016
First Edition: 1979
Reprinted: 1980, 1981, 1982, 1983, 1984, 1985, 1986, 1987, 1988
Second Edition: 1989
Reprinted: 1990, 1991, 1992, 1993, 1994
Third Edition: 1995
Reprinted: 1996, 1997, 1998, 1999, 2000, 2001, 2002, 2003, 2004
Fourth Edition: 2004
Reprinted: 2005, 2006, 2007, 2008, 2009
Fifth Edition: 2010
Reprinted: 2011, 2012
Sixth Edition: 2013
Reprinted: 2014, 2015

Published by Satish Kumar Jain and produced by Varun Jain for

CBS Publishers & Distributors Pvt Ltd
4819/XI Prahlad Street, 24 Ansari Road, Daryaganj, New Delhi 110 002
Ph: 23289259, 23266861, 23266867 Fax: 011-23243014 Website: www.cbspd.com
e-mail: delhi@cbspd.com; cbspubs@airtelmail.in

Corporate Office: 204 FIE, Industrial Area, Patparganj, Delhi 110 092
Ph: 4934 4934 Fax: 4934 4935 e-mail: publishing@cbspd.com; publicity@cbspd.com

Branches

• **Bengaluru:** Seema House 2975, 17th Cross, K.R. Road,
Banasankari 2nd Stage, Bengaluru 560 070, Karnataka
Ph: +91-80-26771678/79 Fax: +91-80-26771680 e-mail: bangalore@cbspd.com
• **Chennai:** 7, Subbaraya Street, Shenoy Nagar, Chennai 600 030, Tamil Nadu
Ph: +91-44-26260666, 26208620 Fax: +91-44-42032115 e-mail: chennai@cbspd.com
• **Kochi:** Ashana House, No. 39/1904, AM Thomas Road, Valanjambalam, Eranakulam 682 018, Kochi, Kerala
Ph: +91-484-4059061-65 Fax: +91-484-4059065 e-mail: kochi@cbspd.com
• **Kolkata:** No. 6/B, Ground Floor, Rameswar Shaw Road, Kolkata-700014 (West Bengal), India
Ph: +91-33-2289-1126, 2289-1127, 2289-1128 e-mail: kolkata@cbspd.com
• **Mumbai:** 83-C, Dr E Moses Road, Worli, Mumbai-400018, Maharashtra
Ph: +91-22-24902340/41 Fax: +91-22-24902342 e-mail: mumbai@cbspd.com

Representatives

• **Hyderabad** 0-9885175004 • **Nagpur** 0-9021734563 • **Patna** 0-9334159340
• **Pune** 0-9623451994 • **Vijayawada** 0-9000660880

Printed at Thomson Press (India) Ltd.

to
_____

my teacher
Shri Uma Shankar Nagayach

— BD Chaurasia

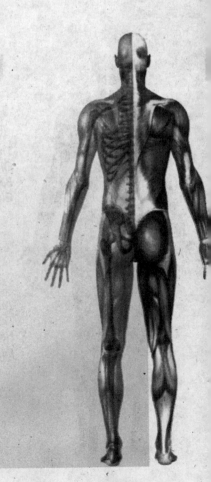

Volume **1**

UPPER LIMB and THORAX

Volume **2**

LOWER LIMB, ABDOMEN and PELVIS

Volume **3**

HEAD and NECK

Volume **4**

BRAIN–NEUROANATOMY

This human anatomy is not systemic but regional
Oh yes, it is theoretical as well as practical
Besides the gross features, it is chiefly clinical
Clinical too is very much diagrammatical.

Lots of tables for the muscles are provided
Even methods for testing are incorporated
Improved colour illustrations are added
So that right half of brain gets stimulated

Tables for muscles acting on joints are given
Tables for branches of nerves and arteries are given
Hope these volumes turn highly useful
Editor's hardwork under Almighty's guidance prove fruitful

Preface to the Seventh Edition

Suggestions from our esteemed readers to add line diagrams based on the concepts followed in the earlier editions of this monumental book have enthused us to move ahead with the seventh edition. A large number of line diagrams in each volume have been modified and redrawn to bring in simplicity. New figures of histology with three points as Facts to Remember have been added, to provide a holistic understanding of a particular topic. Many flowcharts are prepared to make learning easier, faster and interesting. Some real dissection photographs have been given to give a virtual look of anatomy. Anatomy is a visual subject and ideal means of visual recall are simple line diagrams drawn in colour thematically.

The reining feature of this edition is splitting up of the earlier last edition into two: Volume 3 containing head and neck, and Volume 4 brain and neuroanatomy. The material on brain and neuroanatomy has been extensively revised, reinforced and presented with fresh visual and textual appeals to help the students understand and retain the topics with ease and clarity. The topic of neuroanatomy has been given crisply, yet adequate enough to meet all the requirements of the medical students.

Volume 4 will also serve as a useful text for the students of dental sciences, physiotherapy, occupational therapy and other concerned courses. Postgraduate students in neurology, neurosurgery, ophthalmology and otorhinolaryngology will find it as a convenient handbook before embarking upon the study of advanced topics in their respective specialties.

The wall charts accompanying Volumes 1–3 are like ready-reckoner to recollect the numerous names in anatomy. Nomenclature of various structures has been prepared by senior anatomists after profound thoughts. Just the name tells us very important aspect of the part concerned.

Table of contents has been compiled extensively; and index elaborated upon and improved with addition of keywords on dissection, histology and development. It would make search for a particular component easier.

Steps of dissection, actual dissection photographs, paper models, spots, videos, X-rays, etc. will help and guide the students in their practical training. Anatomy is a practical subject: Feeling various structures in one's own body, marking arteries, nerves, veins, viscera, etc., with sketch-pens (containing washable inks) make strategic understanding of landmark features in human anatomy.

As we are aware that examinations are an extension of teaching so the knowledge acquired is tested by Multiple Choice Questions (MCQs). To these MCQs, we have now added Frequently Asked Questions (FAQs) to judge their writing skills and power of expression.

As human anatomy is the fundamental subject of clinical practice, clinical anatomy with relevant text, clinicoanatomical problems at the end of each chapter, and clinical terms at the end of every section, written in easy and lucid language, have been given.

We are encouraged by the fact that the volumes have been translated into other international langauges and the publishers are being approached for translation rights globally.

I am hopeful that the volumes would satisfy the requirements of most of the teachers and students. Suggestions are welcome for further improvement of the volumes.

Any suggestions from the teachers and readers for rectification and improvement are welcome at our email ID editors_bdc@cbspd.com.

Krishna Garg
Chief Editor

Preface to the First Edition

(Excerpts)

The necessity of having a simple, systematized and complete book on anatomy has long been felt. The urgency for such a book has become all the more acute due to the shorter time now available for teaching anatomy, and also to the falling standards of English language in the majority of our students in India. The national symposium on "Anatomy in Medical Education" held at Delhi in 1978 was a call to change the existing system of teaching the unnecessary minute details to the undergraduate students.

This attempt has been made with an object to meet the requirements of a common medical student. The text has been arranged in small classified parts to make it easier for the students to remember and recall it at will. It is adequately illustrated with simple line diagrams which can be reproduced without any difficulty, and which also help in understanding and memorizing the anatomical facts that appear to defy memory of a common student. The monotony of describing the individual muscles separately, one after the other, has been minimised by writing them out in tabular form, which makes the subject interesting for a lasting memory. The relevant radiological and surface anatomy have been treated in separate chapters. A sincere attempt has been made to deal, wherever required, the clinical applications of the subject. The entire approach is such as to attract and inspire the students for a deeper dive in the subject of anatomy.

The book has been intentionally split in three parts for convenience of handling. This also makes a provision for those who cannot afford to have the whole book at a time.

It is quite possible that there are errors of omission and commission in this mostly single-handed attempt. I would be grateful to the readers for their suggestions to improve the book from all angles.

I am very grateful to my teachers and the authors of numerous publications, whose knowledge has been freely utilised in the preparation of this book. I am equally grateful to my professor and colleagues for their encouragement and valuable help. My special thanks are due to my students who made me feel their difficulties, which was a great incentive for writing this book. I have derived maximum inspiration from Prof. Inderbir Singh (Rohtak), and learned the decency of work from Shri SC Gupta (Jiwaji University, Gwalior).

I am deeply indebted to Shri KM Singhal (National Book House, Gwalior) and Mr SK Jain (CBS Publishers & Distributors, Delhi), who have taken unusual pains to get the book printed in its present form. For giving it the desired get-up, Mr VK Jain and Raj Kamal Electric Press are gratefully acknowledged. The cover page was designed by Mr Vasant Paranjpe, the artist and photographer of our college; my sincere thanks are due to him. I acknowledge with affection the domestic assistance of Munne Miyan and the untiring company of my Rani, particularly during the odd hours of this work.

BD Chaurasia

Acknowledgements

Foremost acknowledgment is the extreme gratefulness to almighty for "All Time Guidance" during the preparation of the seventh edition. I am blessed to have Dr Pragati Sheel Mittal and Dr Mrudula Chandrupatla as editors of this book and am thankful to them for their continuous help in compiling and modifying the text and illustrations, and their expert opinions. Dr Mittal has given many sittings with the graphic designers despite his busy schedule.

The suggestions provided by Dr DC Naik, Dr NA Faruqui, Dr SN Kazi, Dr Ved Prakash, Dr Mohini Kaul, Dr Indira Bahl, Dr SH Singh, Dr Rewa Choudhary, Dr Shipra Paul, Dr Anita Tuli, Dr Shashi Raheja, Dr Sneh Aggarwal, Dr Mangala Kohli, Dr Gayatri Rath, Dr RK Suri, Dr Vadana Mehta, Dr Veena Bharihoke, Dr Mahindra Nagar, Dr Renu Chauhan, Dr Sunita Kalra, Dr Vivek Parashar, Mr Buddhadev Ghosh, Mr Kaushik Saha, Dr Neelam Vasudeva, Dr Sabita Mishra, Dr Dinesh Kumar, Dr Nisha Kaul, Dr Satyam Khare, Dr AK Garg, Dr Archana Sharma, Dr Shipli Jain, Dr Poonam Kharab, Dr Mahindra K Anand, Dr Daisy Sahni, Dr Kiran Vasudeva, Dr Rashmi Bhardwaj, Dr Azmi Mohsin, Dr Arqam Miraj, Dr Joseph, Dr Harsh Piumal, HA Buch, Umang Sharma and many friends and colleagues is gratefully acknowledged. They have been providing help and guidance to sustain the responsibility of upkeeping the standard of these volumes.

Videos of bones and soft parts of human body, prepared at Kathmandu University School of Medical Sciences, have been added in the CDs along with the Frequently Asked Questions. I am grateful to Dr R Koju, CEO of KUSMS and Dhulikhel Hospital, for his generosity.

The moral support of the family members is appreciated. The members are Dr DP Garg, Mr Satya Prakash Gupta, Mr Ramesh Gupta, Dr Suvira Gupta, Dr JP Gupta, Mr Manoj, Ms Rekha, Master Shikhar, Mr Sanjay, Mrs Meenakshi, Kriti, Kanika, Dr Manish, Dr Shilpa, Meera, Raghav. Dr Surbhi Garg, the granddaughter has been giving continuous input for improvement of text and diagrams. Dr Medha Joshi has always found solutions to my myriad problems. Dr Shilpa Mittal (KDMC and RC, Mathura, UP), Ms Madhu Chhanda Mohanty (DDUIPH, New Delhi) and Dr Sushant Rit have been encouraging and inspiring us in the preparation of the volumes.

Many students have been assisting in various ways. They are Simral Behl (SAMC and PGI, Indore, MP), Shweta Yadav, Sushmita Rana, Chetan Sood, Gaurav Gupta, Anjali Gupta, Himanshi Gupta, Himakshi Eklaviya and many others of DDUIPH, New Delhi.

The magnanimity shown by Mr SK Jain (Chairman) and Mr Varun Jain (Director), CBS Publishers & Distributors Pvt Ltd, has been ideal and always forthcoming.

The unquestionable support of Mr YN Arjuna (Senior Vice-President Publishing, Editorial and Publicity) and his entire team comprising Ms Ritu Chawla (AGM Production), Sanjay Chauhan (graphic artist) with his untiring efforts on drawings, Mr Tarun Rajput (DTP operator) for excellent formatting, Mr S Jha and Mr Kshirod Sahoo (proof-readers), and Ms Sugandha have done excellent work to bring out the seventh edition. I am really obliged to all of them.

Krishna Garg
Chief Editor

Thus spoke the cadaver

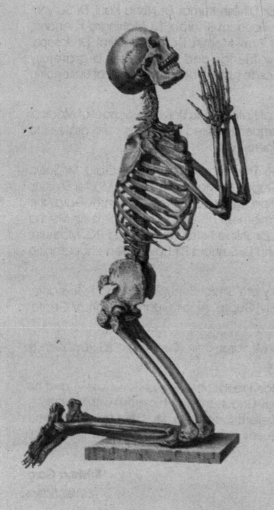

Handle me with little love and care
As I had missed it in my life affair
Was too poor for cremation or burial
That is why am lying in dissection hall

You dissect me, cut me, section me
But your learning anatomy should be precise
Worry not, you would not be taken to court
As I am happy to be with the bright lot

Couldn't dream of a fridge for cold water
Now my body parts are kept in refrigerator
Young students sit around me with friends
A few dissect, rest talk, about food, family and movies
How I enjoy the dissection periods
Don't you? Unless you are interrogated by a teacher

When my parts are buried post-dissection
Bones are taken out for the skeleton
Skeleton is the crown glory of the museum
Now I am being looked up by great enthusiasm

If not as skeletons as loose bones
I am in their bags and in their hostel rooms
At times, I am on their beds as well
Oh, what a promotion to heaven from hell

I won't leave you, even if you pass anatomy
Would follow you in forensic medicine and pathology
Would be with you even in clinical teaching
Medicine line is one where dead teach the living

One humble request I'd make
Be sympathetic to persons with disease
Don't panic, you'll have enough money
And I bet, you'd be singularly happy

Contents

Head and Neck

Anatomy Made Easy

Ichchak dana, bichchak dana, dane upar dana
Hands naache, feet naache, brain hai khushnama Ichhak dana
Teen inch lambi hai, pink aur khurdari hai,
chat pakori, pizza hut chalte iske bal se
Soch vichar express hote hai iske dum se,
achha bolna, thoda bolna, sukh se reh jana
Kehna hai aasan, magar mushkil hai nibhana
Ichhak dana
Bolo kya—tongue, bolo kya—tongue

Introduction and Osteology

Uneasy lies the head that wears the crown
—Shakespeare

INTRODUCTION

Head and neck is the uppermost part of the body. Head comprises skull and lodges the brain covered by meninges, hypophysis cerebri, special senses, teeth and blood vessels. Brain is the highest seat of intelligence. Human is the most evolved animal so far, as there is maximum nervous tissue. To accommodate the increased volume of nervous tissue, the cranial cavity had to enlarge. Correspondingly the lower jaw or mandible had to retract. The eyes also had come more anteriorly, on each side of the nose. The external nose also got prominent. External ear becomes vestigeal and chin is pushed forwards to accommodate the broad tongue. Tongue, the organ for speech, is securely placed in the oral cavity for articulation of words, i.e. speech. In human, the vocalisation centre is quite big to articulate various words and speak distinctly. Speech is a special and chief characteristic of the human.

Skull comprises a number of bones and their respective regions are:

Frontal: Lies in front of skull.

Parietal: Lies on top of skull, formed chiefly by the parietal bones. It is seen from the top.

Occipital: Forms back of skull.

Temporal: It is the area above the ears. The sense of hearing and balance is appreciated and understood in the temporal lobe of brain situated on its inner aspect.

Ocular region: It is the region around the large orbital openings, containing the precious eyeball, muscles to move the eyeball, nerves and blood vessels to supply those muscles. There are accessory structures like the lacrimal apparatus and protective eyelids.

Auricular region: The region of the external ear with external auditory meatus comprises the auricular region. Air waves enter the ear through the meatus which change into fluid waves and finally into nerve impulses to be received in the temporal lobe of the cerebrum.

Nasal region: The region of the external nose, its muscles and the associated cavity comprise the nasal region. Sense of smell is perceived from this region.

Oral region: Comprises upper and lower lips and the angle of the mouth, where the lips join on each side. Numerous muscles are present here, to express the feelings and emotions. These muscles are part of the muscles of facial expression. They show the feelings, without words.

Oral cavity: It houses the mobile talking tongue. Tongue is not swallowed though everything put on the tongue passes downwards. It is held in position by extrinsic muscles arising from surrounding bones. It says so much and manages to hide inside the oral cavity to be protected by 32 teeth in adult.

Parotid region: Lies on the side of the face. It contains the biggest serous parotid salivary gland, which lies around the external auditory meatus.

Head is followed by the tubular neck which continues downwards with chest or thorax.

Each half of the neck comprises two triangles between anterior median line and posterior median line.

Posterior triangle: Lies between sternocleidomastoid, the *neck and chin turning muscle;* trapezius, *the shrugging muscle* and middle one-third of the clavicle. It contains proximal parts of the important brachial plexus, subclavian vessels with its branches and tributaries. Its apex is above and base below.

Anterior triangle: Lies between the anterior median line and the anterior border of sternocleidomastoid muscle. Its apex is in lower part of neck, close to sternum and base above. It contains the common carotid artery and its numerous branches. Isthmus of thyroid gland lies in the lower part of the triangle.

Bones of head and neck include the skull, i.e. cranium with mandible, seven cervical vertebrae, the hyoid, and six ossicles of the ear.

The skull cap formed by frontal, parietal, squamous temporal and a part of occipital bones, develop by intra-membranous ossification, being a quicker one stage process.

The base of the skull in contrast ossifies by intra-cartilaginous ossification which is a two-stage process (membrane-cartilage-bone).

Skull lodges the brain, teeth and also special senses like cochlear and vestibular apparatus, retina, olfactory mucous membrane, and taste buds.

The weight of the brain is not felt as it is floating in the cerebrospinal fluid. Our personality, power of speech, attention, concentration, judgement, and intellect are because of the brain that we possess and its proper use.

SKULL

Terms

The skeleton of the head is called the *skull*. It consists of several bones that are joined together to form the *cranium*. The term skull also includes the mandible or lower jaw which is a separate bone. However, the two terms skull and cranium, are often used synonymously.

The skull can be divided into two main parts:
a. The *calvaria* or *brain box* is the upper part of the cranium which encloses the brain.
b. The facial skeleton constitutes the rest of the skull and includes the mandible.

Bones of the Skull

The skull consists of the 28 bones which are named as follows.
a. The calvaria or brain case is composed of 14 bones including 3 paired ear ossicles.

Paired	Unpaired
1. Parietal (2)	1. Frontal (1)
2. Temporal (2)	2. Occipital (1)
3. Malleus (2)	3. Sphenoid (1)
4. Incus (2)	4. Ethmoid (1)
5. Stapes (2)	

3, 4, 5 are described in Chapter 18

b. The *facial skeleton* is composed of 14 bones.

Paired	Unpaired
1. Maxilla (2)	1. Mandible (1)
2. Zygomatic (2)	2. Vomer (1)
3. Nasal (2)	
4. Lacrimal (2)	
5. Palatine (2)	
6. Inferior nasal concha (2)	

Please Thank Me in S

Skull Joints

The joints in the skull are mostly sutures, a few primary cartilaginous joints and three pairs of synovial joints. Two pairs of synovial joints are present between the ossicles of middle ear. One pair is the largest temporo-mandibular joint. This mobile joint permits us to speak, eat, drink and laugh.

Sutures are:

Plane	– internasal suture
Serrate	– coronal suture
Denticulate	– lambdoid suture
Squamous	– parietotemporal suture

Anatomical Position of Skull

The skull can be placed in proper orientation by considering any one of the two planes.

1 Reid's base line is a horizontal line obtained by joining the infraorbital margin to the centre of external acoustic meatus, i.e. auricular point.
2 The Frankfurt's horizontal plane of orientation is obtained by joining the infraorbital margin to the upper margin of the external acoustic meatus (Fig. 1.1).

Methods of Study of the Skull

The skull can be studied as a whole.

The whole skull can be studied from the outside or externally in different views:
a. Superior view or norma verticalis.
b. Posterior view or norma occipitalis.
c. Anterior view or norma frontalis.
d. Lateral view or norma lateralis.
e. Inferior view or norma basalis.

The whole skull can be studied from the inside or internally after removing the roof of the calvaria or skull cap:

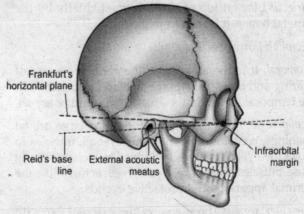

Frankfurt's horizontal plane

Reid's base line   External acoustic meatus   Infraorbital margin

Fig. 1.1: Anatomical position of skull

a. Internal surface of the cranial vault.
b. Internal surface of the cranial base which shows a natural subdivision into anterior, middle and posterior cranial fossae.

The skull can also be studied as individual bones. Mandible, maxilla, ethmoid and zygomatic, etc. have been described.

Peculiarities of Skull Bones

1 Base of skull ossifies in cartilage while the skull cap ossifies in membrane.
2 At birth, skull comprises one table only. By 4 years or so, two tables are formed. Between the two tables, there are diploes (Greek *double*), i.e. spaces containing red bone marrow forming RBCs, granular series of WBCs and platelets. Four diploic veins drain the formed blood cells into neighbouring veins.
3 At birth, the 4 angles of parietal bone have membranous gaps or fontanelles. These allow overlapping of bones during vaginal delivery, if required. These also allow skull bones to increase in size after birth, for housing the delicate brain.
4 Some skull bones have air cells in them and are called pneumatic bones, e.g. frontal, maxilla.
  a. They reduce the weight of skull.
  b. They maintain humidity of inspired air.
  c. They give resonance to voice.
  d. These may get infected resulting in sinusitis.
5 Skull bones are united mostly by sutures.
6 Skull has foramina for "emissary veins" which connect intracranial venous sinuses with extracranial veins. These try to relieve raised intracranial pressure. Infection may reach through the emissary veins into cranial venous sinuses as these veins are valveless.
7 Petrous temporal is the densest bone of the body. It lodges internal ear, middle ear including three ossicles, i.e. malleus, incus and stapes. Ossicles are "bones within the bone" and are fully formed at birth.
8 Skull lodges brain, meninges, CSF, glands like hypophysis cerebri and pineal, venous sinuses, teeth, special senses like retina of eyeball, taste buds of tongue, olfactory epithelium, cochlear and vestibular nerve endings.

EXTERIOR OF THE SKULL

NORMA VERTICALIS

Shape

When viewed from above the skull is usually oval in shape. It is wider posteriorly than anteriorly. The shape may be more nearly circular.

Bones Seen in Norma Verticalis

1 Upper part of frontal bone anteriorly.
2 Uppermost part of occipital bone posteriorly.
3 A parietal bone on each side.

Sutures

1 *Coronal suture:* This is placed between the frontal bone and the two parietal bones. The suture crosses the cranial vault from side to side and runs downwards and forwards (Fig. 1.2).
2 *Sagittal suture:* It is placed in the median plane between the two parietal bones.
3 *Lambdoid suture:* It lies posteriorly between the occipital and the two parietal bones, and it runs downwards and forwards across the cranial vault.
4 *Metopic* (Latin *forehead*) *suture:* This is occasionally present in about 3 to 8% individuals. It lies in the median plane and separates the two halves of the frontal bone. Normally, it fuses at 6 years of age.

Some other Named Features

1 *Vertex* is the highest point on sagittal suture.
2 *Vault* of skull is the arched roof for the dome of skull.
3 *Bregma/anterior fontanella* is the meeting point between the coronal and sagittal sutures. In the foetal skull, this is the site of a membranous gap, called the anterior fontanelle, which closes at 18 to 24 months of age. It allows growth of brain (Fig. 1.3).
4 The *lambda/posterior fontanella* is the meeting point between the sagittal and lambdoid sutures. In the foetal skull, this is the site of the posterior fontanelle which closes at birth—2 to 3 months of age.

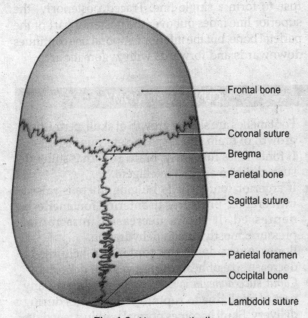

Fig. 1.2: Norma verticalis

- Frontal bone
- Coronal suture
- Bregma
- Parietal bone
- Sagittal suture
- Parietal foramen
- Occipital bone
- Lambdoid suture

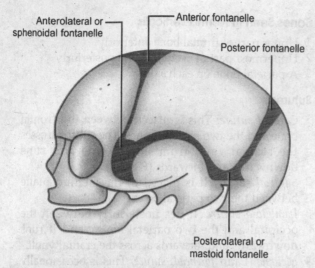

Fig. 1.3: Fontanelles of skull

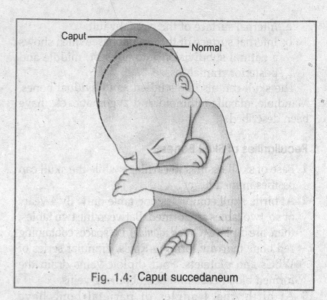

Fig. 1.4: Caput succedaneum

5   The *parietal tuber (eminence)* is the area of maximum convexity of the parietal bone. This is a common site of fracture of the skull.

6   The *parietal foramen,* one on each side, pierces the parietal bone near its upper border, 2.5 to 4 cm in front of the lambda. The *parietal* foramen transmits an emissary vein from the veins of scalp to superior sagittal sinus (Fig. 1.2).

7   The *obelion* is the point on the sagittal suture between the two parietal foramina.

8   The *temporal lines* begin at the zygomatic process of the frontal bone, arch backwards and upwards, and cross the frontal bone, the coronal suture and the parietal bone. Over the parietal bone, there are two lines, superior and inferior. Traced anteriorly, they fuse to form a single line. Traced posteriorly, the superior line fades out over the posterior part of the parietal bone, but the inferior temporal line continues downwards and forwards with zygomatic arch.

CLINICAL ANATOMY

- Fontanelles are sites of growth of skull, permitting growth of brain and helps to determine age.
- If fontanelles fuse early, brain growth is stunted; such children are less intelligent.
- If anterior fontanelle is bulging, there is raised intracranial pressure. If anterior fontanelle is depressed, it shows decreased intracranial pressure, mostly due to dehydration.
- Bones override at the fontanelle helping to decrease size of head during vaginal delivery.
- *Caput succedaneum* is soft tissue swelling on any part of skull due to rupture of capillaries during delivery. Skull becomes normal within a few days in postnatal life (Fig. 1.4).

NORMA OCCIPITALIS

Norma occipitalis is convex upwards and on each side, and is flattened below.

Bones Seen

1   Posterior parts of the parietal bones, above.

2   Upper part of the squamous part of the occipital bone below (Fig. 1.5).

3   Mastoid part of the temporal bone, on each side.

Sutures

1   The *lambdoid suture* lies between the occipital bone and the two parietal bones. Sutural or wormian bones are common along this suture.

2   The *occipitomastoid suture* lies between the occipital bone and mastoid part of the temporal bone.

3   The *parietomastoid suture* lies between the parietal bone and mastoid part of the temporal bone.

4   The posterior part of the *sagittal suture* is also seen.

Other Features

1   *Lambda, parietal foramina* and *obelion* have been examined in the norma verticalis.

2   The *external occipital protuberance* is a median prominence in the lower part of this norma. It marks the junction of the head and the neck. The most prominent point on this protuberance is called the *inion*.

3   The *superior nuchal lines* are curved bony ridges passing laterally from the protuberance. These also mark the junction of the head and the neck. The area below the superior nuchal lines will be studied with the norma basalis.

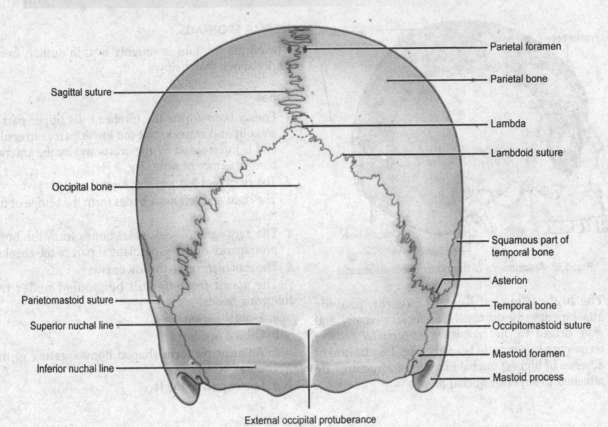

Fig. 1.5: Norma occipitalis

4 The *highest nuchal lines* are not always present. They are curved bony ridges situated about 1 cm above the superior nuchal lines. They begin from the upper part of the external occipital protuberance and are more arched than the superior nuchal lines.

5 The *occipital point* is a median point a little above the inion. It is the point farthest from the glabella.

6 The *mastoid* (Greek *breast*) *foramen* is located on the mastoid part of the temporal bone at or near the occipitomastoid suture. Internally, it opens at the sigmoid sulcus. The mastoid foramen transmits an emissary vein (Table 1.1) and the meningeal branch of the occipital artery.

7 The *interparietal bone* (inca bone) is occasionally present. It is a large triangular bone located at the apex of the squamous occipital. This is not a sutural or accessory bone but represents the membranous part of the occipital bone which has failed to fuse with the rest of the bone.

Attachments

1 The upper part of the external occipital protuberance gives origin to the *trapezius,* and the lower part gives attachment to the upper end of the *ligamentum nuchae* (Fig. 1.14).

2 The medial one-third of the superior nuchal line gives origin to the trapezius, and the lateral part provides insertion to the *sternocleidomastoid* above and to the *splenius capitis* below.

Table 1.1: The emissary veins of the skull			
Name	*Foramen of skull*	*Veins outside skull*	*Venous sinus*
1. Parietal emissary vein	Parietal foramen	Veins of scalp	Superior sagittal
2. Mastoid emissary vein	Mastoid foramen	Veins of scalp	Sigmoid sinus
3. Emissary vein	Hypoglossal canal	Internal jugular vein	Sigmoid sinus
4. Condylar emissary vein	Posterior condylar foramen	Suboccipital venous plexus	Sigmoid sinus
5. 2–3 emissary veins	Foramen lacerum	Pharyngeal venous plexus	Cavernous sinus
6. Emissary vein	Foramen ovale	Pterygoid venous plexus	Cavernous sinus
7. Emissary vein	Foramen caecum	Veins of roof of nose	Superior sagittal

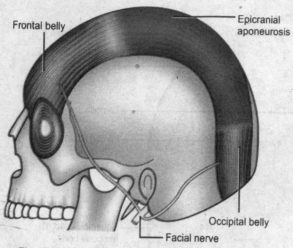

Fig. 1.6: Attachments of the occipitofrontalis muscle

3 The highest nuchal lines, if present, provide attachment to the *epicranial aponeurosis* medially, and give origin to the *occipitalis* or *occipital belly of occipitofrontalis* muscle laterally (Fig. 1.6). In case of absence of highest nuchal lines, these structures are attached to superior nuchal lines.

NORMA FRONTALIS

The norma frontalis is roughly oval in outline, being wider above than below.

Bones

1 *Frontal* bone forms the forehead. Its upper part is smooth and convex, but the lower part is irregular and is interrupted by the orbits and by the anterior bony aperture of nose (Fig. 1.7).
2 The right and left *maxillae* form the upper jaw.
3 The right and left *nasal* bones form the bridge of the nose.
4 The *zygomatic* (Greek *yoke*) bones form the bony prominence of the superolateral part of the cheeks.
5 The *mandible* forms the lower jaw.

The *norma frontalis* will be studied under the following heads:

  a. Frontal region.
  b. Orbital opening.
  c. Anterior piriform-shaped bony aperture of the nose.
  d. Lower part of the face.

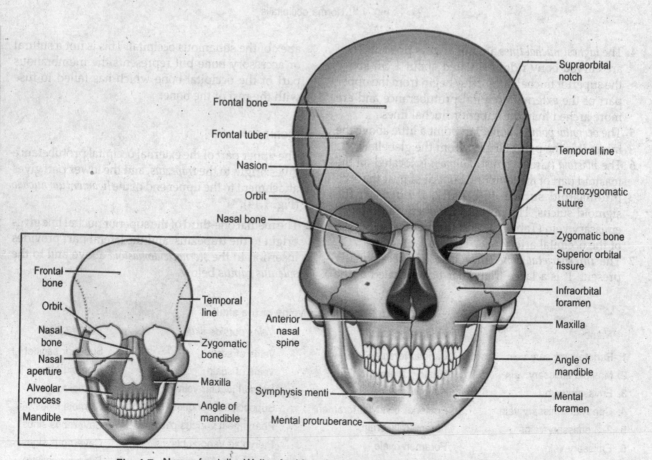

Fig. 1.7: Norma frontalis: Walls of orbit and nasal aperture. Inset showing apertures

Frontal Region

The frontal region presents the following features:

1 The *superciliary arch* is a rounded, curved elevation situated just above the medial part of each orbit. It overlies the frontal sinus and is better marked in males than in females.
2 *The glabella* is a median elevation connecting the two superciliary arches. Below the glabella, the skull recedes to frontonasal suture at root of the nose.
3 The *nasion* is a median point at the root of the nose where the internasal suture meets with the frontonasal suture.
4 The *frontal tuber* or *eminence* is a low rounded elevation above the superciliary arch, one on each side. It is more prominent in females and in children.

Orbital Openings

Each orbital (Latin *circle*) opening is quadrangular in shape and is bounded by the following four margins.

1 The *supraorbital margin* is formed by the frontal bone. At the junction of its lateral two-thirds and its medial one-third, it presents the supraorbital notch or foramen (Fig. 1.7).
2 The *infraorbital margin* is formed by the zygomatic bone laterally, and maxilla medially.
3 The *medial orbital margin* is ill-defined. It is formed by the frontal bone above, and by the lacrimal crest of the frontal process of the maxilla below.
4 The *lateral orbital margin* is formed mostly by the frontal process of zygomatic bone but is completed above by the zygomatic process of frontal bone. *Frontozygomatic suture* lies at their union.

Anterior Bony Aperture of the Nose

The anterior bony aperture is pear-shaped, being wide below and narrow above.

Boundaries

Above: By the lower border of the nasal bones.

Below: By the nasal notch of the body of maxilla on each side.

Features

Note the following:
1 *Articulations of the nasal bone:*
   a. *Anteriorly,* with the opposite bone at the internasal suture.
   b. *Posteriorly,* with the frontal process of the maxilla.
   c. *Superiorly,* with the frontal bone at the frontonasal suture.
   d. *Inferiorly,* the upper nasal cartilage is attached to it.
2 The *anterior nasal spine* is a sharp projection in the median plane in the lower boundary of the piriform aperture (Fig. 1.7).
3 Rhinion is the lowermost point of the internasal suture.

CLINICAL ANATOMY

The *nasal bone is one of the most commonly fractured bones of the face.* Mandible and parietal eminence are the next bones to be fractured (Fig. 1.8).

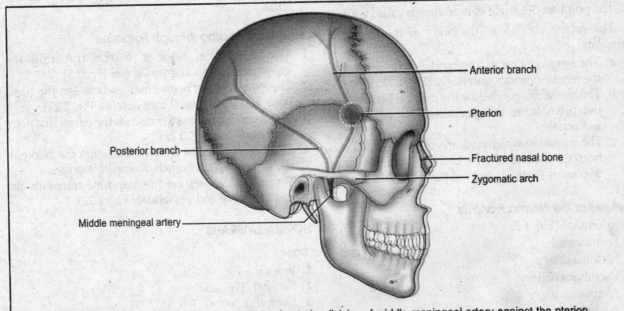

Fig. 1.8: Fractured nasal bone and position of anterior division of middle meningeal artery against the pterion

Anterior branch

Pterion

Fractured nasal bone

Zygomatic arch

Posterior branch

Middle meningeal artery

Head and Neck

Lower Part of the Face

Maxilla

Maxilla contributes a large share in the formation of the facial skeleton. The anterior surface of the body of the maxilla presents:

a. The *nasal notch* medially;

b. The *anterior nasal spine*;

c. The *infraorbital foramen*, 1 cm below the infraorbital margin;

d. The *incisive fossa* above the incisor teeth, and

e. The *canine fossa* lateral to the canine eminence.

In addition, three out of four processes of the maxilla are also seen in this norma.

a. The *frontal process of the maxilla* is directed upwards. It articulates anteriorly with the nasal bone, posteriorly with the lacrimal bone, and superiorly with the frontal bone (Fig. 1.7).

b. The *zygomatic process of the maxilla* is short but stout and articulates with the zygomatic bone.

c. The *alveolar process of the maxilla* bears sockets for the upper teeth.

Zygomatic Bone (Malar Bone)

Zygomatic bone forms the prominence of the cheek. The *zygomaticofacial foramen* is seen on its surface.

Mandible (Lower Law Bone)

Mandible (Latin *to chew*) forms the lower jaw.

The *upper border* or *alveolar arch* lodges the lower teeth.

The *lower border* or *base* is rounded.

The middle point of the base is called the *mental point or gnathion*.

The point on the angle of mandible is called gonion.

The *anterior surface* of the body of the mandible presents:

a. The *symphysis menti*, the *mental protuberance* and the *mental tubercles* anteriorly (Fig. 1.7).

b. The *mental foramen* below the interval between the two premolar teeth, transmitting the *mental nerve and vessels*.

c. The *oblique line* which runs upwards and backwards from the mental tubercle to the anterior border of the ramus (Latin *branch*) of the mandible.

Sutures of the Norma Frontalis

- Internasal (Fig. 1.7)
- Frontonasal
- Nasomaxillary
- Lacrimomaxillary
- Frontomaxillary
- Intermaxillary
- Zygomaticomaxillary
- Zygomaticofrontal.

Attachments

1 The medial part of the superciliary arch gives origin to the *corrugator supercilii* muscle.

2 The *procerus* muscle arises from the nasal bone near the median plane (*see* Fig. 2.9).

3 The orbital part of the *orbicularis oculi* arises from the frontal process of the maxilla and from the nasal part of the frontal bone (*see* Fig. 2.9).

4 The *medial palpebral ligament* is attached to the frontal process of the maxilla between the frontal and maxillary origins of the orbicularis oculi.

5 The *levator labii superioris alaeque nasi* arises from the frontal process of the maxilla in front of the orbicularis oculi (*see* Fig. 2.9).

6 The *levator labii superioris* arises from the maxilla between the infraorbital margin and the infraorbital foramen (*see* Fig. 2.9).

7 The *levator anguli oris* arises from the canine fossa.

8 The *nasalis* and the *depressor septi* arise from the surface of the maxilla bordering the nasal notch.

9 The *incisivus* muscle arises from an area just below the depressor septi. It forms part of orbicularis oris.

10 The *zygomaticus major and minor* arise from the surface of the zygomatic bone (*see* Fig. 2.9).

The *zygomaticus minor* muscle arises below the zygomaticofacial foramen. The *zygomaticus major* arises lateral to the minor muscle (*see* Fig. 2.9).

11 *Buccinator* arises from maxilla and mandible opposite molar teeth and from *pterygomandibular raphe* (*see* Fig. 2.10). It also forms part of orbicularis oris.

Structures Passing through Foramina

1 The *supraorbital notch or foramen* transmits the supraorbital nerves and vessels (*see* Fig. 2.5).

2 The *external nasal nerve* emerges between the nasal bone and upper nasal cartilage (*see* Fig. 2.22).

3 The *infraorbital foramen* transmits the *infraorbital nerve and vessels* (*see* Fig. 2.22).

4 The *zygomaticofacial foramen* transmits the nerve of the same name, a branch of *maxillary nerve*.

5 The *mental foramen* on the mandible transmits the mental nerve and vessels (*see* Fig. 2.22).

NORMA LATERALIS

Bones

1 Frontal

2 Parietal (Fig. 1.9a)

3 Occipital

4 Temporal

5 Sphenoid
6 Zygomatic
7 Mandible
8 Maxilla
9 Nasal

Features

Temporal Lines

The *temporal lines* have been studied in the norma verticalis. The inferior temporal line, in its posterior part, turns downwards and forwards and becomes continuous with the *supramastoid crest* on the squamous temporal bone near its junction with the mastoid temporal. This crest is continuous anteriorly with the posterior root of the zygomatic arch (Fig. 1.9b).

Zygomatic Arch or Zygoma

The *zygomatic arch* is a horizontal bar on the side of the head, in front of the ear, a little above the tragus. It is formed by the temporal process of the zygomatic bone in anterior one-third and the zygomatic process of the temporal bone in posterior two-thirds. The *zygomatico-temporal suture* crosses the arch obliquely downwards and backwards.

Above the zygomatic arch is temporal fossa, which is filled by temporalis muscle. Attached to lower margin of zygomatic arch is masseter muscle; contraction of both temporalis and masseter may be felt by clenching the teeth.

The arch is separated from the side of the skull by a gap which is deeper in front than behind. Its *lateral*

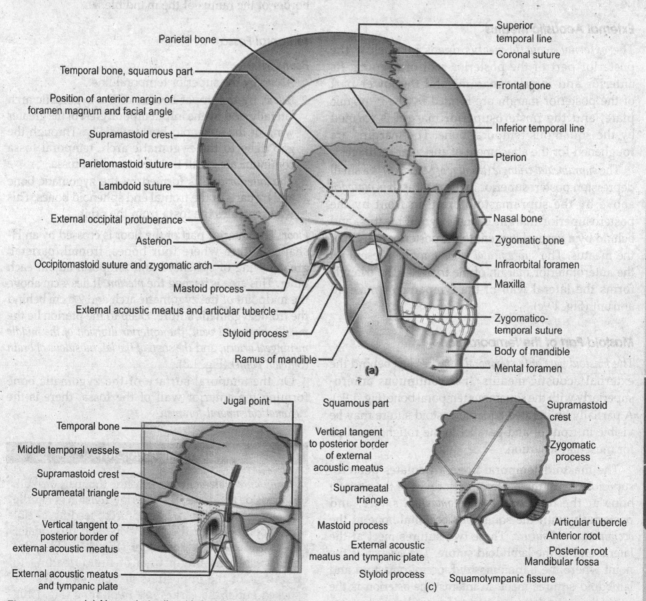

(a)

Parietal bone
Temporal bone, squamous part
Position of anterior margin of foramen magnum and facial angle
Supramastoid crest
Parietomastoid suture
Lambdoid suture
External occipital protuberance
Asterion
Occipitomastoid suture and zygomatic arch
Mastoid process
External acoustic meatus and articular tubercle
Styloid process
Ramus of mandible

Superior temporal line
Coronal suture
Frontal bone
Inferior temporal line
Pterion
Nasal bone
Zygomatic bone
Infraorbital foramen
Maxilla
Zygomatico-temporal suture
Body of mandible
Mental foramen

Jugal point
Temporal bone
Middle temporal vessels
Supramastoid crest
Suprameatal triangle
Vertical tangent to posterior border of external acoustic meatus
External acoustic meatus and tympanic plate

Squamous part
Vertical tangent to posterior border of external acoustic meatus
Suprameatal triangle
Mastoid process
External acoustic meatus and tympanic plate
Styloid process

Supramastoid crest
Zygomatic process
Articular tubercle
Anterior root
Posterior root
Mandibular fossa
Squamotympanic fissure

(c)

Figs 1.9a to c: (a) Norma lateralis with facial angle, (b) bones forming norma lateralis, and (c) tympanic plate forming margins of external acoustic meatus

Head and Neck

surface is subcutaneous. The anterior end of the upper border is called the *jugal point*. The posterior end of the zygomatic arch is attached to the squamous temporal bone by *anterior* and *posterior roots*. The *articular tubercle of the root* of the zygoma lies on its lower border, at the junction of the anterior and posterior roots. The anterior root passes medially in front of the *articular fossa*. The posterior root passes backwards along the lateral margin of the mandibular or articular fossa, then above the external acoustic meatus to become continuous with the supramastoid crest. Two projections are visible in relation to these roots. One is *articular tubercle* at its lower border. Another tubercle is visible just behind the mandibular or articular fossa and is known as *postglenoid tubercle*.

External Acoustic Meatus

The *external acoustic meatus* opens just below the posterior part of the posterior root of zygoma. Its anterior and inferior margins and the lower part of the posterior margin are formed by the tympanic plate, and the posterosuperior margin is formed by the squamous temporal bone. The margins are roughened for the attachment of auricular cartilage.

The *suprameatal triangle (trianlge of Macewen)* is a small depression posterosuperior to the meatus. It is *bounded* above by the supramastoid crest, in front by the posterosuperior margin of the external meatus, and behind by a vertical tangent to the posterior margin of the meatus. The *suprameatal spine* may be present on the anteroinferior margin of the triangle. The triangle forms the lateral wall of the tympanic or mastoid antrum (Fig. 1.9c).

Mastoid Part of the Temporal Bone

The *mastoid part of the temporal bone* lies just behind the external acoustic meatus. It is continuous antero-superiorly with the squamous temporal bone (Fig. 1.9c). A partially obliterated squamomastoid suture may be visible in front of and parallel to the roughened area for muscular insertion.

The mastoid temporal bone articulates postero-superiorly with the posteroinferior part of the parietal bone at the horizontal *parietomastoid suture*, and posteriorly with the squamous occipital bone at the *occipitomastoid suture*. These two sutures meet at the lateral end of the lambdoid suture. The *asterion* is the point where the parietomastoid, occipitomastoid and lambdoid sutures meet. In infants, the asterion is the site of the *posterolateral* or *mastoid fontanelle*, which closes (Fig. 1.3) by 12 months.

The *mastoid process* is a breast-like projection from the lower part of the mastoid temporal bone, postero-inferior to the external acoustic meatus. It appears during the second year of life. The *tympanomastoid fissure* is placed on the anterior aspect of the base of the mastoid process. The *mastoid foramen* lies at or near the occipitomastoid suture (Fig. 1.5).

Styloid Process

The *styloid* (Latin *pen*) *process* is a needle-like thin, long projection from the temporal bone seen in norma basalis situated anteromedial to the mastoid process. It is directed downwards, forwards and slightly medially. Its base is partly ensheathed by the tympanic plate. The apex or tip is usually hidden from view by the posterior border of the ramus of the mandible.

Temporal Fossa

Boundaries

1 *Above,* by the superior temporal line.
2 *Below,* by the upper border of the zygomatic arch laterally, and by the infratemporal crest of the greater wing of the sphenoid bone medially. Through the gap deep to the zygomatic arch, temporal fossa communicates with the infratemporal fossa.
3 The *anterior wall* is formed by the zygomatic bone and by parts of the frontal and sphenoid bones. This wall separates the fossa from the orbit.

Floor: The anterior part of the floor is crossed by an H-shaped suture where four bones, frontal, parietal, greater wing of sphenoid and temporal adjoin each other. This area is termed the *pterion*. It lies 4 cm above the midpoint of the zygomatic arch and 2.5 cm behind the frontozygomatic suture. Deep to the pterion lie the *middle meningeal vein*, the *anterior division of the middle meningeal artery*, and *the stem of the lateral sulcus of brain (Sylvian point)* (Fig. 1.8).

On the temporal surface of the zygomatic bone forming the anterior wall of the fossa, there is the *zygomaticotemporal foramen*.

CLINICAL ANATOMY

Pterion/anterolateral fontanelle is the thin part of skull. In roadside accidents, the anterior division of middle meningeal artery may be ruptured, leading to clot formation between the skull bone and dura mater or extradural haemorrhage (Fig. 1.8). The clot compresses the motor area of brain, leading to paralysis of the opposite side. The clot must be sucked out at the earliest by trephining (Fig. 1.10). The head must be protected by a helmet.

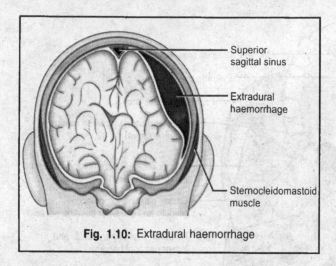

Fig. 1.10: Extradural haemorrhage

Labels: Superior sagittal sinus; Extradural haemorrhage; Sternocleidomastoid muscle

Infratemporal Fossa

Boundaries and the contents are described in Chapter 6.

Pterygopalatine Fossa

Pterygopalatine fossa is described in Chapter 15.

Attachments

1 The *temporal fascia* is attached to the superior temporal line and to the area between the two temporal lines. Inferiorly, it is attached to the outer and inner lips of the upper border of the zygomatic arch.

2 The *temporalis muscle* arises from the whole of the temporal fossa, except the part formed by the zygomatic bone (Fig. 1.14). Beneath the muscle, there lie the *deep temporal vessels* and *nerves*. The *middle temporal vessels* produce vascular markings on the temporal bone just above the external acoustic meatus (Fig. 1.9b).

3 The medial surface and lower border of the zygomatic arch give origin to the *masseter*.

4 The *lateral ligament* of the *temporomandibular joint* is attached to the tubercle of the root of the zygoma (*see* Chapter 6).

5 The *sternocleidomastoid, splenius capitis* and *longissimus capitis* are inserted from before backwards on the posterior part of the lateral surface of the mastoid process (Fig. 1.14). Posterior belly of digastric arises from mastoid notch. The groove obliquely placed behind mastoid notch is due to occipital artery (*see* Fig. 7.3).

6 The *gap* between the zygomatic arch and the side of the skull transmits:
   a. Tendon of the temporalis muscle.
   b. Deep temporal vessels.
   c. Deep temporal nerves.

Structures Passing through Foramina

1 The *tympanomastoid fissure* on the anterior aspect of the base of the mastoid process transmits the *auricular branch* of *vagus nerve*.

2 The mastoid foramen transmits:
   a. An *emissary vein* connecting the *sigmoid sinus* with the *posterior auricular vein* (Table 1.1).
   b. A meningeal branch of the occipital artery.

3 The *zygomaticotemporal foramen* transmits the nerve of the same name and a minute artery (*see* Fig. 2.16).

NORMA BASALIS

For convenience of study, the norma basalis is divided arbitrarily into anterior, middle and posterior parts. The *anterior part* is formed by the hard palate and the alveolar arches. The *middle and posterior parts* are separated by an imaginary transverse line passing through the anterior margin of the foramen magnum (Figs 1.11a and b).

Anterior Part of Norma Basalis

Alveolar Arch

Alveolar arch bears sockets for the roots of the upper teeth.

Hard Palate

1 *Formation:*
   a. Anterior two-thirds, by the palatine processes of the maxilla bones.
   b. Posterior one-third by the horizontal plates of the palatine.

2 *Sutures:* The palate is crossed by a cruciform suture made up of intermaxillary, interpalatine and palatomaxillary sutures.

3 *Dome:*
   a. It is arched in all directions.
   b. Shows pits for the palatine glands.

4 The *incisive foramen* is a deep fossa situated anteriorly in the median plane (Fig. 1.12).
   Two *incisive* canals, right and left, pierce the walls of the incisive foramen, usually one on each side, but occasionally in the median plane, the left being anterior and the right, posterior.

5 The *greater palatine foramen,* one on each side, is situated just behind the lateral part of the palato-maxillary suture. A groove leads from the foramen towards the incisive fossa (Fig. 1.11a).

6 The *lesser palatine foramina,* two or three in number on each side, lie behind the greater palatine foramen, and perforate the pyramidal process of the palatine bone (*see* Fig. 15.14).

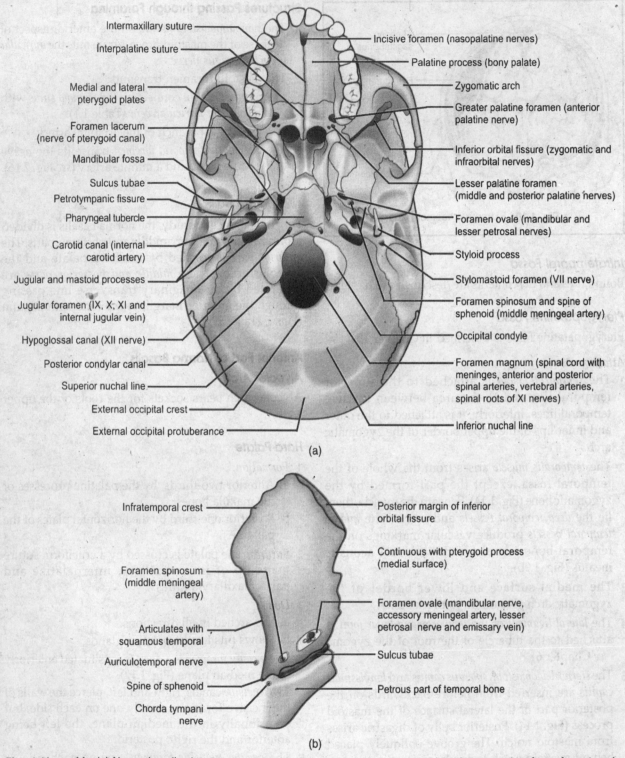

Intermaxillary suture
Interpalatine suture
Medial and lateral pterygoid plates
Foramen lacerum (nerve of pterygoid canal)
Mandibular fossa
Sulcus tubae
Petrotympanic fissure
Pharyngeal tubercle
Carotid canal (internal carotid artery)
Jugular and mastoid processes
Jugular foramen (IX, X, XI and internal jugular vein)
Hypoglossal canal (XII nerve)
Posterior condylar canal
Superior nuchal line
External occipital crest
External occipital protuberance

Incisive foramen (nasopalatine nerves)
Palatine process (bony palate)
Zygomatic arch
Greater palatine foramen (anterior palatine nerve)
Inferior orbital fissure (zygomatic and infraorbital nerves)
Lesser palatine foramen (middle and posterior palatine nerves)
Foramen ovale (mandibular and lesser petrosal nerves)
Styloid process
Stylomastoid foramen (VII nerve)
Foramen spinosum and spine of sphenoid (middle meningeal artery)
Occipital condyle
Foramen magnum (spinal cord with meninges, anterior and posterior spinal arteries, vertebral arteries, spinal roots of XI nerves)
Inferior nuchal line

(a)

Infratemporal crest
Foramen spinosum (middle meningeal artery)
Articulates with squamous temporal
Auriculotemporal nerve
Spine of sphenoid
Chorda tympani nerve

Posterior margin of inferior orbital fissure
Continuous with pterygoid process (medial surface)
Foramen ovale (mandibular nerve, accessory meningeal artery, lesser petrosal nerve and emissary vein)
Sulcus tubae
Petrous part of temporal bone

(b)

Figs 1.11a and b: (a) Norma basalis showing passage of main nerves and arteries, and (b) infratemporal surface of greater wing of sphenoid

7 The *posterior border* of the hard palate is free and presents the *posterior nasal spine* in the median plane.

8 The *palatine crest* is a curved ridge near the posterior border. It begins behind the greater palatine foramen and runs medially (Fig. 1.12).

Middle Part of Norma Basalis

The middle part extends from the posterior border of the hard palate to the arbitrary transverse line passing through the anterior margin of the foramen magnum.

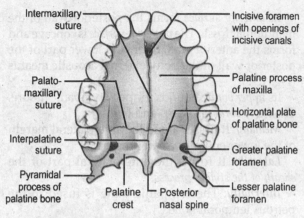

Fig. 1.12: Anterior part of the norma basalis

Median Area

1 The median area shows:
   a. The posterior border of the *vomer*.
   b. A *broad bar of bone* formed by fusion of the posterior part of the body of sphenoid and the basilar part of occipital bone (Fig. 1.13).
2 The vomer separates the two posterior nasal apertures. Its inferior border articulates with the bony palate. The superior border splits into two *alae* and articulates with the *rostrum* of the *sphenoid bone* (Fig. 1.13).
3 The *palatinovaginal canal*. The inferior surface of the vaginal process of the medial pterygoid plate is marked by an anteroposterior groove which is converted into the palatinovaginal canal by the upper surface of the sphenoidal process of the palatine bone. The canal opens anteriorly into the posterior wall of the pterygopalatine fossa (*see* Fig. 15.14).
4 The *vomerovaginal canal*. The lateral border of each ala of the vomer comes into relationship with the vaginal process of the medial pterygoid plate, and may overlap it from above to enclose the vomerovaginal canal (Fig. 1.13).

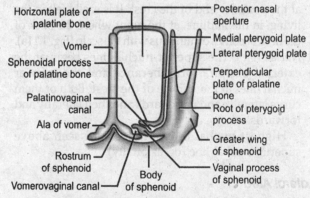

Fig. 1.13: Posterior view of a coronal section through the posterior nasal aperture showing the formation of the palatinovaginal and vomerovaginal canals

5 The broad bar of the bone is marked in the median plane by the *pharyngeal tubercle*, a little in front of the foramen magnum (Fig. 1.11a).

Lateral Area

1 The lateral area shows two parts of the sphenoid bone—pterygoid process and greater wing. Also seen are three parts of the temporal bone, i.e. petrous temporal, tympanic plate and squamous temporal.
2 The *pterygoid process* projects downwards from the junction of greater wing and the body of sphenoid behind the third molar tooth.

   Inferiorly, it divides into the *medial and lateral pterygoid plates* which are fused together anteriorly, but are separated posteriorly by the V-shaped *pterygoid fossa*.

   The fused anterior borders of the two plates articulate medially with the perpendicular plate of the palatine bone, and are separated laterally from the posterior surface of the body of the maxilla by the pterygomaxillary fissure.

   The *medial pterygoid plate* is directed backwards. It has medial and lateral surfaces and a free posterior border.

   The upper end of this border divides to enclose a triangular depression called the *scaphoid fossa*. The lower end of the posterior border is prolonged downwards and laterally to form the *pterygoid hamulus*.

   The *lateral pterygoid plate* is directed backwards and laterally. It has medial and lateral surfaces and a free posterior border. The lateral surface forms the medial wall of the infratemporal fossa. The lateral and medial surfaces give origin to muscles.

   The posterior border sometimes has a projection at its middle called the pterygospinous process which projects towards the spine of the sphenoid.
3 The *infratemporal surface of the greater wing of the sphenoid* is pentagonal:
   a. Its *anterior margin* forms the posterior border of the inferior orbital fissure (Fig. 1.11b).
   b. Its *anterolateral margin* forms the infratemporal crest.
   c. Its *posterolateral margin* articulates with the squamous temporal.
   d. Its *posteromedial margin* articulates with petrous temporal.
   e. *Anteromedially*, it is continuous with the pterygoid process and with the body of the sphenoid bone.
   The posteriormost point between the posterolateral and posteromedial margins projects downwards to form the *spine* of the sphenoid.

   Along the posteromedial margin, the surface is pierced by the following foramina:

a. The *foramen ovale* is large and oval in shape. It is situated posterolateral to the upper end of the posterior border of lateral pterygoid plate (Fig. 1.11b).

b. The *foramen spinosum* is small and circular in shape. It is situated posterolateral to the foramen ovale, and is limited posterolaterally by the spine of sphenoid (Fig. 1.11b).

c. Sometimes there is the *emissary sphenoidal foramen or foramen of Vesalius.* It is situated between the foramen ovale and the scaphoid fossa. Internally, it opens between the foramen ovale and the foramen rotundum.

d. At times, there is a *canaliculus innominatus* situated between the foramen ovale and the foramen spinosum.

The *spine* of the sphenoid may be sharply pointed or blunt (Fig. 1.11b).

The *sulcus tubae* is the groove between the posteromedial margin of the greater wing of the sphenoid and the petrous temporal bone. It lodges the *cartilaginous part of the auditory tube.* Posteriorly, the groove leads to the bony part of the auditory tube which lies within the petrous temporal bone (Fig. 1.11b).

4 The inferior surface of the petrous (Greek *rock*) part of the temporal bone is triangular in shape with its apex directed forwards and medially.

It lies between the greater wing of the sphenoid and the basiocciput. Its *apex* is perforated by the upper end of the carotid canal, and is separated from the sphenoid by the foramen lacerum. The *inferior surface* is perforated by the lower end of the *carotid canal* posteriorly.

The *carotid canal* runs forwards and medially within the petrous temporal bone.

The *foramen lacerum* is a short, wide canal, 1 cm long. Its lower end is bounded posterolaterally by the apex of the petrous temporal, medially by the basiocciput and the body of the sphenoid, and anteriorly by the root of the pterygoid process and the greater wing of the sphenoid bone.

A part of the petrous temporal bone, called the *tegmen tympani*, is present in the middle cranial fossa. It has a down turned edge which is seen in the *squamotympanic fissure* and divides it into the posterior *petrotympanic* and anterior *petrosquamous* fissures (Fig. 1.11a).

5 The *tympanic part of the temporal bone also called as the tympanic plate* is a triangular curved plate which lies in the angle between the petrous and squamous parts.

Its apex is directed medially and lies close to the spine of the sphenoid.

The *base or lateral border* is curved, free and roughened.

Its *anterior surface* forms the posterior wall of the mandibular fossa. The *posterior surface* is concave and forms the anterior wall, floor, and lower part of the posterior wall of the bony external acoustic meatus (Fig. 1.9c).

Its *upper border* bounds the petrotympanic fissure. The *lower border* is sharp and free.

Medially: It passes along the anterolateral margin of the lower end of the carotid canal.

Laterally: It forms the anterolateral part of the *sheath of the styloid process.*

Internally: The tympanic plate is fused to the petrous temporal bone.

6 *The squamous part of the temporal bone* forms:

a. The anterior part of the mandibular articular fossa which articulates with the head of the mandible to form the temporomandibular joint.

b. The articular tubercle which is continuous with the anterior root of the zygoma.

c. A small posterolateral part of the roof of the infratemporal fossa.

Posterior Part of Norma Basalis

Median Area

The median area shows from before backwards:

a. The foramen magnum.
b. The external occipital crest.
c. The external occipital protuberance.
d. Nuchal lines

a. The *foramen magnum* (Latin *great)* is the largest foramen of the skull. It opens upwards into the posterior cranial fossa, and downwards into the vertebral canal. It is oval in shape, being wider behind than in front where it is overlapped on each side by the occipital condyles (Fig. 1.14).

b. The *external occipital crest* begins at the posterior margin of the foramen magnum and ends posteriorly and above at the external occipital protuberance (Fig. 1.11.).

c. The *external occipital protuberance* is a projection located at the posterior end of the crest. It is easily felt in the living, in the midline, at the point where the back of the neck becomes continuous with the scalp (Fig. 1.11a).

d. *Nuchal lines:* The superior nuchal lines begin at the external occipital protuberance and the inferior nuchal lines at the middle of the crest. Both of them curve laterally and backwards and then laterally and forwards.

Highest nuchal line is faded and seen above superior nuchal line (occasionally).

Lateral Area

The *lateral area* shows:

• The condylar part of the occipital bone.
• The squamous part of the occipital bone.

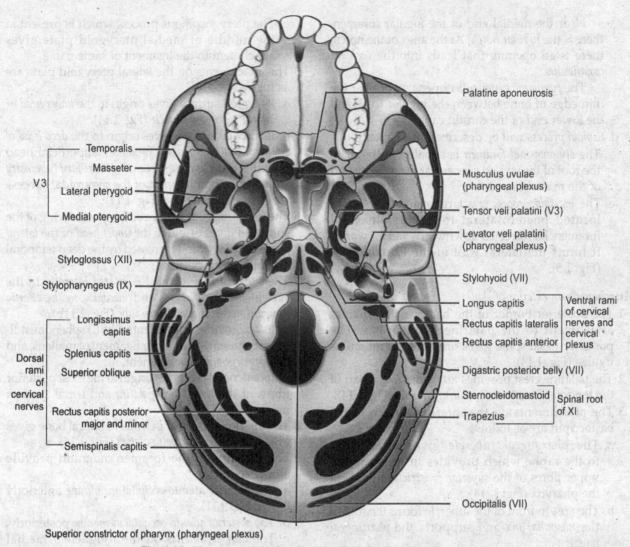

Fig. 1.14: Muscles attached to the base of skull with their nerve supply

- The jugular foramen between the occipital and petrous temporal bones.
- The styloid process of the temporal bone.
- The mastoid part of the temporal bone.
  a. The *condylar or lateral part of the occipital bone* presents the following.
     i. The *occipital condyles* are oval in shape and are situated on each side of the anterior part of the foramen magnum. Their long axis is directed forwards and medially. They articulate with the superior articular facets of the atlas vertebra to form the atlanto-occipital joints (Fig. 1.11).
     ii. The *hypoglossal* or *anterior condylar canal* pierces the bone anterosuperior to the occipital condyle, and is directed laterally and slightly forwards.
     iii. The *condylar* or *posterior condylar canal* is occasionally present in the floor of a condylar

fossa present behind the occipital condyle. Superiorly, it opens into the sigmoid sulcus.
     iv. The *jugular process of the occipital bone* lies lateral to the occipital condyle and forms the posterior boundary of jugular foramen (Fig. 1.11).
  b. *Squamous part of occipital bone* is marked by the superior and inferior nuchal lines mentioned above (Fig. 1.5).
  c. The *jugular foramen* is large and elongated, with its long axis directed forwards and medially. It is placed at the posterior end of the petro-occipital suture (Fig. 1.11a).
     At the posterior end of the foramen, its anterior wall (petrous temporal) is hollowed out to form *jugular fossa* which lodges the superior bulb of the internal jugular vein. The fossa is larger on the right side than on the left.
     The lateral wall of the jugular fossa is pierced by a minute canal, the *mastoid canaliculus.*

Near the medial end of the jugular foramen, there is the *jugular notch*. At the apex of the notch, there is an opening that leads into the *cochlear canaliculus*.

The *tympanic canaliculus* opens on or near the thin edge of bone between the jugular fossa and the lower end of the carotid canal.

d. *Styloid process* will be described in Chapter 8. The *stylomastoid foramen* is situated posterior to the root of the styloid process, at the anterior end of the mastoid notch.

e. The *mastoid process* is a large conical projection located posterolateral to the stylomastoid foramen. It is directed downwards and forwards. It forms the lateral wall of the *mastoid notch* (Fig. 1.5).

Attachments on exterior of skull

1 The posterior border of the hard palate provides attachment to the palatine aponeurosis. The posterior nasal spine gives origin to the musculus uvulae (Fig. 1.14).

2 The palatine crest provides attachment to a part of the tendon of *tensor veli palatini* muscle (Fig. 1.14).

3 The attachments on the inferior surface of the basiocciput are as follows:

a. The *pharyngeal tubercle* gives attachment to the raphe which provides insertion to the upper fibres of the *superior constrictor* muscle of the pharynx (Fig. 1. 14).

b. The area in front of the tubercle forms the roof of the *nasopharynx* and supports the *pharyngeal tonsil*.

c. The *longus capitis* is inserted lateral to the pharyngeal tubercle (Fig. 1.14).

d. The *rectus capitis anterior* is inserted a little posterior and medial to the hypoglossal canal (Fig. 1.14).

4 The attachments on the medial pterygoid plate are as follows:

a. The *pharyngobasilar fascia* is attached below to the processus tuberis.

Processus tuberis is a triangular projection which is present at the middle of the posterior border of medial pterygoid plate. It supports the medial end of cartilaginous part of auditory tube.

b. The lower part of the posterior border, and the pterygoid hamulus, give origin to the *superior constrictor* of the pharynx.

c. The upper part of the posterior border is notched by the *auditory* tube.

d. The *pterygomandibular raphe* is attached to the tip of the *pterygoid hamulus* at one end and to the mandible behind 3rd molar tooth at the other end.

e. The pterygospinous process which is present at the middle of medial pterygoid plate gives attachment to the ligament of same name.

5 The attachments on the lateral pterygoid plate are as follows:

a. Its lateral surface gives origin to the *lower head* of *lateral pterygoid muscle* (Fig. 1.14).

b. Its medial surface gives origin to the *deep head of the medial pterygoid*. The small, superficial head of this muscle arises from the *maxillary tuberosity* and the adjoining part of the pyramidal process of the palatine bone (Fig. 1.14).

6 The infratemporal surface of the greater wing of the sphenoid gives origin to the *upper head* of the *lateral pterygoid muscle*, and is crossed by the deep temporal and masseteric nerves.

7 The *spine* of the *sphenoid is related laterally* to the *auriculotemporal nerve*, and *medially to the chorda tympani nerve* and *auditory tube* (Fig. 1.11b).

Its *tip* provides attachment to the (i) sphenomandibular ligament, (ii) anterior ligament of malleus, and (iii) pterygospinous ligament.

Its *anterior aspect* gives origin to the most posterior fibres of the *tensor veli palatini* and *tensor tympani* muscles.

8 The inferior surface of petrous temporal bone gives origin to the *levator veli palatini* (Fig. 1.14).

9 The margins of the foramen magnum provide attachment to:

a. The *anterior atlanto-occipital membrane* anteriorly (*see* Fig. 9.11).

b. The *posterior atlanto-occipital membrane* posteriorly.

c. The *alar ligaments* on the roughened medial surface of each occipital condyle (*see* Fig. 9.12).

10 The *ligamentum nuchae* is attached to the external occipital protuberance and crest.

11 The *rectus capitis lateralis* is inserted into the inferior surface of the jugular process of the occipital bone (Fig. 1.14).

12 The following are attached to the squamous part of the occipital bone (Fig. 1.14).

The area between the superior and inferior nuchal lines provides insertion medially to the *semispinalis capitis*, and laterally to the *superior oblique* muscle.

The area below the inferior nuchal line provides insertion medially to the *rectus capitis posterior minor*, and laterally to the *rectus capitis posterior major* (Fig. 1.14).

13 The *mastoid notch* gives origin to the *posterior belly of digastric muscle* (Fig. 1.14).

Structures passing through, foramina

1 Each *incisive foramen* transmits:

a. The terminal parts of the *greater palatine vessels* from the palate to the nose.

b. The terminal part of the *nasopalatine nerve* from the nose to the palate (Fig. 1.11a).

2 The *greater palatine foramen* transmits:
a. The *greater palatine vessels*.
b. The *anterior palatine nerve*, both of which run forwards in the groove that passes forwards from the foramen (*see* Fig. 15.16a).

3 The *lesser palatine foramina* transmit the *middle* and *posterior palatine nerves*.

4 The *palatinovaginal canal* transmits:
a. A *pharyngeal branch* from the *pterygopalatine ganglion* (*see* Fig. 15.16a).
b. A small *pharyngeal branch* of the *maxillary artery*.

5 The *vomerovaginal canal* (if patent) transmits branches of the *pharyngeal branch* from pterygopalatine ganglion and vessels.

6 The *foramen ovale* transmits (mnemonic—MALE)
a. The *mandibular nerve* (Fig. 1.11)
b. The *accessory meningeal artery*.
c. The *lesser petrosal nerve*
d. An *emissary vein* connecting the cavernous sinus with the pterygoid plexus of veins.
e. Anterior trunk of middle meningeal vein (occasionally).

7 The *foramen spinosum* transmits the *middle* meningeal artery (Fig. 1.11a), the meningeal branch of the mandibular nerve or nervus spinosus, and the posterior trunk of the middle meningeal vein.

8 The *emissary sphenoidal foramen* (foramen of Vesalius) transmits an *emissary vein* connecting the cavernous sinus with the pterygoid plexus of veins.

9 When present the *canaliculus innominatus* transmits the lesser petrosal nerve, (in place of foramen ovale).

10 The *carotid canal* transmits the *internal carotid artery*, and the *venous* and *sympathetic plexuses* around the artery (Fig. 1.11a).

11 The structures passing through the *foramen lacerum*: During life, the lower part of the foramen is filled with cartilage, and no significant structure passes through the whole length of the canal, except for the meningeal branch of the ascending pharyngeal artery and an emissary vein from the cavernous sinus.

However, the upper part of the foramen is traversed by the internal carotid artery with venous and sympathetic plexuses around it. In the anterior part of the foramen, the *greater petrosal nerve* unites with *the deep petrosal nerve* to form the *nerve of the pterygoid canal* (Vidian's nerve) which leaves the foramen by entering the pterygoid canal in the anterior wall of the foramen lacerum (Fig. 1.15).

12 The medial end of the *petrotympanic fissure* transmits the chorda tympani nerve, anterior ligament of malleus and the anterior tympanic artery (Fig. 1.11a).

13 The *foramen magnum* (Fig. 1.16) transmits the following.

Through the narrow anterior part:
a. Apical ligament of dens.
b. Vertical band of cruciate ligament.
c. Membrana tectoria.

Through wider posterior part:
a. Lowest part of medulla oblongata.
b Three meninges.

Through the subarachnoid space pass:
a. Spinal accessory nerves.
b. Vertebral arteries.
c. Sympathetic plexus around the vertebral arteries.
d. Posterior spinal arteries.
e. Anterior spinal artery.

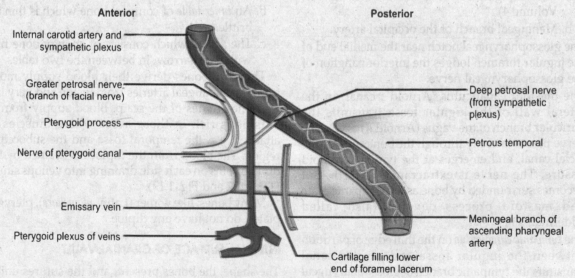

Anterior

Internal carotid artery and sympathetic plexus

Greater petrosal nerve (branch of facial nerve)

Pterygoid process

Nerve of pterygoid canal

Emissary vein

Pterygoid plexus of veins

Posterior

Deep petrosal nerve (from sympathetic plexus)

Petrous temporal

Meningeal branch of ascending pharyngeal artery

Cartilage filling lower end of foramen lacerum

Fig. 1.15: Structures related to the foramen lacerum

Head and Neck

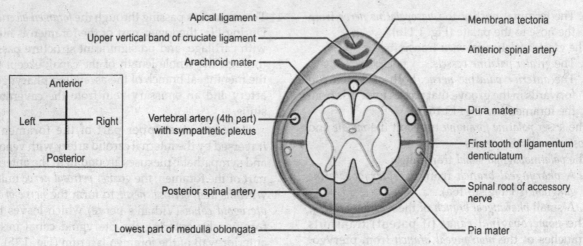

Fig. 1.16: Structures passing through foramen magnum

14 The *hypoglossal* or *anterior condylar* canal transmits the *hypoglossal nerve*, the *meningeal branch* of the hypoglossal nerve (these are the sensory fibres of cervical first spinal nerve supplying the dura mater of posterior cranial fossa) the *meningeal branch* of the ascending pharyngeal artery, and an *emissary vein* connecting the sigmoid sinus with the internal jugular vein (Table 1.1).

15 The *posterior condylar canal* transmits an emissary vein connecting the sigmoid sinus with suboccipital venous plexus (Table 1.1).

16 The *jugular foramen* transmits the following structures:
  i. *Through the anterior part:*
    (a) Inferior petrosal sinus.
    (b) Meningeal branch of the ascending pharyngeal artery.
  ii. *Through the middle part:* IX, X and XI cranial nerves.
  iii. *Through the posterior part:*
    a. Internal jugular vein (Fig. 1.11a, also *see* Fig. 4.46, Volume 4).
    b. Meningeal branch of the occipital artery.
  The glossopharyngeal notch near the medial end of the jugular foramen lodges the inferior ganglion of the glossopharyngeal nerve.

17 The mastoid canaliculus (Arnold's canal) in the lateral wall of the jugular fossa transmits the auricular branch of the vagus (Arnold's nerve). The nerve passes laterally through the bone, crosses the facial canal, and emerges at the tympanomastoid fissure. The nerve is extracranial at birth, but becomes surrounded by bone as the tympanic plate and mastoid process develop (also called Alderman's nerve).

18 The *tympanic canaliculus* on the thin edge of partition between the jugular fossa and carotid canal transmits the tympanic branch of glossopharyngeal nerve (Jacobson's nerve) to the middle ear cavity.

19 The *stylomastoid foramen* transmits the facial nerve and the stylomastoid branch of the posterior auricular artery.

INTERIOR OF THE SKULL

Before beginning a systematic study of the interior, the following general points may be noted.

1 The cranium is lined internally by *endocranium* which is continuous with the pericranium through the foramina and sutures.

2 The *thickness* of the cranial vault is variable. The bones covered with muscles, i.e. temporal and posterior cranial fossae are thinner than those covered with scalp. Further, the bones are thinner in females than in males, and in children than in adults.

3 Most of the cranial bones consist of:
  a. An *outer table* of compact bone which is thick, resilient and tough.
  b. An *inner table* of compact bone which is thin and brittle.
  c. The *diploes* which consists of spongy bone filled with red marrow, in between the two tables.

The skull bones derive their blood supply mostly from the meningeal arteries from inside and very little from the arteries of the scalp. Blood supply from the outside is rich in those areas where muscles are attached, e.g. the temporal fossa and the suboccipital region. The blood from the diploes is drained by four diploic veins on each side draining into venous sinuses (Table 1.2 and Fig. 1.17).

Many bones, like vomer (Latin *plowshare*), pterygoid plates, do not have any diploe.

INTERNAL SURFACE OF CRANIAL VAULT

The shape, the bones present, and the sutures uniting them have been described with the norma verticalis.

Table 1.2: Diploic veins

Vein	Foramen	Drainage
1. Frontal diploic vein	Supraorbital foramen	Drain into supraorbital vein
2. Anterior temporal or parietal diploic vein	In the greater wing of sphenoid	Sphenoparietal sinus or in anterior deep temporal vein
3. Posterior temporal or parietal diploic vein	Mastoid foramen	Transverse sinus
4. Occipital diploic vein (largest)	Foramen in occipital bone	Occipital vein or confluence of sinuses
5. Small unnamed diploic veins	Pierce inner table of skull close to the margins of superior sagittal sinus	Venous lacunae

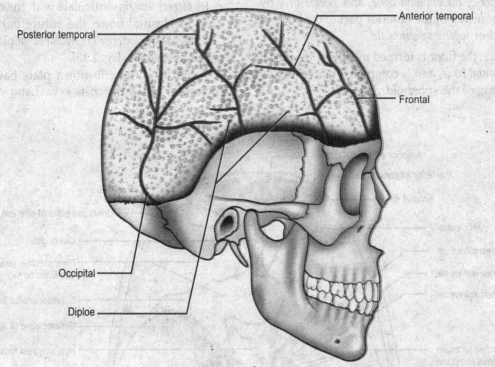

Fig. 1.17: Diploic veins in an adult

The following features may be noted:

a. The *inner table* is thin and brittle. It presents *markings* produced by meningeal vessels, venous sinuses, arachnoid granulations, and to some extent by cerebral gyri. It also presents raised ridges formed by the attachments of the dural folds.

b. The *frontal crest* lies anteriorly in the median plane. It projects backwards.

c. The *sagittal sulcus* runs from before backwards in the median plane. It becomes progressively wider posteriorly. It lodges the superior sagittal sinus.

d. The *granular foveolae* are deep, irregular, large, pits situated on each side of the sagittal sulcus. They are formed by arachnoid granulations. They are larger and more numerous in aged persons.

e. The *vascular markings*. The groove for the anterior branch of the middle meningeal artery, and the accompanying vein runs upwards 1 cm behind the coronal suture. Smaller grooves for the branches from the anterior and posterior branches of the middle meningeal vessels run upwards and backwards over the parietal bone (Fig. 1.8).

f. The *parietal foramina* open near the sagittal sulcus 2.5 to 3.75 cm in front of the lambdoid suture (Fig. 1.2).

g. The *impressions for cerebral gyri* are less distinct. These become very prominent in cases of raised intracranial tension.

INTERNAL SURFACE OF THE BASE OF SKULL

The interior of the base of skull presents natural subdivisions into the anterior, middle and posterior cranial fossae. The dura mater is firmly adherent to the floor of fossae and is continuous with pericranium through the foramina and fissures.

Anterior Cranial Fossa

Boundaries

Anteriorly and on the sides, by the frontal bone (Fig. 1.18).

Posteriorly, it is separated from the middle cranial fossa by the free *posterior border* of the *lesser wing of the sphenoid,* the *anterior clinoid process,* and the *anterior margin of the sulcus chiasmaticus.*

Floor

In the median plane, it is formed anteriorly by the *cribriform plate of the ethmoid bone,* and posteriorly by the superior surface of the anterior part of the body of the sphenoid or *jugum sphenoidale.*

On each side, the floor is formed mostly by the *orbital plate of the frontal bone,* and is completed posteriorly by the lesser wing of the sphenoid.

Other Features

1 The *cribriform plate of the ethmoid bone* separates the anterior cranial fossa from the nasal cavity. It is quadrilateral in shape (Fig. 1.18).
   a. *Anterior* margin articulates with the frontal bone at the *frontoethmoidal suture* which is marked in the median plane by the *foramen caecum.* This foramen is usually blind, but is occasionally patent.
   b. *Posterior margin* articulates with the jugum sphenoidale. At the posterolateral corners, we see the *posterior ethmoidal canals.*
   c. Its *lateral margins* articulate with the orbital plate of the frontal bone: the suture between them presents the *anterior ethmoidal canal* placed behind the crista galli (Fig. 1.18).

Anteriorly, the cribriform plate has a midline projection called the *crista galli* (Latin *cock's comb*).

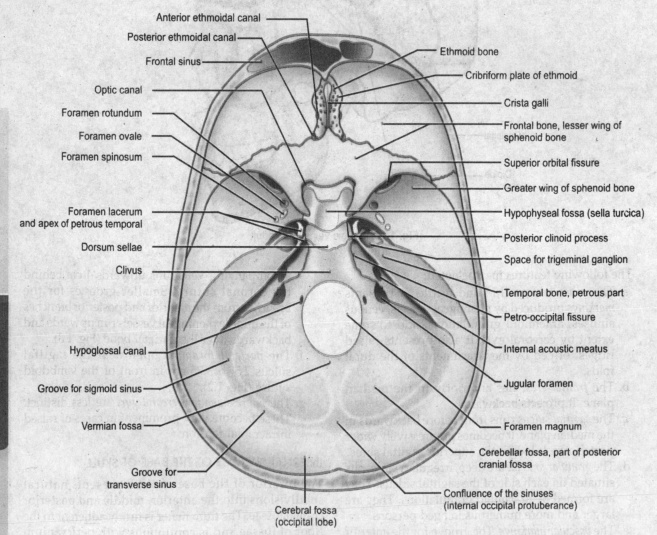

Fig. 1.18: The cranial fossae

On each side of the crista galli, there are foramina through which the *anterior ethmoidal nerve and vessels* pass to the nasal cavity. The plate is also perforated by *numerous foramina* for the passage of olfactory nerve rootlets.

2 The *jugum sphenoidale* separates the anterior cranial fossa from the sphenoidal sinuses.

3 The *orbital plate of the frontal bone* separates the anterior cranial fossa from the orbit. It supports the orbital surface of the frontal lobe of the brain, and presents reciprocal impressions. The *frontal air sinus* may extend into its anteromedial part. The *medial margin* of the plate covers the labyrinth of the ethmoid; and the *posterior margin* articulates with the lesser wing of the sphenoid.

4 The *lesser wing of the sphenoid* is broad medially where it is continuous with the jugum sphenoidale and tapers laterally. The free *posterior border* fits into the *stem of the lateral sulcus of the brain*. It ends medially as a prominent projection, the *anterior clinoid process*. Inferiorly, the posterior border forms the upper boundary of the *superior orbital fissure*. Medially, the lesser wing is connected to the body of the sphenoid by *anterior and posterior roots*, which enclose the *optic canal*.

CLINICAL ANATOMY

Fracture of the anterior cranial fossa may cause bleeding and discharge of cerebrospinal fluid through the nose. It may also cause a condition called *black eye* which is produced by seepage of blood into the eyelid, as frontalis muscle has no bony origin (*see* Fig. 2.8).

Middle Cranial Fossa

It is deeper than the anterior cranial fossa, and is shaped like a butterfly, being narrow and shallow in the middle; and wide and deep on each side.

Boundaries

Anterior

1 Posterior border of the lesser wing of the sphenoid.
2 Anterior clinoid process.
3 Anterior margin of the sulcus chiasmaticus.

Posterior

1 Superior border of the petrous temporal bone.
2 The dorsum sellae of the sphenoid.

Lateral

1 Greater wing of the sphenoid.
2 Anteroinferior angle of the parietal bone.
3 The squamous temporal bone.

Floor

Floor is formed by body of sphenoid in the median region and by greater wing of sphenoid, squamous temporal and anterior surface of petrous temporal on each side.

Other Features

Median area

The body of the sphenoid presents the following features.

1 The *sulcus chiasmaticus* or *optic groove* leads, on each side, to the optic canal. The optic chiasma does not occupy the sulcus, it lies at a higher level well behind the sulcus.

2 The *optic canal* leads to the orbit. It is bounded laterally by the lesser wing of the sphenoid, in front and behind by the two roots of the lesser wing, and medially by the body of sphenoid.

3 The *sella turcica* (pituitary fossa or hypophyseal fossa): The upper surface of the body of the sphenoid is hollowed out in the form of a Turkish saddle, and is known as the *sella turcica*. It consists of the *tuberculum sellae* in front, the *hypophyseal fossa* in the middle and the *dorsum sellae* behind (Fig. 1.18).

The *tuberculum sellae* separates the optic groove from the *hypophyseal fossa*. Its lateral ends form the *middle clinoid process* which may join the anterior clinoid process.

The *hypophyseal fossa* lodges the hypophysis cerebri. Beneath the floor of fossa lie the sphenoidal air sinuses.

The *dorsum sellae* is a transverse plate of bone projecting upwards; it forms the back of the saddle. The superolateral angles of the dorsum sellae are expanded to form the *posterior clinoid processes*.

Lateral area

1 The lateral area is deep and lodges the temporal lobe of the brain.

2 It is related anteriorly to the orbit, laterally to the temporal fossa, and inferiorly to the infratemporal fossa.

3 The *superior orbital fissure* opens anteriorly into the orbit. It is *bounded* above by the lesser wing, below by the greater wing, and medially by the body of the sphenoid (*see* Fig. 13.4).

The medial end is wider than the lateral.

The long axis of the fissure is directed laterally, upwards and forwards. The lower border is marked by a small projection, which provides attachment to the *common tendinous ring of Zinn*. The ring divides the fissure into three parts.

4 The *greater wing of the sphenoid* presents the following features:

a. The *foramen rotundum* leads anteriorly to the pterygopalatine fossa containing pterygopalatine ganglia (*see* Table A.2 in Appendix).

b. The *foramen ovale* lies posterolateral to the foramen rotundum and lateral to the lingula. It leads inferiorly to the infratemporal fossa (Fig. 1.18).

c. The *foramen spinosum* lies posterolateral to the foramen ovale. It also leads, inferiorly, to the infratemporal fossa (Fig. 1.18).

d. The *emissary sphenoidal foramen* or foramen of Vesalius. It carries an emissary vein.

5 The *foramen lacerum* lies at the posterior end of the carotid groove, posteromedial to the foramen ovale.

6 The *anterior surface of the petrous temporal bone* presents the following features:

a. The *trigeminal impression* lies near the apex, behind the foramen lacerum. It lodges the trigeminal ganglion within its dural cave (*see* Fig. 12.4).

b. The *hiatus and groove for the greater petrosal nerve* are present lateral to the trigeminal impression. They lead to the foramen lacerum.

c. The *hiatus and groove for the lesser petrosal nerve* lie lateral to the hiatus for the greater petrosal nerve. They lead to the foramen ovale or to canaliculus innominatus to relay in otic ganglion (Fig. 1.36).

d. Still more laterally there is the *arcuate eminence* produced by the superior semicircular canal.

e. The *tegmen tympani* is a thin plate of bone anterolateral to the arcuate eminence. It forms a continuous sloping roof for the tympanic antrum, for the tympanic cavity and for the canal for the tensor tympani.

The lateral margin of the tegmen tympani is turned downwards, it forms the lateral wall of the bony auditory tube.

Its lower edge is seen in the squamotympanic fissure and divides it into the petrosquamous and petrotympanic fissures.

7 The *cerebral surface of the squamous temporal bone* is concave. It shows impressions for the temporal lobe and grooves for branches of the middle meningeal vessels.

CLINICAL ANATOMY

Fracture of the middle cranial fossa produces:
a. Bleeding and discharge of CSF through the ear.
b. Bleeding through the nose or mouth may occur due to involvement of the sphenoid bone.
c. The seventh and eighth cranial nerves may be damaged, if the fracture also passes through the internal acoustic meatus. If a semicircular canal is damaged, vertigo may occur.

Posterior Cranial Fossa

This is the largest and deepest of the three cranial fossae. The posterior cranial fossa contains the *hindbrain* which consists of the *cerebellum behind and the pons and medulla in front*.

Boundaries

Anterior
1 The superior border of the petrous temporal bone.
2 The dorsum sellae of the sphenoid bone (Fig. 1.18).

Posterior
Squamous part of the occipital bone.

On each side
1 Mastoid part of the temporal bone.
2 The mastoid angle of the parietal bone.

Floor

Median area
1 Sloping area behind the dorsum sellae or clivus in front
2 The foramen magnum in the middle
3 The squamous occipital behind.

Lateral area
1 Condylar or lateral part of occipital bone.
2 Posterior surface of the petrous temporal bone.
3 Mastoid temporal bone.
4 Mastoid angle of the parietal bone.

Other Features

Median area
1 The *clivus* is the sloping surface in front of the foramen magnum. It is formed by fusion of the posterior part of the body of the sphenoid including the dorsum sellae with the basilar part of the occipital bone or basiocciput. It is related to the *basilar plexus of veins*, and supports the pons and medulla (Fig. 1.18).

On each side, the clivus is separated from the petrous temporal bone by the *petro-occipital fissure* which is grooved by the inferior petrosal sinus, and is continuous behind with the jugular foramen.

2 The *foramen magnum* lies in the floor of the fossa. The anterior part of the foramen is narrow because it is *overlapped* by the medial surfaces of the occipital condyles.

3 The *squamous part of the occipital bone* shows the following features:

a. The *internal occipital protuberance* lies opposite the external occipital protuberance. It is related to the confluence of sinuses, and is grooved on each side by the beginning of transverse sinuses.

b. The *internal occipital crest* runs in the median plane from the internal occipital protuberance to the foramen magnum where it forms a shallow depression, the *vermian fossa* (Fig. 1.18).
c. The *transverse sulcus* is quite wide and runs laterally from the internal occipital protuberance to the mastoid angle of the parietal bone where it becomes continuous with the sigmoid sulcus. The transverse sulcus lodges the *transverse sinus*. The right transverse sulcus is usually wider than the left and is continuous medially with the superior sagittal sulcus (Fig. 1.18).
d. On each side of the internal occipital crest, there are *deep fossae* which lodge the cerebellar hemispheres (Fig. 1.18).

Lateral area
1 The *condylar part of the occipital bone* is marked by the following.
   a. The *jugular tubercle* lies over the occipital condyle.
   b. The *hypoglossal canal* (anterior condylar canal) pierces the bone posteroanterior to the jugular tubercle and runs obliquely forwards and laterally along the line of fusion between the basilar and the condylar parts of the occipital bone.
   c. The *condylar canal* (posterior condylar canal) opens in the lower part of the sigmoid sulcus which indents the jugular process of occipital bone.
2 The *posterior surface of the petrous part of the temporal bone* forms the anterolateral wall of the posterior cranial fossa. The following features may be noted:
   a. The *internal acoustic meatus* opens above the anterior part of the jugular foramen. It is about 1 cm long and runs transversely in a lateral direction. It is closed laterally by a perforated plate of bone known as *lamina cribrosa* which separates it from the internal ear (Fig. 1.18).
   b. The orifice of the *aqueduct of the vestibule* is a narrow slit lying behind the internal acoustic meatus.
   c. The *subarcuate fossa* lies below the arcuate eminence, lateral to the internal acoustic meatus.
3 The *jugular foramen* lies at the posterior end of the petro-occipital fissure. The upper margin is sharp and irregular, and presents the *glossopharyngeal notch*. The lower margin is smooth and regular (see Fig. 4.46, Vol. 4).
4 The *mastoid part of the temporal bone* forms the lateral wall of the posterior cranial fossa just behind the petrous part of the bone. Anteriorly, it is marked by the *sigmoid sulcus* which begins as a downward continuation of the transverse sulcus at the mastoid angle of the parietal bone, and ends at the jugular foramen. The sigmoid sulcus lodges the *sigmoid sinus* which become the internal jugular vein at the jugular foramen (Fig. 1.18). The sulcus is related anteriorly

to the *tympanic antrum*. The *mastoid foramen* opens into the upper part of the sulcus.

Attachments and Relations: Interior of the Skull
Attachment on vault
1 The frontal crest gives attachment to the falx cerebri (see Fig. 12.2).
2 The lips of the sagittal sulcus give attachment to the falx cerebri (see Fig. 12.2).

Anterior cranial fossa
1 The crista galli gives attachment to the falx cerebri.
2 The orbital surface of the frontal bone supports the frontal lobe of the brain.
3 The anterior clinoid processes give attachment to the free margin of the tentorium cerebelli (see Fig. 12.3).

Middle cranial fossa
1 The middle cranial fossa lodges the *temporal lobe of the cerebral hemisphere*.
2 The tuberculum sellae provides attachment to the *diaphragma sellae* (see Fig. 12.5).
3 The hypophyseal fossa lodges the *hypophysis cerebri*.
4 Upper margin of the dorsum sellae provides attachment to the diaphragma sellae, and the posterior clinoid process to anterior end of the attached margin of tentorium cerebelli and to the petrosphenoidal ligament (see Fig. 12.3).
5 One *cavernous sinus* lies on each side of the body of the sphenoid. The internal carotid artery passes through the cavernous sinus (see Fig. 12.6).
6 The superior border of the petrous temporal bone is grooved by the *superior petrosal sinus* and provides attachment to the *attached margin of the tentorium cerebelli*. It is grooved in its medial part by the *trigeminal nerve* (trigeminal impression).

Posterior cranial fossa
1 The posterior cranial fossa contains the hindbrain which consists of the cerebellum behind, and the pons and medulla in front.
2 The lower part of the clivus provides attachment to the *apical ligament of the dens* near the foramen magnum, upper vertical band of cruciate ligament and to the *membrana tectoria* just above the apical ligament (Fig. 1.16).
3 The internal occipital crest gives attachment to the *falx cerebelli*.

4 The jugular tubercle is grooved by the *ninth, tenth and eleventh cranial nerves* as they pass to the jugular foramen.

5 The subarcuate fossa on the posterior surface of petrous temporal bone lodges the *flocculus of the cerebellum.*

Structures Passing through Foramina

The following foramina seen in the cranial fossae have been dealt with under the norma basalis: foramen ovale, foramen spinosum, emissary sphenoidal foramen, foramen lacerum, foramen magnum, jugular foramen, hypoglossal canal, and posterior condylar canal. Additional foramina seen in the cranial fossae are as follows.

1 The *foramen caecum* in the anterior cranial fossa is usually blind, but occasionally it transmits a vein from the upper part of nose to the superior sagittal sinus.

2 The *posterior ethmoidal canal* transmits the vessels of the same name. Note that the posterior ethmoidal nerve *does not pass* through the canal as it terminates earlier.

3 The *anterior ethmoidal canal* transmits the corresponding nerve and vessels.

4 The *optic canal* transmits the optic nerve and the ophthalmic artery.

5 The three parts of the *superior orbital fissure* (*see* Fig. 13.4) transmit the following structures:

Lateral part

a. Lacrimal nerve
b. Frontal nerve
c. Trochlear nerve
d. Superior ophthalmic vein

Middle part

a. Upper and lower divisions of the oculomotor nerve (Table 1.4).
b. Nasociliary nerve in between the two divisions of the oculomotor.
c. The abducent nerve, inferolateral to the foregoing nerves (*see* Fig. 13.4).

Medial part

a. Inferior ophthalmic vein.
b. Sympathetic nerves from the plexus around the internal carotid artery.

6 The *foramen rotundum* transmits the maxillary nerve (*see* Fig. 15.15).

7 The *internal acoustic meatus* transmits the *seventh and eighth cranial nerves* and the *labyrinthine vessels.*

Principles Governing Fractures of the Skull

1 Fractures of the skull are prevented by:
  a. Its elasticity.
  b. Rounded shape.

c. Construction from a number of secondary elastic arches, each made up of a single bone.
d. The muscles covering the thin areas.

2 Since the skull is an elastic sphere filled with the semifluid brain, a violent blow on the skull produces a *splitting effect* commencing at the site of the blow and tending to pass along the lines of least resistance.

3 The *base of the skull is more fragile* than the vault, and is more commonly involved in such fractures, particularly along the foramina.

4 The *inner table is more brittle* than the outer table. Therefore, fractures are more extensive on the inner table. Occasionally, only the inner table is fractured and the outer table remains intact.

5 The *common sites* of fracture in the skull are:
  a. The *parietal area* of the vault.
  b. The *middle cranial fossa* of the base. This fossa is weakened by numerous foramina and canals.

The facial bones commonly fractured are:
a. The *nasal bone*
b. The *mandible.*

THE ORBIT

The orbits are pyramidal bony cavities, situated one on each side of the root of the nose. They provide sockets for rotatory movements of the eyeballs. They also protect the eyeballs.

Shape and Disposition

Each orbit resembles a four-sided pyramid. Thus, it has:

- *An apex* situated at the posterior end of orbit at the medial end of superior orbital fissure.
- *A base* seen as the orbital opening on the face.
- *Four walls*: Roof, floor, lateral and medial walls.

The long axis of the orbit passes backwards and medially. The medial walls of the two orbits are parallel and the lateral walls are set at right angles to each other (Fig. 1.19).

Roof

It is concave from side to side. It is formed:

1 Mainly by the orbital plate of the frontal bone.
2 It is completed posteriorly by the lesser wing of the sphenoid (Fig. 1.20).

Relations

1 It separates the orbit from the anterior cranial fossa.
2 The frontal air sinus may extend into its anteromedial part.

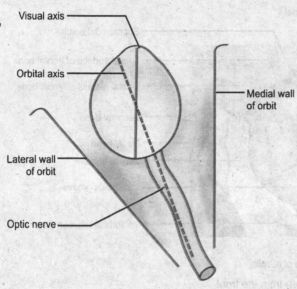

Fig. 1.19: Diagram comparing the orientation of the orbital axis and the visual axis

Named Features

1 The *lacrimal fossa*, placed anterolaterally, lodges the lacrimal gland (Fig. 1.20).

2 The *optic canal lies* posteriorly, at the junction of the roof and medial wall (Figs 1.20 and 1.21).

3 The *trochlear fossa* lies anteromedially. It provides attachment to the fibrous pulley or trochlea for the tendon of the *superior oblique muscle* (Fig. 1.20).

Lateral Wall

This is the thickest and strongest of all the walls of the orbit. It is formed:

1 By the anterior surface of the greater wing of the sphenoid bone posteriorly (Fig. 1.21).

2 By the orbital surface of the frontal process of the zygomatic bone anteriorly.

Relations

1 The greater wing of the sphenoid separates the orbit from the middle cranial fossa.

2 The zygomatic bone separates it from the temporal fossa.

Named Features

1 The *superior orbital fissure* occupies the posterior part of the junction between the roof and lateral wall.

2 The *foramen for the zygomatic nerve* is seen in the zygomatic bone.

3 *Whitnall's* or *zygomatic tubercle* is a palpable elevation on the zygomatic bone just within the orbital margin. It provides attachment to the lateral check ligament of eyeball (Fig. 1.20).

Floor

It slopes upwards and medially to join the medial wall. It is formed:

1 Mainly by the orbital surface of the maxilla (Fig. 1.21).

2 By the lower part of the orbital surface of the zygomatic bone, anterolaterally.

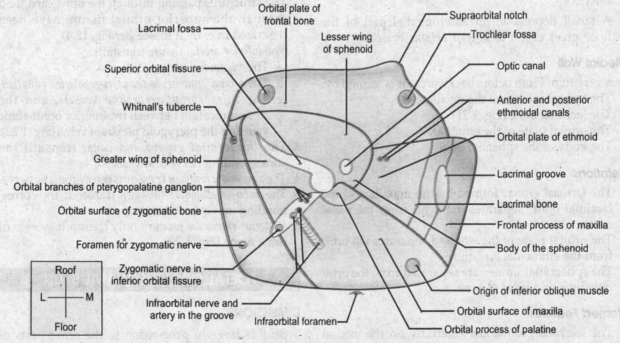

Fig. 1.20: The orbit seen from the front (schematic)

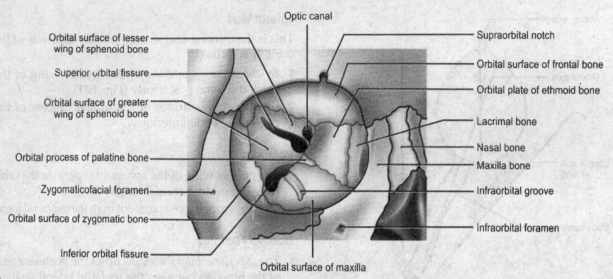

Fig. 1.21: The orbit seen from the front

Labels (clockwise): Optic canal; Supraorbital notch; Orbital surface of frontal bone; Orbital plate of ethmoid bone; Lacrimal bone; Nasal bone; Maxilla bone; Infraorbital groove; Infraorbital foramen; Orbital surface of maxilla; Inferior orbital fissure; Orbital surface of zygomatic bone; Zygomaticofacial foramen; Orbital process of palatine bone; Orbital surface of greater wing of sphenoid bone; Superior orbital fissure; Orbital surface of lesser wing of sphenoid bone

3 The orbital process of the palatine bone, at the posterior angle.

Relation

It separates the orbit from the maxillary sinus.

Named Features

1 The *inferior orbital fissure* occupies the posterior part of the junction between the lateral wall and floor. Through this fissure, the orbit communicates with the infratemporal fossa anteriorly and with the pterygopalatine fossa posteriorly (Figs 1.20 and 1.21).

2 The *infraorbital groove* runs forwards in relation to the floor.

3 A small depression on anteromedial part of the floor gives origin to *inferior oblique muscle*.

Medial Wall

It is very thin. From before backwards, it is formed by:
1 The frontal process of the maxilla.
2 The lacrimal bone (Fig. 1.21).
3 The orbital plate of the ethmoid.
4 The body of the sphenoid bone.

Relations

1 The *lacrimal groove*, formed by the maxilla and the lacrimal bone, separates the orbit from the nasal cavity.

2 The orbital plate of the ethmoid separates the orbit from the ethmoidal air sinuses.

3 The sphenoidal sinuses are separated from the orbit only by a thin layer of bone.

Named Features

1 The lacrimal groove lies anteriorly on the medial wall. It is bounded anteriorly by the lacrimal crest of

the frontal process of the maxilla, and posteriorly by the crest of the lacrimal bone. The floor of the groove is formed by the maxilla in front and by the lacrimal bone behind. The groove lodges the lacrimal sac which lies deep to the lacrimal fascia bridging the lacrimal groove. The groove leads inferiorly, through the nasolacrimal duct, to the inferior meatus of the nose (Fig. 1.21).

2 The *anterior and posterior ethmoidal foramina* lie on the frontoethmoidal suture, at the junction of the roof and medial wall.

Foramina in Relation to the Orbit

1 The structures passing through the optic canal and through the superior orbital fissure have been described in cranial fossae (*see* Fig. 13.4).

2 The *inferior orbital fissure* transmits:
  a. The *zygomatic nerve,*
  b. The *orbital branches of the pterygopalatine ganglion,*
  c. The *infraorbital nerve and vessels*, and the communication between the inferior ophthalmic vein and the pterygoid plexus of veins (Fig. 1.20).

3 The *infraorbital groove and canal* transmit the corresponding nerve and vessels.

4 The *zygomatic foramen* transmits the zygomatic nerve.

5 The *anterior ethmoidal foramen* transmits the corresponding nerve and vessels.

6 *Posterior ethmoidal foramen* only transmits vessels of same name (Fig. 1.20).

FOETAL SKULL/NEONATAL SKULL

DIMENSIONS

1 *Skull* is large in proportion to the other parts of skeleton.

2 *Foetal skeleton* is small as compared to calvaria. In foetal skull, the facial skeleton is 1/7th of calvaria; in adults, it is half of calvaria. The foetal skeleton is small due to rudimentary mandible and maxillae, non-eruption of teeth, and small size of maxillary sinus and nasal cavity. The large size of calvaria is due to precocious growth of brain.

3 *Base of the skull* is short and narrow, though internal ear is almost of adult size, the petrous temporal has not reached the adult length.

STRUCTURE OF BONES

The bones of cranial vault are smooth and unilamellar; there is no diploe. The tables and diploes appear by fourth year of age (Fig. 1.17 and Table 1.2).

Bony Prominences

1 Frontal and parietal tubera are prominent.
2 Glabella, superciliary arches and mastoid processes are not developed.

Paranasal Air Sinuses

These are rudimentary or absent.

Temporal Bone

1 The internal ear, tympanic cavity, tympanic antrum, and ear ossicles are of adult size.
2 The tympanic part is represented by an incomplete tympanic ring.
3 Mastoid process is absent, it appears during the later part of second year.
4 External acoustic meatus is short and straight. Its bony part is unossified and represented by a fibro-cartilaginous plate.
5 Tympanic membrane faces more downwards than laterally due to the absence of mastoid process.
6 Stylomastoid foramen is exposed on the lateral surface of the skull because mastoid portion is flat.
7 Styloid process lies immediately behind the tympanic ring and has not fused with the remainder of the temporal bone.
8 Mandibular fossa is flat and placed more laterally, and the articular tubercle has not developed.
9 The subarcuate fossa is very deep and prominent.
10 Facial canal is short.

Orbits

These are large. The germs of developing teeth lies close to the orbital floor. Orbit comprises base or an outer opening with upper, lower, medial and lateral walls. Its apex lies at the optic foramen/canal. It also has superior and inferior orbital fissures.

OSSIFICATION OF BONES

- Two halves of frontal bone are separated by metopic suture.
- The mandible is also present in two halves. It is a derivative of first branchial arch.
- Occipital bone is in four parts (squamous one, condylar two, and basilar one).
- The four bony elements of temporal bone are separate, except for the commencing union of the tympanic part with the squamous and petrous parts. The second centre for styloid process has not appeared.
- Unossified membranous gaps, a total of 6 fontanelles at the angles of the parietal bones are present (Fig. 1.3).
- Squamous suture between parietal and squamous temporal bone is present.

POSTNATAL GROWTH OF SKULL

The growth of calvaria and facial skeleton proceeds at different rates and over different periods. Growth of calvaria is related to growth of brain, whereas that of the facial skeleton is related to the development of dentition, muscles of mastication, and of the tongue. The rates of growth of the base and vault are also different.

Growth of the Vault

1 *Rate:* Rapid during first year, and then it slows up to the seventh year when it is almost of adult size.
2 *Growth in breadth:* This growth occurs at the sagittal suture, sutures bordering greater wings, occipito-mastoid suture, and the petro-occipital suture at the base.
3 *Growth in height:* This growth occurs at the fronto-zygomatic suture, pterion, squamosal suture, and asterion.
4 *Growth in anteroposterior diameter:* This growth occurs at the coronal and lambdoid sutures.

Growth of the Base

The base grows in anteroposterior diameter at three cartilaginous plates situated between the occipital and sphenoid bones, between the pre- and post-sphenoids, and between the sphenoid and ethmoid.

Growth of the Face

1 Growth of orbits and ethmoid is completed by seventh year.
2 In the face, the growth occurs mostly during first year, although it continues till puberty and even later.

Closure of Fontanelles

Anterior fontanelle (bregma) closes by 18 months, mastoid fontanelle by 12 months, posterior fontanelle (lambda) by 2–3 months and sphenoidal fontanelle also by 2–3 months (Fig. 1.3).

CLINICAL ANATOMY

- Fontanelles help to determine the age in 1–2 years of child.
- Help to know the intracranial pressure. In case of increased pressure, bulging is seen and in case of dehydration, depression is seen at the site of fontanelles.

Thickening of Bones

1 Two tables and diploe appear by fourth year. Differentiation reaches maximum by about 35 years, when the diploic veins produce characteristic marking in the radiographs.
2 Mastoid process appears during second year, and the mastoid air cells during 6th year.

Obliteration of Sutures of the Vault

1 Obliteration begins on the inner surface between 30 and 40 years, and on the outer surface between 40 and 50 years.

2 The timings are variable, but it usually takes place first in the lower part of the coronal suture, next in the posterior part of the sagittal suture, and then in the lambdoid suture.

In Old Age

The skull generally becomes thinner and lighter but in small proportion of cases, it increases in thickness and weight. The most striking feature is reduction in the size of mandible and maxillae due to loss of teeth and absorption of alveolar processes. This causes decrease in the vertical height of the face and a change in the angles of the mandible which become more obtuse.

SEX DIFFERENCES IN THE SKULL

There are no sex differences until puberty. The postpubertal differences are listed in Table 1.3.

Wormian or Sutural Bones

These are small irregular bones found in the region of the fontanelles, and are formed by additional ossification centres.

They are most common at the lambda and at the asterion; common at the pterion (epipteric bone); and rare at the bregma (os Kerkring). Wormian bones are common in hydrocephalic skulls.

Table 1.3: Sex differences in the skull

Features	Males	Females
1. Weight	Heavier	Lighter
2. Size	Larger	Smaller
3. Capacity	Greater in males	10% less than males
4. Walls	Thicker	Thinner
5. Muscular ridges, glabella, superciliary arches, temporal lines, mastoid processes, superior nuchal lines, and external occipital protuberance	More marked	Less marked
6. Tympanic plate	Larger and margins are more roughened	Smaller and margins are less roughened
7. Supraorbital margin	More rounded	Sharp
8. Forehead	Sloping (receding)	Vertical
9. Frontal and parietal tubera	Less prominent	More prominent
10. Vault	Rounded	Somewhat flattened
11. Contour of face	Longer due to greater depth of the jaws. Chin is bigger and projects more forwards. In general, the skull is more rugged due to muscular markings and processes; and zygomatic bones are more massive	Rounded, facial bones are smoother, and mandible and maxillae are smaller.

CRANIOMETRY

Cephalic Index

It expresses the shape of the head, and is the proportion of breadth to length of the skull. Thus:

$$\text{Cephalic index} = \frac{\text{Breadth}}{\text{Length}} \times 100$$

The length or longest diameter is measured from the glabella to the occipital point, the breadth or widest diameter is measured usually a little below the parietal tubera.

Human races may be:

a. *Dolichocephalic* or long-headed when the index is 75 or less.

b. *Mesaticephalic* when the index is between 75 and 80.

c. *Brachycephalic* or short-headed or round-headed when the index is above 80.

d. Dolichocephaly is a feature of primitive races like Eskimos, Negroes, etc.

e. Brachycephaly through mesaticephaly has been a continuous change in the advanced races, like the Europeans.

Facial Angle

This is the angle between two lines drawn from the nasion to the basion or anterior margin of foramen magnum and a line drawn from basion to the prosthion or central point on upper incisor alveolus (Fig. 1.9).

Facial angle is a rough index of the degree of development of the brain because it is the angle between facial skeleton, i.e. splanchnocranium, and the calvaria, i.e. neurocranium, which are inversely proportional to each other. The angle is smallest in the most evolved races of man, it is larger in lower races, and still larger in anthropoids.

Abnormal Crania

Oxycephaly or acrocephaly, tower-skull, or steeple-skull is an abnormally tall skull. It is due to premature closure of the suture between presphenoid and postsphenoid in the base, and the coronal suture in skull cap, so that the skull is very short anteroposteriorly. Compensation is done by the upward growth of skull for the enlarging brain.

Scaphocephaly or boat-shaped skull is due to premature synostosis in the sagittal suture, as a result the skull is very narrow from side to side but greatly elongated.

MANDIBLE

The *mandible*, or the lower jaw, is the largest and the strongest bone of the face. It develops from the *first*

pharyngeal arch. It has a horseshoe-shaped body which lodges the teeth, and a *pair of rami* which project upwards from the posterior ends of the *body*. The rami provide attachment to the muscles of mastication.

BODY

Each half of the body has outer and inner surfaces, and upper and lower borders.

The *outer surface* presents the following features.

a. The *symphysis menti* is the line at which the right and left halves of the bone meet each other. It is marked by a faint ridge (Fig. 1.22).

b. The *mental protuberance* (*mentum* = chin) is a median triangular projecting area in the lower part of the midline. The inferolateral angles of the protuberance form the *mental tubercles*.

c. The *mental foramen* lies below the interval between the premolar teeth (Table 1.4).

d. The *oblique line* is the continuation of the sharp anterior border of the ramus of the mandible. It runs downwards and forwards towards the mental tubercle.

e. The *incisive fossa* is a depression that lies just below the incisor teeth.

The *inner surface* presents the following features.

a. The *mylohyoid line* is a prominent ridge that runs obliquely downwards and forwards from below the third molar tooth to the median area below the genial tubercles (*see* below) (Fig. 1.23).

b. Below the mylohyoid line, the surface is slightly hollowed out to form the *submandibular fossa*, which lodges the submandibular gland.

c. Above the mylohyoid line, there is the *sublingual fossa* in which the sublingual gland lies.

d. The posterior surface of the symphysis menti is marked by four small elevations called the *superior and inferior genial tubercles*.

e. The mylohyoid groove (present on the ramus) extends on to the body below the posterior end of the mylohyoid line.

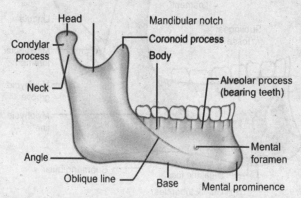

Fig. 1.22: Outer surface of right half of the mandible

The *upper or alveolar border* bears sockets for the teeth. The *lower border* of the mandible is also called the *base*. Near the midline, the base shows an oval depression called the *digastric fossa*.

RAMUS

The ramus is quadrilateral in shape and has:

- Two surfaces—lateral and medial
- Four borders—upper, lower, anterior and posterior
- Two processes—coronoid and condyloid.

The *lateral surface* is flat and bears a number of oblique ridges.

The *medial surface* presents the following:

1. The *mandibular foramen* lies a little above the centre of ramus at the level of occlusal surfaces of the teeth. It leads into the *mandibular canal* which descends into the body of the mandible and opens at the *mental foramen* (Fig. 1.23).

2. The anterior margin of the mandibular foramen is marked by a sharp tongue-shaped projection called the *lingula*. The lingula is directed towards the head or condyloid process of the mandible.

3. The *mylohyoid groove* begins just below the mandibular foramen, and runs downwards and forwards to be gradually lost over the submandibular fossa.

The *upper border* of the ramus is thin and is curved downwards forming the *mandibular notch*.

The *lower border* is the backward continuation of the base of the mandible. Posteriorly, it ends by becoming continuous with the posterior border at the *angle* of the mandible.

The *anterior border* is thin, while the *posterior border* is thick.

The *coronoid* (Greek *crow's beak*) *process* is a flattened triangular upward projection from the anterosuperior part of the ramus. Its anterior border is continuous with the anterior border of the ramus. The posterior border bounds the mandibular notch.

The *condyloid* (Latin *knuckle like*) *process* is a strong upward projection from the posterosuperior part of the ramus. Its upper end is expanded from side to side to form the *head*. The head is covered with fibrocartilage and articulates with the temporal bone to form the temporomandibular joint. The constriction below the head is the *neck*. Its anterior surface presents a depression called the *pterygoid fovea*.

ATTACHMENTS AND RELATIONS OF THE MANDIBLE

1. The oblique line on the lateral side of the body gives origin to the *buccinator* as far forwards as the anterior border of the first molar tooth. In front of this origin, the *depressor labii inferioris* and the *depressor anguli oris* arise from the oblique line below the mental foramen (Fig. 1.24).

2. The incisive fossa gives origin to the *mentalis* and *mental slips of the orbicularis oris*.

3. The parts of both the inner and outer surfaces just below the alveolar margin are covered by the mucous membrane of the mouth.

4. Mylohyoid line gives origin to the *mylohyoid muscle* (Fig. 1.23).

5. *Superior constrictor muscle* of the pharynx arises from an area above the posterior end of the mylohyoid line.

6. *Pterygomandibular raphe* is attached immediately behind the third molar tooth in continuation with the origin of superior constrictor.

7. *Upper genial tubercle* gives origin to the *genioglossus*, and the *lower tubercle* to geniohyoid (Fig. 1.25).

8. *Anterior belly of the digastric* muscle arises from the digastric fossa (Fig. 1.25).

9. *Deep cervical fascia* (investing layer) is attached to the whole length of lower border.

10. The *platysma* is inserted into the lower border (Fig. 1.24).

11. Whole of the lateral surface of ramus except the posterosuperior part provides insertion to the *masseter muscle* (Fig. 1.24).

12. Posterosuperior part of the lateral surface is covered by the *parotid gland*.

13. *Sphenomandibular ligament* is attached to the lingula (Fig. 1.23).

14. The *medial pterygoid muscle* is inserted on the medial surface of the ramus, on the roughened area below and behind the mylohyoid groove (Fig. 1.25).

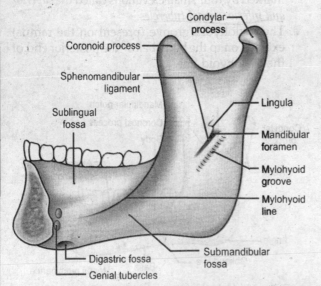

Fig. 1.23: Inner surface of right half of the mandible

Condylar process
Coronoid process
Sphenomandibular ligament
Sublingual fossa
Lingula
Mandibular foramen
Mylohyoid groove
Mylohyoid line
Digastric fossa
Genial tubercles
Submandibular fossa

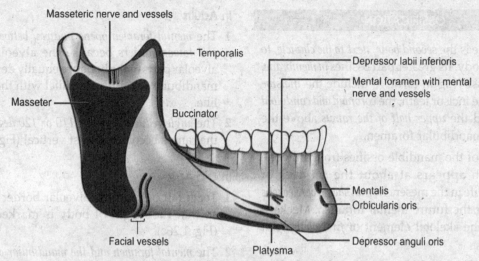

Fig. 1.24: Muscle attachments and relations of outer surface of the mandible

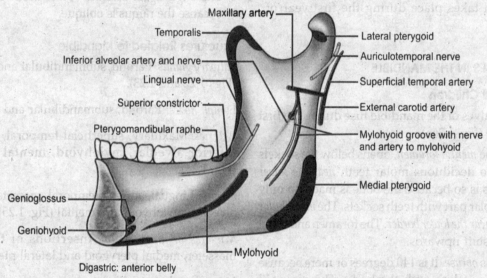

Fig. 1.25: Muscle attachments and relations of inner surface of the mandible

15 The *temporalis* is inserted into the apex and medial surface of the coronoid process. The insertion extends downwards on the anterior border of the ramus (Fig. 1.24).

16 The *lateral pterygoid muscle* is inserted into the pterygoid fovea on the anterior aspect of the neck (Fig. 1.24).

17 The lateral surface of neck provides attachment to the *lateral ligament of the temporomandibular joint* (*see* Fig. 6.9).

FORAMINA AND RELATIONS TO NERVES AND VESSELS

1 The mental foramen transmits the *mental nerve and vessels* (Fig. 1.24).

2 The *inferior alveolar nerve and vessels* enter the *mandibular canal through the mandibular foramen*, and run forwards within the canal.

3 The *mylohyoid nerve and vessels* lie in the *mylohyoid groove* (Fig. 1.25).

4 The *lingual nerve* is related to the medial surface of the ramus in front of the mylohyoid groove (Fig. 1.25).

5 The area above and behind the mandibular foramen is related to the *inferior alveolar nerve and vessels* and to the *maxillary artery* (Fig. 1.25).

6 The *masseteric nerve and vessels* pass through the mandibular notch (Fig. 1.24).

7 The *auriculotemporal nerve* and *superficial temporal artery* are related to the medial side of the neck of mandible (Fig. 1.25).

8 Facial artery is palpable on the lower border of mandible at anteroinferior angle of masseter (Fig. 1.24).

9 Facial and maxillary arteries are not accompanied by respective nerves. The lingual nerve does not get company of its artery.

OSSIFICATION

The mandible is the *second bone, next to the clavicle, to ossify* in the body. Its greater part ossifies *in membrane*. The parts ossifying in *cartilage* include the *incisive part* below the incisor teeth, the *coronoid and condyloid processes*, and the *upper half of the ramus* above the level of the mandibular foramen.

Each half of the mandible ossifies from only one *centre* which appears at about the *6th week* of intrauterine life in the mesenchymal *sheath of Meckel's cartilage* near the future mental foramen. Meckel's cartilage is the skeletal element of *first pharyngeal arch*.

At birth, the mandible consists of two halves connected at the *symphysis menti* by fibrous tissue. Bony union takes place during the first year of life.

AGE CHANGES IN THE MANDIBLE

In Infants and Children

1 The two halves of the mandible fuse during the first year of life (Fig. 1.26a).
2 At birth, the *mental foramen,* opens below the sockets for the two deciduous molar teeth *near the lower border*. This is so because the bone is made up only of the alveolar part with teeth sockets. The *mandibular canal runs near the lower border*. The foramen and canal gradually shift upwards.
3 The angle is *obtuse*. It is 140 degrees or more because the head is in line with the body. The coronoid process is large and projects upwards above the level of the condyle.

In Adults

1 The *mental foramen opens midway between the upper and lower borders* because the alveolar and sub-alveolar parts of the bone are equally developed. The mandibular canal runs parallel with the mylohyoid line.
2 The *angle reduces to about 110 or 120 degrees* because the ramus becomes almost vertical (Fig. 1.26b).

In Old Age

1 Teeth fall out and the alveolar border is absorbed, so that the height of body is markedly reduced (Fig. 1.26c).
2 The *mental foramen and the mandibular canal are close to the alveolar border.*
3 The *angle again becomes obtuse about 140 degrees* because the ramus is oblique.

Structures Related to Mandible

Salivary glands: Parotid, submandibular and sublingual (Figs 1.22 and 1.23).

Lymph nodes: Parotid, submandibular and submental.

Arteries: Maxillary, superficial temporal, masseteric, inferior alveolar, mylohyoid, mental and facial (Fig. 1.24).

Nerves: Lingual, auriculotemporal, masseteric, inferior alveolar, mylohyoid and mental (Fig. 1.25).

Muscles of mastication: Insertions of temporalis, masseter, medial pterygoid and lateral pterygoid.

Ligaments: Lateral ligament of temporomandibular joint, stylomandibular ligament, sphenomandibular and pterygomandibular raphe (Fig. 1.25).

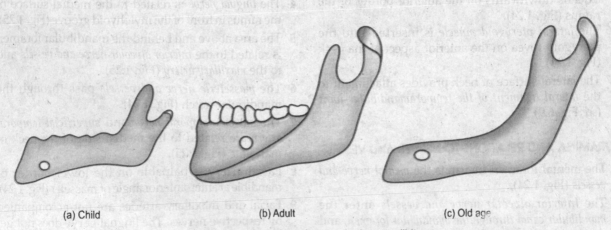

(a) Child   (b) Adult   (c) Old age

Figs 1.26a to c: Age changes in the mandible

CLINICAL ANATOMY

- The mandible is commonly fractured at the canine socket where it is weak. Involvement of the inferior alveolar nerve in the callus may cause neuralgic pain, which may be referred to the areas of distribution of the buccal and auriculotemporal nerves. If the nerve is paralysed, the areas supplied by these nerves become insensitive (Fig. 1.27).
- The next common fracture of the mandible occurs at the angle and neck of mandible (Fig. 1.27).

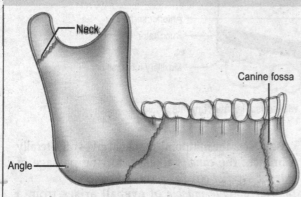

Fig. 1.27: Fracture of the mandible at the neck, at the angle and at canine fossa

MAXILLA

Maxilla is the second largest bone of the face, the first being the mandible. The two maxillae form the whole of the upper jaw, and each maxilla forms a part each in the formation of face, nose, mouth, orbit, the infratemporal and pterygopalatine fossae.

SIDE DETERMINATION

1 Anterior surface ends medially into a deeply concave border, called the *nasal notch*. Posterior surface is convex (Fig. 1.28).
2 Alveolar border with sockets for upper teeth faces downwards with its convexity directed outwards. Frontal process is the longest process which is directed upwards.
3 Medial surface is marked by a large irregular opening, the *maxillary hiatus*/antrum of Highmore for maxillary air sinus.

FEATURES

Each maxilla has a body and four processes—the frontal, zygomatic, alveolar and palatine.

BODY OF MAXILLA

The body of maxilla is pyramidal in shape, with its base directed medially at the nasal surface, and the apex

directed laterally at the zygomatic process. It has four surfaces and encloses a large cavity, the *maxillary sinus* described in Chapter 15.

The surfaces are:
- Anterior or facial,
- Posterior or infratemporal,
- Superior or orbital, and
- Medial or nasal.

Anterior or Facial Surface

1 Anterior surface is directed forwards and laterally.
2 Above the incisor teeth, there is a slight depression, the *incisive fossa*, which gives origin to *depressor septi*. *Incisivus* arises from the alveolar margin below the fossa, and the *nasalis* superolateral to the fossa along the nasal notch.
3 Lateral to canine eminence, there is a larger and deeper depression, the *canine fossa*, which gives origin to *levator anguli oris*.
4 Above the canine fossa, there is *infraorbital foramen*, which transmits *infraorbital nerve and vessels* (Fig. 1.28).
5 *Levator labii superioris* arises between the infraorbital margin and infraorbital foramen.
6 Medially, the anterior surface ends in a deeply concave border, the *nasal notch*, which terminates below into process which with the corresponding process of opposite maxilla forms the anterior nasal spine. Anterior surface bordering the nasal notch gives origin to *nasalis* and *depressor septi*.

Posterior or Infratemporal Surface

1 Posterior surface is convex and directed backwards and laterally.
2 It forms the anterior wall of *infratemporal fossa*, and is separated from anterior surface by the zygomatic process and a rounded ridge which descends from the process to the first molar tooth.
3 Near the centre of the surface open two or three *alveolar canals* for *posterior superior alveolar nerve and vessels*.
4 Posteroinferiorly, there is a rounded eminence, the *maxillary tuberosity*, which articulates superomedially with pyramidal process of palatine bone, and gives origin laterally to the *superficial head of medial pterygoid muscle*.
5 Above the maxillary tuberosity, the smooth surface forms anterior wall of *pterygopalatine fossa*, and is grooved by *maxillary nerve*.

Superior or Orbital Surface

1 Superior surface is smooth, triangular and slightly concave, and forms the greater part of the *floor of orbit*.

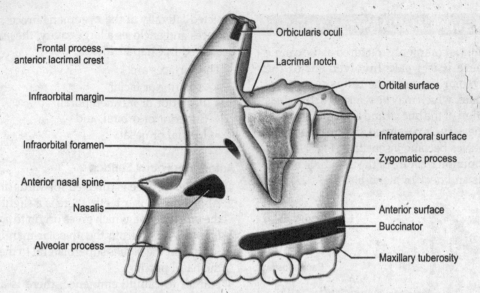

Fig. 1.28: Lateral aspect of maxilla with muscular attachments

2 *Anterior border* forms a part of infraorbital margin. Medially, it is continuous with the lacrimal crest of the frontal process.

3 *Posterior border* is smooth and rounded, it forms most of the anterior margin of inferior orbital fissure. In the middle, it is notched by the infraorbital groove.

4 *Medial border* presents anteriorly the lacrimal notch which is converted into *nasolacrimal canal* by the descending process of lacrimal bone. Behind the notch, the border articulates from before backwards with the *lacrimal, labyrinth of ethmoid, and the orbital process of palatine bone* (Fig. 1.29).

5 The surface presents *infraorbital groove* leading forwards to *infraorbital canal* which opens on the anterior surface as *infraorbital foramen*. The groove, canal and foramen transmit the *infraorbital nerve and*

vessels. Near the midpoint, the canal gives off laterally a branch, the *canalis sinuous*, for the passage of *anterior superior alveolar nerve and vessels.*

6 *Inferior oblique muscle* of eyeball arises from a depression just lateral to lacrimal notch at the anteromedial angle of the surface.

Medial or Nasal Surface

1 Medial surface forms a part of the *lateral wall of nose.*

2 *Posterosuperiorly*, it displays a large irregular opening of the maxillary sinus, the *maxillary hiatus* (Fig. 1.30).

3 Above the hiatus, there are *parts of air sinuses* which are completed by the ethmoid and lacrimal bones.

4 Below the hiatus, the smooth concave surface forms a part of *inferior meatus of nose.*

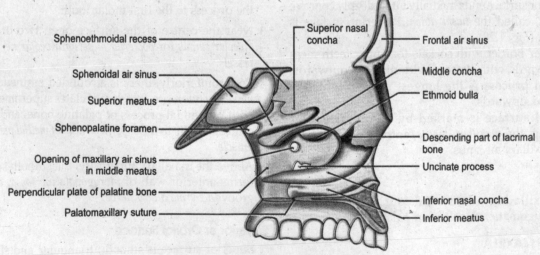

Fig. 1.29: Medial aspect of intact maxilla

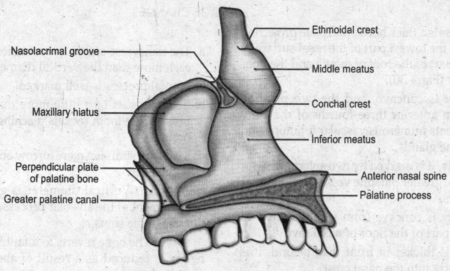

Fig. 1.30: Medial aspect of disarticulated left maxilla

(Labels on figure:)
Nasolacrimal groove
Maxillary hiatus
Perpendicular plate of palatine bone
Greater palatine canal
Ethmoidal crest
Middle meatus
Conchal crest
Inferior meatus
Anterior nasal spine
Palatine process

5 Behind the hiatus, the surface articulates with perpendicular plate of palatine bone, enclosing the *greater palatine canal* which runs downwards and forwards, and transmits *greater palatine vessels and the anterior, middle and posterior palatine nerves* (Fig. 1.12).

6 In front of the hiatus, there is *nasolacrimal groove*, which is converted into the nasolacrimal canal by articulation with the *descending process of lacrimal bone* and the *lacrimal process of inferior nasal concha*. The canal transmits *nasolacrimal duct to the inferior meatus of nose*.

7 More anteriorly, an oblique ridge forms the *conchal crest* for articulation with the inferior nasal concha.

8 Above the conchal crest, the shallow depression forms a part of the *atrium of middle meatus* of nose (*see* Fig. 15.8).

FOUR PROCESSES OF MAXILLA

Zygomatic Process

The zygomatic process is a pyramidal lateral projection on which the anterior, posterior, and superior surfaces of maxilla converge. In front and behind, it is continuous with the corresponding surfaces of the body, but superiorly it is rough for articulation with the zygomatic bone.

Frontal Process

1 The frontal process projects upwards and backwards to *articulate* above with the nasal margin of frontal bone, in front with nasal bone, and behind with lacrimal bone.

2 *Lateral surface* is divided by a vertical ridge, the *anterior lacrimal crest*, into a smooth anterior part and a grooved posterior part.

The lacrimal crest gives attachment to *lacrimal fascia* and the *medial palpebral ligament*, and is continuous below with the infraorbital margin.

The anterior smooth area gives origin to the *orbital part of orbicularis oculi* and *levator labii superioris alaeque nasi*. The posterior grooved area forms the anterior half of the floor of *lacrimal groove* (Fig. 1.45).

3 *Medial surface* forms a part of the lateral wall of nose.

The surface presents following features:

a. Uppermost area is rough for articulation with ethmoid to close the anterior ethmoidal sinuses.

b. *Ethmoidal crest* is a horizontal ridge about the middle of the process. Posterior part of the crest articulates with middle nasal concha, and the anterior part lies beneath the agger nasi (*see* Fig. 15.8).

c. The area below the ethmoidal crest is hollowed out to form the atrium of the middle meatus.

d. Below the atrium is the *conchal crest* which articulates with inferior nasal concha.

e. Below the conchal crest, there lies the inferior meatus of the nose with nasolacrimal groove ending just behind the crest (*see* Fig. 15.8).

Alveolar Process

1 The alveolar process forms half of the alveolar arch, and bears sockets for the roots of upper teeth. In adults, there are eight *sockets: canine socket is deepest; molar sockets are widest* and divided into three minor sockets by septa; the *incisor and second premolar sockets are single;* and the *first premolar socket* is sometimes *divided into two*.

2 *Buccinator* arises from the posterior part of its outer surface up to the first molar tooth (Fig. 1.28).

3 A rough ridge, the *maxillary torus*, is sometimes present on the inner surface opposite the molar sockets.

Head and Neck

Palatine Process

1 Palatine process is a thick horizontal plate projecting medially from the lowest part of the nasal surface. It forms a large part of the roof of mouth and the floor of nasal cavity (Fig. 1.30).

2 *Inferior surface* is concave, and the two palatine processes form anterior three-fourths of the bony palate. It presents numerous vascular foramina and pits for palatine glands.

Posterolaterally, it is marked by two anteroposterior grooves for the greater palatine vessels and anterior palatine nerves.

3 *Superior surface* is concave from side to side, and forms greater part of the floor of nasal cavity.

4 *Medial border* is thicker in front than behind. It is raised superiorly into the nasal crest.

Groove between the nasal crests of two maxillae receives lower border of vomer; anterior part of the ridge is high and is known as *incisor crest* which terminates anteriorly into the anterior nasal spine. Incisive canal traverses near the anterior part of the medial border.

5 *Posterior border* articulates with horizontal plate of palatine bone.

6 *Lateral border* is continuous with the alveolar process.

ARTICULATIONS OF MAXILLA

1 Superiorly, it articulates with three bones—the nasal, frontal and lacrimal.

2 Medially, it articulates with five bones—the ethmoid, inferior nasal concha, vomer, palatine and opposite maxilla.

3 Laterally, it articulates with one bone—the zygomatic.

OSSIFICATION

Maxilla ossifies in membrane from three centres, one for the maxilla proper, and two for os incisivum or *premaxilla*. The centre for maxilla proper appears above the canine fossa during sixth week of intrauterine life.

Of the two premaxillary centres, the main centre appears above the incisive fossa during seventh week of intrauterine life. The second centre (paraseptal or prevomerine) appears at the ventral margin of nasal septum during tenth week and soon fuses with the palatal process of maxilla. Though premaxilla begins to fuse with alveolar process almost immediately after the ossification begins, the evidence of premaxilla as a separate bone may persist until the middle decades.

AGE CHANGES

1 *At birth:*
 a. The transverse and anteroposterior diameters are each more than the vertical diameter.
 b. Frontal process is well marked.
 c. Body consists of a little more than the alveolar process, the tooth sockets reaching to the floor of orbit.
 d. Maxillary sinus is a mere furrow on the lateral wall of the nose.

2 *In the adult:* Vertical diameter is greatest due to development of the alveolar process and increase in the size of the sinus.

3 *In the old:* The bone reverts to infantile condition. Its height is reduced as a result of absorption of the alveolar process.

PARIETAL BONE

Two parietal bones form a large part of the roof and sides of vault of skull. Each bone is roughly quadrilateral in shape with its convexity directed outwards (Fig. 1.31).

SIDE DETERMINATION

Outer surface is convex and smooth, inner surface is concave and depicts vascular markings.

Anteroinferior angle is pointed and shows a groove for anterior division of middle meningeal artery.

FEATURES

Parietal bone has two surfaces, four borders, and four angles.

Surfaces

1 Outer convex
2 Inner concave surface (Fig. 1.32)

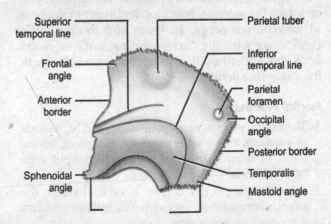

Fig. 1.31: Outer surface of left parietal bone

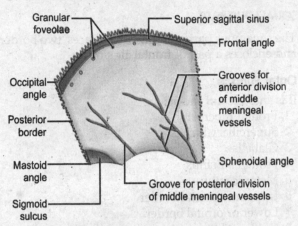

Fig. 1.32: Inner surface of left parietal bone

Borders

1 Superior or sagittal
2 Inferior or squamosal
3 Anterior or frontal
4 Posterior or occipital

Four Angles

1 Anterosuperior or frontal
2 Anteroinferior or sphenoidal
3 Posterosuperior or occipital
4 Posteroinferior or mastoid

At each of the 4 angles are 4 fontanelles. These are:

1 One anterior fontanelle, closes at 18 months.
2 One posterior fontanelles, closes at 3 months
3 Two anterolateral or sphenoidal fontanelles, close at 3 months.

4 Two posterolateral or mastoid fontanelles, close at about 12 months of life.

Details can be studied from norma verticalis and norma lateralis and inner *aspect of skull cap.*

OCCIPITAL BONE

Single occipital bone occupies posterior and inferior parts of the skull (Fig. 1.33).

ANATOMICAL POSITION

It is concave forwards and encloses the largest foramen of skull, foramen magnum, through which cranial cavity communicates with the vertebral canal.

On each side of foramen magnum is the occipital condyle which articulates with atlas vertebra.

FEATURES

Occipital bone is divided into three parts:

1 Squamous part—above, below and behind foramen magnum.
2 Basilar part—lies in front of foramen magnum.
3 Condylar or lateral part—on each side of foramen magnum.

Squamous Part

Comprises two surfaces, three angles and four borders.

Surfaces

External convex surface and internal concave surface.

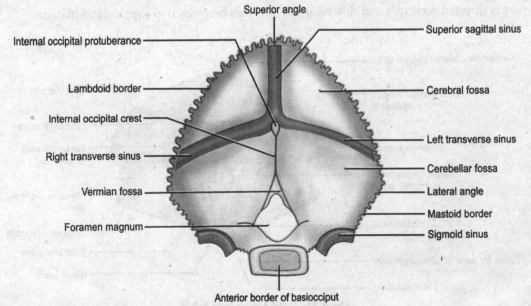

Fig. 1.33: Inner surface of occipital bone

Head and Neck

Angles

One superior angle and two lateral angles.

Borders

Two lambdoid borders in upper part and two mastoid borders in lower part.

Basilar Part

The basilar part of occipital bone is called as basiocciput. It articulates with basisphenoid to form the base of skull. It is quadrilateral in shape and comprises two surfaces and four borders.

Surfaces are superior and inferior.

Borders are anterior, posterior and lateral borders on each side.

Condylar Part

It comprises:
- Superior surface
- Inferior surface which shows occipital condyles and hypoglossal canal.

The details can be read from descriptions of *norma occipitalis* and *posterior cranial fossa*.

FRONTAL BONE

Frontal bone forms the forehead, most of the roof of orbit, most of the floor of anterior cranial fossa. Its parts are squamous, orbital and nasal (Fig. 1.34).

ANATOMICAL POSITION

Squamous part of vertical and is convex forwards.

Two orbital plates are horizontal thin plates projecting backwards.

Nasal part is directed forwards and downwards.

SQUAMOUS PART

The squamous part presents two surfaces, two borders and encloses a pair of frontal air sinuses.

Outer Surface

It is smooth and shows:
1. Frontal tuberosity
2. Superciliary arches
3. Glabella
4. Frontal air sinus
5. Metopic suture
6. Upper or parietal border
7. Lower or orbital border
8. Zygomatic process
9. Temporal line and temporal surfaces

Inner Surface

It is concave and presents following features:
1. Sagittal sulcus
2. Frontal crest

ORBITAL PARTS (PLATES)

Orbital plates are separated from each other by a wide gap, the ethmoidal notch.

Orbital or inferior surface of the plate is smooth and presents lacrimal fossa anterolaterally and trochlear spine anteromedially.

Ethmoidal notch is occupied by cribriform plate of ethmoid bone. On each side of notch are small air spaces which articulates with the labyrinth of ethmoid to complete ethmoidal air sinuses. At the margins are anterior and posterior ethmoidal canals.

NASAL PART

Lies between two supraorbital margins.

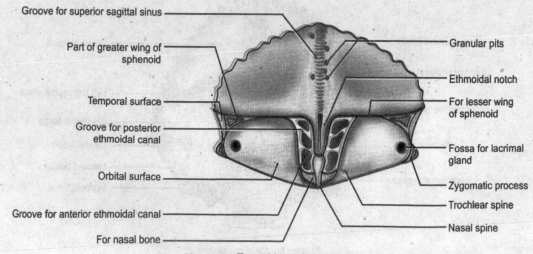

Groove for superior sagittal sinus

Part of greater wing of sphenoid

Temporal surface

Groove for posterior ethmoidal canal

Orbital surface

Groove for anterior ethmoidal canal

For nasal bone

Granular pits

Ethmoidal notch

For lesser wing of sphenoid

Fossa for lacrimal gland

Zygomatic process

Trochlear spine

Nasal spine

Fig. 1.34: Frontal bone from below

The margins of the nasal notch on each side articulate with nasal, frontal process of maxilla and lacrimal bones.

Details can be seen from descriptions of *norma frontalis, norma lateralis, inner aspect of skull cap and anterior cranial fossa.*

TEMPORAL BONE

Temporal bones are situated at the sides and base of skull. It comprises following parts:

a. Squamous part (Fig. 1.35)
b. Petromastoid part
c. Tympanic part
d. Styloid process

SIDE DETERMINATION

- Plate-like squamous part is directed upwards and laterally.
- Strong zygomatic process is directed forwards.
- Petrous part, triangular in shape, is directed medially.
- External acoustic meatus, enclosed between squamous and tympanic parts, is directed laterally.

SQUAMOUS PART

Two surfaces: Outer and inner
Two borders: Superior and anteroinferior

Outer or Temporal Surface

It is smooth and forms a part of temporal fossa.

Above external acoustic meatus, there is a groove for middle temporal artery.

Its posterior part presents supramastoid crest.

Below the anterior end of supramastoid crest and posterosuperior to external acoustic meatus, there is suprameatal triangle.

Zygomatic process springs forwards from the outer surface of squamous part. Its posterior part comprises superior and inferior surfaces. The inferior surface is bounded by two roots which converge at the tubercle of root of the zygoma. Anterior root projects as the articular tubercle in front of mandibular fossa.

Posterior root begins above the external acoustic meatus.

Mandibular fossa lies behind articular tubercle and consists of anterior articular part formed by squamous part of temporal bone and a posterior nonarticular portion formed by tympanic plate.

Inner or Cerebral Surface

It is concave and shows grooves for the middle meningeal vessels. Its superior border articulates with the lower border of parietal bone. Its anteroinferior border articulates with the greater wing of sphenoid.

PETROMASTOID PART

Mastoid Part

Mastoid part (Greek *breast*) forms posterior part of temporal bone. It has:

Two surfaces—outer and inner

Two borders—superior and posterior, and enclose the mastoid air cells. [The outer surface forms a downwards projecting conical process, the mastoid process.]

Two Surfaces

Outer Surface

The outer surface gives attachment to occipitalis muscle. Mastoid foramen opens near its posterior border and transmits an emissary vein and a branch of occipital artery.

Mastoid process appears at the end of 2nd year. Lateral surface gives attachment to sternocleidomastoid, splenius capitis, and longissimus capitis (Fig. 1.14).

Medial surface of the process shows a deep mastoid notch for the origin of posterior belly of digastric. Medial to this notch is a groove for the occipital artery.

Inner Surface

The inner surface is marked by a deep sigmoid sulcus (Fig. 1.36).

Petrous Part

Petreous part (Latin *rock*) triangular in shape. It has a base, an apex, three surfaces—anterior, posterior and inferior; and three borders—superior, anterior and posterior.

Base is fused with squamous and mastoid parts.

Apex is irregular and forms posterolateral boundary of foramen lacerum.

Anterior Surface

Trigeminal impression
   Part forming roof of anterior part of carotid canal.
Arcuate eminence

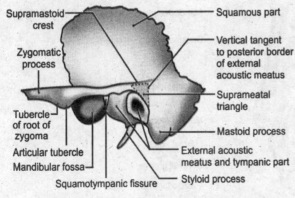

Fig. 1.35: Outer aspect of left temporal bone

Supramastoid crest

Zygomatic process

Tubercle of root of zygoma

Articular tubercle

Mandibular fossa

Squamotympanic fissure

Squamous part

Vertical tangent to posterior border of external acoustic meatus

Suprameatal triangle

Mastoid process

External acoustic meatus and tympanic part

Styloid process

Head and Neck

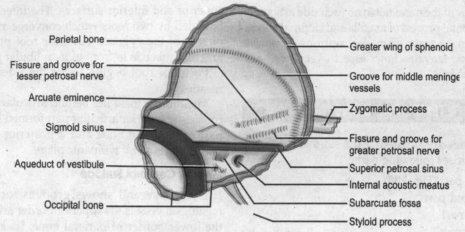

Parietal bone
Fissure and groove for lesser petrosal nerve
Arcuate eminence
Sigmoid sinus
Aqueduct of vestibule
Occipital bone

Greater wing of sphenoid
Groove for middle meningeal vessels
Zygomatic process
Fissure and groove for greater petrosal nerve
Superior petrosal sinus
Internal acoustic meatus
Subarcuate fossa
Styloid process

Fig. 1.36: Inner aspect of the left temporal bone

Tegmen tympani lying most laterally. In the anterior part of tegmen tympani are hiatus and groove for greater petrosal nerve and a smaller hiatus and groove for the lesser petrosal nerve.

Posterior Surface

Internal acoustic meatus is present here.

Aqueduct of vestibule lies behind internal acoustic meatus.

Inferior Surface

Forms part of norma basalis. It shows lower opening of carotid canal (*refer* to norma basalis for details) Jugular fossa lies behind carotid canal (Fig. 1.37).

TYMPANIC PART

It is a curved plate of bone below squamous part and in front of mastoid process. It comprises:

Two Surfaces

Anterior and posterior concave part forming anterior wall, floor and lower part of the posterior wall of external acoustic meatus.

Three Borders

Lateral which forms the margin of external acoustic meatus.

Upper border and lower border which in its lateral part split to enclose the root of styloid process.

External Acoustic Meatus

Bony part of meatus is about 16 mm long.

Its anterior wall, floor and lower part of posterior wall are formed by tympanic part. Its roof and upper half of the posterior wall are formed by the squamous part (Fig. 1.35).

Its inner end is closed by tympanic membrane.

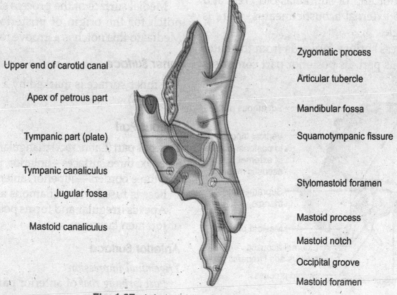

Upper end of carotid canal
Apex of petrous part
Tympanic part (plate)
Tympanic canaliculus
Jugular fossa
Mastoid canaliculus

Zygomatic process
Articular tubercle
Mandibular fossa
Squamotympanic fissure
Stylomastoid foramen
Mastoid process
Mastoid notch
Occipital groove
Mastoid foramen

Fig. 1.37: Inferior view of the temporal bone

STYLOID PROCESS

Styloid (Greek *pillar form*) process is long pointed process directed downwards, forwards and medially between parotid gland and internal jugular vein (Fig. 1.36).

- Its base is related to facial nerve
- Its apex is crossed by external carotid artery.
- It gives attachment to three muscles and 2 ligaments (*see* Chapter 8) (*refer* to norma lateralis for details).

SPHENOID BONE

Sphenoid (Greek *wedge*) bone resembles a bat with outstretched wings. It comprises:

- A body in the centre (Fig. 1.38).
- Two lesser wings from the anterior part of body.
- Two greater wings from the lateral part of body.
- Two pterygoid (wing-like) processes, directed downwards from the junction of body and greater wings.

BODY OF SPHENOID

It comprises six surfaces and enclose a pair of sphenoidal air sinuses.

Superior or Cerebral Surface

It articulates with ethmoid bone anteriorly and basilar part of occipital bone posteriorly. It shows:

1 Jugum sphenoidale
2 Sulcus chiasmaticus
3 Tuberculum sellae
4 Sella turcica
5 Dorsum sellae
6 Clivus

Refer to middle cranial fossa for details.

Inferior Surface

1 Rostrum of sphenoid (Fig. 1.39a)
2 Sphenoid conchae (Fig. 1.39b)
3 Vaginal processes of medial pterygoid plate

Refer to norma basalis for details.

Anterior Surface

Sphenoidal crest articulates with perpendicular plate of ethmoid to form a small part of septum of nose.

Opening of sphenoidal air sinus is seen (Fig. 1.39b).

Sphenoidal conchae close the sphenoid air sinuses leaving the openings. Each half of anterior surface has two parts: superolateral and inferomedial.

The superolateral depression articulates with labyrinth of ethmoid to complete the posterior ethmoidal air sinuses. The inferomedial smooth triangular area forms the posterior part of the root of the nose.

Posterior Surface

It articulates with basilar part of occipital bone.

Lateral Surfaces

Carotid sulcus, a broad groove curved like letter 'f' for lodging cavernous sinus and internal carotid artery. Below the sulcus it articulates with greater wing of sphenoid laterally and with pterygoid process which is directed downwards.

Sphenoidal Air Sinuses

These are asymmetrical air sinuses in the body of sphenoid, and are closed by sphenoidal conchae. The sinus opens into the lateral wall of nose in the spheno-ethmoidal recess above the superior concha.

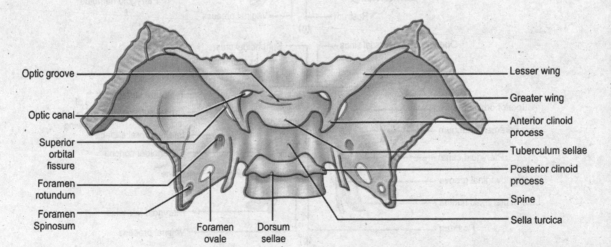

Fig. 1.38: Superior view of the sphenoid bone

Optic groove
Optic canal
Superior orbital fissure
Foramen rotundum
Foramen Spinosum
Foramen ovale
Dorsum sellae
Lesser wing
Greater wing
Anterior clinoid process
Tuberculum sellae
Posterior clinoid process
Spine
Sella turcica

Head and Neck

GREATER WINGS

These are two strong processes which curve laterally and upwards from the sides of the body. It has three surfaces.

Superior or Cerebral Surface

It forms the floor of middle cranial fossa and presents from before backwards:

1 Foramen rotundum (Fig. 1.39a)
2 Foramen ovale
3 Emissary sphenoidale foramen
4 Foramen spinosum

Lateral Surface

A horizontal ridge, the infratemporal crest divides this surface into upper or temporal surface and a lower or infratemporal surface. It is pierced by foramen ovale and foramen spinosum. Its posterior part presents spine of sphenoid.

Refer to norma basalis for details.

Orbital Surface

Forms the posterior wall of the lateral wall of orbit.

Its medial border bears a small tubercle for attachment of a common tendinous ring for the origin of recti muscles of the eyeball. Below the medial end of superior orbital fissure, the grooved area forms the posterior wall of the pterygopalatine fossa and is pierced by foramen rotundum (Fig. 1.39b).

Borders are surrounding the greater wing of sphenoid.

LESSER WINGS

Lesser wings are two triangular plates projecting laterally from the anterosuperior part of the body. It comprises:

- A base forming medial end of the wing. It is connected to the body by two roots which enclose the optic canal.
- Tip forms the lateral end of the wing.
- Superior surface forming floor of anterior cranial fossa.

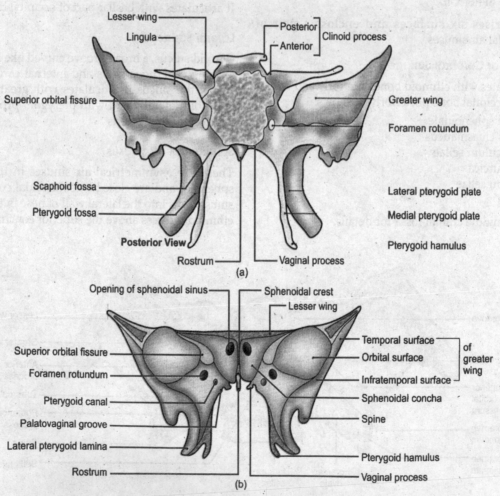

Figs 1.39a and b: (a) Posterior view of sphenoid, and (b) greater and lesser wings of sphenoid

- Inferior surface forming upper boundary of superior orbital fissure.
- Anterior border articulates with the posterior border of orbital plate of frontal bone.
- Posterior border is free and projects into the stem of lateral sulcus of brain. Medially, it terminates into the anterior clinoid process.

Superior Orbital Fissure

It is a triangular gap through which middle cranial fossa communicates with the orbit. The structures passing through it are put in list of foramina and structures passing through them (*see* Fig. 13.4).

PTERYGOID PROCESSES

One pterygoid (Greek *wing*) process on each side projects downwards from the junction of the body with the greater wing of sphenoid (Fig. 1.38).

Each pterygoid process divides inferiorly into the medial and lateral pterygoid plates. The plates are fused together in their upper parts, but are separated in their lower parts by the pterygoid fissure. Posteriorly the pterygoid plates enclose a "V-shaped interval", the pterygoid fossa. The medial pterygoid plate in its upper part presents a scaphoid fossa.

Refer to *norma basalis* for medial and lateral pterygoid plates.

ETHMOID BONE

Ethmoid (Greek *sieve*) is a very light cuboidal bone situated in the anterior of base of cranial cavity between the two orbits. It forms:

1 Part of medial orbital walls
2 Part of nasal septum (Fig. 1.40a)
3 Part of roof of orbit
4 Lateral walls of the nasal cavity

Ethmoid bone comprises:

1 Cribriform plate (Fig. 1.40b)
2 Perpendicular plate
3 A pair of labyrinth

CRIBRIFORM PLATE

It is a horizontal perforated bony lamina, occupying ethmoidal notch of frontal bone. It contains foramina for olfactory nerve rootlets.

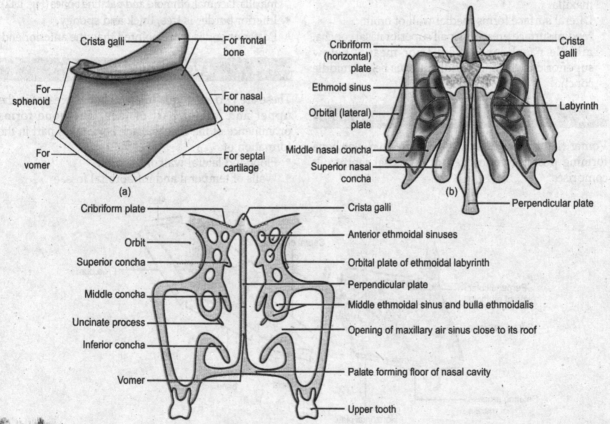

Figs 1.40a to c: (a) Articulations of perpendicular plate, (b) posterior view of the ethmoid bone, and (c) ethmoid bone articulating with neighbouring bones

Crista Galli

Crista galli is a median, tooth-like upward projection in the floor of anterior cranial fossa. Foramen transmitting anterior ethmoidal nerve to nasal cavity is situated by the side of crista galli.

PERPENDICULAR PLATE

It is a thin lamina projecting downwards from the under-surface of the cribriform plate, forming upper part of nasal septum.

LABYRINTHS

These are two light cubical masses situated on each side of the perpendicular plate, suspended from the undersurface of the cribriform plate (Fig. 1.40c).

Each labyrinth also encloses large number of "air cells" arranged in three groups; the anterior, middle and posterior ethmoidal air sinuses. Its surfaces are:

* Anterior surface articulates with frontal process of maxilla to complete anterior ethmoidal air cells.
* Posterior surface articulates with sphenoidal concha to complete posterior ethmoidal air cells.
* Superior surface articulates with orbital plate of frontal bone.
* Inferior surface articulates with nasal surface of maxilla.
* Lateral surface forms medial wall of orbit.
* Medial surface presents small superior nasal concha, middle nasal concha, superior meatus below superior concha, and middle meatus below middle concha.

VOMER

Vomer (Latin *plough share*) is a single thin, flat bone forming posteroinferior part of the nasal septum. It comprises:

* Right and left surfaces marked by nasopalatine nerves which course downwards and forwards.
* Superior border splits into two alae with a groove is occupied by rostrum of sphenoid (Fig. 1.41).
* Inferior border articulates with nasal crests of maxillae and palatine bones.
* Anterior, longest border articulates with perpendicular plate of ethmoid above and with septal cartilage below.
* Posterior border is free and separates the two posterior nasal openings.

INFERIOR NASAL CONCHAE

The inferior nasal conchae are two curved bony laminae, these are horizontally placed in the lower part of lateral walls of the nose. Between this concha and floor of the nose lies the inferior meatus of the nose. It comprises 2 surfaces, 2 borders and 2 ends.

* Medial convex surface is marked by vascular grooves.
* Lateral concave surface forms the medial wall of inferior meatus of the nerve.
* Superior border is irregular and articulates with maxilla, lacrimal, ethmoid and palatine bones (Fig. 1.42).
* Inferior border is free, thick and spongy.
* Posterior end is more pointed than the anterior end.

ZYGOMATIC BONES

These are two small quadrilateral bones present in the upper and lateral part of face. The bone forms prominence of the cheeks. Each bone takes part in the formation of:

* Floor and lateral wall of the orbit
* Walls of temporal and infraorbital fossae

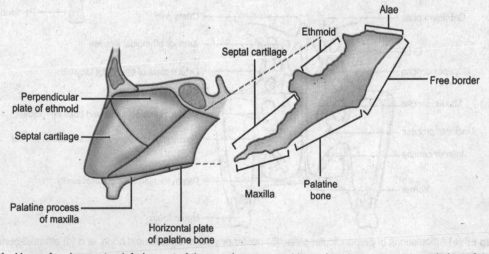

Fig. 1.41: Vomer forming posteroinferior part of the nasal septum and its various borders. Left lateral view of the vomer

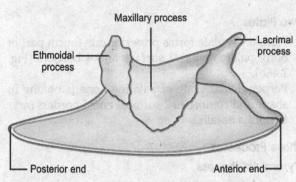

Fig. 1.42: Lateral view of the left inferior nasal concha

Zygomatic bone comprises 3 surfaces, 5 borders and 2 processes.

Surfaces

1 Lateral surface presenting zygomaticofacial foramen (Fig. 1.43a).
2 Temporal surface is smooth and concave and presents zygomaticotemporal foramen (Fig.1.43b).
3 Orbital surface is also smooth and concave one or two zygomaticoorbital foramen on this surface and this bads to zygomaticofacial and zygomatico-temporal foramina (Fig. 1.20).

Borders

1 Anterosuperior or orbital
2 Anteroinferior or maxillary
3 Posteroinferior or temporal border
4 Posteroinferior border
5 Posteromedial border.

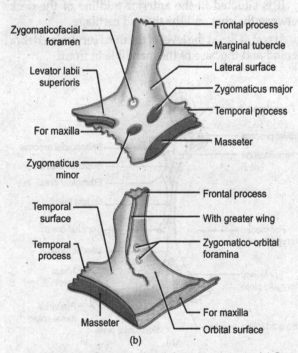

(b)

Figs 1.43a and b: Features of the left zygomatic bone: (a) Outer view, and (b) inner view

Processes

1 Frontal process, which is directed upwards.
2 Temporal process, which is directed backwards.

NASAL BONES

Nasal bones are two small oblong bones, which form the bridge of the nerve.

Each nasal bone has two surfaces and four borders (Fig. 1.44).

Surfaces

1 The outer surface is convex from side to side.
2 The inner surface is concave from side to side and is traversed by a vertical groove or anterior ethmoidal nerve.

Borders

1 Superior border is thick and serrated and articulates with nasal part of frontal bone.
2 Inferior border is thin and notched and articulates with lateral nasal cartilage.
3 Medial border articulates with opposite nasal bone.
4 Lateral border articulates with frontal process of maxilla.

LACRIMAL BONES

Lacrimal bones are extremely delicate and smallest of the skull bones. These form the anterior part of the medial part of the orbit. Each lacrimal bone comprises 2 surfaces and 4 borders.

Surfaces

1 Lateral or orbital surface is divided by posterior lacrimal crest into anterior and posterior parts. The anterior grooved part forms posterior half of the floor

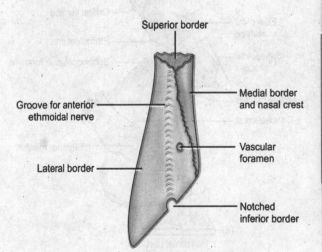

Fig. 1.44: Inner view of the left nasal bone

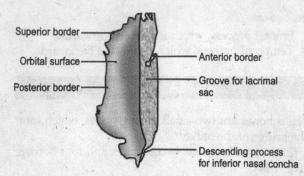

Fig. 1.45: Lateral surface of the left lacrimal bone

of lacrimal groove for lacrimal sac. The posterior smooth part forms part of medial wall of orbit.

2 Medial or nasal surface forms a part of middle meatus of the nose (Fig. 1.45).

Borders

1 Anterior border articulates with frontal process of maxilla.
2 Posterior border with orbital plate of ethmoid.
3 Superior border with frontal bone.
4 Inferior border with orbital surface of maxilla.

PALATINE BONES

Palatine bones are two L-shaped bones present in the posterior part of nasal cavity. Each bone forms:
• Lateral wall and floor of nasal cavity (Fig. 1.46a).
• Roof of mouth cavity
• Floor of the orbit
• Parts of pterygopalatine fossa
Each palatine bone has 2 plates and 3 processes.

Two Plates

1 Horizontal plate forms posterior one-fourth part of bony palate. It has 2 surface and 4 borders (Fig. 1.46b).
2 Perpendicular plate of palatine bone is oblong in shape and comprises 2 surfaces and 4 borders (*refer to norma basalis*).

Three Processes

Pyramidal Process

Pyramidal process projects downwards from the junction of two plates. Its inferior surface is pierced by lesser palatine foramina.

Orbital Process

Orbital process projects upwards and laterally from the perpendicular plate. Its orbital surface is triangular and forms the posterior part of the floor of the orbit (Fig. 1.46b).

Sphenoidal Process

Sphenoidal process projects upwards and medially from the perpendicular plate. Its lateral surface articulates with medial pterygoid plate.

HYOID BONE

The hyoid (Greek *U'shaped*) bone is U-shaped.

It develops from second and third branchial arches.

It is situated in the anterior midline of the neck between the chin and the thyroid cartilage.

At rest, it lies at the level of the third cervical vertebra behind and the base of the mandible in front.

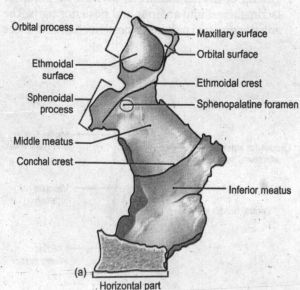

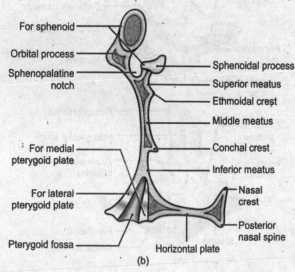

Figs 1.46a and b: (a) Medial view of the left palatine bone, and (b) various processes of palatine bone

It is kept suspended in position by muscles and ligaments (Fig. 1.47).

The hyoid bone provides attachment to the muscles of the floor of the mouth and to the tongue above, to the larynx below, and to the epiglottis and pharynx behind (Fig. 1.47).

The bone consists of the central part, called the body, and of two pairs of cornua—greater and lesser.

Body

It has two surfaces—anterior and posterior, and two borders—upper and lower.

The *anterior surface* is convex and is directed forwards and upwards. It is often divided by a median ridge into two lateral halves.

The *posterior surface* is concave and is directed backwards and downwards.

Each lateral end of the body is continuous posteriorly with the greater horn or cornua. However, till middle life, the connection between the body and greater cornua is fibrous.

Greater Cornua

These are flattened from above downwards. Each cornua tapers posteriorly, but ends in a tubercle. It has two surfaces—upper and lower, two borders—medial and lateral and a tubercle.

Lesser Cornua

These are small conical pieces of bone which project upwards from the junction of the body and greater cornua. The lesser cornua are connected to the body by fibrous tissue. Occasionally, they are connected to the greater cornua by synovial joints which usually persist throughout life, but may get ankylosed.

ATTACHMENTS ON THE HYOID BONE

1 The anterior surface of the body provides insertion to the *geniohyoid* and *mylohyoid* muscles and gives origin to a part of the *hyoglossus* which extends to the greater cornua (Fig. 1.47).

2 The *upper border* of the body provides insertion to the lower fibres of the genioglossi and attachment to the *thyrohyoid membrane*.

The *lower border* of the body provides attachment to the *pretracheal fascia*. In front of the fascia, the *sternohyoid* is inserted medially and the superior belly of *omohyoid* laterally.

Below the omohyoid, there is the linear attachment of the *thyrohyoid*, extending back to the lower border of the greater cornua.

The *medial border* of the greater cornua provides attachment to the *thyrohyoid membrane, stylohyoid muscle* and *digastric pulley*.

The *lateral border* of the greater cornua provides insertion to the thyrohyoid muscle anteriorly. The *investing fascia* is attached throughout its length.

The lesser cornua provides attachment to the *stylohyoid ligament* at its tip. The *middle constrictor* muscle arises from its posterolateral aspect extending on to the greater cornua (*see* Fig. 14.21).

DEVELOPMENT

Upper part of body and lesser cornua develop from second branchial arch, while lower part of body and greater cornua develop from the third arch.

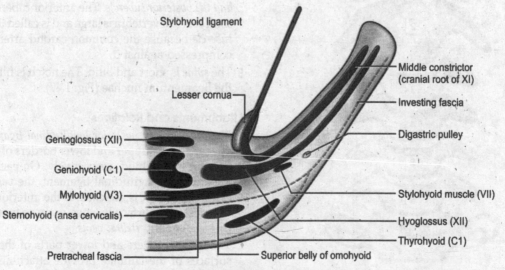

Fig. 1.47: Anterosuperior view of the left half of hyoid bone showing its attachments

Labels:
- Stylohyoid ligament
- Lesser cornua
- Genioglossus (XII)
- Geniohyoid (C1)
- Mylohyoid (V3)
- Sternohyoid (ansa cervicalis)
- Pretracheal fascia
- Middle constrictor (cranial root of XI)
- Investing fascia
- Digastric pulley
- Stylohyoid muscle (VII)
- Hyoglossus (XII)
- Thyrohyoid (C1)
- Superior belly of omohyoid

Head and Neck

CLINICAL ANATOMY

In a suspected case of murder, fracture of the hyoid bone strongly indicates throttling or strangulation.

CERVICAL VERTEBRAE

IDENTIFICATION

The cervical vertebrae are identified by the presence of foramina transversaria.

There are seven cervical vertebrae, out of which the third to sixth are typical, while the first, second and seventh are atypical (Fig. 1.48).

TYPICAL CERVICAL VERTEBRAE

Body

1 The body is *small* and *broader* from side to side than from before backwards.
2 Its *superior surface* is concave transversely with upward projecting lips on each side. The anterior border of this surface may be bevelled.
3 The *inferior surface* is saddle-shaped, being convex from side to side and concave from before backwards. The lateral borders are bevelled and form synovial joints with the projecting lips of the next lower vertebra. The anterior border projects downwards and may hide the intervertebral disc.
4 The *anterior and posterior surfaces* resemble those of other vertebrae (Fig. 1.49).

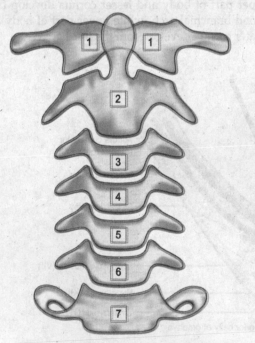

Fig. 1.48: Cervical vertebrae—anterior view

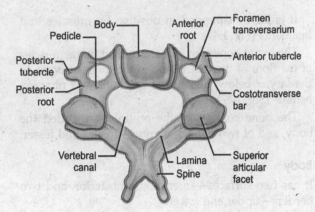

Fig. 1.49: Typical cervical vertebra seen from above

Vertebral Foramen

Vertebral foramen is larger than the body. It is triangular in shape because the pedicles are directed backwards and laterally.

Vertebral Arch

1 The *pedicles* are directed backwards and laterally. The superior and inferior vertebral notches are of equal size.
2 The *laminae* are relatively long and narrow, being thinner above than below.
3 The *superior and inferior articular processes* form articular pillars which project laterally at the junction of pedicle and the lamina. The superior articular facets are flat. They are directed backwards and upwards. The inferior articular facets are also flat but are directed forwards and downwards.
4 The *transverse processes* are pierced by foramina transversaria. Each process has *anterior* and *posterior roots* which end in tubercles joined by the *costotransverse bar*. The costal element is represented by the *anterior root, anterior tubercle, the costotransverse bar and the posterior tubercle.* The anterior tubercle of the sixth cervical vertebra is large and is called the *carotid tubercle* because the common carotid artery can be compressed against it.
5 The *spine* is short and bifid. The notch is filled up by the ligamentum nuchae (Fig. 1.49).

Attachments and Relations

1 The *anterior and posterior longitudinal ligaments* are attached to the upper and lower borders of the body in front and behind, respectively. On each side of the anterior longitudinal ligament, the *vertical part of the longus colli* is attached to the anterior surface. The posterior surface has two or more foramina for passage of *basivertebral veins*.
2 The upper borders and lower parts of the anterior surfaces of the laminae provide attachment to the *ligamenta flava*.

3 The *foramen transversarium* transmits the *vertebral artery*, the *vertebral veins* and a *branch from the inferior cervical ganglion*. The *anterior tubercles* give origin to the *scalenus anterior*, the *longus capitis*, and the *oblique part of the longus colli*.

4 The *costotransverse bars* are grooved by the *anterior primary rami* of the corresponding cervical nerves.

5 The *posterior tubercles* give origin to the *scalenus medius*, *scalenus posterior*, the *levator scapulae*, the *splenius cervicis*, the *longissimus cervicis*, and the *iliocostalis cervicis* (*see* Fig. 10.3).

6 The spine gives origin to the deep muscles of the back of the neck *interspinales, semispinalis thoracis and cervicis, spinalis cervicis, and multifidus* (*see* Figs 10.2 and 10.4).

OSSIFICATION

A typical cervical vertebra ossifies from three primary and six secondary centres. There is one *primary centre* for each half of the neural arch during 9 to 10 weeks of foetal life and one for the *centrum* in 3 to 4 months of foetal life. The two halves of the neural arch fuse posteriorly with each other during the first year. Synostosis at the neurocentral synchondrosis occurs during the third year.

The *secondary centres, two* for the annular epiphyseal discs for the peripheral parts of the upper and lower surfaces of the body, *two* for the tips of the transverse processes, and *two* for the bifid spine appear during puberty, and fuse with the rest of the vertebra by 25 years.

FIRST CERVICAL VERTEBRA

It is called the *atlas* (Tiltan, who supported the heaven). It can be identified by the following features:

1 It is ring-shaped. It has neither a body nor a spine (Fig. 1.50).

2 The atlas has a short anterior arch, a long posterior arch, right and left lateral masses, and transverse processes.

3 The *anterior arch* is marked by a median *anterior tubercle* on its anterior aspect. Its posterior surface bears an *oval facet* which articulates with the *dens* (Fig. 1.50).

4 The *posterior arch* forms about two-fifths of the ring and is much longer than the anterior arch. Its posterior surface is marked by a median posterior tubercle. The upper surface of the arch is marked behind the lateral mass by a *groove*.

Each *lateral mass* shows the following important features:

a. Its upper surface bears the *superior articular facet*. This facet is elongated (forwards and medially), concave, and is directed upwards and medially. It articulates with the corresponding condyle to form an atlanto-occipital joint.

b. The lower surface is marked by the *inferior articular facet*. This facet is nearly circular, more or less flat, and is directed downwards, medially and backwards. It articulates with the corresponding facet on the axis vertebra to form an atlantoaxial joint.

c. The medial surface of the lateral mass is marked by a small roughened tubercle.

d. The *transverse process* projects laterally from the lateral mass. It is unusually long and can be felt on the surface of the neck between the angle of mandible and the mastoid process. Its long length allows it to act as an effective lever for rotatory movements of the head. The transverse process is pierced by the foramen transversarium.

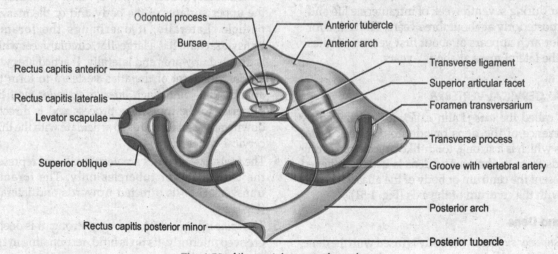

Odontoid process — Anterior tubercle
Bursae — Anterior arch
Rectus capitis anterior — Transverse ligament
Rectus capitis lateralis — Superior articular facet
Levator scapulae — Foramen transversarium
— Transverse process
Superior oblique — Groove with vertebral artery
— Posterior arch
Rectus capitis posterior minor — Posterior tubercle

Fig. 1.50: Atlas vertebra seen from above

Head and Neck

Attachments and Relations

1 The anterior tubercle provides attachment (in the median plane) to the *anterior longitudinal ligament*, and provides insertion on each side to the *upper oblique part of longus colli*.

2 The upper border of the anterior arch gives attachment to the *anterior atlanto-occipital membrane*.

3 The lower border of the anterior arch gives attachment to the lateral fibres of the *anterior longitudinal ligament*.

4 The posterior tubercle provides attachment to the *ligamentum nuchae* in the median plane and gives origin to the *rectus capitis posterior minor* on each side (Fig. 1.50).

5 The groove on the upper surface of the posterior arch is occupied by the *vertebral artery* and by the *first cervical nerve*. Behind the groove, the upper border of the posterior arch gives attachment to the *posterior atlanto-occipital membrane* (*see* Figs 10.5 and 10.6).

6 The lower border of the posterior arch gives attachment to the highest pair of *ligamenta flava*.

7 The tubercle on the medial side of the lateral mass gives attachment to the *transverse ligament of the atlas*.

8 The anterior surface of the lateral mass gives origin to the *rectus capitis anterior*.

9 The transverse process *gives origin to the rectus capitis lateralis* from its upper surface anteriorly, the *superior oblique* from its upper surface posteriorly, the *inferior oblique* from its lower surface of the tip, the *levator scapulae* from its lateral margin and lower border, the *splenius cervicis*, and the *scalenus medius* from the posterior tubercle of transverse process.

OSSIFICATION

Atlas ossifies from three centres, one for each lateral mass with half of the posterior arch, one for the anterior arch. The centres for the lateral masses appear during seventh week of intrauterine life and unite posteriorly at about three years. The centre for anterior arch appears at about first year and unites with the lateral mass at about 7 years.

SECOND CERVICAL VERTEBRA

This is called the *axis* (Latin *axile*). It is identified by the presence of the dens or odontoid (Greek *tooth*) process which is a strong, tooth-like process projecting upwards from the body. The dens is usually believed to represent the centrum or body of the atlas which has fused with the centrum of the axis (Fig. 1.51).

Body and Dens

1 The *superior surface* of the body is fused with the dens, and is encroached upon on each side by the superior

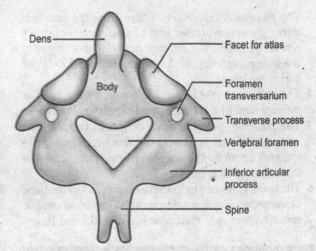

Fig. 1.51: Axis vertebra, posterosuperior view

articular facets. The dens articulates anteriorly with oval fact on posterior surface of the anterior arch of the atlas, and posteriorly with the transverse ligament of the atlas.

2 The *inferior surface* has a prominent anterior margin which projects downwards.

3 The *anterior surface* presents a median ridge on each side of which there are hollowed out impressions.

Vertebral Arch

1 The *pedicles* are concealed superiorly by the superior articular processes. The inferior surface presents a deep and wide *inferior vertebral notch*, placed in front of the inferior articular process. The superior vertebral notch is very shallow and is placed on the upper border of the lamina, behind the superior articular process.

2 The *laminae* are thick and strong.

3 Articular facets: Each *superior articular facet* occupies the upper surfaces of the body and of the massive pedicle. Laterally, it overhangs the foramen transversarium. It is a large, flat, circular facet which is directed upwards and laterally. It articulates with the inferior facet of the atlas vertebra to form the atlantoaxial joint. Each *inferior articular facet* lies posterior to the transverse process and is directed downwards and forwards to articulate with the third cervical vertebra.

4 The *transverse processes* are very small and represent the true posterior tubercles only. The foramen transversarium is directed upwards and laterally (Fig. 1.51).

5 The *spine* is large, thick and very strong. It is deeply grooved inferiorly. Its tip is bifid, terminating in two rough tubercles.

Attachments

1 The dens provides attachment at its apex to the *apical ligament*, and on each side, below the apex to the *alar ligaments* (*see* Fig. 9.12).
2 The anterior surface of the body receives the insertion of the *longus colli*. The *anterior longitudinal ligament* is also attached to the anterior surface.
3 The posterior surface of the body provides attachment, from below upwards, to the *posterior longitudinal ligament*, the *membrana tectoria* and the *vertical limb* of the *cruciate ligament*.
4 The laminae provide attachment to the *ligamenta flava*.
5 The transverse process gives origin by its tip to the *levator scapulae*, the *scalenus medius* anteriorly and the *splenius cervicis* posteriorly. The *intertransverse muscles* are attached to the upper and lower surfaces of the process.
6 The spine gives attachment to the *ligamentum nuchae*, the *semispinalis cervicis*, the *rectus capitis posterior major*, the *inferior oblique*, the *spinalis cervicis*, the *interspinalis* and the *multifidus* (*see* Chapter 10).

SEVENTH CERVICAL VERTEBRA

It is also known as the *vertebra prominens* because of its long spinous process, the tip of which can be felt through the skin at the lower end of the nuchal furrow.

Its spine is thick, long and nearly horizontal. It is not bifid, but ends in a tubercle (Fig. 1.52).

The transverse processes are comparatively large in size, the posterior root is larger than the anterior. The anterior tubercle is absent. The foramen transversarium is relatively small, sometimes double, or may be entirely absent. It does not transmit the vertebral artery.

Attachments

1 The tip of the *spine* provides attachment to the *ligamentum nuchae*, *trapezius*, *rhomboid minor*, *serratus posterior superior*, *splenius capitis*, *semispinalis thoracis*, *spinalis cervicis*, *interspinales*, and the *multifidus* (*see* Fig. 10.3).

2 *Transverse process:* The *foramen transversarium* usually transmits only an accessory vertebral vein. The *posterior tubercle* provides attachment to the *suprapleural membrane*. The lower *border* provides attachment to the *levator costarum*.

The anterior root of the transverse process may sometimes be separate. It then forms a *cervical rib* of variable size.

OSSIFICATION

Its ossification is similar to that of a typical cervical vertebra. In addition, separate centre for each costal process appears during sixth month of intrauterine life and fuses with the body and transverse process during fifth to sixth years of life.

CLINICAL ANATOMY

- The costal element of seventh cervical vertebra may get enlarged to form a cervical rib (Fig. 1.53).
- A cervical rib is an additional rib arising from the C7 vertebra and usually gets attached to the 1st rib near the insertion of scalenus anterior. If the rib is more than 5 cm long, it usually displaces the brachial plexus and the subclavian artery upwards (Fig. 1.54).

  The symptoms are tingling pain along the inner border of the forearm and hand including weakness and even paralysis of the muscles of the palm.
- The intervertebral foramina of the cervical vertebrae, lie anterior to the joints between the articular processes. Arthritic changes in these joints, if occur, cause tiny projections or osteophytes. These osteophytes may press on the

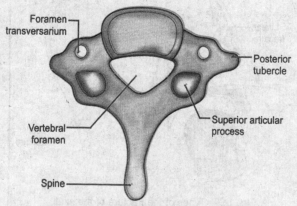

Fig. 1.52: Seventh cervical vertebra seen from above

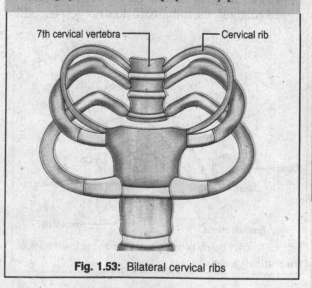

Fig. 1.53: Bilateral cervical ribs

Head and Neck

anteriorly placed cervical spinal nerves in the foramina causing pain along the course and distribution of these nerves (Fig. 1.55).

- The joints in the lateral parts of adjacent bodies of cervical vertebrae are called Luschka's joints. The osteophytes commonly occur in these joints. The cervical nerve roots lying posterolateral to these joints may get pressed causing pain along their distribution (Fig. 1.55).
- The vertebral artery coursing through the foramen transversarium lies lateral to these joints. The osteophytes of Luschka joints may cause distortion of the vertebral artery leading to vertebrobasilar insufficiency. This may cause vertigo, dizziness, etc.
- Prolapse of the intervertebral disc occurs at the junction of different curvatures. So the common site is lower cervical and upper lumbar vertebral region. In the cervical region, the disc involved is above or below 6th cervical vertebra. The nerve roots affected are C6 and C7. There is pain and numbness along the lateral side of forearm and hand. There may be wasting of muscles of thenar eminence.
- During judicial hanging, the odontoid process usually breaks to hit upon the vital centres in the medulla oblongata (Fig. 1.56).
- Atlas may fuse with the occipital bone. This is called *occipitalization of atlas* and this may at times compress the spinal cord which requires surgical decompression.
- The pharyngeal and retropharyngeal inflammations may cause decalcification of atlas vertebra. This may lead to loosening of the attachments of transverse ligament which may eventually yield, causing *sudden death* from *dislocation of dens*.
- Fractures of skull may be depressed, linear and basilar (Fig. 1.57).
- Hangman's fracture occurs due to fracture of the pedicles of axis vertebra. As the vertebral canal gets enlarged, the spinal cord does not get pressed.

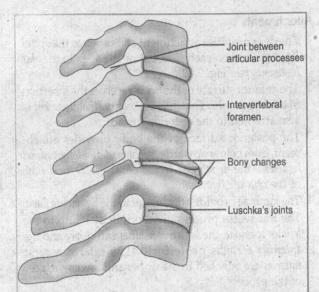

Fig. 1.55: Pressure on the cervical nerve due to bony changes

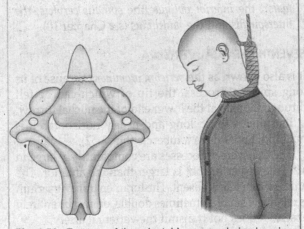

Fig. 1.56: Fracture of the odontoid process during hanging

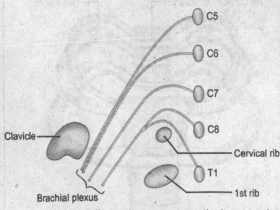

Fig. 1.54: Cervical rib causing pressure on the lower trunk of the brachial plexus

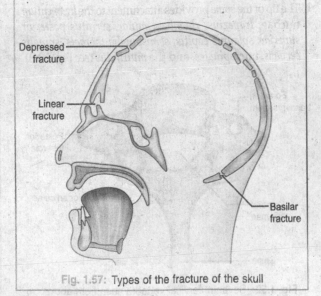

Fig. 1.57: Types of the fracture of the skull

OSSIFICATION OF CRANIAL BONES

Frontal: It ossifies in membrane. Two primary centres appear during eighth week near frontal eminences. At birth, the bone is in two halves, separated by a suture, which soon start to fuse. But remains of metopic suture may be seen in about 3–8% of adult skulls.

Parietal: It also ossifies in membrane. Two centres appear during seventh week near the parietal eminence and soon fuse with each other.

Occipital: It ossifies partly in membrane and partly in cartilage. The part of the bone above highest nuchal line ossifies in membrane by two centres which appear during second month of foetal life, it may remain separate as interparietal bone.

The following centres appear in cartilage:

- Two centres for squamous part below highest nuchal line appear during seventh week. One Kerckring centre appears for posterior margin of foramen magnum during sixteenth week.

- Two centres one for each lateral parts appear during eighth week. One centre appears for the basilar part during sixth week.

Temporal: Squamous and *tympanic* parts ossify in membrane. *Squamous part* by one centre which appears during seventh week. *Tympanic part* from one centre which appears during third month.

Petromastoid and *styloid* parts ossify in cartilage. *Petromastoid part* is ossified by several centres which appear in cartilaginous ear capsule during fifth month. *Styloid process* develops from cranial end of second branchial arch cartilage. Two centres appear in it. Tympanohyal before birth and stylohyal after birth.

Sphenoid: It ossifies in two parts:

Presphenoidal part which lies in front of tuberculum sellae and lesser wings ossifies from six centres in cartilage: Two for body of sphenoid during ninth week; two for the two lesser wings during ninth week; two for the two sphenoidal conchae during fifth month.

Postsphenoidal part consisting of posterior part of body, greater wings and pterygoid processes ossifies from eight centres:

Two centres for two greater wings during eighth week forming the root only; two for postsphenoidal part of body during fourth month; two centres appear for the two pterygoid hamulus during third month of foetal life. These six centres appear in cartilage. Two centres for medial pterygoid plates appear during ninth week and the remaining portion of the greater wings and lateral plates ossify in membrane from the centres for the root of greater wing only.

Ethmoid: It ossifies in cartilage. Three centres appear in cartilaginous nasal capsule. One centre appears in perpendicular plate during first year of life. Two centres one for each labyrinth appear between fourth and fifth months of intra-uterine life.

Mandible: Each half of the body is ossified in membrane by one centre which appears during sixth week near the mental foramen. The upper half of ramus ossifies in cartilage. Ossification spreads in condylar and coronoid processes above the level of the mandibular foramen.

Inferior nasal concha: It ossifies in cartilage. One centre appears during fifth month in the lower border of the cartilaginous nasal capsule.

Palatine: One centre appears during eighth week in perpendicular plate. It ossifies in membrane.

Lacrimal: It ossifies in membrane. One centre appears during twelfth week.

Nasal: It also ossifies in membrane from one centre which appears during third month of intra-uterine life.

Vomer: It ossifies in membrane. Two centres appear during eighth week on either side of midline. These fuse by twelfth week.

Zygomatic: It ossifies in membrane by one centre which appears during eighth week.

Maxilla: It also ossifies in membrane by three centres. One for main body which appears during sixth week above canine fossa.

Two centres appear for premaxilla during seventh week and fuse soon.

Various foramina of anterior, middle and posterior cranial fossae and other foramina with their contents are shown in Table 1.4.

Table 1.4: Foramina of skull bones and their contents

Foramina/apertures	Contents
ANTERIOR CRANIAL FOSSA	
Groove for superior sagittal sinus	Superior sagittal sinus
Foramen caecum	Emissary vein to superior sagittal sinus from upper part of nose
Anterior ethmoidal foramen	Anterior ethmoidal nerve and vessels
Foramina of cribiform plate	Olfactory nerve rootlets
Posterior ethmoidal foramen	Posterior ethmoidal vessels
MIDDLE CRANIAL FOSSA	
Optic canal	Optic nerve and ophthalmic artery
Superior orbital fissure:	
• Lateral part	*Lacrimal and frontal nerves* (branches of ophthalmic nerve); *trochlear nerve*; superior ophthalmic vein; meningeal branch of lacrimal artery; anastomotic branch of middle meningeal artery, which anastomoses with recurrent branch of lacrimal artery.
• Middle part	*Upper and lower divisions of oculomotor nerve* (CN III), *nasociliary nerve, abducent nerve* (CN VI)
• Medial part	Inferior ophthalmic vein; sympathetic nerve from plexus around internal carotid artery.
Foramen rotundum	Maxillary nerve (CN V2)
Foramen ovale	Mandibular nerve (CN V3); accessory meningeal artery; lesser petrosal nerve; emissary vein connecting cavernous sinus with pterygoid plexus (male)
Foramen spinosum	Middle meningeal artery and vein, meningeal branch of mandibular nerve (CN V3)
Emissary sphenoidal foramen	Emissary vein connecting cavernous sinus with pterygoid plexus of veins
Foramen lacerum	During life, the foramen is filled with cartilage
	No significant structure passes through it; internal carotid artery and nerve plexus pass across its superior end; nerve to pterygoid canal passes through its anterior wall; meningeal branch of ascending pharyngeal artery and emissary vein pass through it.
Carotid canal	Internal carotid artery and nerve plexus (sympathetic)
Groove for lesser petrosal nerve	Lesser petrosal nerve
Groove for greater petrosal nerve	Greater petrosal nerve
POSTERIOR CRANIAL FOSSA	
Foramen magnum	Lowest part of medulla oblongata and three meninges; vertebral arteries; spinal roots of CN XI; anterior and posterior spinal arteries; apical ligament; vertical band of cruciate ligament and membrana tectoria.
Jugular foramen	CN IX; X; XI; inferior petrosal and sigmoid sinuses; meningeal branches of ascending pharyngeal and occipital arteries.
Hypoglossal canal/anterior condylar canal	CN XII
Internal acoustic meatus	CN VII; VIII and labyrinthine vessels
External opening of vestibular aqueduct	Endolymphatic duct
Posterior condylar canal	Emissary vein connecting sigmoid sinus with the suboccipital venous plexus
Mastoid foramen	Mastoid emissary vein and meningeal branch of occipital artery
OTHER FORAMINA	
External acoustic meatus	Air waves
External nasal foramen	External nasal nerve
Greater palatine foramen	Greater palatine vessels; anterior palatine nerve
Incisive canal	Greater palatine vessels; terminal part of nasopalatine nerve

(Contd...)

Table 1.4: Foramina of skull bones and their contents (*Contd...*)

Foramina/apertures	Contents
Inferior orbital fissure	Zygomatic nerve; orbital branches of pterygopalatine ganglion; infraorbital nerve and vessels
Infraorbital foramen	Infraorbital nerve and vessels
Lesser palatine foramen	Middle and posterior palatine nerves
Mandibular foramen/canal	Inferior alveolar nerve and vessels
Mandibular notch	Masseteric nerve and vessels
Mastoid canaliculus	Auricular branch of vagus nerve
Mental foramen	Mental nerve and vessels
Palatinovaginal canal	Pharyngeal branch from pterygopalatine ganglion; pharyngeal branch of maxillary artery
Parietal foramen	Emissary vein from scalp to superior sagittal sinus
Petrotympanic fissure	Chorda tympanic nerve and anterior tympanic artery
Pterygoid canal	Nerve to pterygoid canal and vessels
Pterygomaxillary fissure	Maxillary nerve
Pterygopalatine fossa	Pterygopalatine ganglion
Stylomastoid foramen	Facial nerve; stylomastoid branch of posterior auricular artery.
Supraorbital foramen	Supraorbital nerve and vessels
Tympanic canaliculus	Tympanic branch of glossopharyngeal nerve
Tympanomastoid fissure	Auricular branch of vagus nerve
Vomerovaginal canal	Branch of pharyngeal nerve and vessels
Zygomatic foramen	Zygomatic nerve
Zygomaticofacial foramen	Zygomaticofacial nerve
Zygomaticotemporal foramen	Zygomaticotemporal nerve

 FACTS TO REMEMBER

- Eight bones in the calvaria and 14 facial bones make up the skull.

- Most of the joints are 'suture' type of joints. The joint between teeth and gums is gomphosis. There is a pair of temporomandibular joints, which is of synovial variety.

- The bony ossicles are malleus, incus and stapes and are "bone within bone", as these are present in the petrous temporal bone. Between these three ossicles are two synovial joints.

- Diploe veins contain manufactured RBCs, granulocytes and platelets. These drain into the neighbouring veins.

- Paranasal sinuses give resonance to the voice, besides humidifying and warming up the inspired air.

CLINICOANATOMICAL PROBLEM

A young woman complains of pain and numbness along the lateral side of forearm and hand, with wasting of the muscles of thenar eminence.
- Why is there pain in forearm and hand with no injury to the affected area?
- Why are thenar muscles getting weaker?

Ans: There is no obvious injury in the hand or forearm. These symptoms are nervous in nature. One has to look for the nerve root which supplies this area. The nerve root is cervical 6. Feel the cervical spine for any pain. An X-ray/CT scan may reveal prolapse of the intervertebral disc between C6 and C7 vertebrae compressing the cervical 6 nerve root. These roots form part of lateral cutaneous nerve of forearm, and median nerves. Since median nerve (C6) supplies thenar muscles, there is wasting/weakness of these muscles. As lateral cutaneous nerve of forearm is pressed, there is numbness on lateral side of forearm and hand.

Head and Neck

FREQUENTLY ASKED QUESTIONS

1. Enumerate the muscles attached to the hyoid bone. Give their nerve supply.
2. Name the structures traversing foramen magnum. Depict these with the help of a diagram.
3. Write short notes/enumerate:

    a. Structures passing though superior orbital fissure

    b. Pterion bones meeting at this point and its clinical importance

    c. Attachments of muscles on mastoid process with their nerve supply

    d. Ligaments/membranes attached to atlas vertebra

    e. Structure passing through jugular foramen

    f. Name paired bones of cranium and face

MULTIPLE CHOICE QUESTIONS

1. Which of the following structures does not pass through foramen magnum?
    a. Accessory pharyngeal artery
    b. Vertebral artery
    c. Spinal accessory nerve
    d. Vertical band of cruciate ligament
2. Which of the following nerves does not pass through jugular foramen?
    a. Vagus
    b. Hypoglossal
    c. Glossopharyngeal
    d. Accessory
3. Which is the thickest boundary of the orbit?
    a. Lateral
    b. Medial
    c. Roof
    d. Floor
4. Which bone is not a "bone within the bone" in petrous temporal bone?
    a. Malleus
    b. Hyoid
    c. Incus
    d. Stapes
5. Which of the parasympathetic ganglia does not have a secretomotor root?
    a. Submandibular
    b. Pterygopalatine
    c. Otic
    d. Ciliary

ANSWERS

1. a   2. b   3. a   4. b   5. d

Scalp, Temple and Face

Kiss is the anatomical juxtaposition of two orbicularis oris in a state of contraction

INTRODUCTION

Face is the most prominent part of the body. Facial muscles, being the muscles of facial expression, express a variety of emotions like happiness, joy, sadness, anger, frowning, grinning, etc. The face, therefore, is an *index of mind*. One's innerself is expressed by the face itself as it is controlled by the higher centres.

FEATURES THAT CAN BE IDENTIFIED

1 The *forehead* is the part of the face between the hairline of adolescent's scalp and the eyebrows. The superolateral prominence of the forehead is known as the *frontal eminence*.

2 Identify the following in relation to the nose: The prominent ridge separating the right and left halves of the nose is called the *dorsum*. The upper narrow end of the nose just below the forehead, is the *root of the nose*. The lower end of the dorsum is in the form of a somewhat rounded *tip*. At the lower end of the nose, we see the right and left *nostrils* or *anterior nares*. The two nostrils are separated by a soft median partition called the *columella*. This is continuous with the *nasal septum* which separates the two nasal cavities. Each nostril is bounded laterally by the *ala*.

3 The *palpebral fissure* is an elliptical opening between the two eyelids. The lids are joined to each other at the medial and lateral angles or *canthi* of the eye. The free margin of each eyelid has eyelashes or cilia arranged along its outer edge (Fig. 2.1).

Through the palpebral fissure are seen:

a. The opaque sclera or white of the eye.

b. The transparent circular *cornea* through which the coloured iris and the dark circular *pupil* can be seen.

The eyeballs are lodged in bony sockets, called the *orbits*.

The *conjunctiva* is a moist, transparent membrane. The part which covers the anterior surface of the

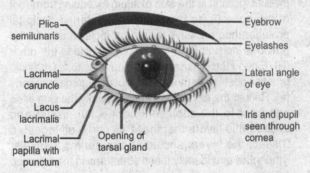

Fig. 2.1: Some features to be seen on the face around the left eye

eyeball is the *bulbar conjunctiva*, and the part lining the inner surfaces of the lids is the *palpebral conjunctiva*. The line along which the bulbar conjunctiva becomes the palpebral conjunctiva is known as the *conjunctival fornix*. The space between the two is the *conjunctival* sac.

4 The *oral fissure* or mouth is the opening between the upper and lower *lips*. It lies opposite the cutting edges of the upper incisor teeth. The angle of the mouth usually lies just in front of first upper premolar tooth. Each lip has a *red margin* at mucocutaneous junction and a *dark margin*, with a nonhairy thin skin intervening between the two margins. The lips normally close the mouth along their red margins. The *philtrum* is the median vertical groove on the upper lip.

5 The *external ear* is made up of two parts: A superficial projecting part, called the *auricle or pinna*; and a deep canal, called the *external acoustic meatus*. The mobile auricle helps in catching the sound waves, and is a characteristic feature of mammals. Details of the structure of the auricle will be considered later.

6 The *supraorbital margin* lies beneath the upper margin of the eyebrow. The supraorbital notch is palpable at the junction of the medial one-third with the lateral two-thirds of the supraorbital margin. A vertical line drawn from the supraorbital notch to the base of the

S - Skin
C - Connective tissue (dense)
A - Aponeurotic layer
L - Loose aleolar tissue
P - Pericranium

mandible, passing midway between the lower two premolar teeth, crosses the infraorbital foramen 5 mm below the infraorbital margin, and the mental foramen midway between the upper and lower borders of the mandible.

7 The *superciliary* arch is a curved bony ridge situated immediately above the medial part of each supraorbital margin. The *glabella* is the median elevation connecting the two superciliary arches, and corresponds to elevation between the two eyebrows.

SCALP AND SUPERFICIAL TEMPORAL REGION

DISSECTION

Place 2–3 wooden blocks under the head to raise it about 10–12 cm from the table. Figure 2.2 shows a median incision in the skin of scalp extending from root of the nose (i), to the prominent external occipital protuberance (ii). Give a coronal incision across the previous incision from root of one auricle to the other (iii). Extend the incision from the auricles to the mastoid process posteriorly (iv), and to root of zygoma anteriorly (v). Reflect the skin in four flaps. Usually the skin is so adherent to the subjacent connective tissue and aponeurotic layers that these all come off together. Dissect the layers, including the nerves, vessels, lymphatics and identify these structures in the cadaver.

SCALP

The soft tissues covering the cranial vault form the scalp (Fig. 2.3).

Extent of Scalp

Anteriorly, supraorbital margins; posteriorly, external occipital protuberance and superior nuchal lines; and on each side, the superior temporal lines.

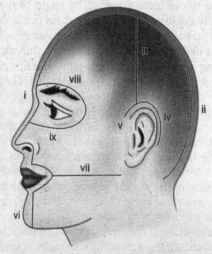

Fig. 2.2: Lines of dissection for scalp, face and eyelids

Structure

Conventionally, the superficial temporal region is studied with the scalp, and the following description, therefore, will cover both the regions.

The scalp is made up of five layers (mnemonic SCALP)

a. Skin
b. Superficial fascia (Connective tissue)
c. Deep fascia in the form of the epicranial aponeurosis or galea aponeurotica with the occipitofrontalis muscle
d. Loose areolar tissue
e. Pericranium (Figs 2.3a and b).

The *skin* is thick and hairy. It is adherent to the epicranial aponeurosis through the dense superficial fascia, as in the palms and soles. It has more number of sweat glands and sebaceous glands.

The *subcutaneous* or *superficial fascia* is more fibrous and dense in the centre than at the periphery of the head. It contains many blood vessels.

It binds the skin to the subjacent aponeurosis, and provides the proper medium for passage of vessels and nerves to the skin.

The *occipitofrontalis muscle* has two bellies, occipital or occipitalis and frontal or frontalis, both of which are inserted into the epicranial aponeurosis. The *occipital bellies* are small and separate. Each arises from the lateral two-thirds of the superior nuchal line, and is supplied by the *posterior auricular* branch of the *facial nerve*.

The *frontal bellies* are longer, wider and partly united in the median plane. Each arises from the skin of the upper eyelid and forehead, mingling with the orbicularis oculi and the corrugator supercilii. It is supplied by the *temporal branch* of the facial nerve (see Fig. 1.6).

The muscle raises the eyebrows and causes horizontal wrinkles in the skin of the forehead (Fig. 2.4).

The temporoparietalis muscle is present on lateral side which arises from temporal fascia and fuses with epicranial aponeurosis. It is supplied by temporal branch of facial nerve.

The *epicranial aponeurosis*, or galea aponeurotica is freely movable on the pericranium along with the overlying and adherent skin and fascia (Figs 2.3a and 2.9). Anteriorly, it receives the insertion of the frontalis, posteriorly, it receives the insertion of the occipitalis and is attached to the external occipital protuberance, and to the highest nuchal lines in between the occipital bellies. On each side, the aponeurosis is attached to the superior temporal line, but sends down a thin expansion which passes over the temporal fascia and is attached to the zygomatic arch (Fig. 2.3b).

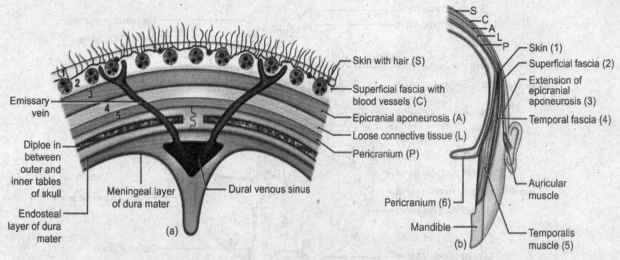

Figs 2.3a and b: (a) Layers of the scalp, and (b) layers of superficial temporal region

First three layers of scalp are called *surgical layers of the scalp*. These are called as scalp proper also.

The fourth layer of the scalp is made up of *loose areolar tissue*. It extends anteriorly into the eyelids (Fig. 2.4) because the frontalis muscle has no bony attachment; posteriorly to the highest and superior nuchal lines; and on each side to the superior temporal lines. It gives passage to the emissary veins which connect extracranial veins to intracranial venous sinuses (Fig. 2.3a).

The fifth layer of the scalp, called the *pericranium*, is loosely attached to the surface of the bones, but is firmly adherent to their sutures where the sutural ligaments bind the pericranium to the endocranium (Fig. 2.3a).

SUPERFICIAL TEMPORAL REGION

It is the area between the superior temporal line and the zygomatic arch. This area contains the following 6 layers (Fig. 2.3b):

1 Skin
2 Superficial fascia
3 Thin extension of epicranial aponeurosis which gives origin to extrinsic muscles of the auricle
4 Temporal fascia
5 Temporalis muscle
6 Pericranium.

Tempus means time. Greying of hair first starts here.

Arterial Supply of Scalp and Superficial Temporal Region

In front of the auricle, the scalp is supplied from before backwards by the:

- *Supratrochlear*
- *Supraorbital*
- *Superficial temporal* arteries (Fig. 2.5).

The first two are branches of the ophthalmic artery which in turn is a branch of the internal carotid artery. The superficial temporal is a branch of the external carotid artery.

Behind the auricle, the scalp is supplied from before backwards by the:

- *Posterior auricular*
- *Occipital* arteries, both of which are branches of the external carotid artery.

Thus, the scalp has a *rich blood supply* derived from both the internal and the external carotid arteries, the two systems anastomosing over the temple.

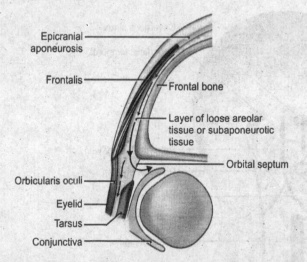

Fig. 2.4: Schematic section through the scalp and upper eyelid to show how fluids can pass from the subaponeurotic space or layer of loose areolar tissue of the scalp into the eyelid, and into the subconjunctival area. Note that this is possible because the frontalis muscle has no bony attachment

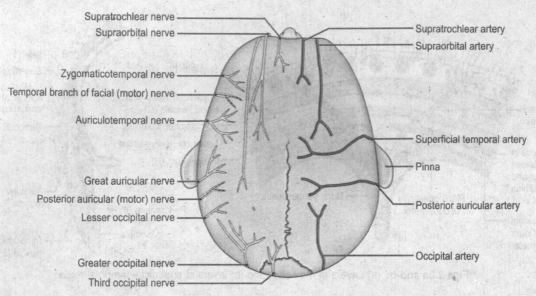

Fig. 2.5: Arterial and nerve supply of scalp and superficial temporal region

Venous Drainage

The veins of the scalp accompany the arteries and have similar names. The *supratrochlear* and *supraorbital* veins unite at the medial angle of the eye forming the *angular* vein which continues down as the *facial* vein.

The *superficial temporal vein* descends in front of the tragus, enters the parotid gland, and joins the maxillary vein to form the *retromandibular* vein. This vein divides into two divisions.

The anterior division of the retromandibular vein unites with the facial vein to form the common facial vein which drains into the internal jugular vein.

The posterior division of the retromandibular vein unites with the *posterior auricular vein* to form the *external jugular vein* which ultimately drains into the *subclavian vein*. The occipital veins terminate in the suboccipital venous plexus (Fig. 2.6).

Emissary veins connect the extracranial veins with the intracranial venous sinuses to equalise the pressure. These veins are valveless. The *parietal emissary vein* passes through the parietal foramen to enter the superior sagittal sinus. The *mastoid emissary vein* passes through the mastoid foramen to reach the sigmoid sinus. Remaining emissary veins are shown in Table 1.1.

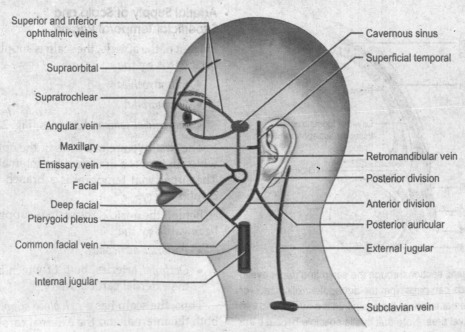

Fig. 2.6: The veins of the scalp, face and their deep connections with the cavernous sinus and the pterygoid plexus of veins

Extracranial infections may spread through these veins to intracranial venous sinuses.

Diploic veins start from the cancellous bone within the two tables of skull. These carry the newly formed blood cells into the general circulation. These are four veins on each side (*see* Fig. 1.17).

The *frontal diploic vein* emerges at the supraorbital notch open into the supraorbital vein. *Anterior temporal diploic vein* ends in anterior deep temporal vein or sphenoparietal sinus. *Posterior temporal diploic vein* ends in the transverse sinus. The *occipital diploic vein* opens either into the occipital vein, or into the transverse sinus near the median plane (*see* Table 1.2).

Lymphatic Drainage

The anterior part of the scalp drains into the pre-auricular or parotid lymph nodes, situated on the surface of the parotid gland. The posterior part of the scalp drains into the posterior auricular or mastoid and occipital lymph nodes.

Nerve Supply

The scalp and temple are supplied by ten nerves on each side. Out of these, five nerves (four sensory and one motor) enter the scalp in front of the auricle. The remaining five nerves (again four sensory and one motor) enter the scalp behind the auricle (Fig. 2.5 and Table 2.1).

Table 2.1: Nerves of the scalp and superficial temporal region

In front of auricle	Behind the auricle
Sensory nerves	*Sensory nerves*
• Supratrochlear, branch of the frontal (ophthalmic division of trigeminal nerve)	• Posterior division of great auricular nerve (C2, C3) from cervical plexus
• Supraorbital, branch of frontal (ophthalmic division of trigeminal nerve)	• Lesser occipital nerve (C2), from cervical plexus
• Zygomaticotemporal, branch of zygomatic nerve (maxillary division of trigeminal nerve)	• Greater occipital nerve (C2, dorsal ramus)
• Auriculotemporal branch of mandibular division of trigeminal nerve	• Third occipital nerve (C3, dorsal ramus)
Motor nerve	*Motor nerve*
• Temporal branch of facial nerve	• Posterior auricular branch of facial nerve

CLINICAL ANATOMY

- Wounds of the scalp gape when the epicranial aponeurosis is divided transversely.
- Because of the abundance of sebaceous glands, the scalp is a common site for sebaceous cysts (Fig. 2.7).
- Wounds of the scalp bleed profusely because the vessels are prevented from retracting by the fibrous fascia. Bleeding can be arrested by applying pressure at the site of injury by a tight cotton bandage against the bone.
- Because of the density of fascia, subcutaneous haemorrhages are never extensive, and the inflammations in this layer cause little swelling but much pain.
- Because the pericranium is adherent to sutures, collections of fluid deep to the pericranium known as *cephalhaematoma* take the shape of the bone concerned when there is fracture of particular bone.
- The layer of loose areolar tissue is known as the *dangerous area of the scalp* because the emissary veins, which course here may transmit infection from the scalp to the cranial venous sinuses (Fig. 2.3a).
- Collection of blood in the layer of loose connective tissue causes generalised swelling of the scalp. The blood may extend anteriorly into the root of the nose and into the eyelids (as frontalis muscle has no bony origin) causing resulting in black eye (Fig. 2.4). The posterior limit of such haemorrhage is not seen. If bleeding is due to local injury, the posterior limit of haemorrhage is seen (Fig. 2.8).
- Because of the spread of blood, compression of brain is not seen and so this layer is also called safety layer.
- Since the blood supply of scalp and superficial temporal region is very rich; avulsed portions need not be cut away. They can be replaced in position and stitched: they usually take up and heal well.

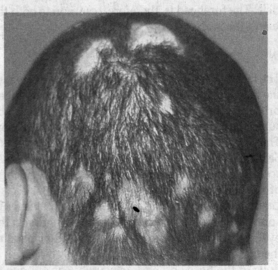

Fig. 2.7: Bilateral sebaceous cysts

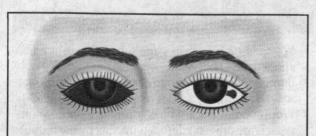

Fig. 2.8: Right eye—black eye due to injury to the scalp; left eye—black eye due to local injury

FACE

DISSECTION

Give a median incision from the root of nose, across the dorsum of nose, centre of philtrum of upper lip, to centre of lower lip to the chin (vi). Give a horizontal incision from the angle of the mouth to posterior border of the mandible (vii). Reflect the lower flap towards and up to the lower border of mandible (Fig. 2.2; line with dots). Direct and reflect the upper flap till the auricle. Subjacent to the skin, the facial muscles are directly encountered as these are inserted in the skin. Identify the various functional groups of facial muscles.

Trace the various motor branches of facial nerve emerging from the anterior border of parotid gland to supply these muscles. Amongst these motor branches on the face are the sensory branches of the three divisions of the trigeminal nerve. Try to identify all these with the help of their course given in the text (Fig. 2.12a).

Features

The face, or countenance, extends superiorly from the adolescent position of hairline, inferiorly to the chin and the base of the mandible, and on each side to the auricle. The forehead is, therefore, common to both the face and the scalp.

SKIN

1 The facial skin is *very vascular*. Rich vascularity makes the face blush and blanch. Wounds of the face bleed profusely but heal rapidly. The results of plastic surgery on the face are excellent for the same reason.
2 The facial skin is *rich in sebaceous and sweat glands*. Sebaceous glands keep the face oily, but also cause *acne* in young adults. Sweat glands help in regulation of the body temperature.
3 *Laxity* of the greater part of the skin facilitates rapid spread of oedema. Renal oedema appears first in the eyelids and face before spreading to other parts of the body.
4 Boils in the nose and ear are acutely painful due to the *fixity* of the skin to the underlying cartilages.

5 Facial skin is very *elastic and thick* because the facial muscles are inserted into it. The wounds of the face, therefore, tend to gape.

SUPERFICIAL FASCIA

It contains: (i) The facial muscles, all of which are inserted into the skin, (ii) the vessels and nerves, to the muscles and to the skin, and (iii) a variable amount of fat. Fat is absent from the eyelids, but is well developed in the cheeks, forming the buccal pads that are very prominent in infants in whom they help in sucking.

The *deep fascia is absent* from the face, except over the parotid gland where it forms the parotid fascia, and over the buccinator where it forms the *buccopharyngeal fascia*.

FACIAL MUSCLES

The facial muscles, or the muscles of facial expression, are subcutaneous muscles. They bring about different facial expressions. These have small motor units.

Embryologically, they develop from the mesoderm of the second branchial arch, and are, therefore, supplied by the facial nerve.

Morphologically, they represent the best remnants of the *panniculus carnosus*, a continuous subcutaneous muscle sheet seen in some animals. All of them are inserted into the skin.

Topographically, the muscles are grouped under the following six heads.

Functionally, most of these muscles may be regarded primarily as regulators of the three openings situated on the face, namely the palpebral fissures, the nostrils and the oral fissure. Each opening has a single sphincter, and a variable number of dilators. Sphincters are naturally circular and the dilators radial in their arrangement. These muscles are better developed around the eyes and mouth than around the nose (Table 2.2).

Table 2.2: Functional groups of facial muscles		
Opening	*Sphincter*	*Dilators*
A. Palpebral fissure	Orbicularis oculi	1. Levator palpebrae superioris 2. Frontalis part of occipitofrontalis
B. Oral fissure	Orbicularis oris	All the muscles around the mouth, except the orbicularis oris, the sphincter, and the mentalis which do not mingle with orbicularis oris (*see above*)
C. Nostrils	Compressor naris	1. Dilator naris 2. Depressor septi 3. Medial slip of levator labii superioris alaeque nasi

Muscle of the Scalp

Occipitofrontalis—described in scalp.

Muscles of the Auricle

Situated around the ear:

1 Auricularis anterior
2 Auricularis superior
3 Auricularis posterior

These are vestigeal muscles.

Muscles of the Eyelids/Orbital Openings

1 Orbicularis oculi (Fig. 2.9 and Table 2.3)
2 Corrugator (Latin *to wrinkle*) supercilii (Fig. 2.9 and Table 2.3)
3 Levator palpebrae superioris (an extraocular muscle, supplied by sympathetic fibres and the third cranial nerve) is described in Chapter 13.

Muscles of the Nose

1 Procerus (Fig. 2.9)
2 Compressor naris.

3 Dilator naris
4 Depressor septi

Muscles around the Mouth

1 Orbicularis oris (Fig. 2.9)
2 Buccinator (Latin *cheek*) (Fig. 2.10)
3 Levator labii superioris alaeque nasi (Fig. 2.10)
4 Zygomaticus major (Fig. 2.9)
5 Levator labii superioris (Fig. 2.9, inset)
6 Levator anguli oris
7 Zygomaticus minor
8 Depressor anguli oris (Fig. 2.10)
9 Depressor labii inferioris
10 Mentalis (Latin *chin*)
11 Risorius (Latin *laughter*)

Muscles of the Neck

Platysma (Greek *broad*)
    Details of the other muscles are given in Table 2.3.

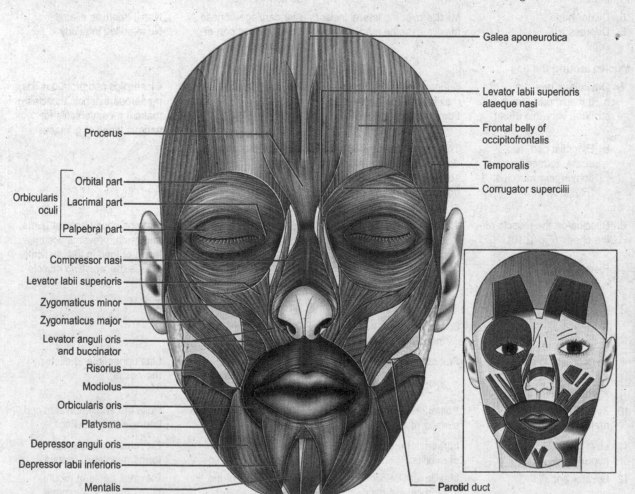

Fig. 2.9: The facial muscles

Table 2.3: The facial muscles

Name	Origin	Insertion	Actions
Muscles of eyelid/orbital opening			
1. Corrugator supercilii (Fig. 2.9)	Medial end of superciliary arch	Skin of mid-eyebrow	Vertical lines in forehead, as in frowning
2. Orbicularis oculi (Fig. 2.9) a. Orbital part, on and around the orbital margin	Medial part of medial palpebral ligament, frontal process of maxilla and nasal part of frontal bone	Concentric rings return to the point of origin	Protects eye from bright light, wind and rain. Cause forceful closure of eyelids
b. Palpebral part, in the lids	Lateral part of medial palpebral ligament	Lateral palpebral raphe	Closes lids gently as in blinking and sleeping
c. Lacrimal part, lateral and deep to the lacrimal sac	Lacrimal fascia and posterior lacrimal crest, forms sheath for lacrimal sac	Pass laterally in front of tarsal plates of eyelids to the lateral palpebral raphe	Dilates lacrimal sac for sucking of lacrimal fluid into the sac, directs lacrimal puncta into lacus lacrimalis; supports the lower lid
Muscles around nasal opening			
3. Procerus	Nasal bone and upper part of lateral nasal cartilage	Skin of forehead between eyebrows and on bridge of the nose	Causes transverse wrinkles
4. Compressor naris	Maxilla just lateral to nose	Aponeurosis across dorsum of nose	Nasal aperture compressed
5. Dilator naris	Maxilla over the lateral incisor	Alar cartilage of nose	Nasal aperture dilated
6. Depressor septi	Maxilla over the medial incisor	Lower mobile part of nasal septum	Nose pulled inferiorly
Mucles around the lips			
7. Orbicularis oris a. Intrinsic part, deep stratum, very thin sheet	Superior incisivus, from maxilla; inferior incisivus, from mandible	Angle of mouth	Closes lips and protrudes lips, numerous extrinsic muscles make it most versatile for various types of grimaces
b. Extrinsic part, two strata, formed by converging muscles (Fig. 2.9)	Thickest middle stratum, derived from buccinator; thick superficial stratum, derived from elevators and depressors of lips and their angles	Lips and the angle of the mouth	
8. Buccinator, the muscle of the cheek (Fig. 2.10)	1. Upper fibres, from maxilla opposite molar teeth	1. Upper fibres, straight to the upper lip	Flattens cheek against gums and teeth; prevents accumulation of food in the vestibule. This is the *whistling muscle*
Pierced by – Parotid duct and – Buccal branch of mandibular nerve	2. Lower fibres, from mandible, opposite molar teeth	2. Lower fibres, straight to the lower lip	
	3. Middle fibres, from pterygomandibular raphe	3. Middle fibres decussate	
9. Levator labii superioris alaeque nasi	Frontal process of maxilla	Upper lip and alar cartilage of nose	Lifts upper lip and dilates the nostril
10. Zygomaticus major	Posterior aspect of lateral surface of zygomatic bone	Skin at the angle of the mouth	Pulls the angle upwards and laterally as in smiling
11. Levator labii superioris	Infraorbital margin of maxilla	Skin of upper lateral half of the upper lip	Elevates the upper lip, forms nasolabial groove
12. Levator anguli oris	Maxilla just below infraorbital foramen	Skin of angle of the mouth	Elevates angle of mouth, forms nasolabial groove

(Contd...)

Table 2.3: The facial muscles (*Contd...*)

Name	Origin	Insertion	Actions
13. Zygomaticus minor	Anterior aspect of lateral surface of zygomatic bone	Upper lip medial to its angle	Elevates the upper lip
14. Depressor anguli oris	Oblique line of mandible below first molar, premolar and canine teeth	Skin at the angle of mouth and fuses with orbicularis oris	Draws angle of mouth downwards and laterally
15. Depressor labii inferioris	Anterior part of oblique line of mandible	Lower lip at midline, fuses with muscles from opposite side	Draws lower lip downward
16. Mentalis	Mandible inferior to incisor teeth	Skin of chin	Elevates and protrudes lower lip as it wrinkles skin on chin
17. Risorius	Fascia on the masseter muscle	Skin at the angle of the mouth	Retracts angle of mouth
Muscles of the neck			
18. Platysma (Fig. 2.9)	Upper parts of pectoral and deltoid fasciae Fibres run upwards and medially	Anterior fibres, to the base of the mandible; posterior fibres to the skin of the lower face and lip, and may be continuous with the risorius	Releases pressure of skin on the subjacent veins; depresses mandible; pulls the angle of the mouth downwards as in horror or fright

Modiolus: It is a compact, mobile fibromuscular structure present at about 1.25 cm lateral to the angle of the mouth opposite the upper second premolar tooth. The five muscles interlacing to form the modiolus are: zygomaticus major, buccinator, levator anguli oris, risorius and depressor anguli oris.

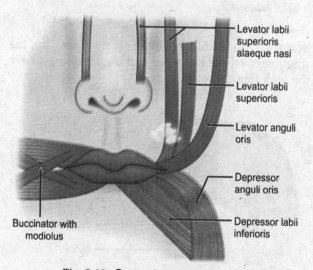

Fig. 2.10: Some of the facial muscles

Labels: Levator labii superioris alaeque nasi; Levator labii superioris; Levator anguli oris; Depressor anguli oris; Depressor labii inferioris; Buccinator with modiolus

4 *Anger:* Dilator naris and depressor septi.
5 *Dislike:* Corrugator supercilii and procerus.
6 *Horror, terror and fright:* Platysma
7 *Surprise:* Frontalis
8 *Doubt:* Mentalis
9 *Grinning:* Risorius
10 *Contempt:* Zygomaticus minor.
11 *Closing the mouth:* Orbicularis oris
12 *Whistling:* Buccinator, and orbicularis oris.

NERVE SUPPLY OF FACE

Motor Nerve Supply

The *facial nerve* is the motor nerve of the face. Its five terminal branches, temporal, zygomatic, buccal, marginal mandibular and cervical emerge from the parotid gland and diverge to supply the various facial muscles as follows.

Temporal—frontalis, auricular muscles, orbicularis oculi (Fig. 2.12a).

Zygomatic—orbicularis oculi (lower eyelid part).

Buccal—muscles of the cheek and upper lip.

Marginal mandibular—muscles of lower lip.

Cervical—platysma.

A few of the *common facial expressions* and the muscles producing them are given below (Fig. 2.11):

1 *Smiling and laughing:* Zygomaticus major.
2 *Sadness:* Levator labii superioris and levator anguli oris.
3 *Grief:* Depressor anguli oris.

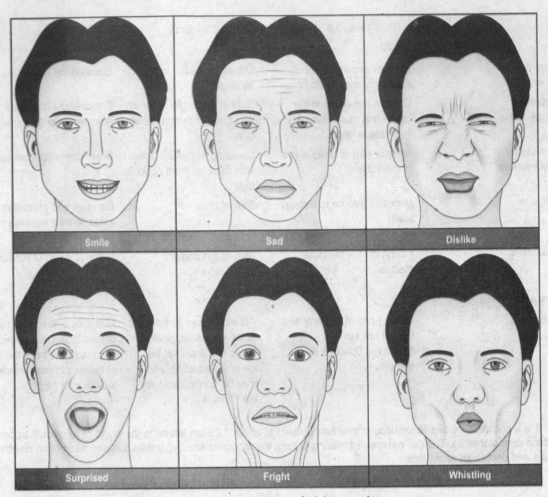

Fig. 2.11: Some common facial expressions

This can be understood by putting your right wrist on the right ear and spreading five digits; the thumb over the temporal region, the index finger on the zygomatic bone, middle finger on the upper lip, the ring finger on the lower lip and the little finger over the neck (Fig. 2.12b).

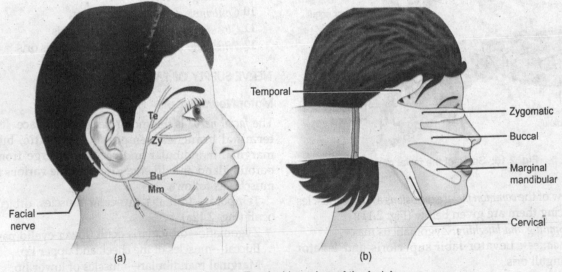

Figs 2.12 a and b: Terminal branches of the facial nerve

CLINICAL ANATOMY

- The facial nerve is examined by testing the following facial muscles (Fig. 2.13).
  a. *Frontalis:* Ask the patient to look upwards without moving his head, and look for the normal horizontal wrinkles on the forehead (Fig. 2.13a).
  b. *Dilators of mouth:* Showing the teeth (Fig. 2.13b).
  c. *Orbicularis oculi:* Tight closure of the eyes (Fig. 2.13c).
  d. *Buccinator:* Puffing the mouth and then blowing forcibly as in whistling (Fig. 2.13d).
- Infranuclear lesion (Fig. 2.14) of the facial nerve, at the stylomastoid foramen is known as Bell's palsy, upper and lower quarters of the face on the same side get paralysed. The face becomes asymmetrical and is drawn up to the normal side. The affected side is motionless. Wrinkles disappear from the forehead. The eye cannot be closed. Any attempt to smile draws the mouth to the normal side. During mastication, food accumulates between the teeth and the cheek. Articulation of labials is impaired.
- In supranuclear lesions of the facial nerve; usually a part of hemiplegia, with injury of corticonuclear fibres, only the lower quarter of the opposite side of face is paralysed. The upper quarter with the frontalis and orbicularis oculi escapes due to its bilateral representation in the cerebral cortex (Fig. 2.15). Only voluntary movements are affected and emotional expressions remain normal as there are separate pathways for voluntary and emotional movements.

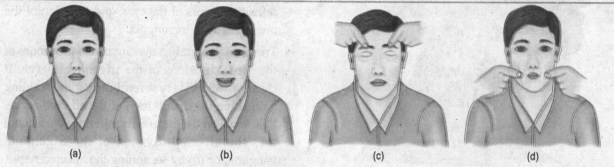

Figs 2.13a to d: (a) Test for frontalis, (b) test for dilators of mouth, (c) test for orbicularis oculi, and (d) test for buccinator

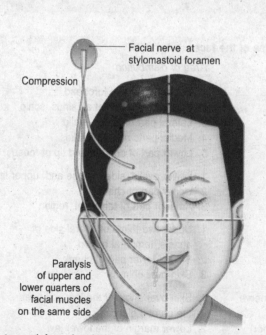

Fig. 2.14: Infranuclear lesion of right facial nerve or Bell's palsy

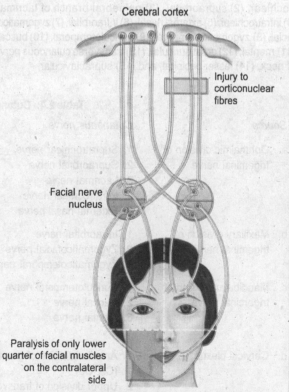

Fig. 2.15: Supranuclear lesion of right facial nerve

Head and Neck

Sensory Nerve Supply

The *trigeminal nerve* through its three branches is the chief sensory nerve of the face (Fig. 2.16 and Table 2.4). The skin over the angle of the jaw and over the parotid gland is supplied by the great auricular nerve (C2, C3).

In addition to most of the skin of the face, the sensory distribution of the trigeminal nerve is also to the nasal cavity, the paranasal air sinuses, the eyeball, the mouth cavity, palate, cheeks, gums, teeth and anterior two-thirds of tongue and the supratentorial part of the dura mater, including that lining the anterior and middle cranial fossae (Fig. 2.16).

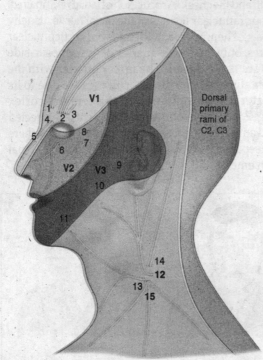

Fig. 2.16: The sensory nerves of the face and neck. (1) Supra-trochlear, (2) supraorbital, (3) palpebral branch of lacrimal, (4) infratrochlear, (5) external nasal, (6) infraorbital, (7) zygomatico-facial, (8) zygomaticotemporal, (9) auriculotemporal, (10) buccal, (11) mental, (12) great auricular, (13) transverse cutaneous nerve of neck, (14) lesser occipital, and (15) supraclavicular

CLINICAL ANATOMY

- The sensory distribution of the trigeminal nerve explains why headache is a uniformly common symptom in involvements of the nose (common cold, boils), the paranasal air sinuses (sinusitis), infections and inflammations of teeth and gums, refractive errors of the eyes, and infection of the meninges as in meningitis.

- Trigeminal neuralgia may involve one or more of the three divisions of the trigeminal nerve. It causes attacks of very severe burning and scalding pain along the distribution of the affected nerve. Pain is relieved either: (a) By injecting 90% alcohol into the affected division of the trigeminal ganglion, or (b) by sectioning the affected nerve, the main sensory root, or the spinal tract of the trigeminal nerve which is situated superficially in the medulla. The procedure is called medullary tractotomy.

Source	Cutaneous nerve	Area of distribution
Table 2.4: Cutaneous nerves of the face		
a. Ophthalmic division of trigeminal nerve	1. Supratrochlear nerve 2. Supraorbital nerve 3. Lacrimal nerve 4. Infratrochlear nerve 5. External nasal nerve	1. Upper eyelid and forehead 2. Upper eyelid, frontal air sinus, scalp 3. Lateral part of upper eyelid 4. Medial parts of both eyelids 5. Lower part of dorsum and tip of nose
b. Maxillary division of trigeminal nerve	1. Infraorbital nerve 2. Zygomaticofacial nerve 3. Zygomaticotemporal nerve	1. Lower eyelid, side of nose and upper lip 2. Upper part of cheek 3. Anterior part of temporal region
c. Mandibular division of trigeminal nerve	1. Auriculotemporal nerve 2. Buccal nerve 3. Mental nerve	1. Upper two-thirds of lateral side of auricle, temporal region 2. Skin of lower part of cheek 3. Skin over chin
d. Cervical plexus	1. Anterior division of great auricular nerve (C2, C3) 2. Upper division of transverse (anterior) cutaneous nerve of neck (C2, C3)	1. Skin over angle of the jaw and over the parotid gland 2. Lower margin of the lower jaw

ARTERIES OF THE FACE

DISSECTION

Tortuous facial artery enters the face at the lower border of mandible. Dissect its course from the anteroinferior angle of masseter muscle running to the angle of mouth till the medial angle of eye, reflecting off some of the facial muscles, if necessary (Fig. 2.17).

Straight facial vein runs on a posterior plane than the artery.

Identify buccopharyngeal fascia on the external surface of buccinator muscle. Clean the deeply placed buccinator muscle situated lateral to the angle of mouth.

Identify parotid duct, running across the cheek 2 cm below the zygomatic arch. The duct pierces buccal pad of fat, buccopharyngeal fascia, buccinator muscle, mucous membrane of the mouth to open into its vestibule opposite second upper molar tooth (Fig. 2.20).

FEATURES

The face is richly vascular. It is supplied by:
1 The facial artery,
2 The transverse facial artery, and
3 Arteries that accompany the cutaneous nerves.

These are small branches of ophthalmic, maxillary and superficial temporal arteries.

Facial Artery (Facial Part)

The facial artery is the chief artery of the face (Fig. 2.17). It is a branch of the external carotid artery given off in the carotid triangle just above the level of the tip of the greater cornua of the hyoid bone. In its cervical course, it passes through the submandibular region, and finally enters the face.

Course

1 It enters the face by winding around the base of the mandible, and by piercing the deep cervical fascia, at the anteroinferior angle of the masseter muscle. It can be palpated here and is called 'anaesthetist's artery'.
2 First it runs upwards and forwards to a point 1.25 cm lateral to the angle of the mouth. Then it ascends by the side of the nose up to the medial angle of the eye, where it terminates by supplying the lacrimal sac; and by anastomosing with the dorsal nasal branch of the ophthalmic artery.
3 The facial artery is very tortuous. The tortuosity of the artery prevents its walls from being unduly stretched during movements of the mandible, the lips and the cheeks.
4 It lies between the superficial and deep muscles of the face.

The course of the artery in the neck is described in submandibular region.

Branches

The anterior branches on the face are large and named. They are:
1 *Inferior labial*, to the lower lip.
2 *Superior labial*, to the upper lip and the anteroinferior part of the nasal septum.
3 *Lateral nasal*, to the ala and dorsum of the nose.

The posterior branches are *small* and unnamed.

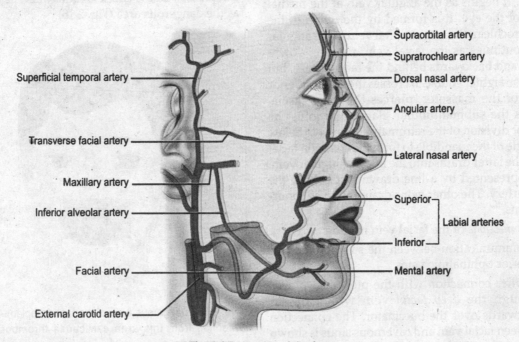

Fig. 2.17: Arteries of the face

Anastomoses

1 The large anterior branches anastomose with similar branches of the opposite side and with the mental artery. In the lips, anastomoses are large, so that cut arteries spurt from both ends.

2 Small posterior branches anastomose with the transverse facial and infraorbital arteries.

3 At the medial angle of the eye, terminal branches of the facial artery anastomose with branches of the ophthalmic artery. This is, therefore, a site for anastomoses between the branches of the external and internal carotid arteries.

Transverse Facial Artery

This small artery is a branch of the superficial temporal artery. After emerging from the parotid gland, it runs forwards over the masseter between the parotid duct and the zygomatic arch, accompanied by the upper buccal branch of the facial nerve. It supplies the parotid gland and its duct, masseter and the overlying skin, and ends by anastomosing with neighbouring arteries (Fig. 2.17).

VEINS OF THE FACE

1 The veins of the face accompany the arteries and drain into the common facial and retromandibular veins. They communicate with the cavernous sinus.

2 The veins on each side form a 'W-shaped' arrangement. Each corner of the 'W' is prolonged upwards into the scalp and downwards into the neck (Fig. 2.6).

3 The *facial vein* is the largest vein of the face with no valves. It begins as the angular vein at the medial angle of the eye. It is formed by the union of the supratrochlear and supraorbital veins. The angular vein continues as the facial vein, running downwards and backwards behind the facial artery, but with a straighter course. It crosses the anteroinferior angle of the masseter, pierces the deep fascia, crosses the submandibular gland, and joins the anterior division of the retromandibular vein below the angle of the mandible to form the common facial vein. The latter drains into the internal jugular vein. It is represented by a line drawn just behind the facial artery. The other veins drain into neighbouring veins.

4 *Deep connections* of the facial vein include:

   a. A communication between the supraorbital and superior ophthalmic veins.

   b. Another connection with the pterygoid plexus through the *deep facial* vein which passes backwards over the buccinator. The connection between facial vein and cavernous sinus is shown in Flowchart 2.1.

Flowchart 2.1: Connection between facial vein and cavernous sinus

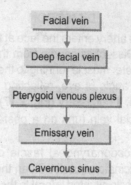

Facial vein
↓
Deep facial vein
↓
Pterygoid venous plexus
↓
Emissary vein
↓
Cavernous sinus

Dangerous Area of Face

The facial vein communicates with the cavernous sinus through emissary veins. Infections from the face can spread in a retrograde direction and cause *thrombosis* of the cavernous sinus. This is specially likely to occur in the presence of infection in the upper lip and in the lower part of the nose. This area is, therefore, called the *dangerous area of the face* (Fig. 2.18).

CLINICAL ANATOMY

The facial veins and its deep connecting veins are devoid of valves, making an uninterrupted passage of blood to cavernous sinus. Squeezing the pustules or pimples in the area of the upper lip or side of nose or even the cheeks may cause infection which may be carried to the cavernous sinus leading to its thrombosis. So the cheek area may also be included as the dangerous area (Fig. 2.18).

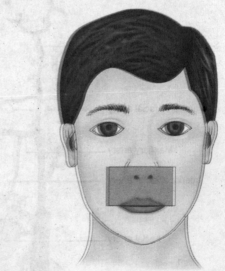

Fig. 2.18: Dangerous area of the face (stippled). Spread of infection from this area can cause thrombosis of the cavernous sinus

LYMPHATIC DRAINAGE OF THE FACE

The face has three lymphatic territories:

1. *Upper territory*, including the greater part of the forehead, lateral halves of eyelids, conjunctiva, lateral part of the cheek and parotid area, drains into the *preauricular parotid nodes*.

2. *Middle territory*, including a strip over the median part of the forehead, external nose, upper lip, lateral part of the lower lip, medial halves of the eyelids, medial part of the cheek, and the greater part of lower jaw, drains into the *submandibular nodes*.

3. *Lower territory*, including the central part of the lower lip and the chin, drains into the *submental nodes* (Fig. 2.19).

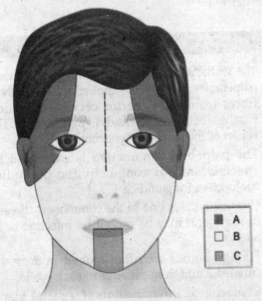

Fig. 2.19: The lymphatic territories of the face. Area (A) drains into the preauricular nodes, area (B) drains into the submandibular nodes, and area (C) drains into the submental nodes

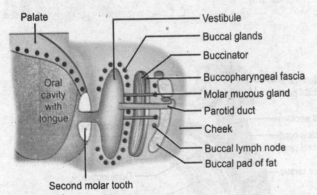

Fig. 2.20: Scheme of coronal section showing structures in the cheek. The parotid duct pierces buccal pad of fat, buccopharyngeal fascia, buccinator muscle and the mucous membrane to open into the vestibule of mouth opposite the crown of the upper second molar tooth

Labial, Buccal and Molar Mucous Glands

The labial and buccal mucous glands are numerous. They lie in the submucosa of the lips and cheeks. The molar mucous glands, four or five, lie on the buccopharyngeal fascia around the parotid duct. All these glands open into the vestibule of the mouth (Fig. 2.20).

EYELIDS OR PALPEBRAE

DISSECTION

Give a circular incision around the roots of eyelids (Fig. 2.2—viii and ix). This will separate the orbital part of orbicularis oculi from the palpebral parts. Carefully reflect the palpebral part towards the palpebral fissure. Identify the structures present beneath the muscle as given in the text.

The upper and lower eyelids are movable curtains which protect the eyes from foreign bodies and bright light. They keep the cornea clean and moist. The upper eyelid is larger and more movable than the lower eyelid (Figs 2.21a and b).

Features

The space between the two eyelids is the palpebral fissure. The two lids are fused with each other to form the medial and lateral angles or *canthi* of the eye. At the inner canthus, there is a small triangular space, the *lacus lacrimalis*. Within it, there is an elevated *lacrimal caruncle*, made up of modified skin and skin glands. Lateral to the caruncle, the bulbar conjunctiva is pinched up to form a vertical fold called the *plica semilunaris* (Fig. 2.1).

Each eyelid is attached to the margins of the orbital opening. Its free edge is broad and has a rounded outer lip and a sharp inner lip. The outer lip presents two or more rows of eyelashes or cilia, except in the boundary of the lacus lacrimalis. At the point where eyelashes cease, there is a *lacrimal papilla* on the summit of which there is the *lacrimal punctum* (Fig. 2.1). Near the inner lip of the free edge, there is a row of openings of the tarsal glands.

The free margin of both the eyelids is subdivided into: lateral 5/6th, the ciliary part with eyelashes and medial 1/6th, the lacrimal part, which lacks cilia.

Structure

Each lid is made up of the following layers from without inwards:

1. The *skin* is thin, loose and easily distensible by oedema fluid or blood.

2 The *superficial fascia* is without any fat. It contains the palpebral part of the orbicularis oculi. Deep to the muscle is loose areolar tissue which is continuous with loose areolar tissue of the scalp.

3 The *palpebral fascia* of the two lids forms the *orbital septum*. Its thickenings form *tarsal plates* or *tarsi* in the lids and the *palpebral ligaments* at the angles. Tarsi are thin plates of condensed fibrous tissue located near the lid margins. They give stiffness to the lids (Müller's muscles) (Fig. 2.21a).

The palpebral fascia (orbital septum) is pierced by: (a) palpebral part of lacrimal gland, (b) fibres of levator palpebral superioris, (c) vessels and nerves entering the face from the orbit.

The upper tarsus receives two tendinous slips from the *levator palpebrae superioris*, one from voluntary part and another from involuntary part Müller's muscle (Fig. 2.21b). *Tarsal glands* or meibomian glands are embedded in the posterior surface of the tarsi; their ducts open in a row behind the cilia.

4 The *conjunctiva* lines the posterior surface of the tarsus.

Apart from the usual glands of the skin, and mucous glands in the conjunctiva, the larger glands found in the lids are:

a. Large sebaceous glands also called as *Zeis's glands* at the lid margin associated with cilia.

b. Modified sweat glands or *Moll's glands* at the lid margin closely associated with Zeis's glands and cilia.

c. Sebaceous or *tarsal glands* are also known as *meibomian glands*.

Blood Supply

The eyelids are supplied by:

1 The superior and inferior palpebral branches of the ophthalmic artery.

2 The lateral palpebral branch of the lacrimal artery. They form an arcade in each lid.
The veins drain into the ophthalmic and facial veins.

Nerve Supply

The upper eyelid is supplied by the lacrimal, supraorbital, supratrochlear and infratrochlear nerves from lateral to medial side.

The lower eyelid is supplied by the infraorbital and infratrochlear nerves (Fig. 2.16).

Lymphatic Drainage

The medial halves of the lids drain into the submandibular nodes, and the lateral halves into the preauricular nodes (Fig. 2.19).

CLINICAL ANATOMY

- The Müller's muscle or involuntary part of levator palpebrae superioris is supplied by sympathetic fibres from the superior cervical ganglion. Paralysis of this muscle leads to partial ptosis. This is part of the Horner's syndrome.

- The palpebral conjunctiva is examined for anaemia and for conjunctivitis; the bulbar conjunctiva for jaundice.

- Conjunctivitis is one of the commonest diseases of the eye. It may be caused by infection or by allergy.

- Foreign bodies are often lodged in a groove situated 2 mm from the edge of each eyelid.

- Chalazion is inflammation of a tarsal gland, causing a localized swelling pointing inwards.

- Ectropion is due to eversion of the lower lacrimal punctum. It usually occurs in old age due to laxity of skin.

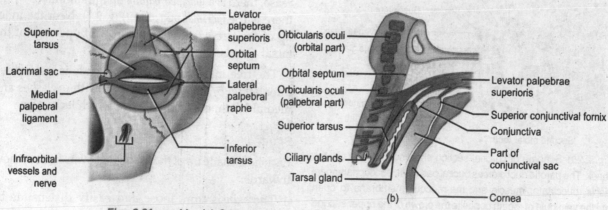

Figs 2.21a and b: (a) Orbital septum, and (b) sagittal section of the upper eyelid

- Trachoma is a contagious granular conjunctivitis caused by the trachoma virus. It is regarded as the commonest cause of blindness.
- Stye or hordeolum is a suppurative inflammation of one of the glands of Zeis. The gland is swollen, hard and painful, and the whole of the lid is oedematous. The pus points near the base of one of the cilia.
- Blepharitis is inflammation of the eyelids, specially of the lid margin.

LACRIMAL APPARATUS

DISSECTION

On the lateral side of the upper lid, cut the palpebral fascia. This will show the presence of the lacrimal gland deep in this area. Its palpebral part is to be traced in the upper eyelid. On the medial ends of both the eyelids look for lacrimal papilla. Palpate and dissect the medial palpebral ligament binding the medial ends of the eyelids. Try to locate the small lacrimal sac behind this ligament.

COMPONENTS

The structures concerned with secretion and drainage of the lacrimal or tear fluid constitute the lacrimal apparatus. It is made up of the following parts:

1 Lacrimal gland and its ducts (Figs 2.22a and b)
2 Conjunctival sac
3 Lacrimal puncta and lacrimal canaliculi
4 Lacrimal sac
5 Nasolacrimal duct.

Lacrimal Gland

It is a *serous gland* situated chiefly in the lacrimal fossa on the anterolateral part of the roof of the bony orbit and partly on the upper eyelid. Small *accessory lacrimal glands* are found in the conjunctival fornices. These are also called as Krause's gland.

The gland is 'J' shaped, being indented by the tendon of the *levator palpebrae superioris* muscle. It has:

a. An *orbital part* which is larger and deeper, and
b. A *palpebral part* smaller and superficial, lying within the eyelid (Figs 2.22a and b).

About a dozen of its *ducts* pierce the conjunctiva of the upper lid and open into the conjunctival sac near the superior fornix. Most of the ducts of the orbital part pass through the palpebral part. Removal of the latter is functionally equivalent to removal of the entire gland. After removal, the conjunctiva and cornea are moistened by accessory lacrimal glands.

The gland is supplied by the lacrimal branch of the ophthalmic artery and by the *lacrimal nerve*. The nerve has both sensory and secretomotor fibres. Flowchart 2.2 shows the secretomotor fibres for lacrimal gland.

The lacrimal fluid secreted by the lacrimal gland flows into the conjunctival sac where it lubricates the front of the eye and the deep surface of the lids. Periodic blinking helps to spread the fluid over the eye. Most of the fluid evaporates. The rest is drained by the lacrimal canaliculi. When excessive, it overflows as *tears*.

Conjunctival Sac

The conjunctiva lining the deep surfaces of the eyelids is called palpebral conjunctiva and that lining the front of the eyeball is bulbar conjunctiva. The potential space between the palpebral and bulbar parts is the

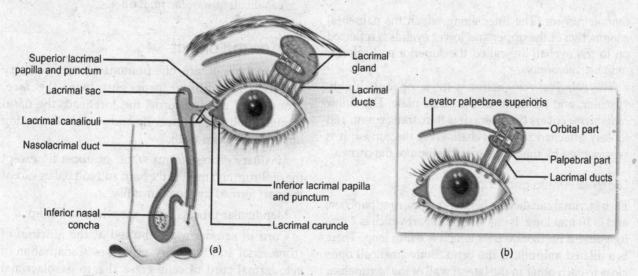

Figs 2.22a and b: Lacrimal apparatus: (a) Components, and (b) two parts of the lacrimal gland

Head and Neck

Flowchart 2.2: Secretomotor fibres for lacrimal gland

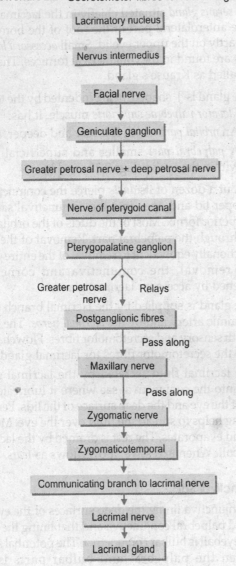

Lacrimal Sac

It is membranous sac 12 mm long and 5 mm wide, situated in the lacrimal groove behind the medial palpebral ligament. Its upper end is blind. The lower end is continuous with the nasolacrimal duct.

The sac is related anteriorly to the medial palpebral ligament and to the orbicularis oculi. Medially, the lacrimal groove separates it from the nose. Laterally, it is related to the lacrimal fascia and the lacrimal part of the orbicularis oculi.

Nasolacrimal Duct

It is a membranous passage 18 mm long. It begins at the lower end of the lacrimal sac, runs downwards, backwards and laterally, and opens into the inferior meatus of the nose. A fold of mucous membrane called the *valve of Hasner* forms an imperfect valve at the lower end of the duct.

CLINICAL ANATOMY

- Inflammation of the lacrimal sac is called *dacrocystitis*.
- The ducts of lacrimal gland open through its palpebral part into the conjunctival sac. Because of this arrangement, the removal of palpebral part necessitates the removal of the orbital part as well.
- Excessive secretion of the lacrimal fluid overflowing on the cheeks is called epiphora. Epiphora may result due to obstruction in the lacrimal fluid pathway, either at the level of punctum or canaliculi or nasolacrimal duct.

DEVELOPMENT OF FACE

Five processes of face, one frontonasal, two maxillary and two mandibular processes form the face. Frontonasal process forms the forehead, the nasal septum, philtrum of upper lip and premaxilla bearing upper four incisor teeth.

Maxillary process forms whole of upper lip except the philtrum and most of the hard and soft palate except the part formed by the premaxilla.

Mandibular process forms the whole lower lip.

Cord of ectoderm gets buried at the junction of frontonasal and maxillary processes. Canalisation of ectodermal cord of cells gives rise to nasolacrimal duct.

conjunctival sac. The lines along which the palpebral conjunctiva of the upper and lower eyelids is reflected on to the eyeball are called the superior and inferior conjunctival fornices.

The *palpebral conjunctiva* is thick, opaque, highly vascular, and adherent to the tarsal plate. The *bulbar conjunctiva* covers the sclera. It is thin, transparent, and loosely attached to the eyeball. Over the cornea, it is represented by the anterior epithelium of the cornea.

Lacrimal Puncta and Canaliculi

Each lacrimal canaliculus begins at the *lacrimal punctum*, and is 10 mm long. It has a vertical part which is 2 mm long and a horizontal part which is 8 mm long. There is a dilated ampulla at the bend. Both canaliculi open close to each other in the lateral wall of the lacrimal sac behind the medial palpebral ligament.

Mnemonics

Bell's palsy

Blink reflex abnormal
Ear ache
Lacrimation (deficient)
Loss of taste in anterior two-thirds of tongue
Sudden onset
Palsy of muscles of facial expression all symptoms are unilateral

Five branches of the facial nerve (VII)

(**T**en **Z**ebras **B**it **M**y **C**at)
Temporal
Zygomatic
Buccal
Marginal mandibular
Cervical

FACTS TO REMEMBER

- Forehead is common to both the scalp and the face.
- There are 5 layers in scalp and 6 layers in the superficial temporal region.
- Impulses from skin of the face reach the three branches of trigeminal nerve, whereas the muscles of facial expression are supplied by the facial nerve. To establish the reflex arc, nucleus of VII nerve comes closer to the spinal nucleus of V nerve at the level of lower pons. This is called "neurobiotaxis".
- Facial nerve though courses through the parotid gland, does not give any branch to the largest salivary gland.
- Buccinator is an accessory muscle of mastication, as it prevents food entering the vestibule of mouth.
- Part of the face is called as "dangerous area of face" as the facial vein communicates with cavernous venous sinus situated in the cranial cavity. Any infection from this part of face can infect the intracranial venous sinus, i.e. cavernous sinus.
- Levator palpebrae superioris is supplied partly by oculomotor nerve and partly by sympathetic fibres.
- The facial muscles are subcutaneous in position and represents morphologically remnants of panniculus carnosus.

CLINICOANATOMICAL PROBLEMS

Case 1

A man of about 30 years comes to OPD with inability to close his left eye, tears overflowing on the left cheek and saliva dribbling from his left angle of the mouth.

- What is the reason for his sad condition?
- What nerve is damaged and how is the integrity of the nerve tested?

Ans: The reason for the patient's sad condition is paralysis of his left facial nerve at the stylomastoid foramen. It is called Bell's palsy. It is treated by physiotherapy and medicines.

Facial nerve is tested by:

Asking the patient:

   i. To look upwards without moving his head, and look for the normal horizontal wrinkles on the forehead.

   ii. To show the teeth

   iii. Tightly close the eyes to test the orbicularis oculi muscle.

   iv. Puffing the mouth and then blowing out air forcibly to test the buccinator muscle.

Case 2

A teenage girl with infected acne tried to drain the pustules on her upper lip with her bare hands. After few days she noticed severe weakness in her eye muscles.

- How are the pustules connected to nerves supplying eye muscles?

Ans: Infection from pustules travels via facial vein, deep facial vein, pterygoid venous plexus, emissary vein to cavernous venous sinus and III, IV and VI cranial nerves related in its lateral wall. Since the nerves are infected, the extraocular muscles get weak and may get paralysed.

FREQUENTLY ASKED QUESTIONS

1. Describe the arterial supply and venous drainage of the face, add a note on its clinical importance.

2. Enumerate the layers of the scalp. Give its blood supply, nerve supply and clinical importance.

3. Write short notes/enumerate:
   a. Buccinator muscle
   b. Sensory nerve supply of face
   c. Components of lacrimal apparatus
   d. Features of Bell's palsy
   e. Emissary veins

MULTIPLE CHOICE QUESTIONS

1. Nasolacrimal duct opens into:
   a. Anterior part of inferior meatus
   b. Vestibule of nose
   c. Middle meatus
   d. Superior meatus

2. Dangerous area of face is named because of connection of cavernous sinus with facial vein through which vein?
   a. Maxillary
   b. Anterior ethmoidal
   c. Posterior ethmoidal
   d. Deep facial

3. Which of the following muscle separates the orbital and palpebral parts of the lacrimal gland?
   a. Superior oblique
   b. Superior rectus

   c. Inferior oblique
   d. Levator palpabrae superioris

4. Infection in dangerous area of face usually leads to:
   a. Superior sagittal sinus thrombosis
   b. Transverse sinus thrombosis
   c. Cavernous sinus thrombosis
   d. Brain abscess

5. Supraorbital artery is a branch of:
   a. Maxillary   b. External carotid
   c. Ophthalmic   d. Internal carotid

6. Which of the following nerve ascends along with occipital artery in the scalp?
   a. Greater occipital   b. Lesser occipital
   c. Third occipital   d. Suboccipital

ANSWERS

1. a   2. d   3. d   4. c   5. c   6. a

Side of the Neck

Life is a continuous process of adjustment
—Indira Gandhi

INTRODUCTION

The beauty of the neck lies in its deep or cervical fascia. The sternocleidomastoid is an important landmark between the anterior and posterior triangles. The posterior triangle contains the spinal root of accessory nerve deep to its fascial roof and the roots and trunks of brachial plexus deep to its fascial floor. It also contains a part of the subclavian artery, which continues as the axillary artery for the upper limb. Arteries like the rivers are named according to the regions they pass through. Congestive cardiac failure can be seen at a glance by the raised jugular venous pressure. This external jugular vein lies in the superficial fascia (Fig. 3.1a) and if cut, leads to air embolism, unless the deep fascia pierced by the vein is also cut to collapse the vein.

LANDMARKS

1 The *sternocleidomastoid* muscle is seen prominently when the neck and chin are turned to the opposite side. The ridge raised by the muscle extends from the clavicle and sternum to the mastoid process (Fig. 3.1b).
2 The *external jugular vein* crosses the sternocleidomastoid obliquely, running downwards and backwards from near the auricle to the clavicle. It is better seen in old age.
3 The *greater supraclavicular fossa* lies above and behind the middle one-third of the clavicle. It overlies the cervical part of the brachial plexus and the third part of the subclavian artery.
4 The *lesser supraclavicular fossa* is a small depression between the sternal and clavicular parts of the sterno-cleidomastoid. It overlies the internal jugular vein.
5 The *mastoid process* is a large bony projection behind the auricle.
6 The *transverse process of the atlas vertebra* can be felt on deep pressure midway between the angle of the

mandible and the mastoid process, immediately anteroinferior to the tip of the mastoid process.
7 The *fourth cervical transverse process* is just palpable at the level of the upper border of the thyroid cartilage; and the *sixth cervical transverse process* at the level of the cricoid cartilage.
8 The anterior tubercle of the *transverse process of the sixth cervical vertebra* is the largest of all such processes and is called the *carotid tubercle* of Chassaignac. The common carotid artery can be best pressed against this tubercle, deep to the anterior border of the sternocleidomastoid muscle.
9 The *anterior border of the trapezius muscle* becomes prominent on elevation of the shoulder against resistance.

THE NECK

DISSECTION

Give a median incision from the chin downwards towards the suprasternal notch situated above the manubrium of sternum.

Make one incision in the skin of base of mandible. Continue it by oblique incision along posterior border of ramus of mandible up to mastoid process and further along the superior nuchal line till the external occipital protuberance.

One incision is given along the upper border of clavicle (Fig. 3.1a). Reflect only the skin up towards the anterior border of trapezius muscle.

Platysma, a part of the subcutaneous muscle is visible. Reflect the platysma towards the mandible. Identify the anterior or transverse cutaneous nerve of the neck in the upper part of superficial fascia. Anterior jugular vein running vertically close to the median plane is also encountered. Remove the superficial fascia till the deep fascia of neck is seen (Fig. 3.1b).

External jugular vein is seen above the clavicle.

To open up the suprasternal space, make a horizontal incision just above the sternum. Extend this incision along the anterior border of sternocleidomastoid muscle for 3–4 cm. Reflect the superficial lamina to expose the suprasternal space and identify its contents.

Define the attachments of investing layer, pretracheal layer, prevertebral layer and carotid sheath.

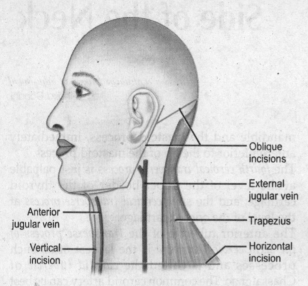

Fig. 3.1a: Lines of dissection

Oblique incisions
External jugular vein
Trapezius
Horizontal incision
Anterior jugular vein
Vertical incision

BOUNDARIES

The side of the neck is roughly quadrilateral in outline. It is *bounded* anteriorly, by the anterior median line; posteriorly, by the anterior border of trapezius; superiorly, by the base of mandible, a line joining angle of the mandible to mastoid process, and superior nuchal line; and inferiorly, by the clavicle.

This quadrilateral space is divided obliquely by the sternocleidomastoid muscle into the *anterior and posterior triangles* (Fig. 3.1b).

SKIN

The skin of the neck is supplied by the second, third and fourth cervical nerves. The anterolateral part is supplied by anterior primary rami through the (i) anterior cutaneous, (ii) great auricular, (iii) lesser occipital and (iv) supraclavicular nerves. A broad band of skin over the posterior part is supplied by dorsal or posterior primary rami (*see* Fig. 2.16).

First cervical spinal nerve has no cutaneous distribution. Cervical fifth, sixth, seventh, eighth and thoracic first nerves supply the upper limb through the brachial plexus; and, therefore, do not supply the neck. The territory of fourth cervical nerve extends into the pectoral region through the supraclavicular nerves and meets second thoracic dermatome at the level of the second costal cartilage.

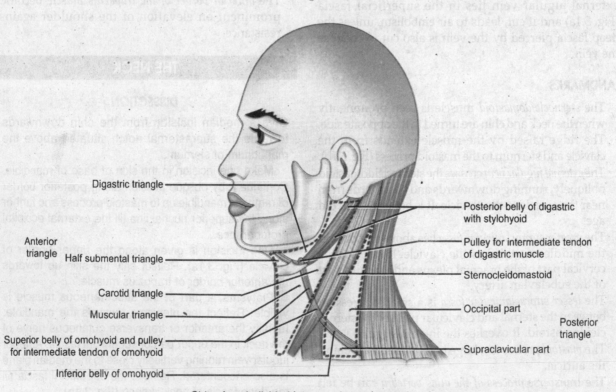

Digastric triangle
Anterior triangle
Half submental triangle
Carotid triangle
Muscular triangle
Superior belly of omohyoid and pulley for intermediate tendon of omohyoid
Inferior belly of omohyoid

Posterior belly of digastric with stylohyoid
Pulley for intermediate tendon of digastric muscle
Sternocleidomastoid
Occipital part
Posterior triangle
Supraclavicular part

Fig. 3.1b: Side of neck divided into anterior and posterior triangles

SUPERFICIAL FASCIA

Superficial fascia contains areolar tissue with platysma (*see* Table 2.3). Lying deep to platysma are cutaneous nerves (Fig. 3.6), superficial veins (*see* Fig. 2.6), *lymph vessels, lymph nodes* and small arteries.

CLINICAL ANATOMY

The surgeon has to stitch platysma muscle separately so that skin does not adhere to deeper neck muscles, otherwise the skin will get an ugly scar.

DEEP CERVICAL FASCIA (FASCIA COLLI)

The deep fascia of the neck is condensed to form the following layers:

1 Investing layer (Fig. 3.2)
2 Pretracheal fascia
3 Prevertebral fascia
4 Carotid sheath
5 Buccopharyngeal fascia
6 Pharyngobasilar fascia.

INVESTING LAYER

It lies deep to the platysma, and surrounds the neck like a collar. It forms the roof of the posterior triangle of the neck (Fig. 3.3).

Attachments

Superiorly

a. External occipital protuberance
b. Superior nuchal line
c. Mastoid process
d. External acoustic meatus
e. Base of the mandible.

Between the angle of the mandible and the mastoid process, the fascia splits to enclose the parotid gland (Fig. 3.4).

The superficial lamina named as *parotid fascia* is thick and dense, and is attached to the zygomatic arch. The deep lamina is thin and is attached to the styloid process, the tympanic plate and the mandible. Between the styloid process and the angle of the mandible, the deep lamina is thick and forms the *stylomandibular ligament* which separates the parotid gland from the submandibular gland, and is pierced by the external carotid artery.

At the base of mandible, it encloses submandibular gland. The superficial lamina is attached to lower border of body of mandible and deep lamina to the mylohyoid line.

Inferiorly

a. Spine of scapula,   b. Acromion process,
c. Clavicle, and   d. Manubrium.

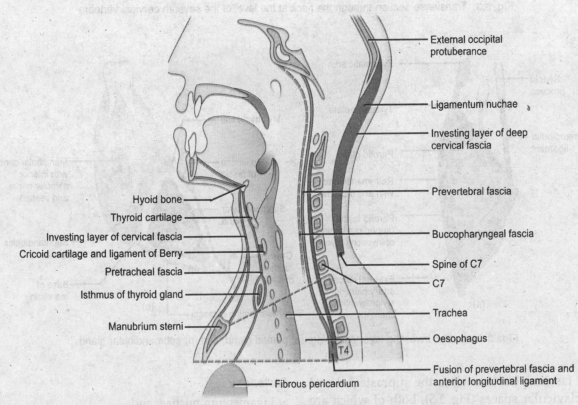

Hyoid bone
Thyroid cartilage
Investing layer of cervical fascia
Cricoid cartilage and ligament of Berry
Pretracheal fascia
Isthmus of thyroid gland
Manubrium sterni
Fibrous pericardium

External occipital protuberance
Ligamentum nuchae
Investing layer of deep cervical fascia
Prevertebral fascia
Buccopharyngeal fascia
Spine of C7
C7
Trachea
Oesophagus
Fusion of prevertebral fascia and anterior longitudinal ligament

T4

Fig. 3.2: Vertical extent of the first three layers of the deep cervical fascia

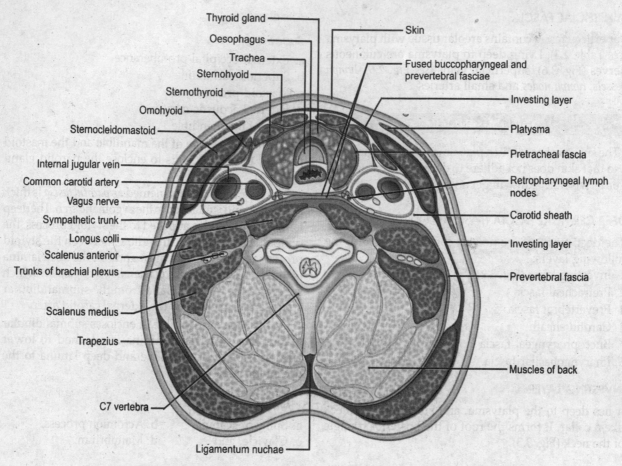

Fig. 3.3: Transverse section through the neck at the level of the seventh cervical vertebra

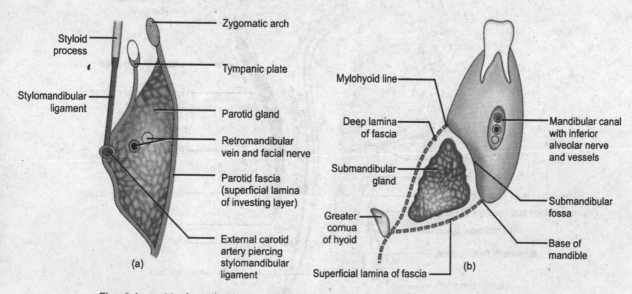

Figs 3.4a and b: Investing layer enclosing: (a) parotid gland, and (b) submandibular gland

The fascia splits to enclose the suprasternal and supraclavicular spaces (Fig. 3.5), both of which are described as follows.

Posteriorly

a. Ligamentum nuchae; and
b. Spine of seventh cervical vertebra.

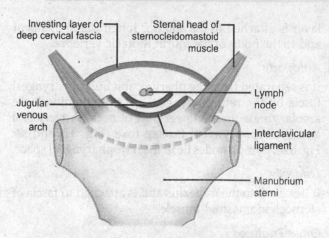

Fig. 3.5: Contents of suprasternal space

Anteriorly

a. Symphysis menti.
b. Hyoid bone.

Both above and below the hyoid bone, it is continuous with the fascia of the opposite side.

Other Features

1 The investing layer of deep cervical fascia *splits* to enclose:
   a. *Muscles*: Trapezius and sternocleidomastoid (Fig. 3.3).
   b. *Salivary glands*: Parotid and submandibular (Fig. 3.4).
   c. *Spaces*: Suprasternal and supraclavicular.

The *suprasternal space* or space of Burns contains:
- The sternal heads of the right and left sterno-cleidomastoid muscles (Fig. 3.5),

- The jugular venous arch,
- A lymph node, and
- The interclavicular ligament.

The *supraclavicular space* is traversed by:
- The external jugular vein (Fig. 3.6),
- The supraclavicular nerves, and
- Cutaneous vessels, including lymphatics.

2 It also forms *pulleys* to bind the tendons of the digastric and omohyoid muscles (Fig. 3.1b).
3 Forms roof of anterior and posterior triangles.
4 Forms stylomandibular ligament (Fig. 3.4b) and parotidomasseteric fascia.

CLINICAL ANATOMY

- Parotid swellings are very painful due to the unyielding nature of parotid fascia.

- While excising the submandibular salivary gland, the external carotid artery should be secured before dividing it, otherwise it may retract through the stylomandibular ligament and cause serious bleeding (Fig. 3.4). The figure also shows the superior attachment of investing layer of deep cervical fascia.

- Division of the external jugular vein in the supra-clavicular space may cause air embolism and consequent death because the cut ends of the vein are prevented from retraction and closure by the fascia, attached firmly to the vein (Fig. 3.6 and inset).

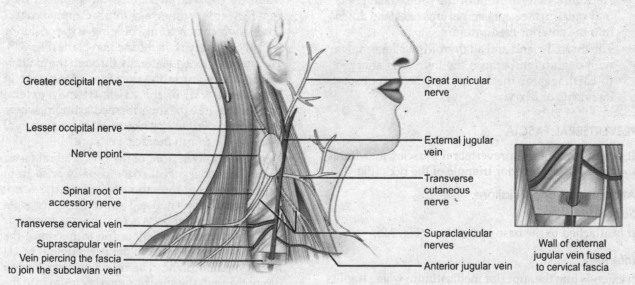

Fig. 3.6: Structures seen in relation to the fascial roof of the posterior triangle and structures seen in supraclavicular space

Head and Neck

PRETRACHEAL FASCIA

The importance of this fascia is that it encloses and suspends the thyroid gland and forms its false capsule (Fig. 3.2).

Attachments

Superiorly

1 Hyoid bone in the median plane.
2 Oblique line of thyroid cartilage laterally.
3 Cricoid cartilage—more laterally.

Inferiorly

Below the thyroid gland, it encloses the inferior thyroid veins, passes behind the brachiocephalic veins, and finally blends with the arch of the aorta and fibrous pericardium.

On Either Side

It forms the front of the carotid sheath, and fuses with the fascia deep to the sternocleidomastoid (Fig. 3.3).

Other Features

1 The posterior layer of the thyroid capsule is thick. On either side, it forms a *suspensory ligament* for the thyroid gland known as *ligament of Berry* (*see* Fig. 8.4). The ligaments are attached chiefly to the cricoid cartilage, and may extend to the thyroid cartilage. They support the thyroid gland, and do not let it sink into the mediastinum. The capsule of the thyroid is very weak along the posterior borders of the lateral lobes.
2 The fascia provides a slippery surface for free movements of the trachea during swallowing.

CLINICAL ANATOMY

- Neck infections in front of the pretracheal fascia may bulge in the suprasternal area or extend down into the anterior mediastinum.
- The thyroid gland and all thyroid swellings move with deglutition because the thyroid is attached to cartilages of the larynx by the suspensory ligaments of Berry.

PREVERTEBRAL FASCIA

It lies in front of the prevertebral muscles, and forms the floor of the posterior triangle of the neck (Fig. 3.2).

Attachments and Relations

Superiorly

It is attached to the base of the skull (Fig. 3.2).

Inferiorly

It extends into the superior mediastinum where it splits into anterior and posterior layers. Anterior layer/alar fascia blends with buccopharyngeal fascia and posterior layer is attached to the anterior longitudinal ligament and to the body of the fourth thoracic vertebra.

Anteriorly

It is separated from the pharynx and buccopharyngeal fascia by the retropharyngeal space containing loose areolar tissue. In the lower part of neck, prevertebral and buccopharyngeal fasciae fuse (Fig. 3.3 and *see* Fig. 8.4). Lymph nodes lie in the retropharyngeal space.

Laterally

It lies deep to the trapezius and is attached to fascia of sternocleidomastoid muscle.

Other Features

1 The cervical and brachial plexuses lie behind the prevertebral fascia. The fascia is pierced by the four cutaneous branches of the cervical plexus (Fig. 3.6).
2 As the trunks of the brachial plexus and the subclavian artery pass laterally through the interval between the scalenus anterior and the scalenus medius, they carry with them a covering of the prevertebral fascia known as the *axillary sheath* which extends into the axilla. The subclavian and axillary veins lie outside the sheath and as a result they can dilate during increased venous return from the limb.
3 Fascia provides a fixed base for the movements of the pharynx, the oesophagus and the carotid sheaths during movements of the neck and during swallowing.

CLINICAL ANATOMY

- Neck infections behind the prevertebral fascia arise usually from tuberculosis of the cervical vertebrae or cervical caries. Pus produced as a result may extend in various directions. It may pass forwards forming a chronic retropharyngeal abscess which may form a bulging in the posterior wall of the pharynx, in the median plane (Fig. 3.7). The pus may extend laterally through the axillary sheath and point in the posterior triangle, or in the lateral wall of the axilla. It may extend downwards into the superior mediastinum, where its descent is limited by fusion of the prevertebral fascia to the fourth thoracic vertebra.
- Neck infections in front of the prevertebral fascia in the retropharyngeal space usually arise from suppuration, i.e. formation of pus in the retropharyngeal lymph nodes. The pus forms an acute retropharyngeal abscess which bulges forwards in the paramedian position due to fusion of the buccopharyngeal fascia to the prevertebral fascia in the median plane. The infection may extend down through the superior mediastinum into the posterior mediastinum (*see* Fig. 8.4).

Anterior = Ansa Cervicalis
Posterior = Cervical Sympathetic Chain
Overlapped = Ant. Border of Sternocleidomastoid
+is fused to layers of deep
cervical fascia

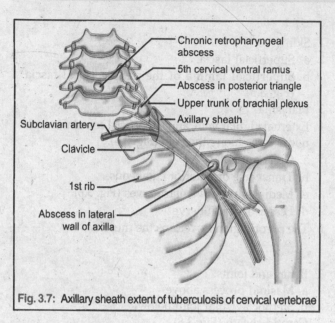

Fig. 3.7: Axillary sheath extent of tuberculosis of cervical vertebrae

CAROTID SHEATH

It is a condensation of the fibroareolar tissue around the main vessels of the neck.

Formation: It is formed on anterior aspect by pretracheal fascia and on posterior aspect by prevertebral fascia.

Contents: The contents are the common or internal carotid arteries, internal jugular vein and the vagus nerve. It is thin over the vein (Figs 3.8a and b). In the upper part of sheath there are IX, XI, XII nerves also. These nerves pierce the sheet at different points.

Relations:

1 The ansa cervicalis lies embedded in the anterior wall of the carotid sheath (Figs 3.8a and b).

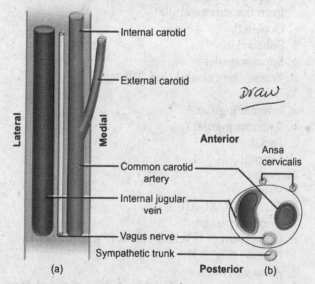

Draw

Figs 3.8a and b: Right carotid sheath with its contents: (a) Surface view, and (b) sectional view

2 The cervical sympathetic chain lies behind the sheath, plastered to the prevertebral fascia.
3 The sheath is overlapped by the anterior border of the sternocleidomastoid, and is fused to the layers of the deep cervical fascia.

BUCCOPHARYNGEAL FASCIA

This fascia covers the superior constrictor muscle externally and extends on to the superficial aspect of the buccinator muscle (*see* Fig. 14.14).

PHARYNGOBASILAR FASCIA

This fascia is especially thickened between the upper border of superior constrictor muscle and the base of the skull. It lies deep to the pharyngeal muscles (*see* Figs 14.14 and 14.21).

PHARYNGEAL SPACES

RETROPHARYNGEAL SPACE

Situation:	Dead space behind pharynx.
Function:	Acts as a bursa for expansion of pharynx during deglutition
Boundaries:	Anterior: Buccopharyngeal fascia Posterior: Prevertebral fascia Sides: Carotid sheath (Fig. 3.3)
Superior:	Base of skull
Inferior:	Open and continuous with superior mediastinum.
Contents:	Retropharyngeal lymph nodes, pharyngeal plexus of vessels and nerves, loose areolar tissue.
Clinical anatomy:	Pus collection due to lymph node abscess. It should be differentiated from cold abscess of spine of cervical vertebrae (*see* Fig. 8.4).

LATERAL PHARYNGEAL SPACE

Situation:	Side of pharynx
Boundaries:	Medial: Pharynx Posterolateral: Parotid gland Anterolateral: Medial pterygoid Posterior: Carotid sheath
Contents:	Maxillary nerve and branches of maxillary artery Fibrofatty tissue
Clinical anatomy:	Pus collection/Ludwig's angina.

STERNOCLEIDOMASTOID MUSCLE (STERNOMASTOID)

The sternocleidomastoid and trapezius are large superficial muscles of the neck. Both of them are supplied by

Head and Neck

he spinal root of the accessory nerve. The trapezius, because of its main action on the shoulder girdle, is considered with the upper limb (*see* Volume 1, Section 1). The sternocleidomastoid is described below.

Origin

1 The *sternal head* is tendinous and arises from the superolateral part of the front of the manubrium sterni (Fig. 3.1b).
2 The *clavicular head* is musculotendinous and arises from the medial one-third of the superior surface of the clavicle. It passes deep to the sternal head, and the two heads blend below the middle of the neck. Between the two heads, there is a small triangular depression of the lesser supraclavicular fossa, overlying the internal jugular vein.

Insertion

It is inserted:

1 By a thick tendon into the lateral surface of *mastoid process*, from its tip to superior border.
2 By a thin aponeurosis into the lateral half of the *superior nuchal line* of the occipital bone.

Nerve Supply

1 The spinal accessory nerve provides the motor supply. It passes through the muscle.
2 Branches from the ventral rami of C2 and C3 are proprioceptive (Fig. 3.9).

Blood Supply

Arterial supply—one branch each from superior thyroid artery and suprascapular artery and, two branches from the occipital artery supply the big muscle. Veins follow the arteries.

Actions

1 When one muscle contracts:
   a. It turns the chin to the opposite side.
   b. It can also tilt the head towards the shoulder of same side.
2 When both muscles contract together:
   a. They draw the head forwards, as in eating and in lifting the head from a pillow.
   b. With the longus colli, they flex the neck against resistance.
   c. It also helps in forced inspiration.

Relations

The sternocleidomastoid is enclosed in the investing layer of deep cervical fascia, and is pierced by the accessory nerve and by the four sternocleidomastoid arteries. It has the following relations:

Superficial

1 Skin
2 a. Superficial fascia.
   b. Superficial lamina of the deep cervical fascia (Fig. 3.3).
3 Platysma.
4 External jugular vein, and superficial cervical lymph nodes lying along the vein (Fig. 3.6).
5 a. Great auricular.
   b. Transverse or anterior cutaneous.
   c. Medial supraclavicular nerves (Fig. 3.6).
   d. Lesser occipital nerve
6 The parotid gland overlaps the muscle.

Deep

1 Bones and joints:
   a. Mastoid process above
   b. Sternoclavicular joint below.
2 Carotid sheath (Fig. 3.8).
3 Muscles:
   a. Sternohyoid
   b. Sternothyroid
   c. Omohyoid
   d. Three scaleni
   e. Levator scapulae (Fig. 3.9, inset 1)
   f. Splenius capitis
   g. Longissimus capitis
   h. Posterior belly of digastric.
4 Arteries:
   a. Common carotid
   b. Internal carotid
   c. External carotid
   d. Sternocleidomastoid arteries, two from the occipital artery, one from the superior thyroid, one from the suprascapular
   e. Occipital
   f. Subclavian
   g. Suprascapular
   h. Transverse cervical (Fig. 3.9).
5 Veins:
   a. Internal jugular
   b. Anterior jugular
   c. Facial
   d. Lingual
6 Nerves:
   a. Vagus
   b. Parts of IX, XI, XII
   c. Cervical plexus
   d. Upper part of brachial plexus (Fig. 3.9, inset 1)
   e. Phrenic (Fig. 3.9)
   f. Ansa cervicalis
7 Lymph nodes, superficial and deep cervical (*see* Figs 8.28 and 8.29).

- Figure 3.5 shows inferior attachment of investing layer of deep cervical fascia. Fascia of supraclavicular space is pierced by external jugular vein to drain into subclavian vein (Fig. 3.6).
- Torticollis is a deformity in which the head is bent to one side and the chin points to the other side. This is a result of spasm or contracture of the muscles supplied by the spinal accessory nerve, these being the sternocleidomastoid and trapezius. Although there are many varieties of torticollis depending on the causes, the common types are:
  a. Rheumatic torticollis due to exposure to cold or draught.
  b. Reflex torticollis due to inflamed or suppurating cervical lymph nodes which irritate the spinal accessory nerve.
  c. Congenital torticollis due to birth injury.

Wry neck: Shortening of the muscle fibres due to intravascular clotting of veins within the muscle. It usually occurs during difficult delivery of the baby.

DISSECTION

Try to dissect and clean the cutaneous nerves (Fig. 3.6) which pierce the investing layer of fascia at the middle of posterior border of sternocleidomastoid muscle.

Demarcate the course of external jugular vein. Cut carefully the deep fascia of posterior border of sternocleidomastoid muscle and reflect it towards trapezius muscle. Identify the accessory nerve lying just deep to the investing layer seen at the middle of the posterior border of sternocleidomastoid muscle and across the posterior triangle to reach the anterior border of trapezius which it supplies (Fig. 3.9).

Define the boundaries, roof, floor, divisions and contents of the posterior triangle (Fig. 3.1b).

Identify and clean the inferior belly of omohyoid. Find the transverse cervical artery along the upper border of this muscle. Trace it both ways. Deep to this muscle is the upper or supraclavicular part of brachial plexus. Identify the roots, trunks and their branches carefully. The branches are suprascapular nerve, dorsal scapular nerve, long thoracic nerve, nerve to subclavius (Fig. 3.10). Medial to the brachial plexus locate the third part of subclavian artery.

Follow the terminal part of external jugular vein through the deep fascia into the deeply placed subclavian vein (Fig. 3.6). Identify suprascapular artery running just above the clavicle (Fig. 3.9).

Define the attachments and relations of sternocleidomastoid muscle. To expose scalenus anterior muscle, cut across the clavicular head of sternocleidomastoid muscle and push it medially. Scalenus anterior muscle covered by well-defined prevertebral fascia can be identified. Clean the subclavian artery and upper part of brachial plexus deep to the scalenus anterior muscle.

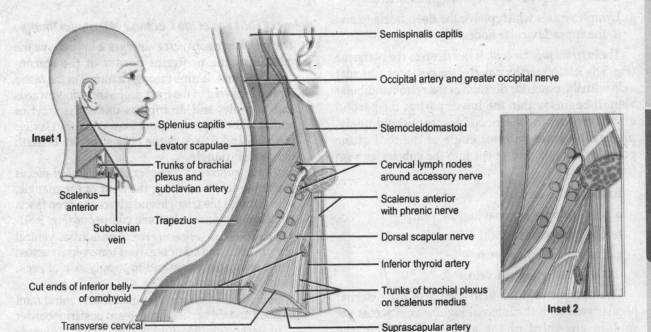

Inset 1

Splenius capitis
Levator scapulae
Trunks of brachial plexus and subclavian artery
Scalenus anterior
Subclavian vein
Trapezius
Cut ends of inferior belly of omohyoid
Transverse cervical

Semispinalis capitis
Occipital artery and greater occipital nerve
Sternocleidomastoid
Cervical lymph nodes around accessory nerve
Scalenus anterior with phrenic nerve
Dorsal scapular nerve
Inferior thyroid artery
Trunks of brachial plexus on scalenus medius
Suprascapular artery

Inset 2

Fig. 3.9: The posterior triangle of neck and its contents

Features

The posterior triangle is a space on the side of the neck situated behind the sternocleidomastoid muscle.

Boundaries

Anterior

Posterior border of sternocleidomastoid (Fig. 3.1b).

Posterior

Anterior border of trapezius.

Inferior or base

Middle one-third of clavicle.

Apex

Lies on the superior nuchal line where the trapezius and sternocleidomastoid meet.

Roof

The roof is formed by the *investing layer of deep cervical fascia*. The superficial fascia over the posterior triangle contains:

1 The platysma.
2 The external jugular and posterior external jugular veins.
3 Parts of the supraclavicular, great auricular, transverse cutaneous and lesser occipital nerves (Fig. 3.6).
4 Unnamed arteries derived from the occipital, transverse cervical and suprascapular arteries.
5 Lymph vessels which pierce the deep fascia to end in the supraclavicular nodes.

The *external jugular vein:* It lies deep to the platysma (Fig. 3.6). It is formed by union of the posterior auricular vein with the posterior division of the retromandibular vein. It begins within the lower part of the parotid gland, crosses the sternocleidomastoid obliquely, pierces the anteroinferior angle of the roof of the posterior triangle, and opens into the subclavian vein (*see* Fig. 2.6).

Its tributaries are:

a. The posterior external jugular vein.
b. The transverse cervical vein.
c. The suprascapular vein.
d. The anterior jugular vein.

The oblique jugular vein connects the external jugular vein with the internal jugular vein across the middle one-third of the anterior border of the sternocleidomastoid.

- The right external jugular vein is *examined to assess the venous pressure;* the right atrial pressure is reflected in it because there are no valves in the entire course of this vein and it is straight.
- As external jugular vein pierces the fascia, the margins of the vein get adherent to the fascia. So if the vein gets cut, it cannot close and air is sucked in due to negative intrathoracic pressure. That causes air embolism. To prevent this, the deep fascia has to be cut.

Floor

The floor of the posterior triangle is formed by the prevertebral layer of deep cervical fascia, covering the following muscles:

1 Splenius capitis.
2 Levator scapulae.
3 Scalenus medius (Fig. 3.9).
4 Semispinalis capitis may also form part of the floor.

Division of the Posterior Triangle

It is subdivided by the inferior belly of omohyoid into:

1 A larger upper part, called the *occipital triangle.*
2 A smaller lower part, called the *supraclavicular* or the *subclavian triangle* (Fig. 3.1b).

Contents of the Posterior Triangle

These are enumerated in Table 3.1. Some of the contents are considered below.

Relevant Features of the Contents of Posterior Triangle

1 The *spinal accessory nerve* emerges a little above the middle of the posterior border of the sterno-cleidomastoid. It runs through a tunnel in the fascia forming the roof of the triangle, passing downwards and laterally, and disappears under the anterior border of the trapezius about 5 cm above the clavicle (Figs 3.6 and 3.9). It is the only structure beneath the roof of triangle.
2 The four *cutaneous branches of the cervical plexus* pierce the fascia covering the floor of the triangle, pass through the triangle and pierce the deep fascia at different points to become cutaneous (Fig. 3.6).

   a. *Transverse cutaneous nerve:* Arises from ventral rami of C2 and C3 nerves runs transversely across the sternocleidomastoid to supply skin of neck, till the sternum.
   b. *Supraclavicular nerves:* Formed from ventral rami of C3 and C4 nerves. Emerges at posterior border of sternocleidomastoid. It descends downwards and diverges into three branches. Medial one

Table 3.1: Contents of the posterior triangle

Contents	Occipital triangle	Subclavian triangle

A. Nerves	1. Spinal accessory nerve (Fig. 3.9, inset 2)
	2. Four cutaneous branches of cervical plexus (Fig. 3.6):
	  a. Lesser occipital (C2)
	  b. Great auricular (C2, C3)
	  c. Anterior cutaneous nerve of neck (C2, C3)
	  d. Supraclavicular nerves (C3, C4)
	3. Muscular branches:
	  a. Two small branches to the levator scapulae (C3, C4)
	  b. Two small branches to the trapezius (C3, C4)
	  c. Nerve to rhomboids (proprioceptive) (C5)
		1. Roots and trunks of brachial plexus
		2. Nerve to serratus anterior (long thoracic, C5–C7)
		3. Nerve to subclavius (C5, C6)
		4. Suprascapular nerve (C5, C6)

B. Vessels	1. Transverse cervical artery and vein 2. Occipital artery	1. Third part of subclavian artery and subclavian vein 2. Suprascapular artery and vein 3. Commencement of transverse cervical artery and termination of the corresponding vein 4. Lower part of external jugular vein
C. Lymph nodes	Along the posterior border of the sternocleidomastoid, more in the lower part—the supraclavicular nodes and a few at the upper angle—the occipital nodes	A few members of the supraclavicular chain

supplies the skin over the manubrium till manubriosternal joint. Intermediate nerve crosses the clavicle to supply skin of first intercostal space till the second rib. Lateral nerve runs across the lateral side of clavicle and acromion to supply skin over the upper half of the deltoid muscle.

c. *Great auricular nerve:* It is the largest ascending branch of cervical plexus. Arises from ventral rami of C2 and C3 nerves. Ascends on the sternocleidomastoid muscle to reach parotid gland, where it divides into anterior and posterior branches. Anterior branch supplies lower one-third of skin on lateral surface of pinna and skin over the parotid gland and connects the gland to the auriculotemporal nerve. This cross-connection is the anatomical basis for Frey's syndrome. Posterior branch supplies lower one-third of skin on medial surface of the pinna.

d. *Lesser occipital:* Arises from ventral ramus of C2 segment of spinal cord. Seen at the posterior border of sternocleidomastoid muscle. It then winds around and ascends along its posterior border to supply skin of upper two-thirds of medial surface of pinna adjoining part of the scalp.

3 *Muscular branches to the levator scapulae and to the trapezius* (C3, C4) appear about the middle of the sternocleidomastoid. Those to the levator scapulae soon end in it; those to the trapezius run below and parallel to the accessory nerve across the middle of the triangle. Both nerves lie deep to the fascia of the floor.

4 Three trunks of the *brachial plexus* emerge between the scalenus anterior and medius, and carry the axil-lary sheath around them. The sheath contains the brachial plexus and the subclavian artery. These structures lie deep to the floor of posterior triangle. If prevertebral *fascia is left intact, all these structures are safe* (Fig. 3.9).

5 The *nerve to the rhomboid* is from C5 root, pierces the scalenus medius and passes deep to the levator scapulae to reach the back where it lies deep or anterior to the rhomboid muscles (Fig. 3.10).

6 The *nerve to the serratus anterior* (C5–C7) arises by three roots. The roots from C5 and C6 pierce the scalenus medius and join the root from C7 over the first digitation of the serratus anterior. The nerve passes behind the brachial plexus. It descends over the serratus anterior in the medial wall of the axilla and gives branches to the digitations of the muscle (Fig. 3.10).

7 The *nerve to the subclavius* (C5, C6) descends in front of the brachial plexus and the subclavian vessels, but behind the omohyoid, the transverse cervical and suprascapular vessels and the clavicle to reach the deep surface of the subclavius muscle. As it runs near the lateral margin of the scalenus anterior, it sometimes gives off the *accessory phrenic nerve* which joins the phrenic nerve in front of the scalenus anterior.

8 The *suprascapular nerve* (C5, C6) arises from the upper trunk of the brachial plexus and crosses the lower part of the posterior triangle just above and lateral to the brachial plexus, deep to the transverse cervical vessels and the omohyoid. It passes backwards over the shoulder to reach the scapula. It supplies the supraspinatus and infraspinatus muscles (Fig. 3.10).

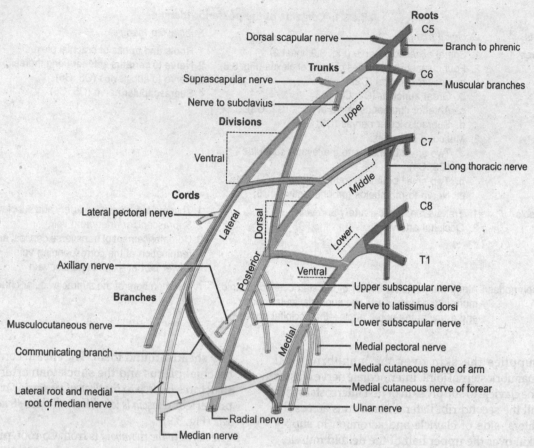

Fig. 3.10: Brachial plexus

9 The *subclavian artery* passes behind the tendon of the scalenus anterior, over the first rib (Fig. 3.9, inset 1).

10 The *transverse cervical artery* is a branch of the thyrocervical trunk. It crosses the scalenus anterior, the phrenic nerve, the upper trunks of the brachial plexus, the nerve to the subclavius, the suprascapular nerve, and the scalenus medius. At the anterior border of the levator scapulae, it divides into superficial and deep branches. The inferior belly of the omohyoid crosses the artery.

11 The *suprascapular artery* is also a branch of the thyrocervical trunk. It passes laterally and backwards behind the clavicle.

12 The *occipital artery* crosses the apex of the posterior triangle superficial to the splenius capitis.

13 The subclavian vein passes in front of the tendon of scalenus anterior muscle.

CLINICAL ANATOMY

- The most common swelling in the posterior triangle is due to enlargement of the supraclavicular lymph nodes. While doing biopsy of the lymph node, one must be careful in preserving the accessory nerve which may get entangled amongst enlarged lymph nodes (Fig. 3.9).

- Supraclavicular lymph nodes are commonly enlarged in tuberculosis, Hodgkin's disease, and in malignant growths of the breast, arm or chest.

- Block dissection of the neck for malignant diseases is the removal of cervical lymph nodes along with other structures involved in the growth. This procedure does not endanger those nerves of the posterior triangle which lie deep to the prevertebral fascia, i.e. the brachial and cervical plexuses and their muscular branches.

- A cervical rib may compress the second part of subclavian artery. In these cases, blood supply to upper limb reaches via anastomoses around the scapula.

- Dysphagia caused by compression of the oesophagus by an abnormal subclavian artery is called *dysphagia lusoria*.

- Elective arterial surgery of the common carotid artery is done for aneurysms, AV fistulae or arteriosclerotic occlusions. It is better to expose the common carotid artery in its upper part where it is superficial. While ligating the artery, care should be taken not to include the vagus nerve or the sympathetic chain.

• Second part of the subclavian artery may get pressed by the scalenus anterior muscle, resulting in decreased blood supply to the upper limb. If the muscle is divided, the effects are abolished (Fig. 3.11).

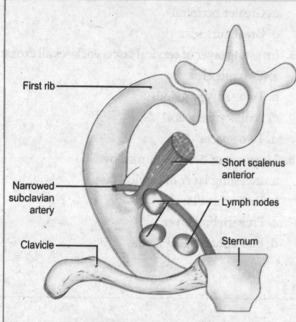

Fig. 3.11: Second part of subclavian artery narrowed by the short scalenus anterior

Mnemonics

Cervical plexus: Arrangement of the important nerves "GLAST":

Great auricular

Lesser occipital

Accessory nerve pops out between L and S

Supraclavicular

Transverse cervical

FACTS TO REMEMBER

Investing layer of deep cervical fascia encloses 2 muscles, 2 salivary glands; forms 2 pulleys; encloses 2 spaces and forms roof of posterior triangle.

• Prevertebral fascia forms the axillary sheath.

• Pretracheal fascia suspends the thyroid gland.

• Cold abscess of caries spine can track down to the posterior triangle or axilla.

• Occipital part of posterior triangle contains the spinal root of accessory nerve as the most important constituent.

• Supraclavicular part of posterior triangle contains roots, trunks, branches of brachial plexus and third part of subclavian artery.

• Sternocleidomastoid divides the side of neck into anterior and posterior triangles.

CLINICOANATOMICAL PROBLEM

A middle-aged woman had a deep cut in the middle of her right posterior triangle of neck. The bleeding was arrested and wound was sutured. The patient later felt difficulty in combing her hair.

• What blood vessel is severed?

• Why did the patient have difficulty in combing her hair?

Ans: The external jugular vein was severed. It passes across the sternocleidomastoid muscle to join the subclavian vein above the clavicle. Her accessory nerve is also injured as it crosses the posterior triangle close to its roof, causing paralysis of trapezius muscle. The trapezius with serratus anterior causes overhead abduction required for combing the hair. Due to paralysis of trapezius, she felt difficulty in combing her hair.

FREQUENTLY ASKED QUESTIONS

1. Describe the cervical fascia under following headings:

   a. Attachments and structures en closed by investing layer of cervical fascia

   b. Clinical importance of pretracheal fascia

   c. Contents of carotid sheath

2. Enumerate the boundaries and contents of posterior triangle of neck. How is external jugular vein formed and what is its clinical importance?

3. Write short notes/enumerate:

   a. Sternocleidomastoid muscle

   b. Contents of suprasternal space

   c. Suspensary ligament of Berry

MULTIPLE CHOICE QUESTIONS

1. All of the following structures are seen in the posterior triangle of neck *except*:
   a. Spinal accessory nerve
   b. Transverse cervical artery
   c. Middle trunk of brachial plexus
   d. Superior belly of omohyoid

2. Spinal root of accessory nerve innervates:
   a. Serratus anterior
   b. Stylohyoid
   c. Styloglossus
   d. Sternocleidomastoid

3. Suprasternal space contains all *except* one of the following structures:
   a. Sternal heads of right and left sternocleido-mastoid muscles
   b. Jugular venous arch
   c. Interclavicular ligament
   d. Sternohyoid muscles

4. All the following nerves are present in the posterior triangle *except*:
   a. Spinal accessory
   b. Lesser occipital
   c. Greater occipital
   d. Great auricular

5. Investing layer of cervical fascia encloses all *except*:
   a. Two muscles
   b. Two salivary glands
   c. Axillary vessels
   d. Two spaces

6. Ligament of Berry is formed by:
   a. Investing layer of cervical fascia
   b. Pretracheal layer
   c. Prevertebral layer
   d. Buccopharyngeal fascia

ANSWERS

1. d   2. d   3. d   4. c   5. c   6. b

Anterior Triangle of the Neck

One picture is worthe more than thousand words
—Anonymous

INTRODUCTION

The anterior triangle of the neck lies between midline of the neck and sternocleidomastoid muscle. It is subdivided into smaller triangles.

SURFACE LANDMARKS

1 The *mandible* forms the lower jaw (Fig. 4.1). The lower border of its horseshoe-shaped body is known as the *base of the mandible*. Anteriorly, this base forms the *chin*, and posteriorly it can be traced to the *angle of the mandible*.

2 The body of the U-shaped *hyoid bone* can be felt in the median plane just below and behind the chin, at the junction of the neck with the floor of the mouth. On each side, the body of hyoid bone is continuous posteriorly with the *greater cornua* which is overlapped in its posterior part by the sternocleidomastoid muscle.

3 The *thyroid cartilage* of the larynx forms a sharp protuberance in the median plane just below the hyoid bone. This protuberance is called the *laryngeal prominence or Adam's apple*. It is more prominent in males.

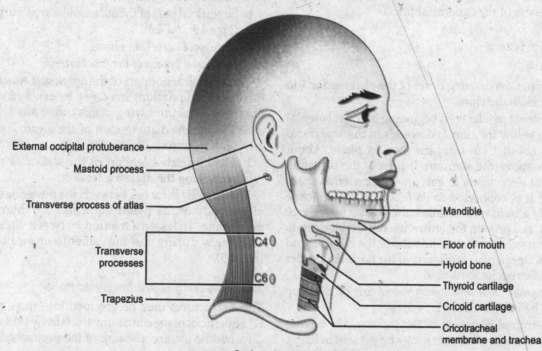

External occipital protuberance

Mastoid process

Transverse process of atlas

Transverse processes

Trapezius

C4

C6

Mandible

Floor of mouth

Hyoid bone

Thyroid cartilage

Cricoid cartilage

Cricotracheal membrane and trachea

Fig. 4.1: Surface landmarks of neck

Head and Neck

4 The rounded arch of the *cricoid cartilage* lies below the thyroid cartilage at the upper end of the trachea.

5 The trachea runs downwards and backwards from the cricoid cartilage. It is identified by its cartilaginous rings. However, it is partially masked by the *isthmus of the thyroid gland* which lies against second to fourth tracheal rings. The trachea is commonly palpated in the *suprasternal notch* which lies between the tendinous heads of origin of the right and left sternocleidomastoid muscles. In certain diseases, the trachea may shift to one side from the median plane. This indicates a shift in the mediastinum.

STRUCTURES IN THE ANTERIOR MEDIAN REGION OF THE NECK

DISSECTION

The skin over the anterior triangle has already been reflected following dissection in Chapter 3. Platysma is also reflected upwards. Identify the structures present in the superficial fascia and structures present in the anterior median region of neck.

Features

This region includes a strip 2 to 3 cm wide extending from the chin to the sternum. The structures encountered are listed below from superficial to deep.

Skin

It is freely movable over the deeper structures due to the looseness of the superficial fascia.

Superficial Fascia

It contains:

1 The upper decussating fibres of the *platysma* for 1 to 2 cm below the chin.

2 The *anterior jugular veins* beginning in the submental region below the chin. It descends in the superficial fascia about 1 cm from the median plane. About 2.5 cm above the sternum, it pierces the investing layer of deep fascia to enter the suprasternal space where it is connected to its fellow of the opposite side by a transverse channel, the *jugular venous arch* (Fig. 4.2). The vein then turns laterally, runs deep to the sternocleidomastoid just above the clavicle, and *ends in the external jugular vein* at the posterior border of the sternocleidomastoid.

3 A few small *submental lymph nodes* lying on the deep fascia below the chin (Fig. 4.3).

4 The terminal filaments of the *transverse or anterior cutaneous nerve* of the neck may be present in it.

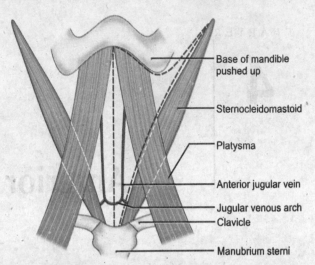

Fig. 4.2: Anterior triangles of the neck showing the platysma and the anterior jugular veins in the superficial fascia

Labels: Base of mandible pushed up — Sternocleidomastoid — Platysma — Anterior jugular vein — Jugular venous arch — Clavicle — Manubrium sterni

Deep Fascia

Above the hyoid bone the investing layer of deep fascia is a single layer in the median plane, but splits on each side to enclose the submandibular salivary gland (*see* Fig. 7.6).

Between the hyoid bone and the cricoid cartilage, it is a single layer extending between the right and left sternocleidomastoid muscles.

Below the cricoid, the fascia splits to enclose the suprasternal space (*see* Fig. 3.5).

Deep Structures Lying above the Hyoid Bone

The *mylohyoid muscle* is overlapped by:

a. Anterior belly of *digastric* above the hyoid bone.

b. Superficial part of the *submandibular salivary gland* (Figs 4.3 and 4.4).

c. *Mylohyoid nerve and vessels.*

d. *Submental branch of the facial artery.*

The anteroinferior part of the *hyoglossus muscle* with its superficial relations may also be exposed during dissection. Structures lying in this corner are:

a. The intermediate tendon of the *digastric* muscle with its fibrous pulley (Fig. 4.3).

b. The bifurcated tendon of the *stylohyoid* muscle embracing the digastric tendon.

The *subhyoid bursa* lies between the posterior surface of the body of the hyoid bone and the thyrohyoid membrane. It lessens friction between these two structures during the movements of swallowing (Fig. 4.5).

Structures Lying Below the Hyoid Bone

These structures may be grouped into three planes: (1) Superficial plane containing the infrahyoid muscles, (2) a middle plane consisting of the pretracheal fascia

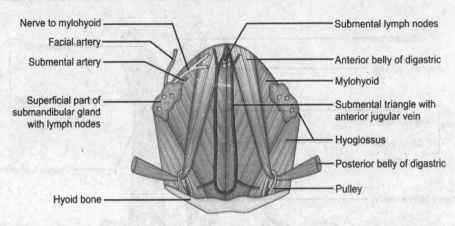

Fig. 4.3: Suprahyoid region, contents of submental and digastric triangles also shown

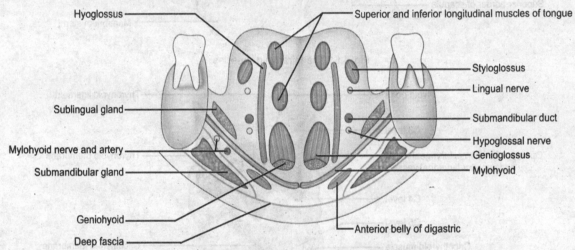

Fig. 4.4: Coronal section through the floor of the mouth

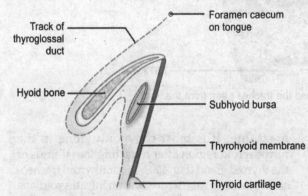

Fig. 4.5: Sagittal section through the hyoid region of the neck showing the subhyoid bursa and its relations

and the thyroid gland, and (3) a deep plane containing the larynx, trachea and structures associated with them.

1 *Infrahyoid muscles*
   a. Sternohyoid
   b. Sternothyroid
   c. Thyrohyoid

d. Superior belly of omohyoid. These are described in Table 4.1 and Fig. 4.6.

2 *Pretracheal fascia:* It forms the *false capsule of the thyroid gland* and the *suspensory ligaments of Berry* which attach the thyroid gland to the cricoid cartilage (*see* Fig. 8.4).

3 Deep to the pretracheal fascia, there are:
   a. The *thyrohyoid membrane* deep to the thyrohyoid muscle: It is pierced by the internal laryngeal nerve and the superior laryngeal vessels (Fig. 4.7).
   b. *Thyroid cartilage.*
   c. *Cricothyroid membrane* with the anastomosis of the cricothyroid arteries on its surface.
   d. Arch of the *cricoid cartilage.*
   e. *Cricothyroid muscle* supplied by the external laryngeal nerve.
   f. *Trachea,* partly covered by the isthmus of the thyroid gland from the second to fourth rings.
   g. *Carotid sheaths* lie on each side of the trachea (*see* Fig. 3.3).

Head and Neck

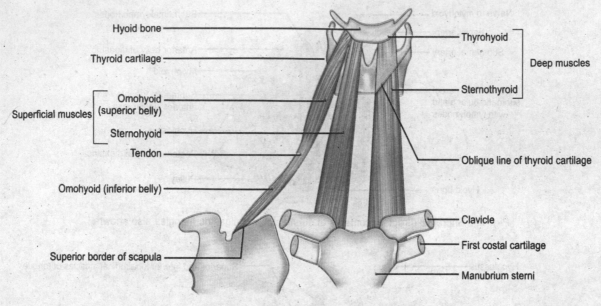

Fig. 4.6: The infrahyoid muscles

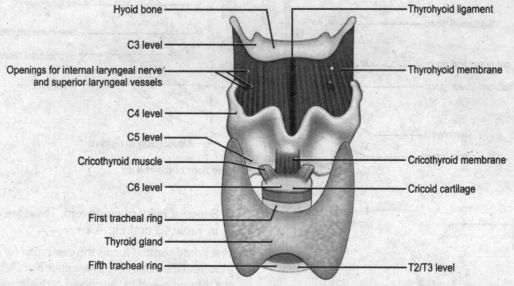

Fig. 4.7: The thyroid gland, the larynx and the trachea seen from the front

CLINICAL ANATOMY

- The common anterior midline swellings of the neck are:
  a. Enlarged submental lymph nodes and sublingual dermoid in the submental region.
  b. Thyroglossal cyst and inflamed subhyoid bursa just below the hyoid bone.
  c. Goitre, carcinoma of larynx and enlarged lymph nodes in the suprasternal region.
- Tracheostomy is an operation in which the trachea is opened and a tube inserted into it to facilitate breathing. It is most commonly done in the retrothyroid region after retracting the isthmus of the thyroid gland (Fig. 4.8). A suprathyroid tracheostomy is liable to stricture, and an infrathyroid one is difficult due to the depth of the trachea and is also dangerous because numerous vessels lie anterior to the trachea here.
- Cut throat wounds are most commonly situated just above or just below the hyoid bone. The main vessels of the neck usually escape injury because they are pushed backwards to a deeper plane during voluntary extension of the neck.

Base of mandible +
Superior: Line joining angle of mandible to mastoid process
medial: Anterior median plane of neck
lateral: Sternocleidomastoid

ANTERIOR TRIANGLE OF THE NECK   97

- Skin incisions to be made parallel to natural creases or Langer's lines (Fig. 4.9).
- Ludwig's angina is the cellulitis of the floor of the mouth. The infection spreads above the mylohyoid forcing the tongue upwards. Mylohyoid is pushed downwards. There is swelling within the mouth as well as below the chin.

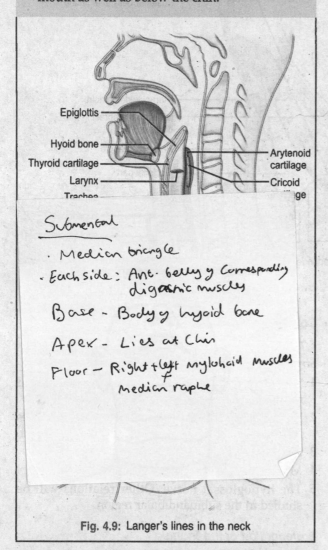

Fig. 4.9: Langer's lines in the neck

Handwritten note:

Submental
- Median triangle
- Each side: Ant. belly of Corresponding digastric muscles
Base – Body of hyoid bone
Apex – Lies at Chin
Floor – Right + left mylohoid muscles + median raphe

SUBMENTAL AND DIGASTRIC TRIANGLES

DISSECTION

Remove the deep fascia from anterior bellies of digastric muscles to expose parts of two mylohyoid muscles. Clean the boundaries and contents of the submental triangle.

Cut the deep fascia from the mandible and reflect it downwards to expose the submandibular gland. Identify and clean anterior and posterior bellies of digastric muscles, which form the boundaries of digastric triangle. Identify the intermediate tendon of digastric after pulling

the submandibular gland laterally. Clean the stylohyoid muscle which envelops the tendon of digastric and is lying along with the posterior belly of digastric muscle. Identify the contents of digastric triangle (Fig. 4.10).

ANTERIOR TRIANGLE

BOUNDARIES

The boundaries of the anterior triangle of neck are:

The anterior median plane of the neck medially; sternocleidomastoid laterally; base of the mandible and a line joining the angle of the mandible to the mastoid process, superiorly (Fig. 4.10).

SUBDIVISIONS

The anterior triangle is subdivided (by the digastric muscle and the superior belly of the omohyoid into:

a. Submental
b. Digastric
c. Carotid
d. Muscular triangles (Fig. 4.10).

SUBMENTAL TRIANGLE

This is a median triangle. It is bounded as follows.

On each side, there is the anterior belly of the corresponding digastric muscles. Its base is formed by the body of the hyoid bone. Its apex lies at the chin. The floor of the triangle is formed by the right and left mylohyoid muscles and the median raphe uniting them (Fig. 4.3).

Contents

1 Two to four small *submental lymph nodes* are situated in the superficial fascia between the anterior bellies of the digastric muscles (Fig. 4.3). They drain:
   a. Superficial tissues below the chin.
   b. Central part of the lower lip.
   c. The adjoining gums.
   d. Anterior part of the floor of the mouth.
   e. The tip of the tongue. Their efferents pass to the submandibular nodes.
2 Small submental veins join to form the anterior jugular veins.

DIGASTRIC TRIANGLE

The area between the body of the mandible and the hyoid bone is known as the submandibular region. The superficial structures of this region lie in the submental and digastric triangles. The deep structures of the floor of the mouth and root of the tongue will be studied separately at a later stage under the heading of submandibular region in Chapter 7.

Head and Neck

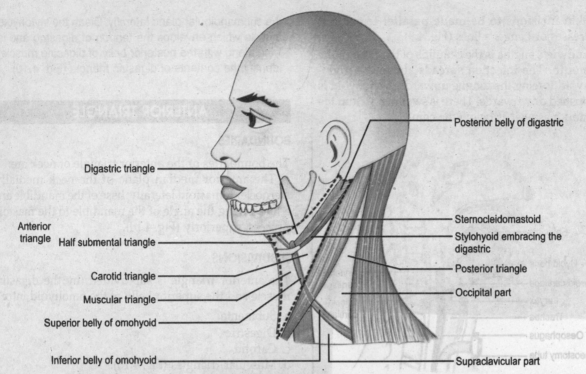

Fig. 4.10: The triangles of the neck. The anterior triangle is subdivided by digastrics and superior belly of omohyoid. Posterior triangle is subdivided by inferior belly of omohyoid

Boundaries

The boundaries of the digastric triangle are as follows.

Anteroinferiorly: Anterior belly of digastric.

Posteroinferiorly: Posterior belly of digastric and the stylohyoid.

Superiorly or base: Base of the mandible and a line joining the angle of the mandible to the mastoid process (Fig. 4.10).

Roof

The roof of the triangle is formed by:

1 Skin.
2 Superficial fascia, containing:
   a. The platysma.
   b. The cervical branch of the facial nerve.
   c. The ascending branch of the transverse or anterior cutaneous nerve of the neck.
3 Deep fascia, which splits to enclose the submandibular salivary gland (*see* Fig. 7.6).

Floor

The *floor* is formed by the mylohyoid muscle anteriorly, and by the hyoglossus posteriorly. A small part of the middle constrictor muscle of the pharynx, appears in the floor (Fig. 4.11).

Contents

Anterior Part of the Triangle

Structures superficial to mylohyoid are:

1 Superficial part of the submandibular salivary gland (Fig. 4.3 and *see* Fig. 7.1).
2 The facial vein and the submandibular lymph nodes are superficial to it and the facial artery is deep to it.
3 Submental artery.
4 Mylohyoid nerve and vessels (Fig. 4.4).
5 The hypoglossal nerve. Other relations will be studied in the submandibular region.

Posterior Part of the Triangle

1 *Superficial structures* are:
   a. Lower part of the parotid gland.
   b. The external carotid artery before it enters the parotid gland.
2 *Deep structures,* passing between the external and internal carotid arteries are:
   a. The styloglossus.
   b. The stylopharyngeus.
   c. The glossopharyngeal nerve (Fig. 4.13).
   d. The pharyngeal branch of the vagus nerve.
   e. The styloid process (*see* Fig. 5.2).
   f. A part of the parotid gland.

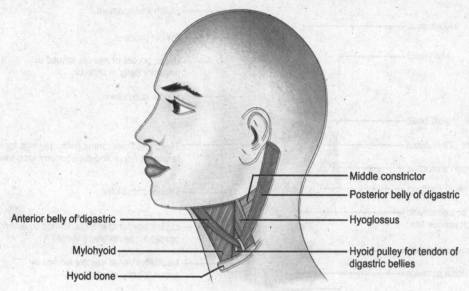

Fig. 4.11: Floor of the digastric triangle

3. *Deepest structures* include:
a. The internal carotid artery.
b. The internal jugular vein.
c. The vagus nerve (*see* Fig. 3.8b).
Most of these structures will be studied later.

CAROTID TRIANGLE

DISSECTION

Clean the area situated between posterior belly of digastric and superior belly of omohyoid muscle, to expose the three carotid arteries with internal jugular vein. Trace IX, X, XI and XII nerves in relation to these vessels (Fig. 4.10).

Identify middle and inferior constrictors of pharynx and thyrohyoid membrane forming its floor (Fig. 4.12).

Carefully clean and preserve superior root, the loop and inferior root of ansa cervicalis in relation to anterior aspect of carotid sheath. Locate the sympathetic trunk situated posteromedial to the carotid sheath (*see* Fig. 3.8b). Dissect the branches of external carotid artery (Figs 4.13 and 4.14).

Identify and preserve internal laryngeal nerve in the thyrohyoid interval. Trace it posterosuperiorly till vagus. Also look for external laryngeal nerve supplying the cricothyroid muscle (Fig. 4.13).

The carotid triangle provides a good view of all the large vessels and nerves of the neck, particularly when its posterior boundary is retracted slightly backwards.

BOUNDARIES

Anterosuperiorly: Posterior belly of the digastric muscle; and the stylohyoid (Fig. 4.12).

Anteroinferiorly: Superior belly of the omohyoid.

Posteriorly: Anterior border of the sternocleidomastoid muscle.

Roof

1 Skin.
2 Superficial fascia containing:
a. The plastysma.
b. The cervical branch of the facial nerve.
c. The transverse cutaneous nerve of the neck.
3 Investing layer of deep cervical fascia.

Floor

It is formed by parts of:
a. The middle constrictor of pharynx.
b. The inferior constrictor of the pharynx (Fig. 4.12).
c. Thyrohyoid membrane.

CONTENTS

Arteries

1 The common carotid artery with the carotid sinus and the carotid body at its termination
2 Internal carotid artery
3 The external carotid artery with its superior thyroid, lingual, facial, ascending pharyngeal and occipital branches (Fig. 4.12).

Veins

1 The internal jugular vein.
2 The common facial vein draining into the internal jugular vein.
3 A pharyngeal vein which usually ends in the internal jugular vein.
4 The lingual vein which usually terminates in the internal jugular vein.

Head and Neck

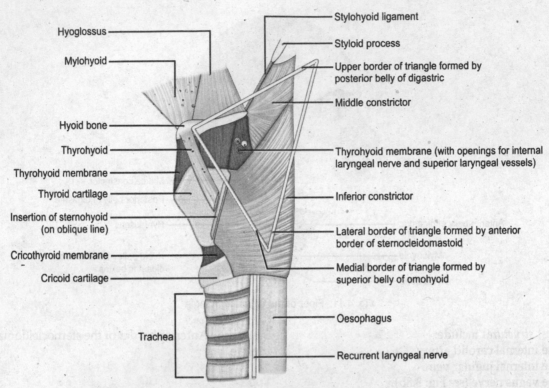

Fig. 4.12: Floor of the carotid triangle

Labels (clockwise from top):
Stylohyoid ligament
Styloid process
Upper border of triangle formed by posterior belly of digastric
Middle constrictor
Thyrohyoid membrane (with openings for internal laryngeal nerve and superior laryngeal vessels)
Inferior constrictor
Lateral border of triangle formed by anterior border of sternocleidomastoid
Medial border of triangle formed by superior belly of omohyoid
Oesophagus
Recurrent laryngeal nerve
Trachea
Cricoid cartilage
Cricothyroid membrane
Insertion of sternohyoid (on oblique line)
Thyroid cartilage
Thyrohyoid membrane
Thyrohyoid
Hyoid bone
Mylohyoid
Hyoglossus

Nerves

1 The vagus running vertically downwards.
2 The superior laryngeal branch of the vagus, dividing into the external and internal laryngeal nerves.
3 The spinal accessory nerve running backwards over the internal jugular vein.
4 The hypoglossal nerve running forwards over the external and internal carotid arteries. The hypo-glossal nerve gives off the upper root of the ansa cervicalis or descendens hypoglossi, and another branch to the thyrohyoid (Fig. 4.16).
5 Sympathetic chain runs (*see* Fig. 3.8b) vertically downwards posterior to the carotid sheath.
   Carotid sheath with its contents (*see* Fig. 3.8).

Lymph nodes: The deep cervical lymph nodes are situated along the internal jugular vein, and include the jugulodigastric node below the posterior belly of the digastric and the jugulo-omohyoid node above the inferior belly of the omohyoid (*see* Fig. 8.28).

Common Carotid Artery

The right common carotid artery is a branch of the brachio-cephalic artery. It begins in the neck behind the right sternoclavicular joint (Fig. 4.14, also *see* Fig. 8.17). The left common carotid artery is branch of the arch of the aorta.

Carotid Sinus

The termination of the common carotid artery, or the beginning of the internal carotid artery shows a slight dilatation, known as the carotid sinus. In this region, the tunica media is thin, but the adventitia is relatively thick and receives a rich innervation from the glossopharyngeal and sympathetic nerves. The carotid sinus acts as a *baro-receptor* or *pressure receptor* and regulates blood pressure.

Carotid Body

Carotid body is a small, oval reddish brown structure situated behind the bifurcation of the common carotid artery. It receives a rich nerve supply mainly from the glossopharyngeal nerve, but also from the vagus and sympathetic nerves. It acts as a *chemoreceptor* and responds to changes in the oxygen, carbon dioxide and pH content of the blood.

Other *allied chemoreceptors* are found near the arch of the aorta, the ductus arteriosus, and the right subclavian artery. These are supplied by the vagus nerve.

CLINICAL ANATOMY

- The carotid sinus is richly supplied by nerves. In some persons, the sinus may be hypersensitive. In such persons, sudden rotation of the head may cause slowing of heart. This condition is called as "carotid sinus syndrome".
- The supraventricular tachycardia may be controlled by carotid sinus massage, due to inhibitory effects of vagus nerve on the heart.
- The necktie should not be tied tightly, as it may compress both the internal carotid arteries, supplying the brain.

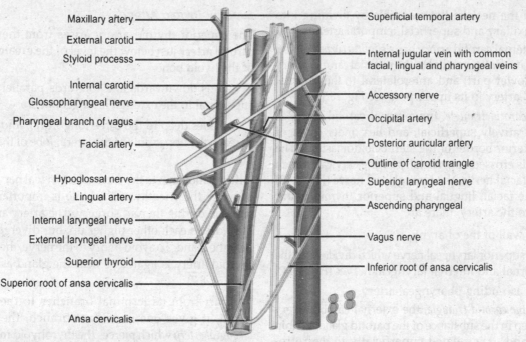

Fig. 4.13: The ninth, tenth, eleventh and twelfth cranial nerves and their branches related to the carotid arteries and to the internal jugular vein, in and around the left carotid triangle

External Carotid Artery

External carotid artery is one of the terminal branches of the common carotid artery. In general, it lies anterior to the internal carotid artery, and is the chief artery of supply to structures in the front of the neck and in the face (Fig. 4.14, also *see* Fig. 8.17).

Course and Relations

1 The external carotid artery begins in the carotid triangle at the level of the upper border of the thyroid cartilage opposite the disc between the third and fourth cervical vertebrae. It runs upwards and slightly backwards and laterally, and terminates

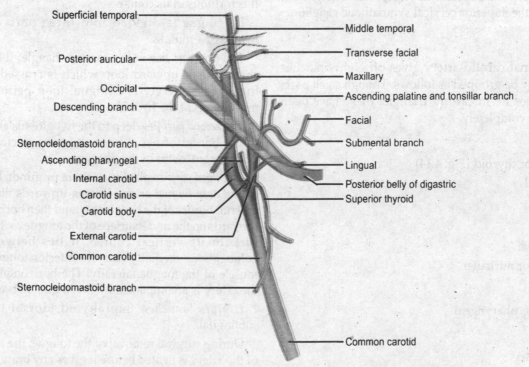

Fig. 4.14: Right carotid arteries including branches of the external carotid artery

behind the neck of the mandible by dividing into the maxillary and superficial temporal arteries.

2 The external carotid artery has a *slightly curved course*, so that it is anteromedial to the internal carotid artery in its lower part, and anterolateral to the internal carotid artery in its upper part (*see* Fig. 20.11).

3 *In the carotid triangle*, the external carotid artery is comparatively superficial, and lies under cover of the anterior border of the sternocleidomastoid. The artery is crossed superficially by the cervical branch of the facial nerve, the hypoglossal nerve (Fig. 4.13) and the facial, lingual and superior thyroid veins. Deep to the artery, there are:

a. The wall of the pharynx.

b. The superior laryngeal nerve which divides into the external and internal laryngeal nerves (Fig. 4.14).

c. The ascending pharyngeal artery.

4 *Above the carotid triangle*, the external carotid artery lies deep in the substance of the parotid gland. Within the gland, it is related superficially to the retro-mandibular vein and the facial nerve (*see* Fig. 5.4). Deep to the external carotid artery, there are:

a. The internal carotid artery.

b. Structures passing between the external and internal carotid arteries; these being styloglossus, stylo-pharyngeus both arising from the styloid process, IX nerve, pharyngeal branch of X (Fig. 4.13).

c. Two structures deep to the internal carotid artery, namely the superior laryngeal nerve (Fig. 4:13) and the superior cervical sympathetic ganglion.

Branches

The external carotid artery gives off eight branches which may be grouped as follows. Though small parts of branches lie in carotid triangle, these have been described completely.

Anterior

1 Superior thyroid (Fig. 4.14)

2 Lingual

3 Facial

Posterior

1 Occipital

2 Posterior auricular.

Medial

Ascending pharyngeal.

Terminal

1 Maxillary

2 Superficial temporal (Fig. 4.14).

Superior Thyroid Artery

The superior thyroid artery arises from the external carotid artery just below the level of the greater cornua of the hyoid bone.

It runs downwards and forwards parallel and just superficial to the external laryngeal nerve.

It passes deep to the three long infrahyoid muscles to reach the upper pole of the lateral lobe of the thyroid gland.

Its relationship to the external laryngeal nerve, which supplies the cricothyroid muscle is important to the surgeon during thyroid surgery. The artery and nerve are close to each other higher up, but diverge slightly near the gland. To avoid injury to the nerve, the superior thyroid artery is ligated as near the gland as possible (*see* Fig. 8.7).

Apart from its terminal branches to the thyroid gland, it gives one important branch, the *superior laryngeal artery* which pierces the thyrohyoid membrane in company with the internal laryngeal nerve (Fig. 4.7). The superior thyroid artery also gives a sternocleido-mastoid branch to that muscle and a cricothyroid branch that anastomoses with the artery of the opposite side in front of the cricovocal membrane.

Lingual Artery

The lingual artery arises from the external carotid artery opposite the tip of the greater cornua of the hyoid bone. It is tortuous in its course.

Its course is divided into three parts by the hyoglossus muscle.

The *first part* lies in the carotid triangle. It forms a characteristic upward loop which is crossed by the hypoglossal nerve. The lingual loop permits free movements of the hyoid bone.

The *second part* lies deep to the hyoglossus along the upper border of hyoid bone. It is superficial to the middle constrictor of the pharynx.

The *third part* is called the arteria profunda linguae, or the *deep lingual artery*. It runs upwards along the anterior border of the hyoglossus, and then horizontally forwards on the undersurface of the tongue as the *fourth part*. In its vertical course, it lies between the genioglossus medially and the inferior longitudinal muscle of the tongue laterally. The horizontal part of the artery is accompanied by the lingual nerve.

It gives branches: Suprahyoid, dorsal lingual, sublingual.

During surgical removal of the tongue, the first part of the artery is ligated before it gives any branch to the tongue or to the tonsil.

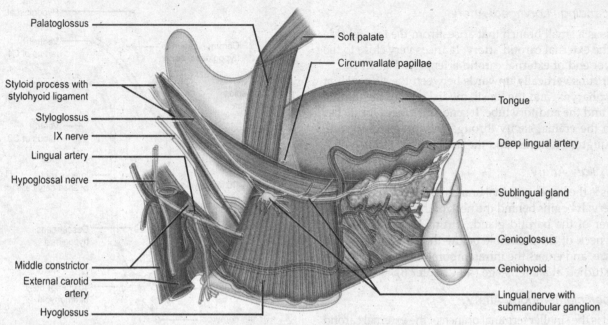

Fig. 4.15: Lingual artery

Facial Artery

The facial artery arises from the external carotid just above the tip of the greater cornua of the hyoid bone.

It runs upwards first in the neck as cervical part and then on the face as facial part. The course of the artery in both places is tortuous. The tortuosity in the neck allows free movements of the pharynx during deglutition. On the face, it allows free movements of the mandible, the lips and the cheek during mastication and during various facial expressions. The artery escapes traction and pressure during these movements.

The *cervical part* of the facial artery runs upwards on the superior constrictor of pharynx deep to the posterior belly of the digastric, with the stylohyoid and to the ramus of the mandible.

It grooves the posterior border of the submandibular salivary gland. Next the artery makes an S-bend (two loops) first winding down over the submandibular gland, and then up over the base of the mandible (*see* Fig. 7.7).

The *facial part* of the facial artery enters the face at anteroinferior angle of masseter muscle, runs upwards close to angle of mouth, side of nose till medial angle of eye. It is described in Chapter 2.

The cervical part of the facial artery gives off the ascending palatine, tonsillar, submental, and glandular branches for the submandibular salivary gland and lymph nodes.

The *ascending palatine artery* arises near the origin of the facial artery. It passes upwards between the styloglossus and the stylopharyngeus, crosses over the upper border of the superior constrictor and supplies the tonsil and the root of the tongue.

The *submental branch* is a large artery which accompanies the mylohyoid nerve, and supplies the submental triangle and the sublingual salivary gland (Fig. 4.3).

Occipital Artery

The occipital artery arises from the posterior aspect of the external carotid artery, opposite the origin of the facial artery.

It is crossed at its origin by the hypoglossal nerve.

In the carotid triangle, the artery gives two sternocleidomastoid branches. The upper branch accompanies the accessory nerve, and the lower branch arises near the origin of the occipital artery.

The further course of the artery in scalp has been described in Chapter 10 (*see* Fig. 10.5).

Posterior Auricular Artery

The posterior auricular artery arises from the posterior aspect of the external carotid just above the posterior belly of the digastric (Fig. 4.14).

It runs upwards and backwards deep to the parotid gland, but superficial to the styloid process. It crosses the base of the mastoid process, and ascends behind the auricle.

It supplies the back of the auricle, the skin over the mastoid process, and over the back of the scalp. It is cut in incisions for mastoid operations. Its *stylomastoid branch* enters the stylomastoid foramen, and supplies the middle ear, the mastoid antrum and air cells, the semicircular canals, and the facial nerve.

Ascending Pharyngeal Artery

This is a small branch that arises from the medial side of the external carotid artery. It arises very close to the lower end of external carotid artery (*see* Fig. 4.14).

It runs vertically upwards between the side wall of the pharynx, and the tonsil, medial wall of the middle ear and the auditory tube. It sends meningeal branches into the cranial cavity through the foramen lacerum, the jugular foramen and the hypoglossal canal.

Maxillary Artery

This is the larger terminal branch of the external carotid artery. It begins behind the neck of the mandible under cover of the parotid gland. It runs forwards deep to the neck of the mandible below the auriculotemporal nerve, and enters the infratemporal fossa where it will be studied at a later stage (*see* Chapter 6).

Superficial Temporal Artery

1 It is the smaller terminal branch of the external carotid artery. It begins, behind the neck of the mandible under cover of the parotid gland (*see* Fig. 5.5a).

2 It runs vertically upwards, crossing the root of the zygoma or preauricular point, where its *pulsations* can be easily felt. About 5 cm above the zygoma, it divides into anterior and posterior branches which supply the temple and scalp. The anterior branch anastomoses with the supraorbital and supra-trochlear branches of the ophthalmic artery.

3 In addition to the branches which supply the temple, the scalp, the parotid gland, the auricle and the facial muscles, the superficial temporal artery gives off a *transverse facial artery*, already studied with the face, and a *middle temporal artery* which runs on the temporal fossa deep to the temporalis muscle.

Ansa Cervicalis or Ansa Hypoglossi

This is a thin nerve loop that lies embedded in the anterior wall of the carotid sheath over the lower part of the larynx. It supplies the infrahyoid muscles (Fig. 4.16).

Formation

It is formed by a superior and an inferior root. The *superior root* is the continuation of the descending branch of the hypoglossal nerve. Its fibres are derived from the first cervical nerve. This root descends over the internal carotid artery and the common carotid artery.

The *inferior root* or descending cervical nerve is derived from second and third cervical spinal nerves. As this root descends, it winds round the internal jugular vein, and then continues anteroinferiorly to join the superior root in front of the common carotid artery (Fig. 4.16).

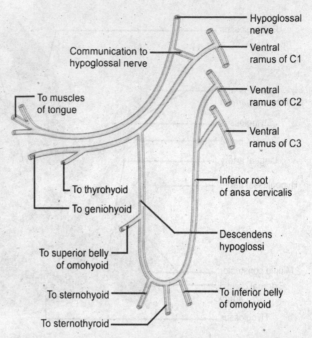

Fig. 4.16: Ansa cervicalis, and branches of the first cervical nerve distributed through the hypoglossal nerve

Distribution

Superior root: To the superior belly of the omohyoid.

Ansa cervicalis: To the sternohyoid, the sternothyroid.

Inferior root: To the inferior belly of the omohyoid.

Note that the thyrohyoid and geniohyoid are supplied by separate branches from the first cervical nerve through the hypoglossal nerve (Fig. 4.15).

MUSCULAR TRIANGLE

DISSECTION

Identify the infrahyoid muscles on each side of the median plane. Cut through the origin of sternocleido-mastoid muscle and reflect it upwards. Trace the nerve supply of infrahyoid muscles.

The superficial structures in the infrahyoid region are included in this triangle. The deeper structures (thyroid gland, trachea, oesophagus, etc.) will be studied separately at a later stage.

BOUNDARIES

Anteriorly: Anterior median line of the neck from the hyoid bone to the sternum.

Posterosuperiorly: Superior belly of the omohyoid muscle (Fig. 4.10).

Posteroinferiorly: Lower part of anterior border of the sternocleidomastoid muscle (Fig. 4.17).

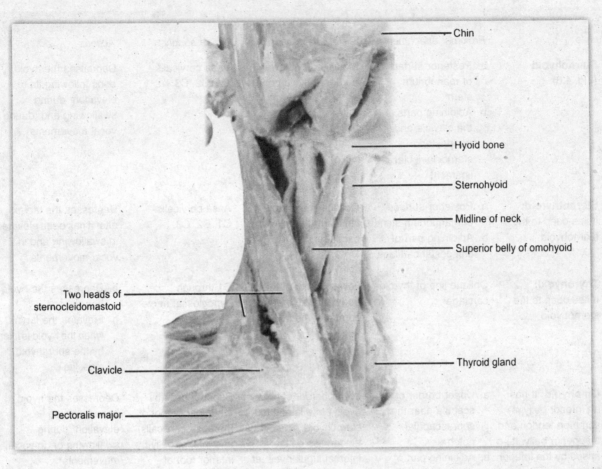

Fig. 4.17: Dissection of muscular triangle

Contents

The infrahyoid muscles are the chief contents of the triangle. These muscles may also be regarded arbitrarily as forming the floor of the triangle (Fig. 4.6).

The *infrahyoid muscles* are:

a. Sternohyoid

b. Sternothyroid

c. Thyrohyoid

d. Omohyoid.

These ribbon muscles have the following general features.

a. They are arranged in two layers, superficial (sternohyoid and omohyoid) and deep (sternothyroid and thyrohyoid) (Fig. 4.6).

b. All of them are supplied by the ventral rami of first, second and third cervical spinal nerves.

c. Because of their attachment to the hyoid bone and to the thyroid cartilage, they move these structures.

d. Sternohyoid, superior belly of omohyoid, sternothyroid lie superficial to the lateral or superficial convex surface of the thyroid gland (*see* Fig. 8.4).

e. The anterior surface of isthmus of thyroid gland is covered by right and left sternothyroid and sternohyoid muscles (*see* Fig. 8.4).

The specific details of infrahyoid muscles are shown in Table 4.1.

Mnemonics

External carotid artery branches

Superior thyroid (anterior)

Ascending pharyngeal (medial)

Lingual (anterior)

Facial (anterior)

Occipital (posterior)

Posterior auricular (posterior)

Superficial temporal (terminal)

Maxillary (terminal)

Table 4.1: Infrahyoid muscles

Muscle	Proximal attachment	Distal attachment	Nerve supply	Actions
1. **Sternohyoid** (Fig. 4.6)	a. Posterior surface of manubrium sterni b. Adjoining parts of the clavicle and the posterior sternoclavicular ligament	Medial part of lower border of hyoid bone	Ansa cervicalis C1, C2, C3	Depresses the hyoid bone following its elevation during swallowing and during vocal movements
2. **Sternothyroid:** It lies deep to the sternohyoid	a. Posterior surface of manubrium sterni b. Adjoining part of first costal cartilage	Oblique line on the lamina of the thyroid cartilage	Ansa cervicalis C1, C2, C3	Depresses the larynx after it has been elevated in swallowing and in vocal movements
3. **Thyrohyoid:** It lies deep to the sternohyoid	Oblique line of thyroid cartilage	Lower border of the body and the greater cornua of the hyoid bone	C1 through hypoglossal nerve	a. Depresses the hyoid bone b. Elevates the larynx when the hyoid is fixed by the suprahyoid muscles
4. **Omohyoid:** It has an inferior belly, a common tendon and a superior belly. It arises by the inferior belly, and is inserted through the superior belly	a. Upper border of scapula near the suprascapular notch b. Adjoining part of suprascapular ligament	Lower border of body of hyoid bone lateral to the sternohyoid. The central tendon lies on the internal jugular vein at the level of the cricoid cartilage and is bound to the clavicle by a fascial pulley	Superior belly by the superior root of the ansa cervicalis, and inferior belly by inferior root of ansa cervicalis	Depresses the hyoid bone following its elevation during swallowing or in vocal movements

FACTS TO REMEMBER

- Apex of anterior triangle of neck is close to the sternum, while that of posterior triangle is close to the mastoid process.
- Submental triangle is half on each side of the midline.
- Maximum blood vessels are present in the carotid triangle
- Superficial temporal artery can be palpated at the preauricular point.
- The necktie should not be tied tightly, as it may compress both the internal carotid arteries, supplying the brain.

CLINICOANATOMICAL PROBLEM

A patient is undergoing abdominal surgery. Anaesthetist is sitting at the head end of the table and monitoring patient's pulse by palpating arteries in the head and neck region

- What artery is the anaesthetist palpating?
- Name the other palpable arteries in the body.

Ans: The anaesthetist has been monitoring the pulse by palpating the common carotid artery at the anterior border of sternocleidomastoid muscle. He need not get up to feel the radial pulse repeatedly.

Other palpable arteries in head and neck are superficial temporal and facial. In upper limb palpable arteries are third part of axillary artery, brachial artery and radial pulse.

In abdomen, one can feel abdominal aorta pulsation when one lies supine.

Palpable arteries in lower limb are femoral at head of femur, popliteal, dorsalis pedis and posterior tibial.

FREQUENTLY ASKED QUESTIONS

1. Describe carotid triangle under following headings:
   a. Boundaries
   b. Contents
   c. Nerves
   d. Arteries
2. Describe the boundaries and contents of digastric triangle.

3. Write short notes/enumerate:
   a. Branches of external carotid artery
   b. Infrahyoid muscles
   c. Ansa cervicalis
   d. Facial artery—cervical part
   e. Lingual artery

MULTIPLE CHOICE QUESTIONS

1. Only medial branch external carotid artery is:
   a. Superior thyroid
   b. Lingual
   c. Ascending pharyngeal
   d. Maxillary
2. All the following are branches of external carotid except:
   a. Posterior ethmoidal
   b. Occipital
   c. Lingual
   d. Facial
3. Muscles forming boundaries of carotid triangle are all except:
   a. Posterior belly of digastric
   b. Superior belly of omohyoid
   c. Inferior belly of omohyoid
   d. Sternocleidomastoid

4. Hyoid bone develops from:
   a. 1st and 2nd arches b. 2nd and 3rd arches
   c. 3rd and 4th arches d. 1st, 2nd and 3rd arches
5. Which of the following is not a palpable artery in head and neck?
   a. Facial artery
   b. Superficial temporal artery
   c. Lingual artery
   d. Common carotid artery
6. Which of the following is not a infrahyoid muscle?
   a. Sternohyoid   b. Sternothyoid
   c. Thyrohyoid   d. Omohyoid—inferior belly
7. Which of the following nerve runs with vagus between internal carotid artery and internal jugular vein till the angle of the mandible?
   a. Hypoglossal   b. Accessory
   c. Glossopharyngeal d. Maxillary

ANSWERS

1. c   2. a   3. c   4. b   5. c   6. d   7. a

Head and Neck

Parotid Region

Eat, drink and feel no sorrow; For there many not be a tomorrow

INTRODUCTION

Parotid region contains the largest serous salivary gland and the "queen of the face", the facial nerve. Parotid gland contains vertically disposed blood vessels and horizontally situated facial nerve and its various branches. Parotid gland gets affected by virus of mumps, which can extend the territory of its attack up to gonads as well. One must be careful of the branches of facial nerve while incising the parotid abscess by giving horizontal incision. Facial nerve is described in Chapter 4, Volume 4.

SALIVARY GLANDS

There are three pairs of large salivary glands—the parotid, submandibular and sublingual. In addition, there are numerous small glands in the tongue, the palate, the cheeks and the lips. These glands produce saliva which keeps the oral cavity moist, and helps in chewing and swallowing. The saliva also contains enzymes that aid digestion.

PAROTID GLAND

DISSECTION

Carefully cut through the fascial covering of the parotid gland from the zygomatic arch above to the angle of mandible below. While removing tough fascia, dissect the structures emerging at the periphery of the gland.

Trace the duct of the parotid gland anteriorly till the buccinator muscle. Trace one or more of the branches of facial nerve till its trunk in the posterior part of the gland. The trunk can be followed till the stylomastoid foramen. Trace its posterior auricular branch. Trace the course of retromandibular vein and external carotid artery in the gland, removing the glands in pieces. Clean the facial nerve already dissected. Study the entire course of facial nerve from its beginning to the end.

Facial nerve is the main nerve of the face, supplying all the muscles of facial expression, carrying secretomotor fibres to submandibular, sublingual salivary glands, including those in tongue and floor of mouth. It is also secretomotor to glands in the nasal cavity, palate and the lacrimal gland. It is responsible enough for carrying the taste fibres from anterior two-thirds of tongue also except from the vallate papillae (*see* Chapter 4 of Volume 4).

Features

(*Para* = around; *otic* = ear)
The parotid is the largest of the salivary glands. It weighs about 25 g. It is situated below the external acoustic meatus, between the ramus of the mandible and the sternocleidomastoid. The gland overlaps these structures. Anteriorly, the gland also overlaps the masseter muscle (Fig. 5.1). Skin over the gland is supplied by great auricular nerve (C2, 3).

Capsule of Parotid Gland

The investing layer of the deep cervical fascia forms a capsule for the gland (Fig. 5.2). It is supplied by great auricular nerve. The fascia splits (between the angle of

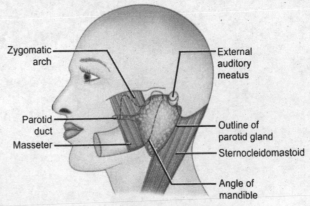

Fig. 5.1: Position of parotid gland

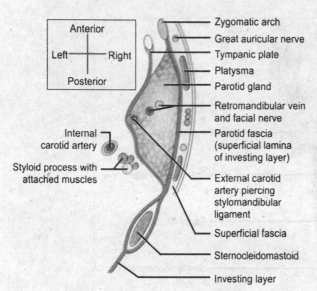

Fig. 5.2: Capsule of the parotid gland

the mandible and the mastoid process) to enclose the gland. The superficial lamina/parotidomassetric fascia, thick and adherent to the gland, is attached above to the zygomatic arch. The deep lamina is thin and is attached to the styloid process, tympanic plate, the angle and posterior border of the ramus of the mandible. A portion of the deep lamina, extending between the styloid process and the mandible, is thickened to form the *stylomandibular ligament* which separates the parotid gland from the submandibular salivary gland. The ligament is pierced by the external carotid artery (*see* Fig. 3.4).

- *Parotid swellings* are very painful due to the unyielding nature of the parotid fascia.
- *Mumps* is an infectious disease of the salivary glands (usually the parotid) caused by a specific virus. Viral parotitis or mumps characteristically does not suppurate. Its complications are orchitis and pancreatitis.

External Features

The gland resembles a three-sided pyramid.

The apex of the pyramid is directed downwards (Figs 5.3a and b).

The gland has four surfaces:
a. Superior (base of the pyramid)
b. Superficial (Fig. 5.3a)
c. Anteromedial
d. Posteromedial (Fig. 5.4a).

The surfaces are separated by three borders:
a. Anterior (Fig. 5.4b)
b. Posterior
c. Medial/pharyngeal

Relations

The *apex* (Fig. 5.3a) overlaps the posterior belly of the digastric and the adjoining part of the carotid triangle. The cervical branch of the facial nerve and the two divisions of the retromandibular vein emerge near the apex.

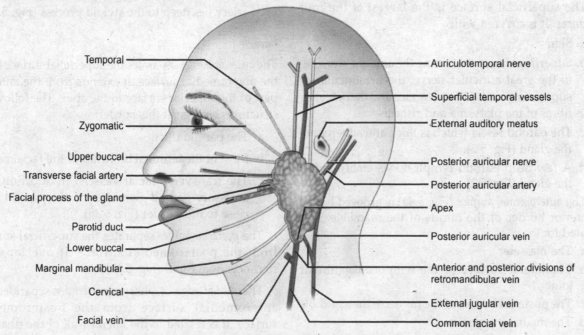

Fig. 5.3a: Structures emerging at the periphery of the parotid gland

Head and Neck

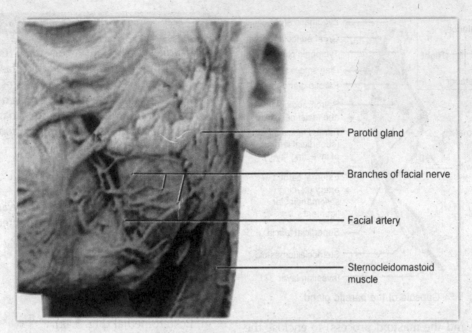

Parotid gland

Branches of facial nerve

Facial artery

Sternocleidomastoid muscle

Fig. 5.3b: Parotid gland

Surfaces

The superior surface or base forms the upper end of the gland which is small and concave. It is related to:

a. The cartilaginous part of the external acoustic meatus.

b. The posterior surface of the temporomandibular joint (Fig. 5.3b).

c. The superficial temporal vessels.

d. The auriculotemporal nerve (Fig. 5.3a).

The superficial surface is the largest of the four surfaces. It is covered with:

a. Skin

b. Superficial fascia containing the anterior branches of the great auricular nerve, the preauricular or superficial parotid lymph nodes and the posterior fibres of the platysma and risorius.

c. The parotid fascia which is thick and adherent to the gland (Fig. 5.2).

d. A few deep parotid lymph nodes embedded in the gland (Fig. 5.2).

The *anteromedial surface* (Fig. 5.4a) is grooved by the posterior border of the ramus of the mandible. It is related to:

a. The masseter

b. The lateral surface of the temporomandibular joint.

c. The posterior border of the ramus of the mandible

d. The medial pterygoid

e. The emerging branches of the facial nerve.

The *posteromedial surface* (Fig. 5.4a) is moulded to the mastoid and the styloid processes and the structures attached to them. Thus, it is related to:

a. The mastoid process, with the sternocleido-mastoid and the posterior belly of the digastric.

b. The styloid process, with structures attached to it.

c. The external carotid artery and facial nerve enter the gland through this surface. The internal carotid artery lies deep to the styloid process (Fig. 5.4a).

Borders

The *anterior border* separates the superficial surface from the anteromedial surface. It extends from the anterior part of the superior surface to the apex. The following structures emerge at this border:

a. The parotid duct.

b. Most of the terminal branches of the facial nerve.

c. The transverse facial vessels. In addition, the accessory parotid gland lies on the parotid duct close to this border (Fig. 5.3a).

The *posterior border* separates the superficial surface from the posteromedial surface. It overlaps the sternocleidomastoid (Fig. 5.4b).

The *medial edge* or pharyngeal *border* separates the anteromedial surface from the posteromedial surface. It is related to the lateral wall of the pharynx (Fig. 5.4a).

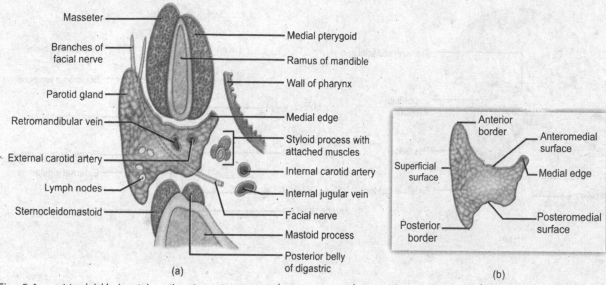

Figs 5.4a and b: (a) Horizontal section through the parotid gland showing its relations and the structures passing through it, and (b) gross features of parotid gland

Structures within the parotid gland

From medial to the lateral side, these are as follows.

1 *Arteries:* The external carotid artery enters the gland through its posteromedial surface (Fig. 5.5a). The maxillary artery leaves the gland through its anteromedial surface. The superficial temporal artery gives transverse facial artery and emerges at the anterior part of the superior surface.

2 *Veins:* The retromandibular vein is formed within the gland by the union of the superficial temporal and maxillary veins. In the lower part of the gland, the vein divides into anterior and posterior divisions which emerge close to the apex (lower pole) of the gland (Fig. 5.5b).

3 The *facial nerve* exits from cranial cavity through stylomastoid foramen and enters the gland through the upper part of its posteromedial surface, and divides into its terminal branches within the gland. The branches leave the gland through its anteromedial surface, and appear on the surface at the anterior border (Fig. 5.5c).

Facial nerve lies in relation to isthmus of the gland which separates large superficial part from small deep part of the gland. Facial nerve divides into two branches (Figs 5.5d and e):

a. *Temporofacial:* Divides into temporal and zygomatic branches.

b. *Cervicofacial:* Divides into buccal, marginal mandibular and cervical branches.

The various branches (5–6) of facial nerve radiate like a goose-foot from the curved anterior border of the parotid gland to supply the respective muscles of facial expression. This pattern of branching is called "pes anserinus".

4 Parotid lymph nodes.

Patey's faciovenous plane

The gland is composed of a large superficial and a small deep part, the two being connected by an 'isthmus' around which facial nerve divides (Fig. 5.5d).

Accessory processes of parotid gland

Facial process—along parotid duct. It lies between zygomatic arch and the parotid duct (Fig. 5.3a).

Pterygoid process—between mandibular ramus and medial pterygoid.

Glenoid process—between external acoustic meatus and temporomandibular joint

Poststyloid process

Parotid Duct/Stenson's Duct

(Dutch Anatomist 1638–86)

Parotid duct is thick-walled and is about 5 cm long. It emerges from the middle of the anterior border of the gland (Fig. 5.1). It runs forwards and slightly downwards on the masseter. Here its relations are:

Superiorly

1 Accessory parotid gland.

2 The transverse facial vessels (Fig. 5.3a).

3 Upper buccal branch of the facial nerve.

Inferiorly

The lower buccal branch of the facial nerve.

At the anterior border of the masseter, the parotid duct turns medially and pierces:

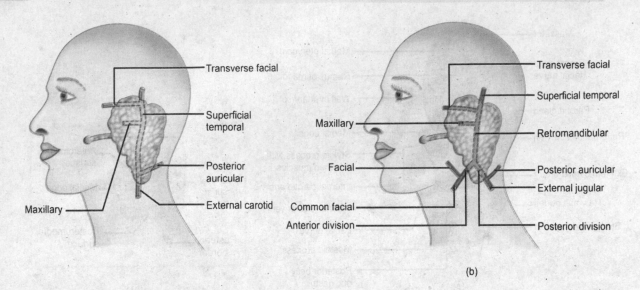

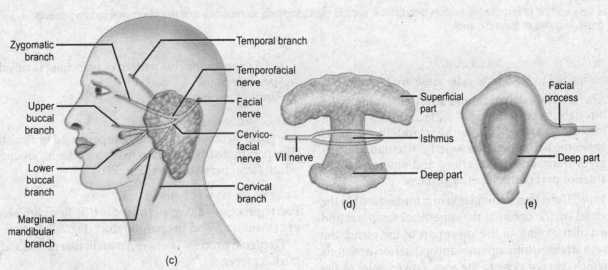

Figs 5.5a to e: Structures within the parotid gland: (a) Arteries, (b) veins, (c) nerves, (d) two parts of the parotid gland are separated by isthmus, and (e) superficial part overlapping the deep part

a. The buccal pad of fat.

b. The buccopharyngeal fascia.

c. The buccinator (obliquely).

Because of the oblique course of the duct through the buccinator, inflation of the duct is prevented during blowing.

The duct runs forwards for a short distance between the buccinator and the oral mucosa. Finally, the duct turns medially and opens into the vestibule of the mouth (gingivobuccal vestibule) opposite the crown of the upper second molar tooth (*see* Fig. 2.20).

Blood Supply

The parotid gland is supplied by the external carotid artery and its branches that arise within the gland. The veins drain into the external jugular vein and internal jugular vein.

Nerve Supply

1 Parasympathetic nerves are secretomotor (Fig. 5.6). They reach the gland through the auriculotemporal nerve.

The preganglionic fibres begin in the inferior salivatory nucleus; pass through the glossopharyngeal nerve, its tympanic branch, the tympanic plexus and the lesser petrosal nerve; and relay in the otic ganglion.

The postganglionic fibres pass through the auriculo-temporal nerve and reach the gland. This is shown in Flowchart 5.1.

2 Sympathetic nerves are vasomotor, and are derived from the plexus around the middle meningeal artery.

3 Sensory nerves to the gland come from the auriculo-temporal nerve, but the parotid fascia is innervated by the sensory fibres of the great auricular nerve (C2, C3).

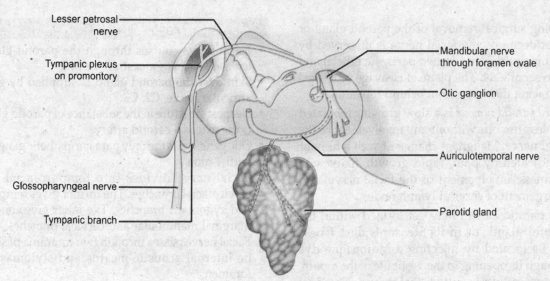

Fig. 5.6: Parasympathetic nerve supply to the parotid gland

Flowchart 5.1: Tracing nerve supply of parotid gland

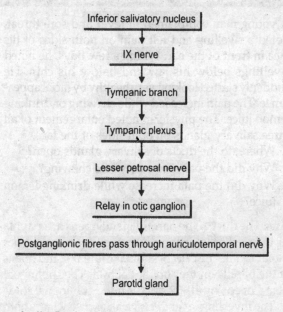

Lymphatic Drainage

Lymph drains first to the parotid nodes and from there to the upper deep cervical nodes.

Parotid Lymph Nodes

The parotid lymph nodes lie partly in the superficial fascia and partly deep to the deep fascia over the parotid gland (Fig. 5.4). They drain:

a. Temple
b. Side of the scalp
c. Lateral surface of the auricle
d. External acoustic meatus
e. Middle ear
f. Parotid gland
g. Upper part of the cheek
h. Parts of the eyelids and orbit.

Efferents from these nodes pass to the upper group of deep cervical nodes.

DEVELOPMENT

The parotid gland is ectodermal in origin. It develops from the buccal epithelium just lateral to the angle of mouth. The outgrowth branches repeatedly to form the duct system and acini. The mesoderm forms the intervening connective tissue septa.

CLINICAL ANATOMY

- A *parotid abscess* may be caused by spread of infection from the opening of parotid duct in the mouth cavity (Fig. 5.7).

- A parotid abscess is best drained by horizontal incision/making many small holes known as Hilton's method (Fig. 5.8) below the angle of mandible.

- Parotidectomy is the removal of the parotid gland. After this operation, at times, there may be regeneration of the secretomotor fibres in the auriculotemporal nerve which join the great auricular nerve. This causes stimulation of the sweat glands and hyperaemia in the area of its distribution, thus producing redness and sweating in the area of skin supplied by the nerve. This clinical entity is called *Frey syndrome*. Whenever, such a person chews there is increased sweating in the region supplied by auriculotemporal nerve. So it is also called 'auriculotemporal syndrome'.

- During surgical removal of the parotid gland or parotidectomy, the facial nerve is preserved by removing the gland in two parts, superficial and deep separately. The plane of cleavage is defined by tracing the nerve from behind forwards.

- *Mixed parotid tumour* is a slow growing lobulated painless tumour without any involvement of the facial nerve. Malignant change of such a tumour is indicated by pain, rapid growth, fixity with hardness, involvement of the facial nerve, and enlargement of cervical lymph nodes.

- The parotid calculi may get formed within the parotid gland or in its Stenson's duct. These can be located by injecting a radiopaque dye through its opening in the vestibule of the mouth. The procedure is called 'Sialogram'. The duct can be examined by a spatula or bidigital examination.

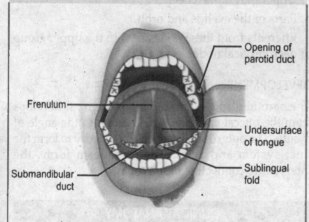

Fig. 5.7: Openings of salivary glands

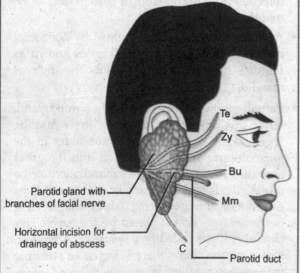

Fig. 5.8: Horizontal incision for draining parotid abscess. Branches of facial nerve also seen

FACTS TO REMEMBER

- Facial nerve courses through the parotid gland, *without supplying any structure in it.*
- Skin over the parotid gland is supplied by great auricular nerve, C2, C3.
- Deepest structure in the substance of parotid gland is the external carotid artery.
- Otic ganglion is the only parasympathetic ganglion with 4 roots.
- Facial nerve divides into temporofacial and cervicofacial branches. The former gives temporal and zygomatic branches. The latter gives buccal, marginal mandibular and cervical branches.
- Facial nerve passes through two foramina of skull, i.e internal acoustic meatus and stylomastoid foramen.

CLINICOANATOMICAL PROBLEM

A young man complained of fever and sore throat, noted a swelling and felt pain on both sides of his face in front of the ear. Within a few days, he noted swellings below his jaw and below his chin. He suddenly started looking very healthy by facial appearance. The pain increased while chewing or drinking lemon juice. The physician noted enlargement of all three salivary glands on both sides of the face.

- Where do the ducts of salivary glands open?
- Why did the pain increase while chewing?
- Why did the pain increase while drinking lemon juice?

Ans: The duct of the parotid gland opens at a papilla in the vestibule of mouth opposite the 2nd upper molar tooth. The duct of submandibular gland opens at the papilla on the sublingual fold. The sublingual gland opens by 10–12 ducts on the sublingual fold.

The investing layer of cervical fascia encloses both the parotid and the submandibular glands and is attached to the lower border of the mandible. As mandible moves during chewing, the fascia gets stretched which results in pain. The fascia and skin are supplied by the great auricular nerve.

While drinking lemon juice, there is lot of pain, as the salivary secretion is stimulated by the acid of the lemon juice.

The investing layer of cervical fascia encloses: Two muscles, the trapezius and the sternocleidomastoid; two spaces, the suprasternal space and the supraclavicular space; two glands, the parotid and the submandibular and forms two pulleys, one for the intermediate tendon of digastric and one for the intermediate tendon of omohyoid muscle.

FREQUENTLY ASKED QUESTIONS

1. Describe parotid gland under the following headings:
   a. Gross anatomy
   b. Structures emerging at various borders, apex and base
   c. Nerve supply
   d. Clinical anatomy

2. Describe briefly the structures present within the parotid gland.

3. Write short notes on/enumerate:
   a. Parotid duct
   b. Histology of parotid gland

MULTIPLE CHOICE QUESTIONS

1. Nerve carrying postganglionic parasympathetic fibres of the parotid gland is:
   a. Facial   b. Auriculotemporal
   c. Inferior alveolar   d. Buccal

2. Somata of postganglionic secretomotor fibres to parotid gland lie in:
   a. Ciliary ganglion
   b. Pterygopalatine ganglion
   c. Otic ganglion
   d. Submandibular ganglion

3. Which of the following artery passes between the roots of the auriculotemporal nerve?
   a. Maxillary
   b. Middle meningeal
   c. Superficial temporal
   d. Accessory meningeal

4. Vein formed by union of posterior division of retromandibular and posterior auricular vein is:
   a. Internal jugular   b. External jugular
   c. Common facial   d. Anterior jugular

5. All of the following are peripheral parasympathetic ganglia *except*:
   a. Otic   b. Ciliary
   c. Pterygopalatine   d. Geniculate

6. Which artery is not inside the parotid gland?
   a. External carotid
   b. Internal carotid
   c. Superficial temporal
   d. Maxillary

7. One of the following nerves is not related to parotid gland:
   a. Temporal branch of facial
   b. Zygomatic branch of facial
   c. Buccal branch of facial
   d. Posterior superior alveolar branch of maxillary

8. Pes anserinus is the arrangement in which of the following nerves?
   a. Vagus   b. Trigeminal
   c. Facial   d. Glossopharyngeal

ANSWERS

1. b   2. c   3. b   4. b   5. d   6. b   7. d   8. c

Temporal and Infratemporal Regions

Best physicians are: Doctor Quiet, Doctor Rest, Doctor Diet and Doctor Merryman
—Regimen of Salerno

INTRODUCTION

Temporal and infratemporal regions include muscles of mastication, which develop from mesoderm of first branchial arch. Only one joint, the temporomandibular joint, is present on each side between the base of skull and mandible to allow movements during speech and mastication.

The parasympathetic ganglion is the otic ganglion, the only ganglion with four roots, i.e. sensory, sympathetic, motor and secretomotor or parasympathetic.

The blood supply of this region is through the maxillary artery. Middle meningeal artery is its most important branch, as its injury results in extradural haemorrhage (*see* Fig. 1.10).

TEMPORAL FOSSA

In order to understand these regions, the osteology of the temporal fossa, and the infratemporal fossa should be studied. The *temporal fossa* lies on the side of the skull, and is bounded by the superior temporal line and the zygomatic arch.

BOUNDARIES

Anterior: Zygomatic and frontal bones (Fig. 6.1).

Posterior: Inferior temporal line and supramastoid crest.

Superior: Superior temporal line

Inferior: Zygomatic arch.

Floor: Parts of frontal, parietal, temporal and greater wing of sphenoid. Temporalis muscle is attached to the floor and inferior temporal line.

CONTENTS

1 Temporalis muscle.
2 Middle temporal artery (branch of superficial temporal artery) (*see* Chapter 4).

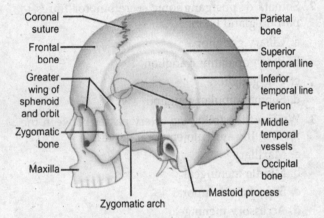

Fig. 6.1: Some features seen on the lateral side of the skull

3 Zygomaticotemporal nerve and artery.
4 Deep temporal nerves for supplying temporalis muscle.
5 Deep temporal artery, branch of maxillary artery.

INFRATEMPORAL FOSSA

It is an irregular space below zygomatic arch.

BOUNDARIES

Anterior: Posterior surface of body of maxilla.

Roof: Infratemporal surface of greater wing of sphenoid.

Medial: Lateral pterygoid plate and pyramidal process of palatine bone.

Lateral: Ramus of mandible (Fig. 6.2).

CONTENTS

1 Lateral pterygoid muscle.
2 Medial pterygoid muscle.

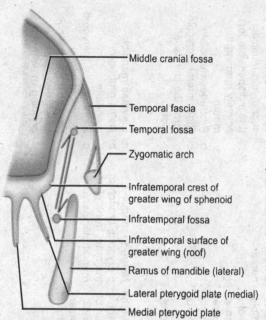

Fig. 6.2: Scheme to show the outline of the temporal and infratemporal fossae in a coronal section

Labels in figure:
- Middle cranial fossa
- Temporal fascia
- Temporal fossa
- Zygomatic arch
- Infratemporal crest of greater wing of sphenoid
- Infratemporal fossa
- Infratemporal surface of greater wing (roof)
- Ramus of mandible (lateral)
- Lateral pterygoid plate (medial)
- Medial pterygoid plate

3 Mandibular nerve with its branches.
4 Maxillary nerve with posterior superior alveolar nerve (*see* Chapter 15).
5 Chorda tympani, branch of VII nerve.
6 1st and 2nd parts of maxillary artery with their branches.
7 Posterior superior alveolar artery, branch of 3rd part of maxillary artery.
8 Accompanying veins.

LANDMARKS ON THE LATERAL SIDE OF THE HEAD

The external ear or pinna is a prominent feature on the lateral aspect of the head.

1 The *zygomatic bone* forms the prominence of the cheek at the inferolateral corner of the orbit. The *zygomatic arch* bridges the gap between the eye and the ear.
2 The head of the mandible lies in front of the tragus. It is felt best during movements of the lower jaw.
3 The *mastoid process* is a large bony prominence situated behind the lower part of the auricle.
4 The superior *temporal line* forms the upper boundary of the temporal fossa which is filled up by the temporalis muscle.
5 The *pterion* is the area in the temporal fossa where four bones (frontal, parietal, temporal and greater wing of sphenoid) adjoin each other across an H-shaped suture (Fig. 6.1).
6 The junction of the back of the head with the neck is indicated by the external occipital protuberance and the superior nuchal lines.

MUSCLES OF MASTICATION

DISSECTION

Identify the masseter muscle extending from the zygomatic arch to the ramus of the mandible (Fig. 6.3). Cut the zygomatic arch in front of and behind the attachment of masseter muscle and reflect it downwards. Divide the nerve and blood vessels to the muscle. Clean the ramus of mandible by stripping off the masseter muscle from it.

Give an oblique cut from the centre of mandibular notch to the lower end of anterior border of ramus of mandible. Turn this part of the bone including the insertion of temporalis muscle upwards (Fig. 6.4). Strip the muscle from the skull and identify deep temporal nerves and vessels.

Make one cut through the neck of the mandible. Give another cut through the ramus at a distance of 4 cm from the neck. Remove the bone carefully in between these two cuts, avoiding injury to the underlying structures. The lateral pterygoid is exposed in the upper part and medial pterygoid in the lower part of the dissection (Fig. 6.5).

FEATURES

The muscles of mastication move the mandible during mastication and speech. They are the masseter, the temporalis, the lateral pterygoid and the medial pterygoid. They develop from the mesoderm of the first branchial arch, and are supplied by the mandibular nerve which is the nerve of that arch. The muscles are enumerated in Table 6.1 and shown in Figs 6.3 to 6.5. Temporal fascia and relations of lateral and medial pterygoid muscles are described.

TEMPORAL FASCIA

The temporal fascia is a thick aponeurotic sheet that roofs over the temporal fossa and covers the temporalis muscle. Superiorly, the fascia is single layered and is attached to the superior temporal line. Inferiorly, it splits into two layers which are attached to the inner and outer lips of the upper border of the zygomatic arch. The small gap between the two layers contains fat, a branch from the superficial temporal artery and the zygomaticotemporal nerve.

The superficial surface of the temporal fascia receives an expansion from the epicranial aponeurosis (*see* Fig. 2.3). This surface gives origin to the auricularis anterior and superior, and is related to the superficial temporal vessels, the auriculotemporal nerve, and the temporal branch of the facial nerve (*see* Fig. 5.3a). The deep surface of the temporal fascia gives origin to some fibres of the temporalis muscle.

Head and Neck

Head and Neck

Table 6.1: Muscles of mastication

Muscle	Origin	Fibres	Insertion	Nerve supply	Actions
1. Masseter Quadrilateral, covers lateral surface of ramus of mandible, has three layers (Fig. 6.3)	a. *Superficial layer* (largest): From anterior two-thirds of lower border of zygomatic arch and adjoining zygomatic process of maxilla b. *Deep layer:* From deep surface of zygomatic arch c. *Middle layer:* From lower border of posterior one-third of zyomatic arch	a. Superficial fibres pass downwards and backwards at 45° b. Deep fibres pass vertically downwards c. Middle fibres pass vertically downwards	a. *Superficial layer* into the lower part of the lateral surface of ramus of mandible b. *Deep layer* into rest of the ramus of the mandible c. *Middle layer* into the central part of ramus of the mandible	Masseteric nerve, a branch of anterior division of mandibular nerve	a. Elevates mandible to close the mouth to bite b. Superficial fibres cause protrusion
2. Temporalis Fan-shaped, fills the temporal fossa (Fig. 6.4)	a. Temporal fossa, excluding zygomatic bone b. Temporal fascia	Anterior fibres run vertically, middle obliquely and posterior horizontally. All converge and pass through gap deep to zygomatic arch	a. Margins and deep surface of coronoid process. b. Anterior border of ramus of the mandible	Two deep temporal branches from anterior division of mandibular nerve	a. Elevates mandible b. Helps in side to side grinding movement c. Posterior fibres retract the protruded mandible
3. Lateral pterygoid Short, conical, has upper and lower heads (Fig. 6.5)	a. *Upper head* (small): From infratemporal surface and crest of greater wing of sphenoid bone b. *Lower head* (larger): From lateral surface of lateral pterygoid plate. Origin is medial to insertion	Fibres run backwards and laterally and converge for insertion	a. Pterygoid fovea on the anterior surface of neck of mandible b. Anterior margin of articular disc and capsule of temporomandibular joint. Insertion is postero-lateral and at a slightly higher level than origin	A branch from anterior division of mandibular nerve	a. Depress mandible to open mouth, with suprahyoid muscles. It is indispensible for actively opening the mouth b. Protrudes mandible c. Right lateral pterygoid turns the chin to left side
4. Medial pterygoid Quadrilateral, has a small superficial and a large deep head (Fig. 6.5)	a. *Superficial head* (small slip): From tuberosity of maxilla and adjoining bone b. *Deep head* (quite large): From medial surface of lateral pterygoid plate and adjoining process of palatine bone	Fibres run downwards, backwards and laterally. The two heads embrace part of the lower head of lateral pterygoid (Fig. 6.5)	Roughened area on the medial surface of angle and adjoining ramus of mandible, below and behind the mandibular foramen and mylohyoid groove	Nerve to medial pterygoid, branch of the main trunk of mandibular nerve	a. Elevates mandible b. Helps protrude mandible c. Right medial pterygoid with right lateral pterygoid turn the chin to left side as part of grinding movements

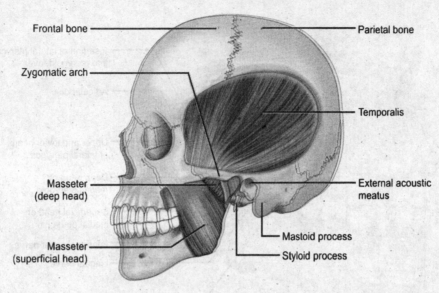

Fig. 6.3: Origin and insertion of the masseter muscle. Origin of temporalis also shown

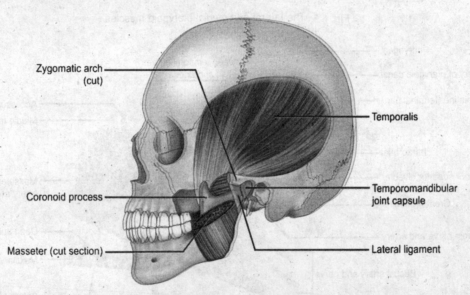

Fig. 6.4: Origin and insertion of the temporalis muscle

The fascia is extremely dense. In some species (e.g. tortoise), the temporal fascia is replaced by bone.

RELATIONS OF LATERAL PTERYGOID

The lateral pterygoid may be regarded as the key muscle of this region because its relations provide a fair idea about the layout of structures in the infra-temporal fossa. The relations are as follows:

Superficial

1 Masseter (Fig. 6.4)
2 Ramus of the mandible
3 Tendon of the temporalis
4 The maxillary artery (Fig. 6.6).

Deep

1 Mandibular nerve
2 Middle meningeal artery (Fig. 6.11).
3 Sphenomandibular ligament
4 Deep head of the medial pterygoid.

Structures Emerging at the Upper Border

1 Deep temporal nerves (Fig. 6.6)
2 Masseteric nerve.

Structures Emerging at the Lower Border

1 Lingual nerve and artery
2 Inferior alveolar nerve
3 The middle meningeal and accessory meningeal arteries pass upwards deep to it (Fig. 6.6).

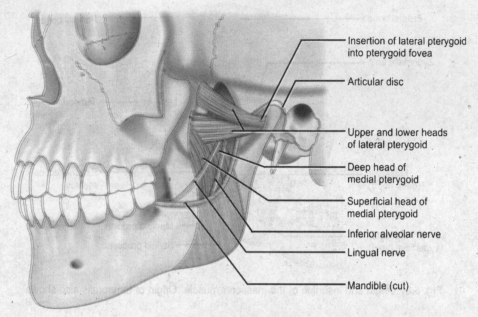

Fig. 6.5: The lateral and medial pterygoid muscles

Labels (top to bottom, right side):
- Insertion of lateral pterygoid into pterygoid fovea
- Articular disc
- Upper and lower heads of lateral pterygoid
- Deep head of medial pterygoid
- Superficial head of medial pterygoid
- Inferior alveolar nerve
- Lingual nerve
- Mandible (cut)

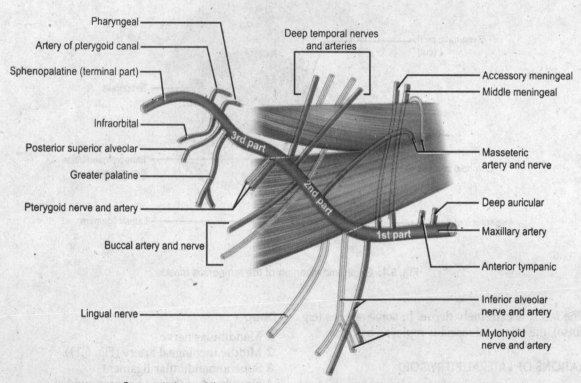

Fig. 6.6: Some relations of the lateral pterygoid muscle and branches of maxillary artery

Labels:
- Pharyngeal
- Artery of pterygoid canal
- Sphenopalatine (terminal part)
- Deep temporal nerves and arteries
- Accessory meningeal
- Middle meningeal
- Infraorbital
- Posterior superior alveolar
- Masseteric artery and nerve
- Greater palatine
- 3rd part
- Pterygoid nerve and artery
- 2nd part
- Deep auricular
- Maxillary artery
- Anterior tympanic
- Buccal artery and nerve
- 1st part
- Lingual nerve
- Inferior alveolar nerve and artery
- Mylohyoid nerve and artery

Structures Passing through the Gap between the Two Heads

1 The maxillary artery enters the gap

2 The buccal branch of the mandibular nerve comes out through the gap (Fig. 6.6).

The pterygoid plexus of veins surrounds the lateral pterygoid.

RELATIONS OF MEDIAL PTERYGOID

The superficial and deep heads of medial pterygoid enclose the lower head of lateral pterygoid muscle (Fig. 6.5).

Superficial Relations

The upper part of the muscle is separated from the lateral pterygoid muscle by:

1 The lateral pterygoid plate
2 The lingual nerve (Fig. 6.5).
3 The inferior alveolar nerve.

Lower down the muscle is separated from the ramus of the mandible by the lingual and inferior alveolar nerves, the maxillary artery, and the sphenomandibular ligament.

Deep Relations

The relations are:
1 Tensor veli palatini
2 Superior constrictor of pharynx
3 Styloglossus
4 Stylopharyngeus attached to the styloid process.

CLINICAL ANATOMY

Temporalis and masseter muscles are palpated by requesting the person to clench the teeth. Medial and lateral pterygoid muscles can be tested by requesting the person to move the lower jaw from one side to other side.

MAXILLARY ARTERY

DISSECTION

External carotid artery divides into its two terminal branches, maxillary and superficial temporal on the anteromedial surface of the parotid gland (see Fig. 5.5a). The maxillary artery, appears in this region. Identify some of its branches. Most important to be identified is the middle meningeal artery. Revise its course and branches given in Chapter 12. Accompanying these branches are the veins and pterygoid venous plexus and the superficial content of infratemporal fossa. Remove these veins. Try to see its communication with the cavernous sinus and facial vein.

Features

This is the larger terminal branch of the external carotid artery, given off behind the neck of the mandible. It has a wide territory of distribution, and supplies:
1 The external and middle ears, and the auditory tube (Fig. 6.7)
2 The dura mater
3 The upper and lower jaws with their teeth
4 The muscles of the temporal and infratemporal regions
5 The nose and paranasal air sinuses
6 The palate
7 The root of the pharynx.

COURSE AND RELATIONS

For descriptive purposes, the maxillary artery is divided into three parts (Fig. 6.7 and Table 6.2).
1 The *first (mandibular) part* runs horizontally forwards, first between the neck of the mandible and the sphenomandibular ligament, below the auriculotemporal nerve, and then along the lower border of the lateral pterygoid.
2 The *second (pterygoid) part* runs upwards and forwards superficial to the lower head of the lateral pterygoid.
3 The *third (pterygopalatine) part* passes between the two heads of the lateral pterygoid and through the pterygomaxillary fissure, to enter the pterygopalatine fossa.

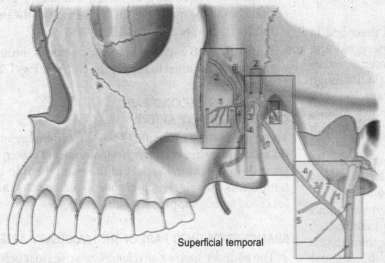

First part of maxillary artery
1. Deep auricular
2. Anterior tympanic
3. Middle meningeal
4. Accessory meningeal
5. Inferior alveolar

Second part of maxillary artery
1. Masseteric
2. Deep temporal
3. Pterygoid
4. Buccal

Third part of maxillary artery
1. Posterior superior alveolar
2. Infraorbital
3. Greater palatine
4. Pharyngeal
5. Artery of pterygoid canal
6. Sphenopalatine

Superficial temporal

External carotid

Fig. 6.7: Branches of three parts of the maxillary artery

Table 6.2: Branches of maxillary artery (Figs 6.6 and 6.7)

Branches	Foramina transmitting	Distribution
A. Of first part		
1. Deep auricular	Foramen in the floor (cartilage or bone) of external acoustic meatus	Skin of external acoustic meatus, and outer surface of tympanic membrane
2. Anterior tympanic	Petrotympanic fissure	Inner surface of tympanic membrane
3. Middle meningeal	Foramen spinosum	Supplies more of bone and less of meninges; also 5th and 7th nerves, middle ear and tensor tympani
4. Accessory meningeal	Foramen ovale	Main distribution is extracranial to pterygoids
5. Inferior alveolar	Mandibular foramen	Lower 8 teeth and mylohyoid muscle
B. Of second part		
1. Masseteric	—	Masseter
2. Deep temporal	—	Temporalis (two branches)
3. Pterygoid	—	Lateral and medial pterygoids
4. Buccal	—	Skin of the cheek
C. Of third part		
1. Posterior superior alveolar	Alveolar canals in body of maxilla	Upper molar and premolar teeth and gums; maxillary sinus
2. Infraorbital	Inferior orbital fissure	Lower orbital muscles; lacrimal sac; maxillary sinus; upper incisor and canine teeth
3. Greater palatine	Greater palatine canal	Soft palate; tonsil; palatine glands and mucosa of upper gums
4. Pharyngeal	Pharyngeal (palatovaginal) canal	Roof of nose and pharynx; auditory tube; sphenoidal sinus
5. Artery of pterygoid canal	Pterygoid canal	Auditory tube; upper pharynx and middle ear
6. Sphenopalatine (terminal part)	Sphenopalatine foramen	Lateral and medial walls of nose and various air sinuses

BRANCHES OF FIRST PART OF THE MAXILLARY ARTERY

1 The *deep auricular artery* supplies the external acoustic meatus, the tympanic membrane and the temporomandibular joint (Fig. 6.7).

2 The *anterior tympanic* branch supplies the middle ear including the medial surface of the tympanic membrane.

3 The *middle meningeal artery* has been described in Chapter 12. It lies between lateral pterygoid and sphenomandibular ligament, then between two roots of auriculotemporal nerve, enters the skull through foramen spinosum to reach middle cranial fossa. It divides into a large frontal branch which courses towards the *pterion* and a smaller parietal branch (Fig. 6.11, also *see* Fig. 12.14).

4 The *accessory meningeal artery* enters the cranial cavity through the foramen ovale. Apart from the meninges, it supplies structures in the infratemporal fossa.

5 The *inferior alveolar artery* runs downwards and forwards medial to the ramus of the mandible to reach the mandibular foramen. Passing through this foramen, the artery enters the mandibular canal (within the body of the mandible) in which it runs downwards and then forwards.

Before entering the mandibular canal, the artery gives off a lingual branch to the tongue; and a mylohyoid branch that descends in the mylohyoid groove (on the medial aspect of the mandible) and runs forwards above the mylohyoid muscle (*see* Fig. 1.25).

Within the mandibular canal, the artery gives branches to the mandible and to the roots of the each tooth attached to the bone.

It also gives off a mental branch that passes through the mental foramen to supply the chin (*see* Fig. 1.24).

BRANCHES OF SECOND PART OF THE MAXILLARY ARTERY

These are mainly muscular. These are: (i) masseteric, (ii) and (iii) *deep temporal* branches (anterior and posterior) ascend on the lateral aspect of the skull deep to the temporalis muscle, (iv) *to the pterygoid muscles,* and (v) *buccal branch* supplies the skin of cheek.

BRANCHES OF THIRD PART OF THE MAXILLARY ARTERY

1 The *posterior superior alveolar artery* arises just before the maxillary artery enters the pterygomaxillary fissure. It descends on the posterior surface of the

maxilla and gives branches that enter canals in the bone to supply the molar and premolar teeth, and the maxillary air sinus.

2 The *infraorbital artery* also arises just before the maxillary artery enters the pterygomaxillary fissure. It enters the orbit through the inferior orbital fissure. It then runs forwards in relation to the floor of the orbit, first in the infraorbital groove and then in the infraorbital canal to emerge on the face through the infraorbital foramen. It gives off some *orbital branches*, for structures in the orbit; *middle superior alveolar branch* for premolar teeth and the *anterior superior alveolar* branches that enter apertures in the maxilla to reach the incisor and canine teeth attached to the bone.

After emerging on the face, the infraorbital artery gives branches to the lacrimal sac, the nose and the upper lip.

The remaining branches of the third part arise within the pterygopalatine fossa (Fig. 6.7).

3 The *greater palatine artery* runs downwards in the greater palatine canal to emerge on the posterolateral part of the hard palate through the greater palatine foramen. It then runs forwards near the lateral margin of the palate to reach the incisive canal (near the midline) through which some terminal branches enter the nasal cavity (*see* Fig. 1.12).

Branches of the artery supply the palate and gums. While still within the greater palatine canal, it gives off the *lesser palatine arteries* that emerge on the palate through the lesser palatine foramina, and run backwards into the soft palate and tonsil.

4 The *pharyngeal branch* runs backwards through a canal related to the inferior aspect of the body of the sphenoid bone (pharyngeal or palatinovaginal canal). It supplies part of the nasopharynx, the auditory tube and the sphenoidal air sinus.

5 The *artery of the pterygoid canal* runs backwards in the canal of the same name and helps to supply the pharynx, the auditory tube and the tympanic cavity.

6 The *sphenopalatine artery* passes medially through the sphenopalatine foramen to enter the cavity of the nose. It gives off *posterolateral nasal* branches to the lateral wall of the nose and to the paranasal sinuses; and *posteromedial branches* to the nasal septum. Sphenopalatine artery is the artery of "epistaxis" (*see* Fig. 15.5).

PTERYGOID PLEXUS OF VEINS

It lies around and within the lateral pterygoid muscle. The tributaries of the plexus correspond to the branches of the maxillary artery. The plexus is drained by the maxillary vein which begins at the posterior end of the plexus and unites with the superficial temporal vein to form the retromandibular vein. Thus, the maxillary vein accompanies only the first part of the maxillary artery.

The plexus communicates:

a. With the inferior ophthalmic vein through the inferior orbital fissure.

b. With the cavernous sinus through the emissary veins.

c. With the facial vein through the deep facial vein.

CLINICAL ANATOMY

- The anterior branch of middle meningeal artery is likely to be injured at the pterion in roadside accidents. It leads to extradural haemorrhage (*see* Fig. 1.10). The clot must be sucked out at the earliest, otherwise it may compress the motor area of brain.
- Bleeding from lower teeth is from branches of inferior alveolar artery (1st part of maxillary artery) and from upper teeth is from branches of 3rd part of maxillary artery. These are posterior superior alveolar and infraorbital arteries.
- Sphenopalatine is the terminal branch of 3rd part of maxillary artery. It anastomoses with neighbouring vessels to form large capillary plexus called Kiesselbach's plexus at the antero inferior angle of the nasal septum. It is a common site of bleeding from nose or epistaxis and is known as Little's area. So sphenopalatine artery is called "the artery of epistaxis."

TEMPOROMANDIBULAR JOINT

DISSECTION

Cut the lateral pterygoid muscle close to its insertion. Dislodge the head of mandible from the articular disc. Locate the articular cartilages covering the head of the mandible and the mandibular fossa. Take out the articular disc as well and study its shape and its role in increasing the varieties of movements.

Type of Joint

This is a synovial joint of the condylar variety.

Articular Surfaces

The upper articular surface is formed by the following parts of the temporal bone:

1 Articular tubercle

2 Anterior part of mandibular fossa (Fig. 6.8).

3 Posterior non-articular part formed by the tympanic plate.

Head and Neck

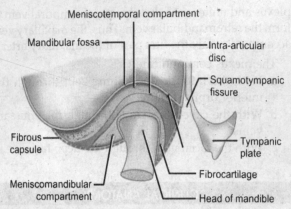

Fig. 6.8: Subdivisions and attachments of the articular disc of TMJ

The inferior articular surface is formed by the head of the mandible.

The articular surfaces are covered with *fibrocartilage*. The joint cavity is divided into upper and lower parts by an intra-articular disc.

Ligaments

The ligaments are the fibrous capsule, the lateral ligament, the sphenomandibular ligament, and the stylomandibular ligament.

1 The *fibrous capsule* is attached *above* to the articular tubercle, the circumference of the mandibular fossa in front and the squamotympanic fissure behind, and *below* to the neck of the mandible. The capsule is loose above the intra-articular disc, and tight below it. The synovial membrane lines the fibrous capsule and the neck of the mandible (Fig. 6.9).

2 The *lateral temporomandibular ligament* reinforces and strengthens the lateral part of the capsular ligament. Its fibres are directed downwards and backwards. It is attached above to the articular tubercle, and below to the posterolateral aspect of the neck of the mandible.

Limits movement of mandible in posterior direction

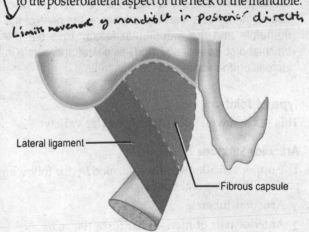

Fig. 6.9: Fibrous capsule and lateral ligament of the temporomandibular joint

3 The *sphenomandibular ligament* is an accessory ligament, that lies on a deep plane away from the fibrous capsule. It is attached superiorly to the spine of the sphenoid, and inferiorly to the lingula of the mandibular foramen. It is a remnant of the dorsal part of Meckel's cartilage.

The ligament is related *laterally* to:
a. Lateral pterygoid muscle (Fig. 6.10).
b. Auriculotemporal nerve.
c. Maxillary artery (Fig. 6.11).

The ligament is related medially to:
a. Chorda tympani nerve.
b. Wall of the pharynx. Near its lower end, it is pierced by the mylohyoid nerve and vessels.

4 The *stylomandibular ligament* is another accessory ligament of the joint. It represents a thickened part of the *deep cervical fascia* which separates the parotid and submandibular salivary glands. It is attached above to the lateral surface of the styloid process, and below to the angle and adjacent part of posterior border of the ramus of the mandible (Fig. 6.11).

ARTICULAR DISC

The *articular disc* is an oval predominantly fibrous plate that divides the joint into an upper and a lower compartments. The upper compartment permits *gliding* movements, and the lower, *rotatory* as well as *gliding* movements.

The disc has a concavo-convex superior surface, and a concave inferior surface. The periphery of the disc is attached to the fibrous capsule. The disc is composed of an anterior extension, anterior thick band, intermediate zone, posterior thick band and bilaminar region (Fig. 6.8) containing venous plexus. The disc represents the degenerated primitive insertion of lateral pterygoid. The disc prevents friction between the articulating surfaces.

It acts as a cushion and helps in shock absorption. It stabilises the condyle by filling up the space between articulating surfaces.

The proprioceptive fibres present in the disc help to regulate movements of the joint.

The disc helps in distribution of weight across the TMJ by increasing the area of contact.

RELATIONS OF TEMPOROMANDIBULAR JOINT

Lateral

1 Skin and fasciae
2 Parotid gland (Fig. 6.11, inset)
3 Temporal branches of the facial nerve.

Medial

1 The tympanic plate separates the joint from the internal carotid artery.

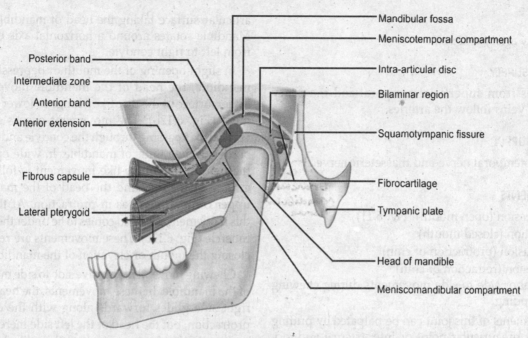

Fig. 6.10: Articular surfaces of the left temporomandibular joint

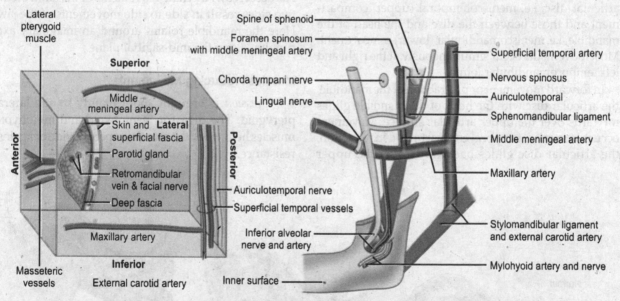

Fig. 6.11: Superficial relations of the sphenomandibular ligament seen after removal of the lateral pterygoid. Medial relations of temporomandibular joint also seen. Inset shows other relations of the joint

2 Spine of the sphenoid, with upper end of the spheno-mandibular ligament attached to it.

3 Auriculotemporal and chorda tympani nerves.

4 Middle meningeal artery (Fig. 6.11).

Anterior

1 Lateral pterygoid

2 Masseteric nerve and artery (Fig. 6.8).

Posterior

1 The parotid gland separates the joint from the external auditory meatus.

2 Superficial temporal vessels.

3 Auriculotemporal nerve (*see* Fig. 5.3).

Superior

1 Middle cranial fossa

2 Middle meningeal vessels.

Inferior

Maxillary artery and vein.

BLOOD SUPPLY

Branches from superficial temporal and maxillary arteries. Veins follow the arteries.

NERVE SUPPLY

Auriculotemporal nerve and masseteric nerve. }2

branches of Mandibular nerve

MOVEMENTS

1 Depression (open mouth) (Fig. 6.11)
2 Elevation (closed mouth)
3 Protrusion (protraction of chin)
4 Retrusion (retraction of chin)
5 Lateral or side to side movements during chewing or grinding.

Movements of this joint can be palpated by putting finger at preauricular point or into external auditory meatus. The movements at the joint can be divided into those between the upper articular surface and the articular disc, i.e. meniscotemporal (upper) compartment and those between the disc and the head of the mandible, i.e. meniscomandibular (lower) compartment. Most movements occur simultaneously at the right and left temporomandibular joints.

In forward movement or protraction of the mandible, the articular disc with the head of the mandible glides forwards over the upper articular surface. Movement occurs in meniscotemporal compartment. In retraction, the articular disc glides backwards over the upper articular surface taking the head of mandible with it. Mandible rotates around a horizontal axis extending from left to right condyle.

In slight opening of the mouth or depression of the mandible, the head of the mandible moves on the undersurface of the disc like a hinge in lower compartment (Fig. 6.12b). The movement occurs around a vertical axis passing through the condyle and posterior border of the ramus of mandible. In wide opening of the mouth, this hinge-like movement is followed by gliding of the disc and the head of the mandible in upper compartment, as in protraction. At the end of this movement, the head comes to lie under the articular tubercle (Fig. 6.12c). These movements are reversed in closing the mouth or elevation of the mandible.

Chewing movements involve side to side movements of the mandible. In these movements, the head of (say) right side glides forwards along with the disc as in protraction, but the head of the left side merely rotates on a vertical axis. As a result of this, the chin moves forwards and to left side (the side on which no gliding has occurred). Alternate movements of this kind on the two sides result in side to side movements of the jaw. Here the mandible rotates around an imaginary axis running along the mid-sagittal plane.

Muscles Producing Movements

↓ *Depression* is brought about mainly by the lateral pterygoid. The digastric, geniohyoid and mylohyoid muscles help when the mouth is opened wide or against resistance.

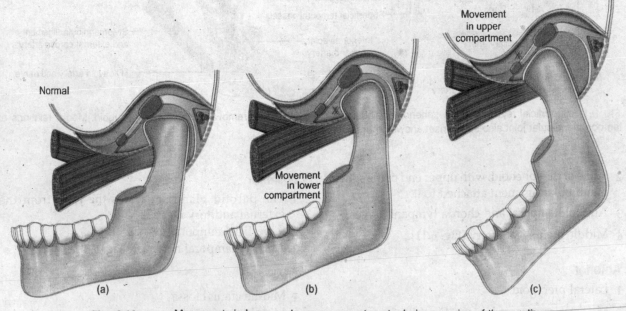

Normal   Movement in lower compartment   Movement in upper compartment

(a)   (b)   (c)

Figs 6.12a to c: Movements in lower and upper compartments during opening of the mouth

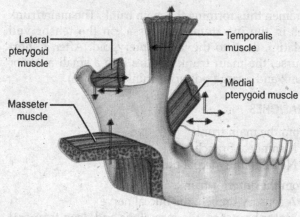

Fig. 6.13: Movements of temporomandibular joint (arrows) by muscles of mastication

The origin of only lateral pterygoid is anterior, slightly lower and medial to its insertion. During contraction, it rotates the head of mandible and opens the mouth. During wide opening, it pulls the articular disc forwards. So movement occurs in both the compartments. It is also done passively by gravity (Figs 6.10 and 6.13).

↑ *Elevation* is brought about by the masseter, the anterior vertical, middle oblique fibres of temporalis, and the medial pterygoid muscles of both sides. These are antigravity muscles.

← *Protrusion* is done by the lateral and medial pterygoids and superficial oblique fibres of masseter.

→ *Retraction* is produced by the posterior horizontal fibres of the temporalis and deep vertical fibres of masseter.

Lateral or side to side movements, e.g. chewing from left side produced by right lateral pterygoid, right medial pterygoid which push the chin to left side. Then left temporalis (anterior fibres), left masseter (deep fibres) (↔) chew the food. Chewing from right side involves left lateral pterygoid, left medial pterygoid, right temporalis and right masseter. Since so many muscles are involved, chewing becomes tiring.

CLINICAL ANATOMY

• Dislocation of mandible: During excessive opening of the mouth, the head of the mandible of one or both sides may slip anteriorly into the infratemporal fossa, as a result of which there is inability to close the mouth. Reduction is done by depressing the jaw with the thumbs placed on the last molar teeth, and at the same time elevating the chin (Fig. 6.14).

• Derangement of the articular disc may result from any injury, like overclosure or malocclusion. This gives rise to clicking and pain during movements of the jaw.

• In operations on the temporomandibular joint, the VII nerve and auriculotemporal nerve, branch of mandibular division of V should be preserved with care (Fig. 6.15).

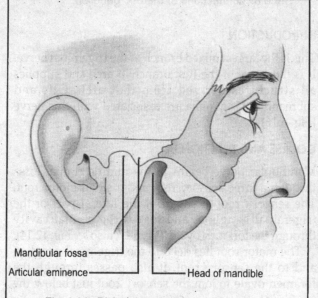

Fig. 6.14: Dislocation of the head of mandible

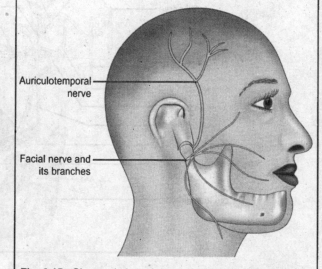

Fig. 6.15: Close relation of the two nerves to the temporomandibular joint

Head and Neck

MANDIBULAR NERVE

DISSECTION

Identify middle meningeal artery arising from the maxillary artery and trace it till the foramen spinosum. Note the two roots of auriculotemporal nerve surrounding the artery. Trace the origin of the auriculo-temporal nerve from mandibular nerve (Fig. 6.11). Dissect all the other branches of the nerve. Identify the chorda tympani nerve joining the lingual branch of mandibular nerve. Lift the trunk of mandibular nerve laterally and locate the otic ganglion.

Trace all connections of the otic ganglion.

INTRODUCTION

This is the largest mixed branch of the trigeminal nerve. It is the nerve of the first branchial arch and supplies all structures derived from that arch. Otic and submandibular ganglia are associated with this nerve (Fig. 6.16).

COURSE AND RELATIONS

Mandibular nerve begins in the middle cranial fossa through a large sensory root and a small motor root. The sensory root arises from the lateral part of the trigeminal ganglion, and leaves the cranial cavity through the foramen ovale (Fig. 6.17, also *see* Fig. 12.14).

The motor root lies deep to the trigeminal ganglion and to the sensory root. It also passes through the foramen ovale to join the sensory root just below the

foramen thus forming the main trunk. The main trunk lies in the infratemporal fossa, on the tensor veli palatini, deep to the lateral pterygoid. After a short course, the main trunk divides into a small anterior trunk and a large posterior trunk (Fig. 6.16).

BRANCHES

From the main trunk:
a. Meningeal branch
b. Nerve to the medial pterygoid.

From the anterior trunk:
a. A sensory branch, the buccal nerve
b. Motor branches, the masseteric and deep temporal nerves and the nerve to the lateral pterygoid.

From the posterior trunk:
a. Auriculotemporal
b. Lingual
c. Inferior alveolar nerves.

Meningeal Branch or Nervus Spinosus

Meningeal branch enters the skull through the *foramen spinosum* with the middle meningeal artery and supplies the dura mater of the middle cranial fossa.

Nerve to Medial Pterygoid

Nerve to medial pterygoid arises close to the otic ganglion and supplies the medial pterygoid from its deep surface. This nerve gives a motor root to the otic ganglion which does not relay and supplies the tensor veli palatini, and the tensor tympani muscles (Fig. 6.17).

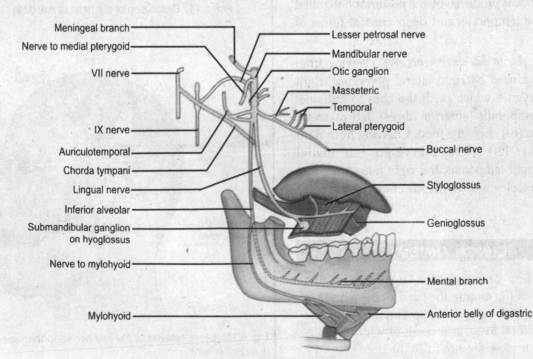

Meningeal branch — — Lesser petrosal nerve
Nerve to medial pterygoid — — Mandibular nerve
VII nerve — — Otic ganglion
— Masseteric
— Temporal
— Lateral pterygoid
IX nerve —
Auriculotemporal —
Chorda tympani — — Buccal nerve
Lingual nerve — — Styloglossus
Inferior alveolar — — Genioglossus
Submandibular ganglion on hyoglossus —
Nerve to mylohyoid — — Mental branch
Mylohyoid — — Anterior belly of digastric

Fig. 6.16: Distribution of mandibular nerve (V3)

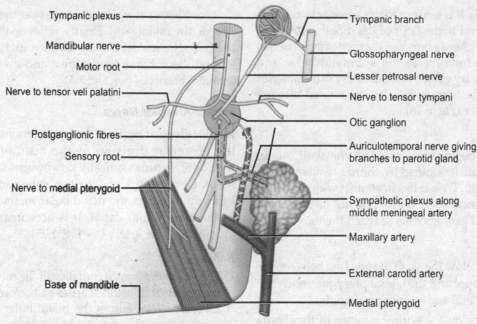

Fig. 6.17: Right otic ganglion seen from medial side

Labels (clockwise from top left):
Tympanic plexus · Mandibular nerve · Motor root · Nerve to tensor veli palatini · Postganglionic fibres · Sensory root · Nerve to medial pterygoid · Base of mandible · Tympanic branch · Glossopharyngeal nerve · Lesser petrosal nerve · Nerve to tensor tympani · Otic ganglion · Auriculotemporal nerve giving branches to parotid gland · Sympathetic plexus along middle meningeal artery · Maxillary artery · External carotid artery · Medial pterygoid

Buccal Nerve

Buccal nerve is the only sensory branch of the anterior division of the mandibular nerve. It passes between the two heads of the lateral pterygoid, runs downwards and forwards, and supplies the skin of cheek and mucous membrane related to the buccinator (Fig. 6.6). It also supplies the labial aspect of gums of molar and premolar teeth.

Masseteric Nerve

Masseteric nerve emerges at the upper border of the lateral pterygoid just in front of the temporomandibular joint, passes laterally through the mandibular notch in company with the masseteric vessels, and enters the deep surface of the masseter. It also supplies the temporomandibular joint (see Fig. 1.24).

Deep Temporal Nerves

Deep temporal nerves are two nerves, anterior and posterior. They pass between the skull and the lateral pterygoid, and enter the deep surface of the temporalis.

Nerve to Lateral Pterygoid

Nerve to lateral pterygoid enters the deep surface of the muscle.

Auriculotemporal Nerve

Auriculotemporal nerve arises by two roots which run backwards, encircle the middle meningeal artery, and unite to form a single trunk (Figs 6.11, 6.16 and 6.17). The nerve continues backwards between the neck of

the mandible and the sphenomandibular ligament, above the maxillary artery. Behind the neck of the mandible, it turns upwards and ascends on the temple behind the superficial temporal vessels.

The *auricular part* of the nerve supplies the skin of the tragus; and the upper parts of the pinna, the external acoustic meatus and the tympanic membrane. (Note that the lower parts of these regions are supplied by the great auricular nerve and the auricular branch of the vagus nerve.) The *temporal part* supplies the skin of the temple (see Fig. 2.5). *In addition*, the auriculotemporal nerve also supplies the parotid gland (secretomotor and also sensory, Fig. 6.17) and the temporomandibular joint (see Table A.2).

Lingual Nerve

Lingual nerve (Table 6.3) is one of the two terminal branches of the posterior division of the mandibular

Table 6.3: Branches of the mandibular nerve (CN V3)

Muscular	Sensory	Others
Temporalis and masseter	Meningeal Auriculotemporal	Carries taste fibres
Medial and lateral pterygoids	Inferior alveolar and mental	Carries secreto-motor fibres
Tensor veli palatini and tensor tympani	Lingual	Articular
Mylohyoid and digastric (anterior belly)	Buccal	—

nerve (Fig. 6.16). It is sensory to the anterior two-thirds of the tongue and to the floor of the mouth. However, the fibres of the chorda tympani (branch of facial nerve) which is secretomotor to the submandibular and sublingual salivary glands and gustatory to the anterior two-thirds of the tongue, are also distributed through the lingual nerve (Fig. 6.18).

Course

Lingual nerve begins one cm below the skull. About 2 cm below skull, it is joined by chorda tympani nerve at an acute angle. Then it lies in contact with mandible medial to 3rd *molar tooth*. Finally, it lies on surface of hyoglossus and genioglossus to reach the tongue.

Relations

It begins 1 cm below the skull. It runs first between the tensor veli palatini and the lateral pterygoid, and then between the lateral and medial pterygoids.

About 2 cm below the skull, it is joined by the chorda tympani nerve (Fig. 6.18).

Emerging at the lower border of the lateral pterygoid, the nerve runs downwards and forwards between the ramus of the mandible and the medial pterygoid. Next it lies in direct contact with the mandible, medial to the third molar tooth between the origins of the superior constrictor and the mylohyoid muscles (*see* Fig. 1.25).

It soon leaves the gum and runs over the hyoglossus deep to the mylohyoid. Finally, it lies on the surface of the genioglossus deep to the mylohyoid. Here it winds around the submandibular duct and divides into its terminal branches (*see* Fig. 7.4).

Inferior Alveolar Nerve

Inferior alveolar nerve is the larger terminal branch of the posterior division of the mandibular nerve (Fig. 6.16). It runs vertically downwards lateral to the medial pterygoid and to the sphenomandibular ligament. It enters the mandibular foramen and runs in the mandibular canal. It is accompanied by the inferior alveolar artery (*see* Fig. 1.25).

Branches

1 The *mylohyoid branch* contains all the motor fibres of the posterior division. It arises just before the inferior alveolar nerve enters the mandibular foramen. It pierces the sphenomandibular ligament with the mylohyoid artery, runs in the mylohyoid groove, and supplies the mylohyoid muscle and the anterior belly of the digastric (Fig. 6.11).

2 While running in the mandibular canal the inferior alveolar nerve gives branches that supply the lower teeth and gums.

3 The *mental nerve* emerges at the mental foramen and supplies the skin of the chin, and the skin and

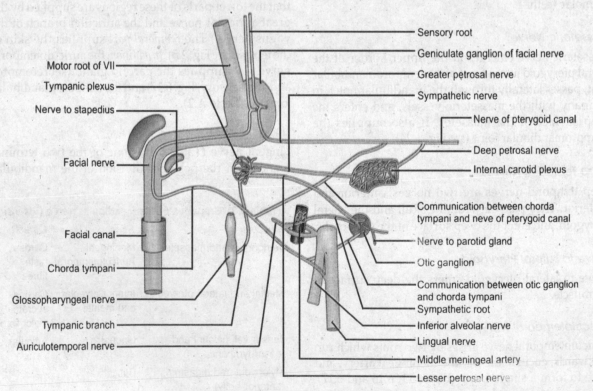

Fig. 6.18: Connections of otic ganglion (schematic)

Sensory root
Geniculate ganglion of facial nerve
Greater petrosal nerve
Sympathetic nerve
Nerve of pterygoid canal
Deep petrosal nerve
Internal carotid plexus
Communication between chorda tympani and neve of pterygoid canal
Nerve to parotid gland
Otic ganglion
Communication between otic ganglion and chorda tympani
Sympathetic root
Inferior alveolar nerve
Lingual nerve
Middle meningeal artery
Lesser petrosal nerve

Motor root of VII
Tympanic plexus
Nerve to stapedius
Facial nerve
Facial canal
Chorda tympani
Glossopharyngeal nerve
Tympanic branch
Auriculotemporal nerve

mucous membrane of the lower lip (Fig. 6.16). Its incisive branch supplies the labial aspect of gums of canine and incisor teeth.

OTIC GANGLION

It is a peripheral parasympathetic ganglion which relays secretomotor fibres to the parotid gland. Topographically, it is intimately related to the mandibular nerve, but functionally, it is a part of the glossopharyngeal nerve (Figs 6.17 and 6.18).

Size and Situation

It is 2 to 3 mm in size, and is situated in the infra-temporal fossa, just below the foramen ovale. It lies medial to the mandibular nerve, and lateral to the tensor veli palatini. It surrounds the origin of the nerve to the medial pterygoid (Fig. 6.16).

Connections and Branches

The secretomotor *motor or parasympathetic root* is formed by the lesser petrosal nerve. Its origin and course is shown in Flowchart 6.1.

The *sympathetic root* is derived from the plexus on the middle meningeal artery. It contains postganglionic fibres arising in the superior cervical ganglion. The fibres pass through the otic ganglion without relay and reach the parotid gland via the auriculotemporal nerve. They are vasomotor in function.

The *sensory root* comes from the auriculotemporal nerve and is sensory to the parotid gland.

Flowchart 6.1: Secretomotor fibres for parotid gland

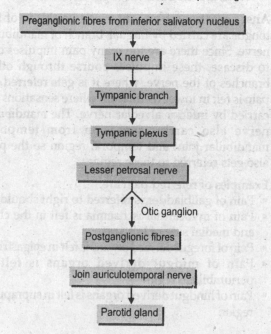

Other fibres passing through the ganglion are as follows:

a. The nerve to medial pterygoid gives a motor root to the ganglion which passes through it without relay and supplies medially placed tensor veli palatini and laterally placed tensor tympani muscles.
b. The chorda tympani nerve is connected to the otic ganglion and also to the nerve of the pterygoid canal (Fig. 6.18). These connections provide an alternative pathway of taste from the anterior two-thirds of the tongue.

CLINICAL ANATOMY

- The motor part of the mandibular nerve is tested clinically by asking the patient to clench her/his teeth and then feeling for the contracting masseter and temporalis muscles on the two sides. If one masseter is paralysed, the jaw deviates to the para-lysed side, on opening the mouth by the action of the normal lateral pterygoid of the opposite side. The activity of the pterygoid muscles is tested by asking the patient to move the chin from side to side.
- *Referred pain:* In cases with cancer of the tongue, pain radiates to the ear and to the temporal fossa, over the distribution of the auriculotemporal nerve as both lingual and auriculotemporal nerves are branches of mandibular nerve. Sometimes the lingual nerve is divided to relieve intractable pain of this kind . This may be done where the nerve lies in contact with the mandible below and behind the last molar tooth, covered only by mucous membrane.
- *Mandibular neuralgia:* Trigeminal neuralgia of the mandibular division is often difficult to treat. In such cases, the sensory root of the nerve may be divided behind the ganglion, and this is now the operation of choice when pain is confined to the distribution of the maxillary and mandibular nerves. During division, the ophthalmic fibres that lie in the superomedial part of the root are spared, to preserve the corneal reflex thus avoiding damage to the cornea (Fig. 6.19).
- Lingual nerve lies in contact with mandible, medial to the third molar tooth. In extraction of malplaced 'wisdom' tooth, care must be taken not to injure the lingual nerve (*see* Fig. 1.25). Its injury results in loss of all sensations from anterior two-thirds of the tongue.
- A lesion at the foramen ovale leads to paraesthesia along the mandible, tongue, temporal region and paralysis of the muscles of mastication. This also leads to loss of jaw-jerk reflex.
- The mandibular nerve supplies both the efferent and afferent loops of the jaw-jerk reflex, as it is a

mixed nerve. Tapping the chin causes contraction of the pterygoid muscles.

- In extraction of mandibular teeth, inferior alveolar nerve needs to be anaesthetised. The drug is given into the nerve before it enters the mandibular canal.
- *Inferior alveolar nerve:* Inferior alveolar nerve as it travels the mandibular canal can be damaged by the fracture of the mandible. This injury can be assessed by testing sensation over the chin.
- During extraction of the 3rd molar, the buccal nerve may get involved by the local anaesthesia causing temporary numbness of the cheek.

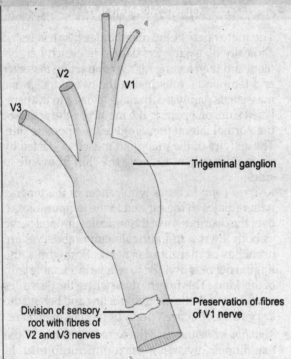

Fig. 6.19: Partial cutting of the sensory root of trigeminal nerve

Labels: V2, V1, V3, Trigeminal ganglion, Preservation of fibres of V1 nerve, Division of sensory root with fibres of V2 and V3 nerves

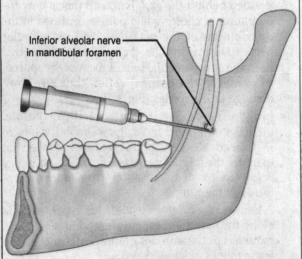

Fig. 6.20: Injection given in mandibular foramen for anaesthetising the inferior alveolar nerve before extraction of last molar tooth

Labels: Inferior alveolar nerve in mandibular foramen

Mnemonics

Function of Lateral (La) vs. Medial (Me) pterygoid muscles

"*La*": Jaw is open, so lateral pterygoid opens mouth.
"*Me*": Jaw is closed, so medial pterygoid closes the mouth.

FACTS TO REMEMBER

- Mandibular nerve is the only mixed branch of trigeminal nerve
- The nerve is associated with two parasympathetic ganglia, i.e. otic and submandibular ganglia
- Maxillary artery gives many branches; some accompany branches of maxillary nerve and others branches of mandibular nerve as there is no mandibular artery
- Only muscle of mastication which depresses the TMJ is the lateral pterygoid muscle
- Spine of sphenoid is related to chorda tympani and auriculotemporal nerves. Injury to the spine will hamper the secretion of 3 salivary glands.
- Auriculotemporal nerve and branches of facial nerve are related to temporomandibular joint.

CLINICOANATOMICAL PROBLEM

A patient of carcinoma in anterior two-thirds of tongue complains of pain in his lower teeth, temporal region and the temporomandibular joint.

- Why is pain of tongue referred to lower teeth?
- Which are the other areas of referred pain?

Ans: Sensations from anterior two-thirds of the tongue are carried by lingual, branch of mandibular nerve. Since there are too many pain impulses due to disease, these impulses course through other branches of the nerve, where it is gets referred. So pain is felt in lower teeth, from where sensations are carried by inferior alveolar nerve. The mandibular nerve also carries sensation from temporomandibular joint and temporal region so the pain also gets referred to these regions.

Examples of referred pain are:
- Pain of gallbladder is referred to right shoulder
- Pain of myocardial ischaemia is felt in the chest and medial side of left arm
- Pain of foregut derived organs is felt in epigastrium
- Pain of midgut derived organs is felt in periumbilical region
- Pain of hindgut derived organs is felt in suprapubic region

FREQUENTLY ASKED QUESTIONS

1. Describe temporomandibular joint under the following headings:
   a. Bones taking part
   b. Capsule and ligaments
   c. Relations
   d. Movements and their muscles
   e. Clinical anatomy
2. Describe muscles of mastication under the following headings:

   a. Origin
   b. Insertion
   c. Actions
   d. Clinical anatomy

3. Write short notes on/enumerate:
   a. Otic ganglion and its connections
   b. Branches of 1st part of maxillary artery
   c. Branches of mandibular nerve
   d. Branches of 3rd part of maxillary artery
   d. Sphenomandibular ligament and the structures piercing it

MULTIPLE CHOICE QUESTIONS

1. Action of lateral pterygoid muscle is:
   a. Elevation and retraction of mandible
   b. Depression and retraction of mandible
   c. Elevation and protrusion of mandible
   d. Depression and protrusion of mandible
2. Which of the following muscles is used for opening the mouth?
   a. Medial pterygoid   b. Temporalis
   c. Lateral pterygoid   d. Masseter
3. Which of the following ligaments is not a ligament of temporomandibular joint?
   a. Pterygomandibular
   b. Sphenomandibular
   c. Lateral ligament
   d. Stylomandibular
4. Which one is not a branch of maxillary artery?
   a. Anterior tympanic b. Anterior ethmoidal
   c. Middle meningeal d. Inferior alveolar
5. Which of the following is not a muscle of mastication?
   a. Medial pterygoid
   b. Masseter
   c. Temporalis
   d. Orbicularis oris

6. Dislocated mandible can be reversed by:
   a. Depressing the jaw posteriorly and elevating the chin
   b. Depressing the jaw and depressing the chin
   c. Elevating the jaw and elevating the chin
   d. Depressing the chin and elevating the jaw posteriorly
7. Nervus spinosus is a branch of:
   a. Maxillary nerve   b. Mandibular nerve
   c. Ophthalmic nerve d. 2nd cervical nerve
8. Lingual nerve is the branch of:
   a. Facial nerve
   b. Glossopharyngeal nerve
   c. Mandibular nerve
   d. Hypoglossal nerve
9. Lingual nerve can be pressed against a bone inside the mouth near the roots of the:
   a. Third upper molar tooth
   b. Second upper molar tooth
   c. Third lower molar tooth
   d. First lower molar tooth
10. Nerve piercing sphenomandibular ligament is:
   a. Nerve to mylohyoid
   b. Inferior alveolar
   c. Buccal
   d. Lingual

ANSWERS

1. d	2. c	3. a	4. b	5. d	6. a	7. b	8. c	9. c	10. a

Submandibular Region

Life is too short for men to take it too seriously
—George Bernard Shaw

INTRODUCTION

Submandibular region includes deeper structures in the area between the mandible and hyoid bone including the floor of the mouth and the root of the tongue.

The submandibular region contains the suprahyoid muscles, submandibular and sublingual salivary glands and submandibular ganglion. Chorda tympani from facial nerve provides preganglionic secretomotor fibres to the glands. Chorda tympani also carries fibres of sensation of taste from anterior two-thirds of tongue except from the circumvallate papillae. Taste from the circumvallate papillae is carried by the glosso-pharyngeal nerve.

SUPRAHYOID MUSCLES

DISSECTION

Cut the facial artery and vein present at the antero-inferior angle of masseter muscle. Separate the origin of anterior belly of digastric muscle from the digastric fossa near the symphysis menti. Push the mandible upwards. Clean and expose the posterior belly of digastric muscle and its accompanying stylohyoid muscle. Identify the digastrics, stylohyoid, mylohyoid, geniohyoid, hyoglossus.

Features

The suprahyoid muscles are the digastric, the stylohyoid, the mylohyoid and the geniohyoid. The muscles are in following layers:

1 First layer formed by digastric (Greek *two bellies*) and stylohyoid (Fig. 7.1).
2 Second layer formed by mylohyoid (Greek *pertaining to hyoid bone*) (Fig. 7.2).
3 Third layer formed by geniohyoid and hyoglossus (Fig. 7.4).

4 Fourth layer formed by genioglossus (Fig. 7.4). The muscles are described in Table 7.1.

RELATIONS OF POSTERIOR BELLY OF DIGASTRIC

Superficial

1 Mastoid process with the sternocleidomastoid, splenius capitis and the longissimus capitis (Fig. 7.3, also *see* Fig. 5.4a)..
2 The stylohyoid.
3 The parotid gland with retromandibular vein.
4 Submandibular salivary gland (Fig. 7.3) and lymph nodes.
5 Angle of the mandible with medial pterygoid.

Deep

1 Transverse process of the atlas with superior oblique and the rectus capitis lateralis.
2 Internal carotid, external carotid, lingual, facial and occipital arteries
3 Internal jugular vein.
4 Vagus, accessory and hypoglossal cranial nerves (Fig. 7.3).
5 The hyoglossus muscle.

Upper Border

1 The posterior auricular artery (*see* Fig. 4.14).
2 The stylohyoid muscle.

Lower Border

Lower border is related to occipital artery (*see* Fig. 4.14).

RELATIONS OF MYLOHYOID

Superficial

1 Anterior belly of digastric (Fig. 7.1)
2 Superficial part of the submandibular salivary gland.
3 Mylohyoid nerve and vessels.
4 Submental branch of the facial artery.

Table 7.1: Suprahyoid muscles

Muscle	Origin	Fibres	Insertion	Nerve supply	Actions
1. **Digastric (DG):** It has two bellies united by an intermediate tendon (Figs 7.1 and 7.2)	a. Anterior belly (DGA): From digastric fossa of mandible b. Posterior belly (DGP): From mastoid notch of temporal bone	a. Anterior belly runs downwards and backwards b. Posterior belly runs downwards and forwards	Both heads meet at the intermediate tendon which perforates SH and is held by a fibrous pulley to the hyoid bone	a. Anterior belly by nerve to mylohyoid b. Posterior belly by facial nerve	a. Depresses mandible when mouth is opened widely or against resistance; it is secondary to lateral pterygoid b. Elevates hyoid bone
2. **Stylohyoid (SH):** Small muscle, lies on upper border of DGP (Fig. 7.2)	Posterior surface of styloid process	Tendon is perforated by DGP tendon	Junction of body and greater cornua of hyoid bone (see Fig. 1.47)	Facial nerve	a. Pulls hyoid bone upwards and backwards b. With other hyoid muscles, it fixes the hyoid bone
3. **Mylohyoid (MH):** Flat, triangular muscle; two mylohyoids form floor of mouth cavity, deep to DGA (Figs 7.1 and 7.2)	Mylohyoid line of mandible (see Fig. 1.23)	Fibres run medially and slightly downwards	a. Posterior fibres: Body of hyoid bone (see Fig. 1.47) b. Middle and anterior fibres; median raphe, between mandible and hyoid bone	Nerve to mylohyoid	a. Elevates floor of mouth in first stage of deglutition b. Helps in depression of mandible, and elevation of hyoid bone
4. **Geniohyoid (GH):** Short and narrow muscle; lies above medial part of MH (Fig. 7.4)	Inferior mental spine (genial tubercle)	Runs backwards and downwards	Anterior surface of body of hyoid bone	C1 through hypoglossal nerve	a. Elevates hyoid bone b. May depress mandible when hyoid is fixed
5. **Hyoglossus:** It is a muscle of tongue. It forms important landmark in this region (Fig. 7.4)	Whole length of greater cornua and lateral part of body of hyoid bone (see Fig. 1.47)	Fibres run upwards and forwards	Side of tongue between styloglossus and inferior longitudinal muscle of tongue	Hypoglossal (XII) nerve	Depresses tongue makes dorsum convex, retracts the protruded tongue

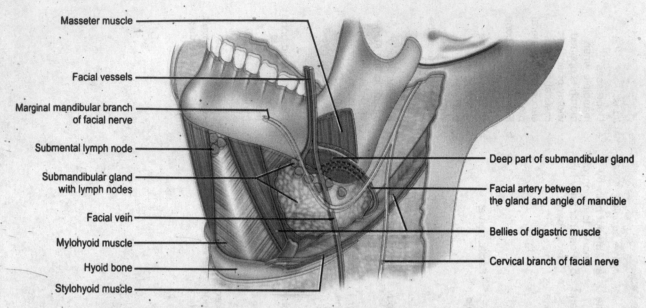

Fig. 7.1: Relation of marginal mandibular branch of facial nerve to the submandibular gland and its lymph nodes

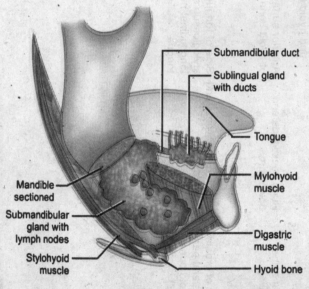

Fig. 7.2: Mylohyoid muscle dividing the gland into two

Deep

1 Hyoglossus with its superficial relations, namely the styloglossus, the lingual nerve, the submandibular ganglion, the deep part of the submandibular salivary gland, the submandibular duct, the hypoglossal nerve, and the venae comitantes hypoglossi (Figs 7.2 and 7.4).

2 The genioglossus with its superficial relations, namely the sublingual salivary gland, the lingual nerve, submandibular duct, the lingual artery, and the hypoglossal nerve (Fig. 7.4).

RELATIONS OF HYOGLOSSUS
Superficial

Styloglossus, lingual nerve, submandibular ganglion, deep part of the submandibular gland, submandibular duct, hypoglossal nerve and veins accompanying it (Fig. 7.4).

Deep

1 Inferior longitudinal muscle of the tongue.
2 Genioglossus.
3 Middle constrictor of the pharynx.
4 Glossopharyngeal nerve.
5 Stylohyoid ligament.
6 Lingual artery.

Structures passing deep to posterior border of hyoglossus, from above downwards:

1 Glossopharyngeal nerve.
2 Stylohyoid ligament.
3 Lingual artery (Fig. 7.4).

SUBMANDIBULAR SALIVARY GLAND

DISSECTION

Submandibular gland is seen in the digastric triangle. On pushing the superficial part of the gland posteriorly, the entire mylohyoid muscle is exposed. The deep part of the gland lies on the superior surface of the muscle. Separate the facial artery from the deep surface of gland and identify its branches in neck. The hyoglossus muscle is recognised as a quadrilateral muscle lying on deeper plane than mylohyoid muscle. Identify lingual nerve with submandibular ganglion, and hypoglossal nerve running on the hyoglossus muscle from lateral to the medial side. Deep part of gland and its duct are also visible on this surface of hyoglossus muscle (Fig. 7.4).

Carefully release the hyoglossus muscle from the hyoid bone and reflect it towards the tongue. Note the structures deep to the muscle, e.g. genioglossus muscle, lingual artery, vein and middle constrictor of the pharynx.

FEATURES

This is a large salivary gland, situated in the anterior part of the digastric triangle. The gland is about the size of a walnut weighing about 15 to 20 g. It is roughly J-shaped, being indented by the posterior border of the mylohyoid which divides it into a larger part superficial to the muscle, and a small part lying deep to the muscle (Fig. 7.5).

Coverings: The gland is partially enclosed between two layers of deep cervical fascia. The superficial (Fig. 7.6) layer of fascia covers the inferior surface of the gland and is attached to the base of the mandible.

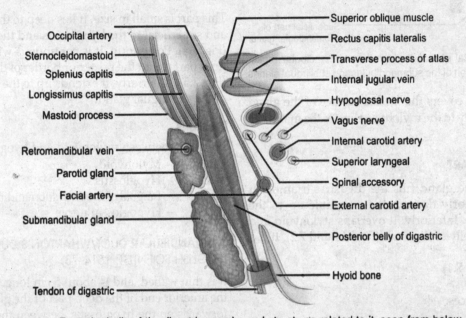

Fig. 7.3: Posterior belly of the digastric muscle, and structures related to it, seen from below

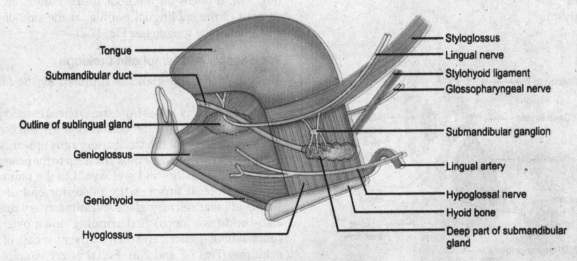

Fig. 7.4: Submandibular region showing the superficial relations of the hyoglossus and genioglossus muscles, the deep part of submandibular gland also shown

Head and Neck

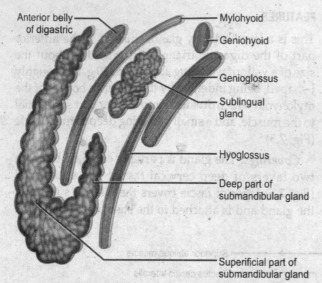

Fig. 7.5: Horizontal section through the submandibular region showing the location of the submandibular and sublingual glands

The deep layer covers the medial surface of the gland and is superiorly to the mylohyoid line of the mandible (Fig. 7.6).

SUPERFICIAL PART

This part of the gland fills the digastric triangle. It extends superiorly deep to the mandible up to the mylohyoid line. Inferiorly: It overlaps stylohyoid and the posterior belly of digastric (Figs 7.1 and 7.2). It has three surfaces:
a. Inferior (Fig. 7.1)
b. Lateral
c. Medial surfaces.

Relations

The **inferior surface** is covered by:
a. Skin
b. Platysma

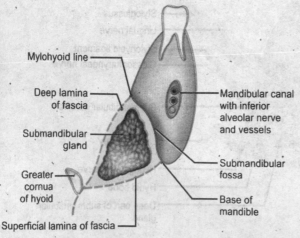

Fig. 7.6: Fascial coverings of the superficial part of the submandibular salivary gland

c. Cervical branch of the facial nerve
d. Deep fascia
e. Facial vein (Fig. 7.7).
f. Submandibular lymph nodes (Fig. 7.1).

The **lateral surface** is related to:
a. The submandibular fossa on the mandible.
b. Insertion of the medial pterygoid (Fig. 7.7).
c. The facial artery (Figs 7.7 and 7.8).

The **medial surface** is related to:
   Mylohyoid, hyoglossus and styloglossus muscles from before backwards (Fig. 7.8).

DEEP PART

This part is small in size. It lies deep to the mylohyoid, and superficial to the hyoglossus and the styloglossus (Fig. 7.4). Posteriorly, it is continuous with the superficial part round the posterior border of the mylohyoid (Fig. 7.5). Anteriorly, it extends up to the posterior end of the sublingual gland.

Relations

Present in between mylohyoid and hyoglossus
Laterally – Mylohyoid
Medially – Hyoglossus
Above   – Lingual nerve with submandibular ganglion
Below   – Hypoglossal nerve

SUBMANDIBULAR DUCT/WHARTON'S DUCT
(ENGLISH SCIENTIST: 1614–73)

It is thin walled, and is about 5 cm long. It emerges at the anterior end of the deep part of the gland and runs forwards on the hyoglossus, between the lingual and hypoglossal nerves. At the anterior border of the hyoglossus, the duct is crossed by the lingual nerve (Fig. 7.4). It opens on the floor of the mouth, on the summit of the sublingual papilla, at the side of the frenulum of the tongue (see Fig. 17.2).

Blood Supply and Lymphatic Drainage

The submandibular gland is supplied by the facial artery.

The facial artery arises from the external carotid just above the tip of the greater cornua of the hyoid bone.

The *cervical part* of the facial artery runs upwards on the superior constrictor of pharynx deep to the posterior belly of the digastric, and stylohyoid to the ramus of the mandible. It grooves the posterior end of the submandibular salivary gland. Next the artery makes an S-bend (two loops) first winding down over the submandibular gland, and then up over the base of the mandible (Figs 7.7 and 7.8). Facial artery is palpable on the base of mandible at the anteroinferior angle of masseter muscle.

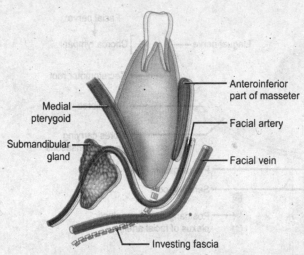

Fig. 7.7: Relationship of the facial vein to the submandibular gland and to the mandible

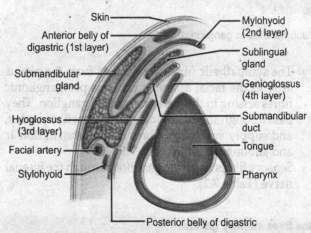

Fig. 7.8: Schematic horizontal section through the submandibular region

The veins drain into the common facial or lingual vein.

Lymph passes to submandibular lymph nodes.

Nerve Supply

It is supplied by branches from the submandibular ganglion. These branches convey:

1 Secretomotor fibres (*see* Table A.2)
2 Sensory fibres from the lingual nerve
3 Vasomotor sympathetic fibres from the plexus on the facial artery.

The secretomotor pathway is shown in Flowchart 7.1.

SUBLINGUAL SALIVARY GLAND

This is smallest of the three salivary glands. It is almond-shaped and weighs about 3 to 4 g. It lies above the mylohyoid, below the mucosa of the floor of the mouth, medial to the sublingual fossa of the mandible and lateral to the genioglossus (Figs 7.2, 7.4 and 7.8).

Flowchart 7.1: Secretomotor fibres to the glands

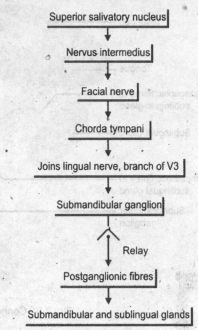

Relations

Front   – Meets opposite side gland
Behind – Comes in contact with deeper part of submandibular gland
Above   – Mucous membrane of mouth
Below   – Mylohyoid muscle
Lateral – Sublingual fossa
Medial – Genioglossus muscles (Fig. 7.8)

About 15 ducts emerge from the gland. Most of them open directly into the floor of the mouth on the summit of the sublingual fold. A few of them join the sub-mandibular duct (Fig. 17.2).

The gland receives its blood supply from the lingual and submental arteries. The nerve supply is similar to that of the submandibular gland.

SUBMANDIBULAR GANGLION

This is a parasympathetic peripheral ganglion. It is a relay station for secretomotor fibres to the submandibular and sublingual salivary glands. Topographically, it is related to the lingual nerve, but functionally, it is connected to the chorda tympani branch of the facial nerve (*see* Table 1.3 and Flowchart 7.1).

The fusiform ganglion lies on the hyoglossus muscle just above the deep part of the submandibular salivary gland, suspended from the lingual nerve by two roots (Fig. 7.9).

CONNECTIONS AND BRANCHES

1 The secretomotor fibres pass from the lingual nerve to the ganglion through the posterior root. These are parasympathetic preganglionic fibres that arise in the *superior salivatory nucleus* and pass through nervus

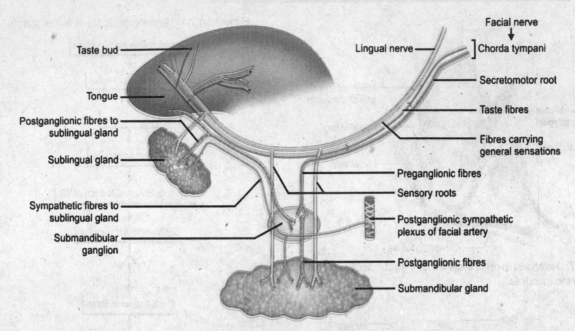

Fig. 7.9: Connection of the submandibular ganglion

intermedius till the facial nerve, the chorda tympani and the lingual nerve to reach the ganglion for relay. Postganglionic fibres for the submandibular gland reach the gland through five or six branches from the ganglion. Postganglionic fibres for the sublingual and anterior lingual glands re-enter the lingual nerve through the anterior root and travel to the gland through the distal part of the lingual nerve (Flowchart 7.1).

2   The sympathetic fibres are derived from the plexus around the facial artery. It contains postganglionic fibres arising in the superior cervical ganglion. They pass through submandibular ganglion without relay, and supply vasomotor fibres to the submandibular and sublingual glands (Fig. 7.9).

3   Sensory fibres reach the ganglion through the lingual nerve (Table 7.2).

	Table 7. 2: Comparison of the three salivary glands		
	Parotid	*Submandibular*	*Sublingual*
Location	In relation to external ear, angle of mandible, mastoid process (*see* Fig. 5.1)	Lies in submandibular fossa close to angle of mandible (Fig. 7.6)	Lies in sublingual fossa on the base of the mandible (Fig. 7.2)
Size	Largest	Medium sized	Smallest
Relation to fascia	Enclosed by investing layer of cervical fascia	Enclosed by investing layer of cervical fascia	Not enclosed
Type of gland	Purely serous secreting (Fig. 7.10)	Mixed, both serous and mucus secreting (Fig. 7.11)	Purely mucus secreting (Fig. 7.12)
Gross features	Comprises 3 surfaces, 3 borders, apex and base one artery, one vein, one nerve and lymph nodes lie within the gland (*see* Chapter 5)	Comprises 3 surfaces, inferior, lateral and medial. One artery which indents the posterior end of the gland. Only lymph nodes lie within it	Related closely to lingual nerve and submandibular duct
Secretomotor root	From IX cranial nerve	From VII cranial nerve	From VII cranial nerve
Sympathetic root	Plexus around middle meningeal artery	Plexus around facial artery	Same as submandibular gland
Sensory	Auriculotemporal	Lingual nerve	Lingual nerve
Development	Ectoderm	Endoderm	Endoderm
Opening or the duct	Vestibule of mouth opposite 2nd upper molar tooth (Fig. 5.7)	Papilla on in sublingual fold in the floor of the mouth (Fig. 17.2)	10–12 ducts open on sublingual fold in the floor of the mouth (Fig. 17.2)

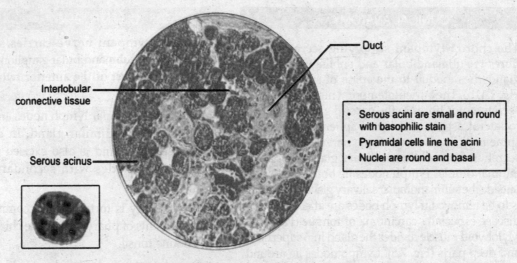

Fig. 7.10: Histology of parotid gland

Labels:
- Duct
- Interlobular connective tissue
- Serous acinus

- Serous acini are small and round with basophilic stain
- Pyramidal cells line the acini
- Nuclei are round and basal

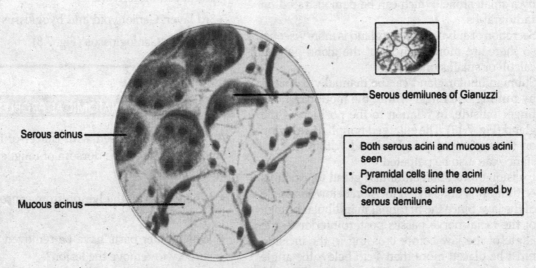

Fig. 7.11: Histology of submandibular gland

Labels:
- Serous demilunes of Gianuzzi
- Serous acinus
- Mucous acinus

- Both serous acini and mucous acini seen
- Pyramidal cells line the acini
- Some mucous acini are covered by serous demilune

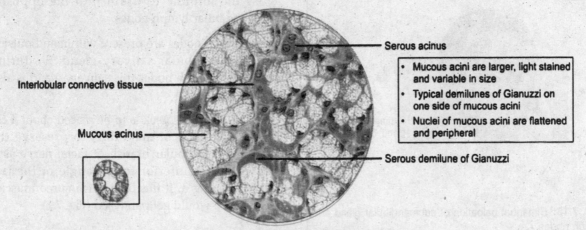

Fig. 7.12: Histology of sublingual gland

Labels:
- Serous acinus
- Interlobular connective tissue
- Mucous acinus
- Serous demilune of Gianuzzi

- Mucous acini are larger, light stained and variable in size
- Typical demilunes of Gianuzzi on one side of mucous acini
- Nuclei of mucous acini are flattened and peripheral

Head and Neck

CLINICAL ANATOMY

- The chorda tympani supplying secretomotor fibres to submandibular and sublingual salivary glands lies medial to the spine of sphenoid (*see* Fig. 1.11b). The auriculotemporal nerve supplying secretomotor fibres to the parotid gland is related to lateral aspect of spine of sphenoid. Injury to spine may involve both these nerves with loss of secretion from all three salivary glands.
- Submandibular lymph nodes lie both within and outside the submandibular salivary gland. The gland is to be removed if lymph nodes are affected in any disease especially carcinoma of tongue (Fig. 7.1).
- Mylohyoid muscle divides the gland into superficial and deep parts (Fig. 7.5). Lymph nodes lie around and within the gland. Cancer of the tongue or of the gland may metastasise into the mandible also (Fig. 7.2).
- The duct of submandibular gland may get impacted by a small stone, which can be demonstrated on radiographs.
- Secretion of submandibular gland is more viscous, so there are more chances of the gland getting calculi or small stones.
- Submandibular gland can be manually palpated by putting one finger within the mouth and one finger outside, in relation to the position of the gland (Fig. 7.13). The enlarged lymph nodes lying on the surface of the gland and within its substance can also be palpated.
- Excision of the submandibular gland for calculus or tumour is done by an incision below the angle of the jaw. Since the marginal mandibular branch of the facial nerve passes posteroinferior to the angle of the jaw before crossing it, the incision must be placed more than 4 cm below the angle to preserve the nerve (Fig. 7.1).

The nerve also passes across the lymph nodes of submandibular region. One should be careful of the nerve while doing biopsy of lymph node.

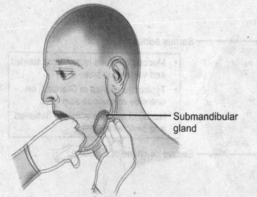

Fig. 7.13: Bimanual palpation of submandibular gland and lymph nodes

FACTS TO REMEMBER

- Chorda tympani nerve carries secretomotor fibres to the submandibular ganglion. It also carries taste from most of the anterior two-thirds of the tongue.
- The submandibular lymph nodes are also present in the submandibular gland. In cancer of the tongue, this gland is also excised to get rid off the lymph nodes with secondaries from the tongue.
- Facial artery is tortuous to accommodate to the movements of pharynx. It is the chief artery of the palatine tonsil.
- Suprahyoid muscles are disposed in four layers:

  1st layer: Digastrics and stylohyoid

  2nd layer: Mylohyoid

  3rd layer: Geniohyoid and hyoglossus

  4th layer: Genioglossus (Fig. 7.8)

CLINICOANATOMICAL PROBLEM

A patient is diagnosed with cancer of the tongue. The lesion was on the dorsum of tongue close to its lateral border.

- Where does all the lymph from cancerous lesion drain?
- Which other parts have be removed during the surgery to remove the lesion?

Ans: The lymph from dorsum of tongue close to lateral border chiefly drains into the submandibular group of lymph nodes. Few lymph vessels may even cross the midline to drain into the opposite submandibular lymph nodes.

These lymph nodes are present within and outside the submandibular salivary gland. So during removal of lymph nodes this salivary gland is also to be removed.

The incision in the neck is to be placed about 4 cm below the angle of mandible, to preserve the marginal mandibular branch of facial nerve as it passes posteroinferior to the angle of the jaw before crossing it. If this branch is injured muscles of lower lip would get paralysed (Fig. 7.1).

FREQUENTLY ASKED QUESTIONS

1. Describe the submandibular salivary gland under the following headings:
   a. Parts
   b. Relations
   c. Nerve supply
   d. Clinical anatomy

2. Describe the attachments, nerve supply and actions of both bellies of digastric muscle.

3. Write short notes on:
   a. Hyoglossus muscle
   b. Mylohyoid muscle
   c. Submandibular ganglion

MULTIPLE CHOICE QUESTIONS

1. One of the following statements about chorda tympani nerve is not true:
   a. Branch of facial nerve
   b. Joins lingual nerve in infratemporal fossa
   c. Carries postganglionic parasympathetic fibres
   d. Carries taste fibres from most of the anterior two-thirds of tongue

2. Nerve carrying preganglionic parasympathetic fibres to submandibular ganglion:
   a. Greater petrosal   b. Lesser petrosal
   c. Deep petrosal   d. Chorda tympani

3. Which of the following nerves lies posteroinferior to angle of mandible?
   a. Zygomatic branch of facial
   b. Buccal branch of facial

   c. Marginal mandibular branch of facial
   d. Cervical branch of facial

4. Submandibular lymph nodes drain all of the following areas *except:*
   a. Lateral side of tongue
   b. External nose, upper lip
   c. Lateral halves of eyelids
   d. Medial halves of eyelids

5. Which muscle divides the submandibular gland into a superficial and deep parts?
   a. Hyoglossus
   b. Mylohyoid
   c. Geniohyoid
   d. Anterior belly of digastric

ANSWERS

1. c   2. d   3. c   4. c   5. b

Structures in the Neck

The extirpation of the thyroid gland for goitre typifies perhaps better than any operation, the supreme triumphs of the surgeon's art
—William S Halsted

INTRODUCTION

The thyroid gland lies in front of the neck. Skin incision for its surgery should be horizontal, for better healing and for cosmetic reasons. Branches of subclavian artery anastomose with those of axillary artery around the scapula.

Scalenus anterior is important. It may compress the subclavian artery to cause "scalenus anterior syndrome".

Lymph nodes are clinically important in deciding the prognosis and treatment of malignancies.

Contents: There are numerous structures in the neck. For convenience, they may be grouped as follows:
- a. *Glands:* Thyroid and parathyroid.
- b. *Thymus:* Involutes at puberty.
- c. *Arteries:* Subclavian and carotid.
- d. *Veins:* Subclavian, internal jugular and brachio-cephalic.
- e. *Nerves:* Glossopharyngeal, vagus, accessory, hypoglossal described in Volume 4.
- f. *Sympathetic trunk:* It has three cervical ganglia.
- g. Lymph nodes and thoracic duct.
- h. Styloid apparatus.

GLANDS

DISSECTION

Sternocleidomastoid muscle has already been reflected laterally from its origin. Cut the sternothyroid muscle near its origin and reflect it upwards. Clean the surface of trachea and identify inferior thyroid vein and remains of the thymus gland (darker in colour than fat).

Isthmus of the thyroid gland lies on the 2nd–4th tracheal rings. Pyramidal lobe if present projects from the upper border of the isthmus. On each side of isthmus is the lateral lobe of the gland. Clean the lobes and identify the vessels of thyroid gland. Identify the recurrent laryngeal nerves tucked between the lateral surfaces of trachea and oesophagus. Look for beaded thoracic duct present on the left of oesophagus. Trace the superior and inferior thyroid arteries. Identify cricothyroid and inferior constrictor muscles lying medial to the lobes of thyroid gland (Figs 8.1 to 8.6).

Thyroid gland

Cut the isthmus of the thyroid gland and turn one of the lobes laterally. Locate an anastomosis between the posterior branch of superior thyroid and ascending branch of inferior thyroid arteries supplying the gland. Identify the two parathyroid glands just lateral to this anastomotic vessel (Figs 8.7 and 8.12).

THYROID GLAND

The thyroid (shield-like) is an endocrine gland with rich blood supply situated in the lower part of the front and sides of the neck. It regulates the basal metabolic rate, stimulates somatic and psychic growth, and plays an important role in calcium metabolism. Since it is placed superficially it can easily be examined. This is the only gland using natural iodine for the synthesis of its hormones which are stored within the follicles to be used according to the needs of the body.

The gland consists of right and left *lobes* that are joined to each other by the *isthmus* (Fig. 8.1). A third, pyramidal lobe, may project upwards from the isthmus (or from one of the lobes). Sometimes a fibrous or fibro-muscular band (levator glandulae thyroidae) descends from the body of the hyoid bone to the isthmus or to the pyramidal lobe (Fig. 8.2).

Situation and Extent

1 The gland lies against vertebrae C5–C7 and T1, embracing the upper part of the trachea (Fig. 8.2).

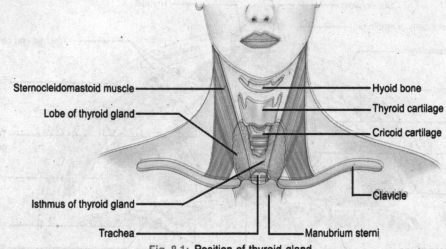

Fig. 8.1: Position of thyroid gland

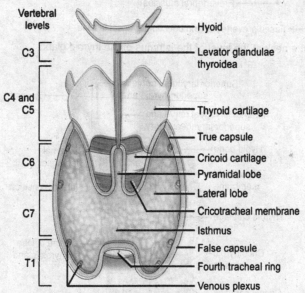

Fig. 8.2: Scheme to show the location and subdivisions of the thyroid gland including the false capsule

2 Each lobe extends from the middle of thyroid cartilage to the fourth or fifth tracheal ring.

3 The isthmus extends from the second to the fourth tracheal ring.

Dimensions and Weight

Each lobe measures about 5 × 2.5 × 2.5 cm, and the isthmus 1.2 × 1.2 cm. On an average, the gland weighs about 25 g. However, it is larger in females than in males, and further increases in size during menstruation and pregnancy.

Capsules of Thyroid

1 The *true capsule* is the peripheral condensation of the connective tissue of the gland.

A dense capillary plexus is present deep to the true capsule. To avoid haemorrhage during operations,

the thyroid is removed along with the true capsule. It can be compared with the prostate in which the venous plexus lies between the two capsules of the gland, and therefore, during prostatectomy both capsules are left behind (Figs 8.3a and b).

2 The *false capsule* is derived from the pretracheal layer of the deep cervical fascia (Fig. 8.2). It is thin along the posterior border of the lobes, but thick on the inner surface of the gland where it forms a suspensory ligament (of Berry), which connects the lobe to the cricoid cartilage (Fig. 8.4).

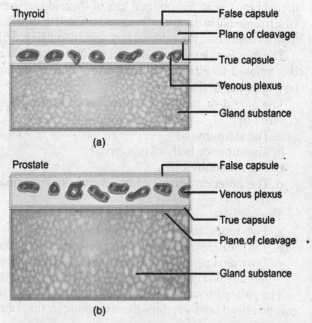

Figs 8.3a and b: Schemes of comparing the relationship of the venous plexuses related to: (a) The thyroid gland, and (b) the prostate, with the true and false capsules around these organs. Note the plane of cleavage along which the organ is separated from neighbouring structures during surgical removal

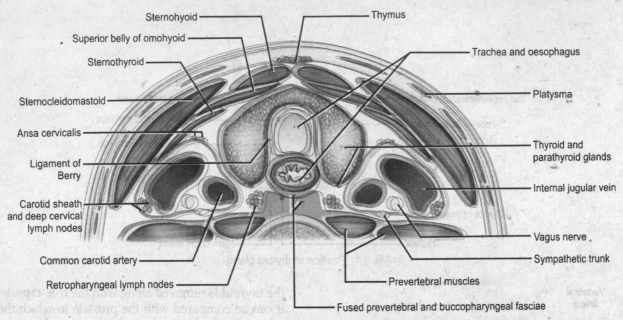

Fig. 8.4: Transverse section through the anterior part of the neck at the level of the isthmus of the thyroid gland

Parts and Relations

The lobes are conical in shape having:

a. An apex
b. A base
c. Three surfaces: Lateral, medial and posterolateral.
d. Two borders: Anterior and posterior.

The *apex* is directed upwards and slightly laterally. It is limited superiorly by the attachment of the sterno-thyroid muscle to the oblique line of thyroid cartilage which is medial to the apex. The apex is related to superior thyroid artery and the external laryngeal nerve (Fig. 8.5).

The *base* is at level with the 4th or 5th tracheal ring. It is related to inferior thyroid artery and recurrent laryngeal nerve (Fig. 8.7).

The *lateral* or *superficial surface* is convex, and is covered by:

a. The sternohyoid
b. The superior belly of omohyoid
c. The sternothyroid
d. The anterior border of the sternocleidomastoid (Fig. 8.4).

The *medial surface* is related to:

a. Two tubes, trachea and oesophagus
b. Two muscles, inferior constrictor and cricothyroid
c. Two nerves, external laryngeal and recurrent laryngeal (Fig. 8.5).

The *posterolateral* or *posterior surface* is related to the carotid sheath and overlaps the common carotid artery (Fig. 8.4).

The *anterior border* is thin and is related to the anterior branch of superior thyroid artery (Fig. 8.7).

The *posterior border* is thick and rounded and separates the medial and posterior surfaces. It is related to:

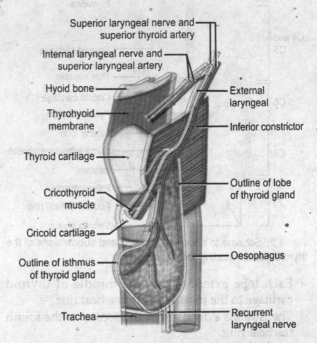

Fig. 8.5: Deep relations of the thyroid gland

a. Inferior thyroid artery.
b. Anastomosis between the posterior branch of superior and ascending branch of inferior thyroid arteries.
c. Parathyroid glands.
d. Thoracic duct only on the left side (Fig. 8.7).

The *isthmus* connects the lower parts of the two lobes. It has:

a. Two surfaces: Anterior and posterior.
b. Two borders: Superior and inferior.

The *anterior surface* is covered by:

a. The right and left sternothyroid and sternohyoid muscles.
b. The anterior jugular veins.
c. Fascia and skin (Fig. 8.4).

The *posterior surface* is related to the second to fourth tracheal rings.

The *upper border* is related to anterior branches of the right and left superior thyroid arteries (Fig. 8.6) which anastomose here.

Lower border: Inferior thyroid veins leave the gland at this border (Fig. 8.8).

Arterial Supply

The thyroid gland is supplied by the superior and inferior thyroid arteries.

1 The *superior thyroid artery* is the first anterior branch of the external carotid artery (Figs 8.6 and 8.7). It runs downwards and forwards in intimate relation to the external laryngeal nerve. After giving branches to adjacent structures, the artery pierces the pretracheal fascia to reach the apex of the lobe where the nerve deviates medially. At the upper pole the artery divides into anterior and posterior branches.

The *anterior branch* descends on the anterior border of the lobe and continues along the upper border of the isthmus to anastomose with its fellow of the opposite side.

The *posterior branch* descends on the posterior border of the lobe and anastomoses with the ascending branch of inferior thyroid artery (Fig. 8.7).

2 The *inferior thyroid artery* is a branch of thyrocervical trunk (which arises from the subclavian artery).

It runs first upwards, then medially, and finally downwards to reach the base of the gland. During its course, it passes behind the carotid sheath and the middle cervical sympathetic ganglion; and in front of the vertebral vessels; and gives off branches to adjacent structures (*see* Fig. 9.5).

Its terminal part is intimately related to the recurrent laryngeal nerve, while proximal part is away from the nerve.

The artery divides into 4 to 5 glandular branches which pierce the fascia separately to reach the lower part of the gland. One *ascending branch* anastomoses with the posterior branch of the superior thyroid artery and supplies the parathyroid glands.

3 Sometimes (in 3% of individuals), the thyroid is also supplied by the *lowest thyroid artery (thyroidea ima artery)* which arises from the brachiocephalic trunk or directly from the arch of the aorta. It enters the lower part of the isthmus.

4 *Accessory thyroid arteries* arising from tracheal and oesophageal arteries also supply the thyroid.

Venous Drainage

The thyroid is drained by the superior, middle and inferior thyroid veins.

The *superior thyroid vein* emerges at the upper pole and accompanies the superior thyroid artery. It ends in the internal jugular vein (Fig. 8.8).

The *middle thyroid vein* is a short, wide channel which emerges at the middle of the lobe and soon enters the internal jugular vein.

The *inferior thyroid veins* emerge at the lower border of isthmus. They form a plexus in front of the trachea, and drain into the left brachiocephalic vein.

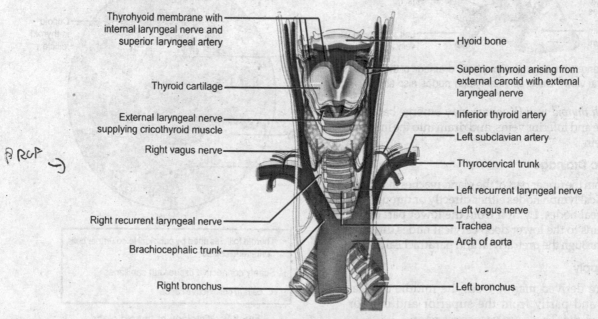

Fig. 8.6: Arterial supply of anterior aspect of thyroid gland

Thyrohyoid membrane with internal laryngeal nerve and superior laryngeal artery

Thyroid cartilage

External laryngeal nerve supplying cricothyroid muscle

Right vagus nerve

Right recurrent laryngeal nerve

Brachiocephalic trunk

Right bronchus

Hyoid bone

Superior thyroid arising from external carotid with external laryngeal nerve

Inferior thyroid artery

Left subclavian artery

Thyrocervical trunk

Left recurrent laryngeal nerve

Left vagus nerve

Trachea

Arch of aorta

Left bronchus

Head and Neck

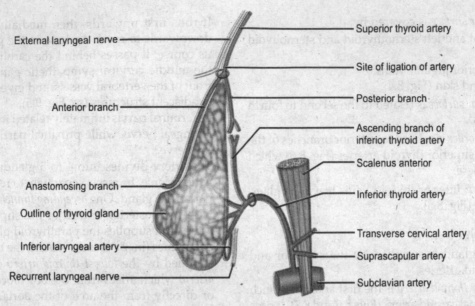

Fig. 8.7: Arterial supply of the surfaces of thyroid gland. Sites of ligatures of the superior and inferior thyroid arteries shown

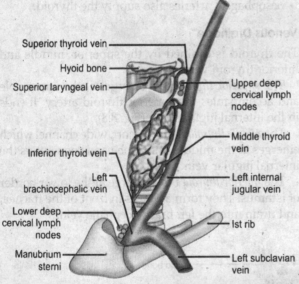

Fig. 8.8: Venous drainage and lymphatic drainage of the thyroid gland (lateral view). Deep cervical lymph nodes also shown

A *fourth thyroid vein* (Kocher) may emerge between the middle and inferior veins, and drain into the internal jugular vein.

Lymphatic Drainage

Lymph from the upper part of the gland reaches the upper deep cervical lymph nodes either directly or through the prelaryngeal nodes. Lymph from the lower part of the gland drains to the lower deep cervical nodes directly, and also through the pretracheal and paratracheal nodes.

Nerve Supply

Nerves are derived mainly from the middle cervical ganglion and partly from the superior and inferior cervical ganglia. These are vasoconstrictor.

HISTOLOGY

The thyroid gland is made up of the following two types of secretory cells.

1 *Follicular cells* lining the follicles of the gland secrete tri-iodothyronin and tetraiodothyronin (thyroxin) which stimulate basal metabolic rate and somatic and psychic growth of the individual. During active phase, the lining of the follicles is columnar, while in resting phase, it is cuboidal. Follicles contain the colloid (the hormone) in their lumina (Fig. 8.9).

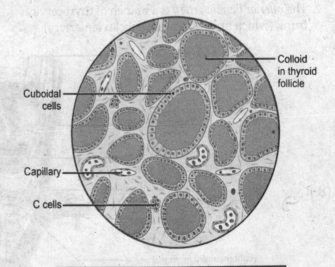

Fig. 8.9: Histology of thyroid gland

- Thyroid follicles lined by cuboidal to columnar cells containing colloid
- Scanty connective tissue with capillaries
- 'C' cells in connective tissue

2 *Parafollicular cells (C cells)* are fewer and light cells. These lie in between the follicles. They secrete thyrocalcitonin which promotes deposition of calcium salts in skeletal and other tissues, and tends to produce hypocalcaemia. These effects are opposite to those of parathormone.

DEVELOPMENT

The thyroid develops from a *median endodermal thyroid diverticulum* which grows down in front of the neck from the floor of the primitive pharynx (foramen caecum), just caudal to the tuberculum impar (Figs 8.10a to d).

The lower end of the diverticulum enlarges to form the gland. The rest of the diverticulum remains narrow and is known as the *thyroglossal duct*. Most of the duct soon disappears. The position of the upper end is marked by the *foramen caecum* of the tongue, and the lower end often persists as the *pyramidal lobe*. The gland becomes functional during third month of development.

Remnants of the thyroglossal duct may form thyroglossal cysts, or a thyroglossal fistula. Thyroid tissue may develop at abnormal sites along the course of the duct resulting in lingual or retrosternal thyroids. Accessory thyroids may be present.

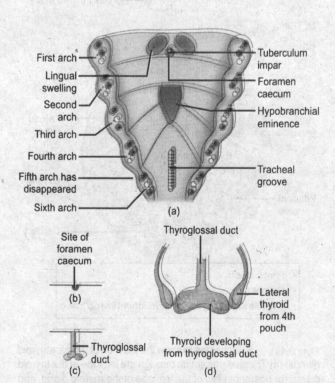

Figs 8.10a to d: Development of thyroid gland

First arch
Lingual swelling
Second arch
Third arch
Fourth arch
Fifth arch has disappeared
Sixth arch

Tuberculum impar
Foramen caecum
Hypobranchial eminence

Tracheal groove

(a)

Site of foramen caecum

(b)

Thyroglossal duct

(c)

Thyroglossal duct

Lateral thyroid from 4th pouch

Thyroid developing from thyroglossal duct

(d)

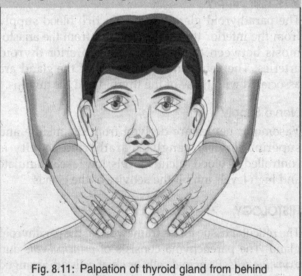

Fig. 8.11: Palpation of thyroid gland from behind

PARATHYROID GLANDS

Parathyroid glands are two pairs (superior and inferior) of small endocrine glands, that usually lie on the posterior border of the thyroid gland, within the false capsule (Figs 8.12a and b). The *superior parathyroids* are also referred to as *parathyroid IV* because they develop from the endoderm of the *fourth pharyngeal pouch*. The *inferior parathyroids*, similarly, are also called *parathyroid III* because they develop from the *third pouch*.

Head and Neck

The parathyroids secrete the hormone *parathormone* which controls the metabolism of calcium and phosphorus along with thyrocalcitonin.

Each parathyroid gland is oval or lentiform in shape, measuring $6 \times 4 \times 2$ mm (the size of a split pea). Each gland weighs about 50 mg.

Position

The anastomosis between the superior and inferior thyroid arteries is usually a good guide to the glands because they usually lie close to it (Fig. 8.12a).

The *superior parathyroid* is more constant in position and usually lies at the middle of the posterior border of the lobe of the thyroid gland. It is usually dorsal to the recurrent laryngeal nerve.

The *inferior parathyroid* is more variable in position. It may lie:

a. Within the thyroid capsule, below the inferior thyroid artery and near the lower pole of the thyroid lobe (Fig. 8.12b).
b. Behind and outside the thyroid capsule, immediately above the inferior thyroid artery.
c. Within the substance of the lobe near its posterior border. It is usually ventral to the recurrent laryngeal nerve.

Vascular Supply

The parathyroid glands receive a rich blood supply from the inferior thyroid artery and from the anastomosis between the superior and inferior thyroid arteries. The veins and lymphatics of the gland are associated with those of the thyroid and the thymus.

Nerve Supply

Vasomotor nerves are derived from the middle and superior cervical ganglia. Parathyroid activity is controlled by blood calcium levels; low levels stimulate and high levels inhibit the activity of the glands.

HISTOLOGY

The reticular tissue forms framework of the parathyroid gland. The parenchyma consists of *principal cells* and *oxyphilic cells*. Principal cells or chief cells are arranged in sheets with numerous sinusoids and capillaries traversing them. The principal cells are polygonal or round with a centrally placed vesicular nuclei and a pale staining acidophilic cytoplasm (Fig. 8.12c).

Oxyphilic cells are a few in number, occur singly or in small groups. These are larger than principal cells. They have darkly staining nuclei and strongly acidophilic cytoplasm. Oxyphilic cells are seen to increase with age.

The principal or chief cells secrete *parathormone* responsible for maintaining the blood calcium level.

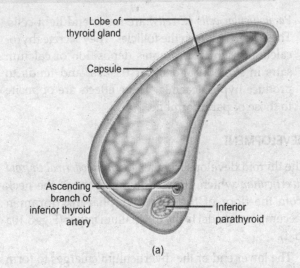

(a)

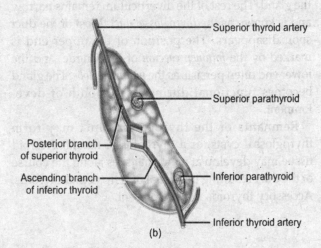

(b)

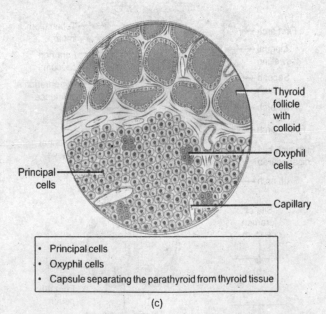

- Principal cells
- Oxyphil cells
- Capsule separating the parathyroid from thyroid tissue

(c)

Figs 8.12a to c: Schemes to show the location of the parathyroid glands: (a) Transverse section through the left lobe of the thyroid gland, (b) posterior view of the left lobe of the thyroid gland, and (c) histology of the parathyroid gland

CLINICAL ANATOMY

- Tumours of the parathyroid glands lead to excessive secretion of parathormone (hyper-parathyroidism). This leads to increased removal of calcium from bone, making them weak and liable to fracture. Calcium levels in blood increase (hypercalcaemia) and increased urinary excretion of calcium can lead to the formation of stones in the urinary tract.
- Hypoparathyroidism may occur spontaneously or from accidental removal of the glands during thyroidectomy. This results in hypocalcaemia leading to increased neuromuscular irritability causing muscular spasm and convulsions (tetany) (Fig. 8.13).
- Parathyroid glands are tough glands and will continue to function if these are transplanted from an excised thyroid gland into the sternocleidomastoid muscle.

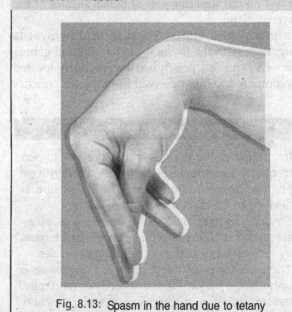

Fig. 8.13: Spasm in the hand due to tetany

THYMUS

The thymus (Greek *thyme leaf*) is an important lymphoid organ, situated in the anterior and superior mediastina of the thorax, extending above into the lower part of the neck. It is well developed at birth, continues to grow up to puberty, and thereafter, undergoes gradual atrophy and replacement by fat.

The thymus is a bilobed structure, made up of two pyramidal lobes of unequal size which are connected together by areolar tissue.

Each lobe develops from the endoderm of the third pharyngeal pouch. It lies on the pericardium, the great vessels of the superior mediastinum, and the trachea.

The thymus weighs 10–15 g at birth, 30–40 g at puberty, and only 10 g after mid-adult life. Thus, after puberty, it becomes inconspicuous due to replacement by fat.

Blood Supply

The thymus is supplied by branches from the internal thoracic and inferior thyroid arteries. Its veins drain into the left brachiocephalic, internal thoracic and inferior thyroid veins.

Nerve Supply

Vasomotor nerves are derived from the stellate ganglion. The capsule is supplied by the phrenic nerve and by the descendens cervicalis.

HISTOLOGY OF THYMUS

Thymus consists of a thin outer fibrous covering known as the capsule. From the capsule extend many thin connective tissue septa dividing it incompletely into various lobules. Each lobule has a peripheral darker cortex and a central lighter medulla. The interlobular septa are partial and do not extend into the medulla, so that there is continuity of the medullary tissue of the various lobules (Fig. 8.14).

Chief cells present in thymus are:

a. *Thymic lymphocytes*: These are situated in the interstices of the thymic reticulum and are immunologically competent but uncommitted cells.

b. *Epithelial reticular cells*: These are flattened cells with pale nuclei. Their processes branch and lie in apposition with the processes of the adjoining cells forming thin membrane. These reticular cells develop from the endoderm of third pharyngeal pouch. These cells secrete hormones, thymosin, thymopoietin, thymulin and thymic humoral factor. These hormones are required for proliferation, differentiation, maturation of T lymphocytes.

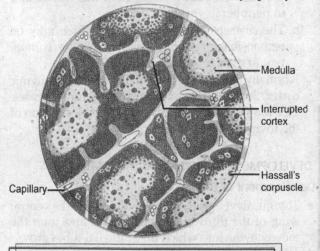

- Trabeculae only in cortical part with dark lymphocytes
- Medulla of adjacent lobules continuous and contains lighter reticular cells
- Hassall's corpuscles made up of concentric lamellae of epithelial cells surrounding a hyaline mass

Fig. 8.14: Histology of thymus

Head and Neck

Functions

1. The thymus controls lymphopoiesis, and maintains an effective pool of circulating lymphocytes, competent to react to innumerable antigenic stimuli.

2. It controls development of the peripheral lymphoid tissues of the body during the neonatal period. By puberty, the main lymphoid tissues are fully developed.

3. The cortical lymphocytes of the thymus arise from stem cells of bone marrow origin. Most (95%) of the lymphocytes (T lymphocytes) produced are autoallergic (act against the host or 'self' antigens), short-lived (3–5 days) and never move out of the organ. They are destroyed within the thymus by phagocytes. Their remnants are seen as Hassall's corpuscles.

   The remaining 5% of the T lymphocytes are long-lived (3 months or more), and move out of the thymus to join the circulating pool of lymphocytes where they act as immunologically competent but uncommitted cells, i.e. they can react to any unfamiliar, new antigen. On the other hand, the other circulating lymphocytes (from lymph nodes, spleen, etc.) are committed cells, i.e. they can mount an immune response only when exposed to a particular antigen. Thymic lymphopoiesis, lympholysis and involution are all intrinsically controlled.

4. The medullary epithelial cells of the thymus are thought to secrete:
   a. *Lymphopoietin*, which stimulates lymphocyte production both in the cortex of the thymus and in peripheral lymphoid organs.
   b. The *competence-inducing factor*, which may be responsible for making new lymphocytes competent to react to antigenic stimuli.

5. Normally there are no germinal centres in the thymic cortex. Such centres appear in autoimmune diseases. This may indicate a defect in the normal function of the thymus.

DEVELOPMENT OF THYMUS AND PARATHYROIDS

Development of Thymus

- Thymus develops from the endoderm of the ventral wing of the third pharyngeal pouch and from the mesenchyme into which the epithelial tubes grow.
- The bilateral primordia of the thymus lose their connections with the pharyngeal wall, come together in the median plane to form bilobed structure which migrates into the superior mediastinum part of the thoracic cavity.
- Thymus continues to grow after birth till puberty, after which it begins to undergo involution.

Consequently, it is difficulty to recognize in old age, as it is atrophied and replaced by fatty tissue.

Development of Parathyroid Glands

Inferior parathyroid glands are derived from the dorsal wing of the third pharyngeal pouch.
- Primordia of the inferior parathyroids along with primordia of thymus lose their connection with the pharyngeal wall.
- The downwards migrating thymus also pulls the inferior parathyroids with it, which finally come to rest on the inferior part of dorsal surface of the thyroid gland.

Superior parathyroid glands are derived from the endoderm of 4th pharyngeal pouch.
- The primordia of superior parathyroid glands, after loosing connection with the pharyngeal wall, come to rest on the superior part of dorsal surface of the thyroid gland.
- As mentioned above, because of downwards migration with the thymus, the parathyroid glands derived from 3rd pouch become inferiorly located as compared to those derived from the 4th pouch.

CLINICAL ANATOMY

- Involution of the thymus is enhanced by hypertrophy of the adrenal cortex, injection of cortisone or of androgenic hormone. The involution is delayed by castration and adrenalectomy.
- Thymic hyperplasia or tumours are often associated with myasthenia gravis, characterized by excessive fatigability of voluntary muscles. The precise role of the thymus in this disease is uncertain; it may influence, directly or indirectly, the transmission at the neuromuscular junction. Figure 8.15 shows drooping of eyelids.
- Thymic tumours may press on the trachea, oesophagus and the large veins of the neck, causing hoarseness, cough, dysphagia and cyanosis.

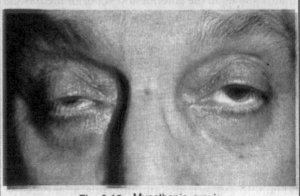

Fig. 8.15: Myasthenia gravis

BLOOD VESSELS OF THE NECK

DISSECTION

Identify scalenus anterior muscle in the anteroinferior part of the neck. Subclavian artery gets divided into three parts by this muscle. Identify vertebral, internal thoracic artery and the thyrocervical trunk with its branches arising from the first part of the artery, costocervical arising from second part and either dorsal scapular or none from the third part.

SUBCLAVIAN ARTERY

This is the principal artery which continues as axillary artery for the upper limb. It also supplies a considerable part of the neck and brain through its branches (Fig. 8.16).

Origin

On the *right side*, it is branch of the brachiocephalic artery. It arises posterior to the sternoclavicular joint. On the *left side*, it is a branch of the arch of the aorta. It ascends and enters the neck posterior to the left sternoclavicular joint. Both arteries pursue a similar course in the neck (Fig. 8.17).

Course

1 Each artery arches laterally from the sternoclavicular joint to the outer border of the first rib where it ends by becoming continuous with the axillary artery (Fig. 8.17).
2 The scalenus anterior muscle crosses the artery anteriorly and divides it into three parts. The first part is medial, the second part posterior, and the third part lateral to scalenus anterior.

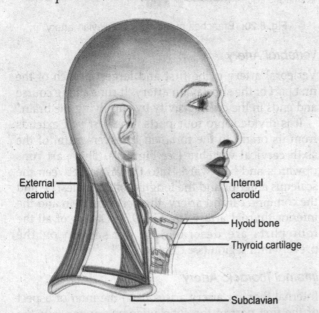

Fig. 8.16: Origin and course of the subclavian arteries

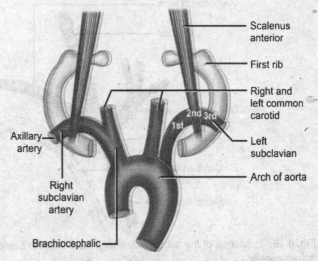

Fig. 8.17: Course of subclavian and carotid arteries

Relations of the First Part
Anterior
Immediate relations from medial to lateral side are:
1 Common carotid artery
2 Vagus
3 Internal jugular vein
4 The sternothyroid and the sternohyoid muscles
5 Sternocleidomastoid.

Posterior (Posteroinferior)
1 Suprapleural membrane
2 Cervical pleura
3 Apex of lung (Fig. 8.18).

Relations of the Second Part
Anterior
1 Scalenus anterior
2 Right phrenic nerve deep to the prevertebral fascia
3 Sternocleidomastoid.

Posterior (Posteroinferior)
1 Suprapleural membrane
2 Cervical pleura
3 Apex of lung.

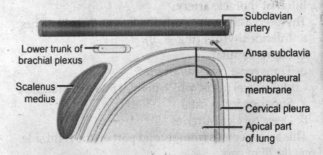

Fig. 8.18: Schematic transverse section through the lower part of neck to show the relations of the left subclavian artery

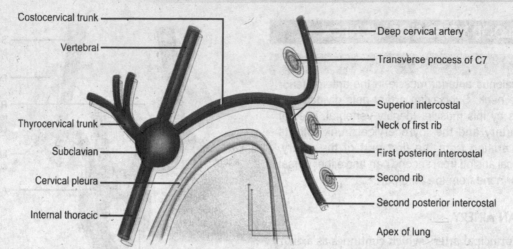

Fig. 8.19: Branches of the subclavian artery. Note that the branches actually arise at different levels, but are shown at one level schematically

Superior

Upper and middle trunks of the brachial plexus.

Relations of the Third Part

Anterior

1 Middle one-third of the clavicle
2 The posterior border of the sternocleidomastoid.

Posterior (Posteroinferior)

1 Scalenus medius
2 Lower trunk of brachial plexus
3 Suprapleural membrane
4 Cervical pleura
5 Apex of lung.

Superior

Upper and middle trunks of brachial plexus.

Inferior

First rib (Fig. 8.19).

Branches

From the first part

1 Vertebral artery (Fig. 8.19).
2 Internal thoracic artery.
3 Thyrocervical trunk, which divides into three branches:
   a. Inferior thyroid (Fig. 8.20).
   b. Suprascapular.
   c. Transverse cervical arteries.
4 Costocervical trunk, which divides into two branches:
   a. Superior intercostal.
   b. Deep cervical arteries.
This artery comes from second part on the right side.

From the third part

Dorsal scapular artery—occasionally.

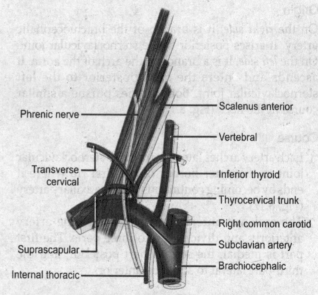

Fig. 8.20: Branches of the right subclavian artery

Vertebral Artery

Vertebral artery is the first and largest branch of the first part of the subclavian artery. It runs a long course and ends in the cranial cavity by supplying the brain.

It is divided into four parts. The *first part* extends from its origin to the foramen transversarium of the sixth cervical vertebra (*see* Fig. 9.2). This part runs upwards and backwards into the angle between the scalenus anterior and the longus colli muscles, behind the common carotid artery, the vertebral vein and the inferior thyroid artery (*see* Fig. 9.5). Details of all the four parts are described in the section on the prevertebral region (*see* Chapter 9).

Internal Thoracic Artery

Internal thoracic artery arises from the inferior aspect of the first part of the subclavian artery opposite the origin of the thyrocervical trunk. The origin lies near the medial border of the scalenus anterior (Fig. 8.20). The artery runs downwards and medially in front of the cervical pleura. Anteriorly, the artery is related to the sternal end of the clavicle. The artery enters the thorax by passing behind the first costal cartilage. It runs till 6th intercostal space where it ends by dividing into superior epigastric and musculophrenic arteries. For course of the artery in the thorax *see* Chapter 14, Volume 1.

Thyrocervical Trunk

Thyrocervical trunk is a short, wide vessel which arises from the front of the first part of the subclavian artery, close to the medial border of the scalenus anterior, and between the phrenic and vagus nerves. It almost immediately divides into the inferior thyroid, suprascapular and transverse cervical arteries (Figs 8.19 and 8.20).

The *inferior thyroid artery* is described with the thyroid gland. In addition to glandular branches to the thyroid, it gives:

a. The ascending cervical artery which runs upwards in front of the transverse processes of cervical vertebrae.
b. The inferior laryngeal artery which accompanies the recurrent laryngeal nerve, and enters the larynx deep to the lower border of the inferior constrictor (Fig. 8.7).
c. Other branches which supply the pharynx, the trachea, the oesophagus and surrounding muscles.

The *suprascapular artery* runs laterally and down-wards, and crosses the scalenus anterior and the phrenic nerve.

It lies behind the internal jugular vein and the sternocleidomastoid. It then crosses the trunks of the brachial plexus and runs in the posterior triangle, behind and parallel with the clavicle, to reach the superior border of the scapula (*see* Fig. 3.9).

It crosses above the suprascapular ligament and takes part in the anastomoses around the scapula (*see* Chapter 6, Volume 1). In addition to branches to surrounding muscles, the artery also supplies the clavicle, scapula, shoulder and acromioclavicular joints.

The *transverse cervical artery* runs laterally above the suprascapular artery (*see* Fig. 3.9).

It crosses the scalenus anterior and the phrenic nerve passing behind the internal jugular vein and the sternocleidomastoid.

It then crosses the brachial plexus and the floor of the posterior triangle to reach the anterior border of trapezius, where it divides into a superficial and deep branches. The superficial branch accompanies the spinal root of accessory nerve till the lower end of the muscle.

The deep branch passes deep to levator scapulae and takes part in the anastomoses around the scapula (*see* Chapter 6, Volume 1).

Sometimes the two branches may arise separately; the superficial from thyrocervical trunk and the deep from the third part of subclavian artery. Then these are named as superficial cervical and dorsal scapular arteries.

Dorsal Scapular Artery

This artery occasionally arises from the third part of subclavian artery. If transverse cervical does not divide into superficial and deep branches but continues as superficial branch, the distribution of deep branch is taken over by dorsal scapular artery.

Costocervical Trunk

Costocervical trunk arises from the posterior surface of the second part of the subclavian artery on the right side; but from the first part of the artery on the left side. It arches backwards over the cervical pleura, and divides into the descending superior intercostal and ascending deep cervical arteries at the neck of the first rib (Fig. 8.19).

The *superior intercostal artery* descends in front of the neck of the first rib, and divides into the first and second posterior intercostal arteries.

The *deep cervical artery* is analogous to the posterior branch of a posterior intercostal artery. It passes backwards between the transverse process of the 7th cervical vertebra and the neck of the first rib. It then ascends between the semispinalis capitis and cervicis up to the axis vertebra. It anastomoses with the occipital and vertebral arteries.

- The third part of the subclavian artery can be effectively compressed against the first rib after depressing the shoulder. The pressure is applied downwards, backwards, and medially in the angle between the sternocleidomastoid and the clavicle.
- A cervical rib may compress the subclavian artery, diminishing the radial pulse (Fig. 8.21).
- The right subclavian artery may arise from the descending thoracic aorta. In that case, it passes posterior to the oesophagus which may be compressed and the condition is known as (dysphagia lusoria).
- An aneurysm may form in the third part of the subclavian artery. Its pressure on the brachial plexus causes pain, weakness, and numbness in the upper limb.

- Obstruction to the subclavian artery proximal to the origin of vertebral artery may lead to "stealing of blood from the brain through the opposite vertebral artery. This may provide necessary blood to the affected side. The nervous symptoms incurred are called "subclavian steal syndrome" (Fig. 8.22).

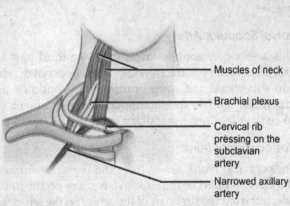

Fig. 8.21: The cervical rib pressing on the subclavian artery narrowing the axillary artery and diminishing the radial pulse

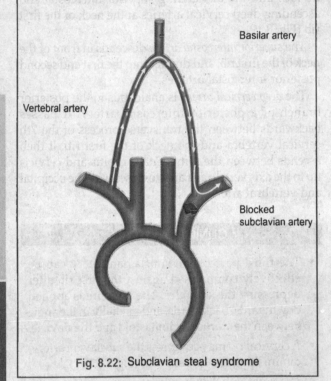

Fig. 8.22: Subclavian steal syndrome

COMMON CAROTID ARTERY

DISSECTION

The common carotid artery has been exposed in the carotid triangle. Clean it in its entire course. Identify the internal carotid artery and trace it till it leaves the neck.

Veins

Identify the tributaries of subclavian, internal jugular and brachiocephalic veins.

Features

The *origin* and *course* of the common carotid arteries has been described in Chapter 4. The common carotid artery is enclosed in the *carotid sheath*.

Course

Common carotid artery begins in the thorax in front of the trachea opposite a point a little to the left of the centre of the manubrium. It ascends to the back of left sternoclavicular joint and enters the neck.

In the neck, both arteries have a similar course. Each artery runs upwards within the carotid sheath, under cover of the anterior border of the sternocleidomastoid. It lies in front of the lower four cervical transverse processes. At the level of the upper border of the thyroid cartilage, the artery ends by dividing into the external and internal carotid arteries.

Relations of the Artery in the Neck

Anterior Relations

1. The common carotid artery is crossed by the superior belly of omohyoid at the level of cricoid cartilage (*see* Fig. 4.14).
2. Below the omohyoid, the artery is deeply situated, and is covered by:
   a. The sternocleidomastoid
   b. The anterior jugular vein
   c. The sternohyoid
   d. The sternothyroid and the middle thyroid vein.

Posterior Relations

1. Transverse process of vertebrae C4–8, and the muscles attached to their anterior tubercles (longus colli, longus capitis, scalenus anterior).
2. The inferior thyroid artery crosses medially at the level of the cricoid cartilage.
3. Vertebral artery (Fig. 8.23).
4. On the left side the thoracic duct crosses laterally behind the artery at the level of vertebra C7, in front of the vertebral vessels.

Medial Relations

1. Thyroid gland
2. Larynx and pharynx; trachea, oesophagus and recurrent laryngeal nerve (Fig. 8.5).

Lateral Relation

Internal jugular vein.

Posterolateral Relation

Vagus nerve (Fig. 8.4).

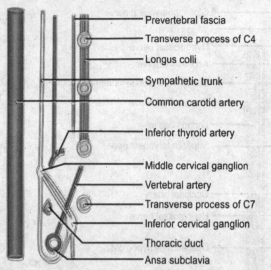

- Prevertebral fascia
- Transverse process of C4
- Longus colli
- Sympathetic trunk
- Common carotid artery
- Inferior thyroid artery
- Middle cervical ganglion
- Vertebral artery
- Transverse process of C7
- Inferior cervical ganglion
- Thoracic duct
- Ansa subclavia

Fig. 8.23: Schematic sagittal section showing posterior relations of the common carotid artery

---

CLINICAL ANATOMY

The pulsation of common carotid artery can be felt by compressing against the carotid tubercle, i.e. the anterior tubercle of the transverse process of vertebra C6 which lies at the level of the cricoid cartilage.

INTERNAL CAROTID ARTERY

The internal carotid artery is one of the two terminal branches of the common carotid artery. It begins at the level of the upper border of the thyroid cartilage opposite the disc between the third and fourth cervical vertebrae, and ends inside the cranial cavity by supplying the brain. This is the principal artery of the brain and the eye. It also supplies the related bones and meninges.

For convenience of description, the course of the artery is divided into four parts:
a. Cervical part, in the neck
b. Petrous part, within the petrous temporal bone (*see* Fig. 12.16)
c. Cavernous part, within the cavernous sinus
d. Cerebral part in relation to base of the brain.

Cervical Part

1 It ascends vertically in the neck from its origin to the base of the skull to reach the lower end of the carotid canal. This part is enclosed in the carotid sheath (with the internal jugular vein and the vagus).
2 No branches arise from the internal carotid artery in the neck.
3 Its initial part usually shows a dilatation, the *carotid sinus* which acts as a baroreceptor (*see* Fig. 4.14).

4 The lower part of the artery (in the carotid triangle) is comparatively superficial. The upper part, above the posterior belly of digastric, is deep to the parotid gland, the styloid apparatus, and many other structures.

Relations

Anterior or superficial
1 In the carotid triangle:
   a. Anterior border of sternocleidomastoid
   b. The external carotid artery is anteromedial to it (Fig. 8.16).
2 Above the carotid triangle (Fig. 8.23):
   a. Posterior belly of digastric
   b. Stylohyoid
   c. Stylopharyngeus
   d. Styloid process
   e. Parotid gland with structures within it.

Posterior
1 Superior cervical ganglion
2 Carotid sheath
3 The glossopharyngeal, vagus, accessory and hypoglossal nerves at the base of the skull.

Medial
1 Pharynx
2 The external carotid is anteromedial to it below the parotid.

Lateral
1 Internal jugular vein
2 Temporomandibular joint (at the base of the skull).

Petrous Part

1 In the carotid canal, the artery first runs upwards, and then turns forwards and medially at right angles. It emerges at the apex of the petrous temporal bone, in the posterior wall of the foramen lacerum where it turns upwards and medially.
2 *Relations:* The artery is surrounded by venous and sympathetic plexuses. It is related to the middle ear and the cochlea (posterosuperiorly); the auditory tube and tensor tympani (anterolaterally); and the trigeminal ganglion (superiorly) (*see* Fig. 12.14).
3 *Branches:*
   a. *Caroticotympanic* branches enter the middle ear, and anastomose with the anterior and posterior tympanic arteries (*see* Fig. 12.16).
   b. The *pterygoid branch* (small and inconstant) enters the pterygoid canal with the nerve of that canal and anastomoses with the greater palatine artery.

Head and Neck

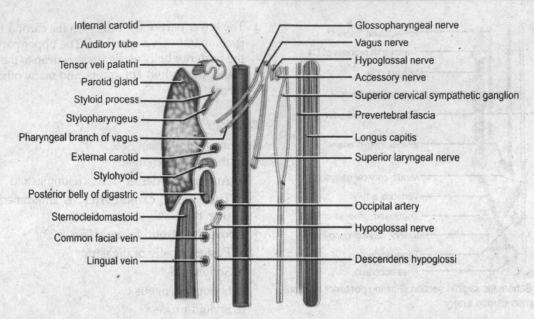

Fig. 8.24: Schematic sagittal section showing the anterior and posterior relations of the internal carotid artery

Cavernous and Cerebral Parts of Internal Carotid Artery

Cavernous part runs in the cavernous sinus (*see* Fig. 12.6). Cerebral part lies at base of skull and gives ophthalmic, anterior cerebral, middle cerebral, posterior communicating and anterior choroidal arteries (*see* Volume 4).

SUBCLAVIAN VEIN

Course

It is a continuation of the axillary vein. It begins at the outer border of the first rib, and ends at the medial border of the scalenus anterior by joining the internal jugular vein to form the brachiocephalic vein.

It lies:

a. In front of the subclavian artery, the scalenus anterior and the right phrenic nerve
b. Behind the clavicle and the subclavius
c. Above the first rib and pleura.

Its tributaries are:

a. The external jugular vein (Fig. 8.25)
b. The dorsal scapular vein
c. The thoracic duct on the left side
d. The right lymphatic duct on the right side.

INTERNAL JUGULAR VEIN

Course

1 It is a direct continuation of the sigmoid sinus. It begins at the jugular foramen, and ends behind the sternal end of the clavicle by joining the subclavian vein to form the brachiocephalic vein.

2 The origin is marked by a dilation, the *superior bulb* which lies in the jugular fossa of the temporal bone,

beneath the floor of the middle ear cavity. The termination of the vein is marked by the *inferior bulb* which lies beneath the lesser supraclavicular fossa.

Relations

Superficial

1 Sternocleidomastoid
2 Posterior belly of digastric
3 Superior belly of omohyoid
4 Parotid gland
5 Styloid process
6 The internal carotid artery, and the glossopharyngeal, vagus, accessory and hypoglossal cranial nerves (at the base of skull).

Posterior

1 Transverse process of atlas
2 Cervical plexus
3 Scalenus anterior
4 First part of subclavian artery.

Medial

1 Internal carotid artery
2 Common carotid artery
3 Vagus nerve.

Tributaries

1 Inferior petrosal sinus
2 Common facial vein
3 Lingual vein
4 Pharyngeal veins
5 Superior thyroid vein
6 Middle thyroid vein (Fig. 8.25).

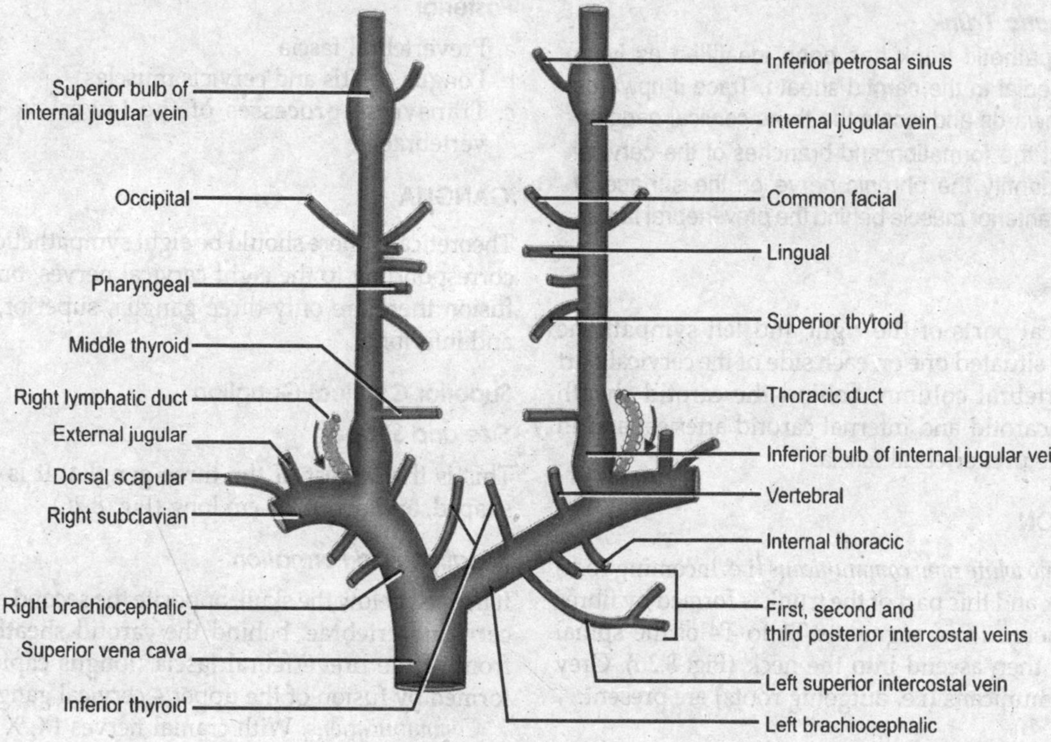
Superior bulb of internal jugular vein
Occipital
Pharyngeal
Middle thyroid
Right lymphatic duct
External jugular
Dorsal scapular
Right subclavian
Right brachiocephalic
Superior vena cava
Inferior thyroid
Inferior petrosal sinus
Internal jugular vein
Common facial
Lingual
Superior thyroid
Thoracic duct
Inferior bulb of internal jugular vein
Vertebral
Internal thoracic
First, second and third posterior intercostal veins
Left superior intercostal vein
Left brachiocephalic

Fig. 8.25: The veins of the neck

The thoracic duct opens into the angle of union between the left internal jugular vein and the left subclavian vein. The right lymphatic duct opens similarly on the right side.

In the middle of the neck, the internal jugular vein may communicate with the external jugular vein through the oblique jugular vein which runs across the anterior border of the sternocleidomastoid.

CLINICAL ANATOMY

- Deep to the lesser supraclavicular fossa, the internal jugular vein is easily accessible for recording of venous pulse tracings. The vein can be cannulated by direct puncture in the interval between sternal and clavicular heads of sternocleidomastoid muscle.
- In congestive cardiac failure or any other disease where venous pressure is raised, the internal jugular vein is markedly dilated and engorged.

BRACHIOCEPHALIC VEIN

1 The right brachiocephalic vein (2.5 cm long) is shorter than the left (6 cm long) (Fig. 8.25).

2 Each vein is formed behind the sternoclavicular joint, by the union of the internal jugular vein and the subclavian vein.

3 The right vein runs vertically downwards. The left vein runs obliquely downwards and to the right behind the upper half of the manubrium sterni. The two brachiocephalic veins unite at the lower border of the right first costal cartilage to form the superior vena cava.

4 The *tributaries* correspond to the branches of the first part of the subclavian artery. These are as follows:

Right Brachiocephalic

a. Vertebral
b. Internal thoracic
c. Inferior thyroid
d. First posterior intercostal.

Left Brachiocephalic

a. Vertebral (Fig. 8.25)
b. Internal thoracic
c. Inferior thyroid
d. First posterior intercostal.
e. Left superior intercostal.
f. Thymic and pericardial veins.

CERVICAL PART OF SYMPATHETIC TRUNK

DISSECTION

The course of IX–XII cranial nerves has been seen in different chapters. Now trace these nerves and their branches. Read their course and branches in Chapter 4 of Volume 4.

Sympathetic Trunk

The sympathetic trunk has been identified as lying posteromedial to the carotid sheath. Trace it upwards and downwards and locate the three cervical ganglia.

Dissect the formation and branches of the cervical plexus. Identify the phrenic nerve on the surface of scalenus anterior muscle behind the prevertebral fascia.

Features

The cervical parts of the right and left sympathetic trunks are situated one on each side of the cervical part of the vertebral column, behind the carotid sheath (common carotid and internal carotid arteries) and in front of the prevertebral fascia.

FORMATION

There are *no white rami communicans* (i.e. incoming root) in the neck and this part of the trunk is formed by fibres which emerge from segments T1 to T4 of the spinal cord, and then ascend into the neck (Fig. 8.26). Grey rami communicans (i.e. outgoing roots) are present.

RELATIONS

Anterior

a. Internal carotid artery
b. Common carotid artery
c. Carotid sheath (Fig. 8.4)
d. Inferior thyroid artery.

Posterior

a. Prevertebral fascia
b. Longus capitis and cervicis muscles
c. Transverse processes of the lower six cervical vertebrae.

GANGLIA

Theoretically there should be eight sympathetic ganglia corresponding to the eight cervical nerves, but due to fusion there are only three ganglia, superior, middle and inferior.

Superior Cervical Ganglion

Size and Shape

This is the largest of the three ganglia. It is spindle-shaped, and about 2.5 cm long (Fig. 8.26).

Situation and Formation

It lies just below the skull, opposite the second and third cervical vertebrae, behind the carotid sheath and in front of the prevertebral fascia (longus capitis). It is formed by fusion of the upper 4 cervical ganglia.

Communications. With cranial nerves IX, X and XII, and with the external and recurrent laryngeal nerves.

Branches

1 Grey rami communicans pass to the ventral rami of upper four cervical nerves (Fig. 8.26).
2 The internal carotid nerve arises from the upper end of the ganglion and forms a plexus around the

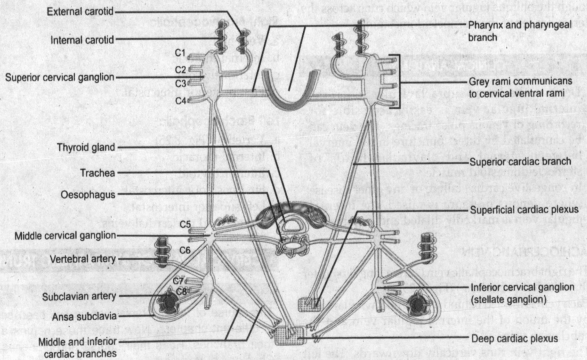

External carotid
Internal carotid
C1
C2
Superior cervical ganglion
C3
C4

Pharynx and pharyngeal branch

Grey rami communicans to cervical ventral rami

Thyroid gland
Trachea
Oesophagus
C5
Middle cervical ganglion
C6
Vertebral artery

Superior cardiac branch

Superficial cardiac plexus

C7
C8
Subclavian artery
Ansa subclavia

Inferior cervical ganglion (stellate ganglion)

Middle and inferior cardiac branches

Deep cardiac plexus

Fig. 8.26: The cervical sympathetic trunks and their branches

internal carotid artery. A part of this plexus supplies the dilator pupillae (*see* Chapter 19). Some of these fibres form the deep petrosal nerve for pterygopalatine ganglion; others give fibres along long ciliary nerve for the ciliary ganglion.

3 The external carotid branches form a plexus around the external carotid artery. Some of these fibres form the sympathetic roots of the otic and submandibular ganglia (*see* Table 1.3).

4 Pharyngeal branches take part in the formation of the pharyngeal plexus.

5 The left superior cervical cardiac branch goes to the superficial cardiac plexus while the right branch goes to the deep cardiac plexus.

Middle Cervical Ganglion

Size and Shape

This ganglion is very small. It may be divided into 2 to 3 smaller parts, or may be absent.

Situation

It lies in the lower part of the neck, in front of vertebra C6 just above the inferior thyroid artery, behind the carotid sheath (Fig. 8.26).

Formation

It is formed by fusion of the fifth and sixth cervical ganglia connections. It is connected with the inferior cervical ganglion directly, and also through a loop that winds round the subclavian artery. This loop is called the ansa subclavia.

Branches

1 Grey rami communicans are given to the ventral rami of the 5th and 6th cervical nerves.

2 Thyroid branches accompany the inferior thyroid artery to the thyroid gland. They also supply the parathyroid glands (Fig. 8.26).

3 Tracheal and oesophageal branches.

4 The middle cervical cardiac branch is the largest of the sympathetic cardiac branches. It goes to the deep cardiac plexus.

Inferior Cervical Ganglion

Size, Shape and Formation

It is formed by fusion of 7th and 8th cervical ganglia. This is often fused with the first thoracic ganglion and is then known as the *cervicothoracic ganglion* or *stellate ganglion* because it is star-shaped.

· It is situated between the transverse process of vertebra C7 and the neck of the first rib. It lies behind the vertebral artery, and in front of ramus of spinal nerve C8. *A cervicothoracic ganglion extends in front of the neck of the first rib.*

Branches

1 Grey rami communicans are given to the ventral rami of nerves C7 and C8.

2 Vertebral branches form a plexus around the vertebral artery.

3 Subclavian branches form a plexus around the subclavian artery. This plexus is joined by branches from the ansa subclavia (Fig. 8.26).

4 An inferior cervical cardiac branch goes to the deep cardiac plexus.

Branches of the cervical sympathetic ganglia put in Table 8.1.

CLINICAL ANATOMY

• The head and neck are supplied by sympathetic nerves arising from the upper four thoracic segments of the spinal cord. Most of these preganglionic fibres pass through the stellate ganglion to relay in the superior cervical ganglion.

• Injury to cervical sympathetic trunk produces Horner's syndrome. It is characterized by:

a. Ptosis—drooping of the upper eyelid.

b. Miosis—constriction of the pupil (Fig. 8.27).

c. Anhydrosis—loss of sweating on that side of the face.

d. Enophthalmos—retraction of the eyeball.

e. Loss of the ciliospinal reflex—pinching the skin on the nape of the neck does not produce dilatation of the pupil (which normally takes place).

• Horner's syndrome can also be caused by a lesion within the central nervous system anywhere at or above the first thoracic segment of the spinal cord involving sympathetic fibres.

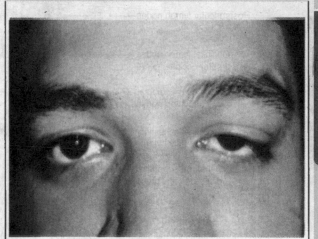

Fig. 8.27: Horner's syndrome on left side

Table 8.1: Branches of cervical sympathetic ganglia

	Superior cervical ganglion	Middle cervical ganglion	Inferior cervical ganglion
Arterial branches	i. Along internal carotid artery as internal carotid nerve	Along inferior thyroid artery	Along subclavian and vertebral arteries
	ii. Along common carotid and external carotid arteries		
Grey rami communicans	Along 1–4 cervical nerves	Along 5 and 6 cervical nerves	Along 7 and 8 cervical nerves
Along cranial nerves	Along cranial nerves IX, X, XI and XII	–	–
Visceral branches	Pharynx, cardiac	Thyroid, cardiac	Cardiac

LYMPHATIC DRAINAGE OF HEAD AND NECK

DISSECTION

Identify the lymph nodes in the submental, the submandibular, the parotid, the mastoid and the occipital regions including the deep cervical nodes. Dissect the main lymph trunk present at the root of the neck.

Features

Lymph nodes in head and neck are as follows:
a. Superficial group
b. Deep group
c. Deepest group

Big man / Please Play On a Lake

SUPERFICIAL GROUP

Buccal and Mandibular Nodes

The buccal node lies on the buccinator, and the mandibular node at the lower border of the mandible near the anteroinferior angle of the masseter, in close relation to the marginal mandibular branch of the facial nerve. They drain part of the cheek and the lower eyelid.

Their efferents pass to the anterosuperior group of deep cervical nodes (Fig. 8.28).

Preauricular Nodes

Drain parotid gland, temporal region, middle ear, etc.

Postauricular (Mastoid) Nodes

The postauricular nodes lie on the mastoid process, superficial to the sternocleidomastoid and deep to the auricularis posterior. They drain a strip of scalp just above and behind the auricle, the upper half of the medial surface and margin of the auricle, and the posterior wall of the external acoustic meatus. Their efferents pass to the posterosuperior group of deep cervical nodes (Fig. 8.28).

Occipital Nodes

The occipital nodes lie at the apex of the posterior triangle superficial to the attachment of the trapezius. They drain the occipital region of the scalp. Their efferents pass to the supraclavicular members of the posteroinferior group of deep cervical nodes.

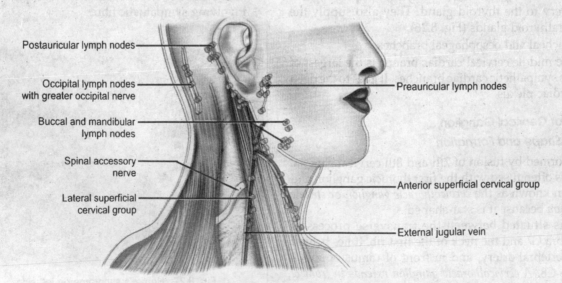

Postauricular lymph nodes

Occipital lymph nodes with greater occipital nerve

Buccal and mandibular lymph nodes

Spinal accessory nerve

Lateral superficial cervical group

Preauricular lymph nodes

Anterior superficial cervical group

External jugular vein

Fig. 8.28: Superficial lymph nodes of the neck

Anterior Superficial Cervical Nodes

The anterior cervical nodes lie along the *anterior jugular vein* and are unimportant. The suprasternal lymph node is a member of this group. They drain the skin of the anterior part of the neck below the hyoid bone. Their efferents pass to the deep cervical nodes of both sides (Fig. 8.28).

Lateral Superficial Cervical Nodes

The superficial cervical nodes lie along the *external jugular vein* superficial to the sternocleidomastoid. They drain the lobule of the auricle, the floor of the external acoustic meatus, and the skin over the lower parotid region and the angle of the jaw. Their efferents pass round both borders of the muscle to reach the upper and lower deep cervical nodes.

DEEP GROUP

It comprises five levels (Fig. 8.29).

Submental and Submandibular Nodes

Submental nodes lie deep to the chin. These drain the lymph from tip of tongue and anterior part of floor of mouth. The submandibular nodes drain lateral surface of tongue, lower gums and teeth and central area of forehead.

The *submandibular lymph nodes* are clinically very important because of their wide area of drainage. They

are very commonly enlarged. The nodes lie beneath the deep cervical fascia on the surface of the submandibular salivary gland. They *drain*:

a. Centre of the forehead.
b. Nose with the frontal, maxillary and ethmoidal air sinuses.
c. The inner canthus of the eye.
d. The upper lip and the anterior part of the cheek with the underlying gum and teeth.
e. The outer part of the lower lip with the lower gums and teeth excluding the incisors.
f. The anterior two-thirds of the tongue excluding the tip, and the floor of the mouth. They also receive efferents from the submental lymph nodes.

The *efferents* from the submandibular nodes pass mostly to the jugulo-omohyoid node and partly to the jugulodigastric node. These nodes are situated along the internal jugular vein and are members of the deep cervical chain (*see* Fig. 8.29).

Upper Lateral Group around Internal Jugular Vein

The *jugulodigastric node* (Fig. 8.29) is a member of this group. It lies below the posterior belly of digastric, between the angle of the mandible and anterior border of the sternocleidomastoid, in the triangle bounded by the posterior belly of digastric, the facial vein and the internal jugular vein. It is the main node draining the *tonsil*.

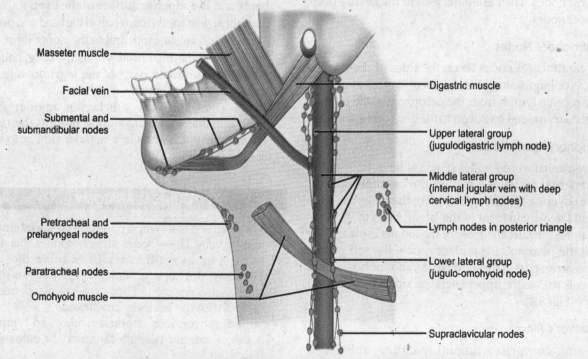

Fig. 8.29: Deep and deepest groups of lymph nodes in the neck

Masseter muscle

Facial vein

Submental and submandibular nodes

Pretracheal and prelaryngeal nodes

Paratracheal nodes

Omohyoid muscle

Digastric muscle

Upper lateral group (jugulodigastric lymph node)

Middle lateral group (internal jugular vein with deep cervical lymph nodes)

Lymph nodes in posterior triangle

Lower lateral group (jugulo-omohyoid node)

Supraclavicular nodes

Head and Neck

Middle Lateral Group around Internal Jugular Vein

These drain thyroid and parathyroid glands. They receive efferents from prelaryngeal, pretracheal and paratracheal lymph nodes.

Lower Lateral Nodes around Internal Jugular Vein

The *jugulo-omohyoid node* is a group. It lies just above the intermediate tendon of the omohyoid, under cover of the posterior border of the sternocleidomastoid. It is the main lymph node of the *tongue*.

Lymph Nodes in Posterior Triangle

The lymph nodes are present around the spinal root of accessory nerve.

Efferents of the deep cervical lymph nodes join together to form the *jugular lymph trunks*, one on each side. The left jugular trunk opens into the thoracic duct. The right trunk may open either into the right lymphatic duct, or directly into the angle of junction between the internal jugular and subclavian veins.

DEEPEST GROUP

Prelaryngeal and Pretracheal Nodes

The prelaryngeal and pretracheal nodes lie deep to the investing fascia, the prelaryngeal nodes on the cricothyroid membrane, and the pretracheal in front of the trachea below the isthmus of the thyroid gland. They drain the larynx, the trachea and the isthmus of the thyroid. They also receive afferents from the anterior cervical nodes. Their efferents pass to the nearby deep cervical nodes.

Paratracheal Nodes

The paratracheal nodes lie on the sides of the trachea and oesophagus along the recurrent laryngeal nerves. They receive lymph from the oesophagus, the trachea and the larynx, and pass it on to the deep cervical nodes.

Retropharyngeal Nodes

The retropharyngeal nodes (Fig. 8.4) lie in front of the prevertebral fascia and behind the buccopharyngeal fascia covering the posterior wall of the pharynx. They extend laterally in front of the lateral mass of the atlas and along the lateral border of the longus capitis. They drain the pharynx, the auditory tube, the soft palate, the posterior part of the hard palate, and the nose. Their efferents pass to the upper lateral group of deep cervical nodes (Fig. 8.4).

Waldeyer's Ring

The ring comprises lingual, palatine, tubal and nasopharyngeal tonsils (*see* Fig. 14.13).

MAIN LYMPH TRUNKS AT THE ROOT OF THE NECK

1 The *thoracic duct* is the largest lymph trunk of the body. It begins in the abdomen from the upper end of the cisterna chyli enters the thorax through aortic opening, traverses the thorax, and ends on the left side of the root of the neck by opening into the angle of junction between the left internal jugular vein and the left subclavian vein (Fig. 8.25). Before its termination, it forms an arch at the level of the transverse process of vertebra C7 rising 3 to 4 cm above the clavicle. The relations of the arch are:

Anterior:
a. Left common carotid artery
b. Vagus
c. Internal jugular vein

Posterior:
a. Vertebral artery and vein
b. Sympathetic trunk
c. Thyrocervical trunk and its branches
d. Prevertebral fascia
e. Phrenic nerve
f. Scalenus anterior.

Apart from its tributaries in the abdomen and thorax, the thoracic duct receives (in the neck):
a. The left jugular trunk
b. The left subclavian trunk
c. The left bronchomediastinal trunk.

It drains most of the body, except for the right upper limb, the right halves of the head, the neck and the thorax and the superior surface of the liver.

2 The right *jugular trunk* drains half of the head and neck.

3 The right *subclavian trunk* drains the upper limb.

4 The *bronchomediastinal trunk* drains the lung, half of the mediastinum and parts of the anterior walls of the thorax and abdomen.

5 On the right side, the subclavian, jugular and bronchomediastinal trunks unite to form the *right lymph trunk* which ends in a manner similar to the thoracic duct (Fig. 8.25).

CLINICAL ANATOMY

- The deep cervical lymph nodes lie on the internal jugular vein. These nodes often become adherent to the vein in malignancy or in tuberculosis. Therefore, during operation on such patients the vein is also resected. These are examined from behind with the neck slightly flexed.

- Superficial cervical, supraclavicular and lymph nodes of anterior triangle can easily be palpated (Fig. 8.30).

- Chronic infection of the palatine tonsil causes enlargement of jugulodigastric lymph nodes which adhere to the internal jugular vein.
- Painful enlargement of the submandibular lymph nodes is common because infections in tongue, mouth and cheek are quite common. These nodes may be affected by tubercular bacteria.
- Spinal root of accessory nerve may get entangled in the enlarged lymph nodes situated in the posterior triangle of neck. While taking biopsy of the lymph node, one must be careful not to injure the accessory nerve lest trapezius gets damaged (*see* Fig. 3.9).

The left supraclavicular nodes are called Virchow's lymph nodes. Cancer from stomach and testis may metastasize into these lymph nodes, which may become palpable.

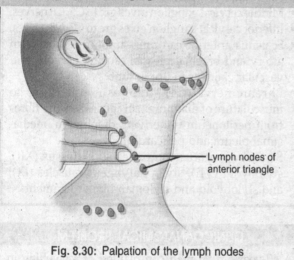

Fig. 8.30: Palpation of the lymph nodes

STYLOID APPARATUS

The styloid process with its attached structures is called the styloid apparatus. The structures attached to the process are three muscles and two ligaments. The muscles are the stylohyoid, styloglossus and stylopharyngeus and ligaments are the stylohyoid and stylomandibular (Figs 8.31a and b).

The apparatus is of diverse origin. The styloid process, the stylohyoid ligament and stylohyoid muscle are derived from the second branchial arch; the stylopharyngeus from the third arch; the styloglossus from occipital myotomes; and the stylomandibular ligament from a part of the deep fascia of neck.

The *five attachments resemble the reins of a chariot.* Two of these reins (ligaments) are nonadjustable, whereas the other three (muscles) are adjustable and are controlled each by a separate cranial nerve, seventh, ninth and twelfth nerves.

The *styloid process* is a long, slender and pointed bony process projecting downwards, forwards and slightly medially from the temporal bone. It descends between the external and internal carotid arteries to reach the side of the pharynx. It is interposed between the parotid gland laterally and the internal jugular vein medially.

The *styloglossus muscle* arises from the anterior surface of the styloid process and is inserted into the side of the tongue.

The *stylopharyngeus muscle* arises from the medial surface of the base of the styloid process and is inserted on the posterior border of the lamina of the thyroid cartilage (*see* Fig. 14.23).

Stylohyoid extends between posterior surface of styloid process and hyoid bone. It splits at its lower end to enclose the intermediate tendon of digastric muscle.

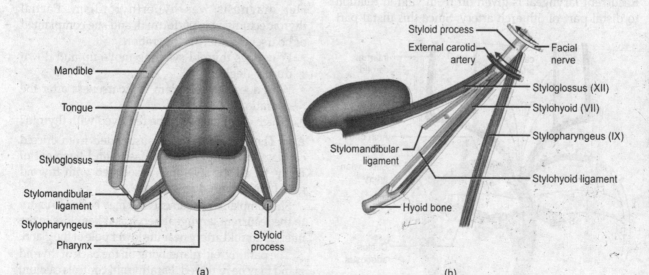

Figs 8.31a and b: The styloid apparatus: (a) Superior view, and (b) lateral view

The *stylomandibular ligament* is attached laterally to styloid process above and angle of mandible below.

The *stylohyoid ligament* extends from the tip of the styloid process to the lesser cornua of the hyoid bone.

Features

1 External carotid artery crosses tip of styloid process superficially and pierces stylomandibular ligament.

2 Facial nerve crosses the base of styloid process laterally after it emerges from stylomastoid foramen.

DEVELOPMENT OF THE ARTERIES

Brachoicephalic artery	:	Right aortic sac
Right subclavian artery	:	Proximal part from the right 4th aortic arch artery and remaining part from right 7th cervical intersegmental artery.
Left subclavian artery	:	Only left 7th cervical intersegmental artery.
Common carotid	:	Third aortic arch proximal to external carotid bud.
Internal carotid artery	:	Third aortic arch, distal to the external carotid bud and original dorsal aorta cranial to the attachment of third aortic arch.
External carotid artery	:	Develop as sprout from the third aortic arch.
Pulmonary trunk	:	Part of truncus arteriosus.
Arch of aorta	:	Left aortic sac
	:	Left 4th aortic arch
	:	Left dorsal aorta.

Relation to recurrent laryngeal nerve (Fig. 8.32). Recurrent laryngeal is given off from vagi in relation to distal part of 6th arch artery. Since this distal part forms ligamentum arteriosum on left side only, the recurrent laryngeal nerve hooks around this ligamentum in thorax to reach tracheo-oesophageal groove.

On the right side there is no ligamentum arteriosum, the recurrent laryngeal nerve slips upwards in the neck and hooks around the right subclavian artery to reach the tracheo-oesophageal groove.

FACTS TO REMEMBER

- Isthmus of thyroid gland acts as a shield for trachea.
- Parathyroid glands lie along the anastomotic channel between posterior branch of superior thyroid artery and ascending branch of inferior thyroid artery.
- Internal carotid artery comprises 4 parts: Cervical, petrous, cavernous and cerebral.
- Superior cervical ganglion gives grey rami communicates (grc) to C1–C4 nerves.
- Middle cervical ganglion gives grc to C5, C6 nerves.
- Inferior cervical ganglion gives grc to C7, C8 nerves.
- Scalenus anterior can press upon the subclavian artery and brachial plexus, causing nervous and vascular changes in upper limb.
- Phrenic nerve (C4) supplies motor fibres to musculature of diaphragm. It carries sensory fibres from peritoneum underlying diaphragm, mediastinal pleura and pericardium.
- Styloid apparatus comprises styloglossus (XII), stylohyoid (VII), stylopharyngeus muscles (IX); and stylohyoid and stylomandibular ligaments.

CLINICOANATOMICAL PROBLEM

A 40-year-old woman complained of a swelling in front of her neck, nervousness and loss of weight. Her diagnosis was hyperthyroidism. Partial thyroidectomy was performed, and she complained of hoarseness after the operation.

- Why does thyroid swelling move up and down during deglutition?
- Why does she complain of hoarseness after the operation?
- Which other gland can be removed with thyroid?

Ans: The thyroid gland is suspended from cricoid cartilage by the pretracheal fascia and ligament of Berry. So all the swellings associated with thyroid gland move with deglutition.

She complains of hoarseness. It may be due to injury to the recurrent laryngeal nerve as it lies close to the inferior thyroid artery near the lower pole of the gland.

The parathyroid gland lying on the back of thyroid gland may be removed. Parathyroid controls calcium level in the blood.

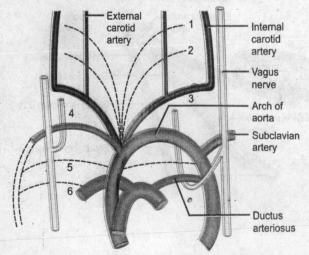

Fig. 8.32: Relation to recurrent laryngeal nerve

FREQUENTLY ASKED QUESTIONS

1. Describe thyroid gland under the following headings:
   a. Position
   b. Gross anatomy
   c. Blood supply
   d. Clinical anatomy
2. Enumerate the various group of lymph nodes in the neck. Mention the areas drained by these nodes.

3. Write short notes on/enumerate:
   a. Styloid apparatus
   b. Branches of subclavian artery
   c. Branches of superior cervical ganglion
   d. Horner's syndrome
   e. Tributaries of internal jugular vein

MULTIPLE CHOICE QUESTIONS

1. Where should the superior thyroid artery should be ligated during thyroidectomy?
   a. Close to its origin from external carotid artery
   b. Close to the upper pole of the lateral lobe
   c. Anterior and posterior branches separately
   d. Anywhere in its course
2. Where should inferior thyroid artery be ligated during thyroidectomy?
   a. Away from the gland
   b. At its distal or terminal part
   c. Anywhere in its course
   d. The branches ligated separately
3. Horner's syndrome produces all symptoms except:
   a. Partial ptosis   b. Miosis
   c. Anhydrosis   d. Exophthalmos
4. Which of the following muscles is not supplied by ansa cervicalis?
   a. Sternohyoid
   b. Sternothyroid
   c. Inferior belly of omohyoid
   d. Geniohyoid
5. One of the following is not a branch of subclavian artery:
   a. Internal thoracic
   b. Vertebral

c. Costocervical trunk
d. Subscapular

6. One of the following symptoms is not seen in Horner's syndrome:
   a. Complete ptosis   b. Miosis
   c. Anhydrosis   d. Enophthalmos
7. One of the following statements about parathyroid gland is not true:
   a. Inferior parathyroid arises from 3rd pharyngeal pouch
   b. Parathyroid glands are supplied by superior thyroid artery
   c. Superior parathyroid arises from 4th pharyngeal pouch
   d. Thymus develops along with inferior parathyroid gland
8. Which one is not a branch of thyrocervical trunk?
   a. Inferior thyroid
   b. Suprascapular
   c. Transverse cervical
   d. Deep cervical
9. Which one is not a component of carotid sheath?
   a. Internal carotid artery
   b. Vagus nerve
   c. Sympathetic trunk
   d. Internal jugular vein

ANSWERS

1. b	2. a	3. d	4. d	5. d	6. a	7. b	8. d	9. c

Head and Neck

Prevertebral and Paravertebral Regions

I profess to learn and to teach anatomy not from books but from dissections,
not from the tenets of philosophers but from the fabric of nature
—William Harvey

INTRODUCTION

The prevertebral region contains four muscles, vertebral artery and joints of the neck. Vertebral artery, a branch of subclavian artery, comprises four parts—1st, 2nd and 3rd are in the neck and the fourth part passes through the foramen magnum to reach the subarachnoid space and the vertebral arteries of two sides unite to form a single median basilar artery which gives branches to supply a part of cerebral cortex, cerebellum, internal ear and pons. Congenital or acquired diseases of cervical vertebrae or their joints give rise to lots of symptoms related to branches of vertebral artery.

The apical ligament of dens is a continuation of notochord. Transverse ligament, which is a part of cruciate ligament, keeps the dens of axis in position. If this ligament is injured by disease or in "capital punishment", there is immediate death due to injury to vasomotor centres in medulla oblongata. Trachea and oesophagus are contents of prevertebral region.

The paravertebral region contains three scalene muscles, cervical plexus, its branches including the phrenic nerve. This region also includes the cervical pleura.

PREVERTEBRAL MUSCLES
(Anterior Vertebral Muscles)

The four prevertebral or anterior vertebral muscles are the longus colli (cervicis), the longus capitis, the rectus capitis anterior and the rectus capitis lateralis (Fig. 9.1). These are weak flexors of the head and neck. They extend from the base of the skull to the superior mediastinum. They partially cover the anterior aspect of the vertebral column. They are covered anteriorly by the thick prevertebral fascia. The muscles are described in Table 9.1.

VERTEBRAL ARTERY

DISSECTION

Remove the scalenus anterior muscle. Identify deeply placed anterior and posterior intertransverse muscles. Cut through the anterior intertransverse muscles to expose the second part of vertebral artery. First part was seen as the branch arising from the first part of the subclavian artery. Its third part was seen in the suboccipital triangle. The fourth part lies in the cranial cavity.

Features

The vertebral artery is one of the two principal arteries which supply the brain. In addition, it also supplies the spinal cord, the meninges, and the surrounding muscles and bones. It arises from the posterosuperior aspect of the first part of the subclavian artery near its commencement. It runs a long course, and ends in the cranial cavity by supplying the brain (Fig. 9.2). The artery is divided into four parts.

First Part

The first part extends from the origin of the artery (from the subclavian artery) to the transverse process of the sixth cervical vertebra.

This part of the artery runs upwards and backwards in the triangular space between the scalenus anterior and the longus colli muscles called as the scalenovertebral triangle (Fig. 9.3).

Relations

Anterior

1 Carotid sheath with common carotid artery
2 Vertebral vein

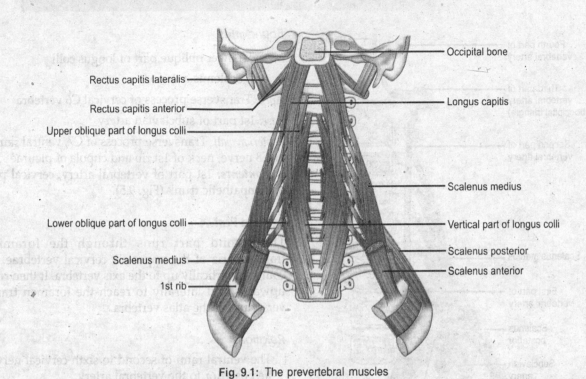

Fig. 9.1: The prevertebral muscles

Table 9.1: The prevertebral muscles

Muscle	Origin	Insertion	Nerve supply	Actions
1. **Longus colli (cervicis).** This muscle extends from the atlas to the third thoracic vertebra. It has upper and lower oblique parts and a middle vertical part (Fig. 9.1)	a. The upper oblique part is from the anterior tubercles of the transverse processes of cervical vertebrae 3, 4, 5 b. Lower oblique part is from bodies of upper 2–3 thoracic vertebrae c. Middle vertical part is from bodies of upper 3 thoracic and lower 3 cervical vertebrae	a. Upper oblique part is into the anterior tubercle of the atlas b. Lower oblique part is into the anterior tubercles of the transverse processes of 5th and 6th cervical vertebrae c. Middle vertical part is into bodies of 2,3,4 cervical vertebrae	Ventral rami of nerves C3–C8	a. Flexes the neck b. Oblique parts flex the neck laterally c. Lower oblique part rotates the neck to the opposite side
2. **Longus capitis.** It overlaps the longus colli. It is thick above and narrow below	Anterior tubercles of transverse processes of cervical 3–6 vertebrae	Inferior surface of basilar part of occipital bone	Ventral rami of nerves C1–C3	Flexes the head
3. **Rectus capitis anterior.** This is a very short and flat muscle. It lies deep to the longus capitis	Anterior surface of lateral mass of atlas in front of the occipital condyle	Basilar part of the occipital bone	Ventral ramus of nerve C1	Flexes the head
4. **Rectus capitis lateralis.** This is a short, flat muscle	Upper surface of transverse process of atlas	Inferior surface of jugular process of the occipital bone	Ventral rami of nerves C1, C2	Flexes the head laterally

3 Inferior thyroid artery

4 Thoracic duct on left side (Fig. 9.3).

Posterior

1 Transverse process of 7th cervical vertebra (Fig. 9.2)

2 Stellate ganglion

3 Ventral rami of nerves C7, C8.

Scalenovertebral Triangle

The triangle is present at the root of the neck.

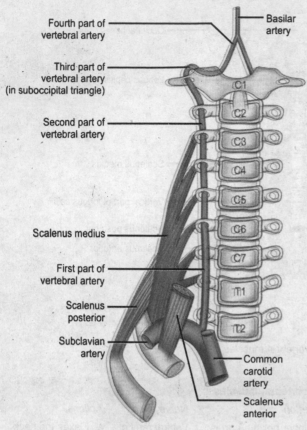

Fourth part of vertebral artery

Basilar artery

Third part of vertebral artery (in suboccipital triangle)

Second part of vertebral artery

Scalenus medius

First part of vertebral artery

Scalenus posterior

Subclavian artery

Common carotid artery

Scalenus anterior

Fig. 9.2: Scheme showing parts of the vertebral artery, as seen from the front

Boundaries

Medial: Lower oblique part of longus colli

Lateral: Scalenus anterior

Apex: Transverse process of cervical C6 vertebra

Base: 1st part of subclavian artery

Posterior wall: Transverse process of C7, ventral ramus of C8 nerve, neck of 1st rib and cupola of pleurae

Contents: 1st part of vertebral artery, cervical part of sympathetic trunk (Fig. 9.5).

Second Part

The second part runs through the foramina transversaria of the upper six cervical vertebrae. Its course is vertically up to the axis vertebra. It then runs upwards and laterally to reach the foramen transversarium of the atlas vertebra.

Relations

1   The ventral rami of second to sixth cervical nerves lie posterior to the vertebral artery.

2   The artery is accompanied by a venous plexus and a large branch from the stellate ganglion (*see* Fig. 8.26).

Third Part

Third part lies in the suboccipital triangle. Emerging from the foramen transversarium of the atlas, the artery

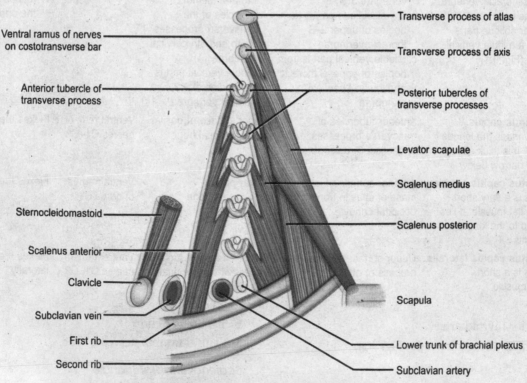

Ventral ramus of nerves on costotransverse bar

Anterior tubercle of transverse process

Sternocleidomastoid

Scalenus anterior

Clavicle

Subclavian vein

First rib

Second rib

Transverse process of atlas

Transverse process of axis

Posterior tubercles of transverse processes

Levator scapulae

Scalenus medius

Scalenus posterior

Scapula

Lower trunk of brachial plexus

Subclavian artery

Fig. 9.3: Schematic sagittal section through the left scalenus anterior to show its relations

winds medially around the posterior aspect of the lateral mass of the atlas. It runs medially lying on the posterior arch of this bone, and enters the vertebral canal by passing deep to the lower arched margin of the posterior atlanto-occipital membrane.

Relations

Anterior: Lateral mass of atlas.

Posterior: Semispinalis capitis.

Lateral: Rectus capitis lateralis.

Medial: Ventral ramus of the first cervical nerve.

Inferior:

1 Dorsal ramus of the first cervical nerve (*see* Fig. 10.6)
2 The posterior arch of the atlas (*see* Fig. 10.6).

Fourth Part

1 The fourth part extends from the posterior atlanto-occipital membrane to the lower border of the pons.
2 In the vertebral canal, it pierces the dura and the arachnoid, and ascends in front of the roots of the hypoglossal nerve. As it ascends, it gradually inclines medially to reach the front of the medulla. At the lower border of the pons, it unites with its fellow of the opposite side to form the basilar artery (Fig. 9.2).

BRANCHES OF VERTEBRAL ARTERY

First part has no branches.

Cervical Branches

1 Spinal branches from the *second part* enter the vertebral canal through the intervertebral foramina and supply the spinal cord, the meninges and the vertebrae.
2 Muscular branches arise from the *third part* and supply the suboccipital muscles.

Cranial Branches

These arise from the *fourth part*. They are:
1 *Meningeal* branches
2 The *posterior spinal*
3 The *anterior spinal* artery
4 The *posterior inferior cerebellar* artery
5 *Medullary* arteries
These are described in Chapter 11, Volume 4.

DEVELOPMENT OF VERTEBRAL ARTERY

Different parts of vertebral artery develop in the following ways.

First part: From a branch of dorsal division of 7th cervical intersegmental artery.

Second part: From postcostal anastomosis.

Third part: From spinal branch of the first cervical intersegmental artery.

Fourth part: From preneural branch of first cervical intersegmental artery.

SCALENE MUSCLES

DISSECTION

Clean and define the cervical parts of the trachea and oesophagus.

Scalenus anterior has been seen in relation to subclavian artery. Scalenus medius is one of the muscle forming floor of posterior triangle of neck. Scalenus posterior lies deep to the medius (*see* Fig. 3.9).

The relations of the cervical pleura are shown in Fig. 9.4.

Features

There are usually three scalene muscles, the scalenus anterior, the scalenus medius and the scalenus posterior. The scalenus medius is the largest, and the scalenus posterior the smallest, of three. These muscles extend from the transverse processes of cervical vertebrae to the first two ribs. They can, therefore, either elevate these ribs or bend the cervical part of the vertebral column laterally (Fig. 9.4).

These muscles are described in Table 9.2.

Additional Features of the Scalene Muscles

1 Sometimes a fourth, rudimentary scalene muscle, the *scalenus minimus* is present. It arises from the anterior border of the transverse process of vertebra C7 and is inserted into the inner border of the first rib behind the groove for the subclavian artery and into the dome of the cervical pleura. The *suprapleural membrane* is regarded as the expansion this muscle. Contraction of the scalenus minimus pulls the dome of the cervical pleura.
2 *Relations of scalenus anterior.* The scalenus anterior is a *key* muscle of the lower part of the neck because of its intimate relations to many important structures in this region. It is a useful surgical landmark.

Anterior:

a. Phrenic nerve covered by prevertebral fascia.
b. Lateral part of carotid sheath containing the internal jugular vein.
c. Sternocleidomastoid (Fig. 9.4).
d. Clavicle.

Posterior:

a. Brachial plexus (Fig. 9.4).
b. Subclavian artery.
c. Scalenus medius.
d. Cervical pleura covered by the suprapleural membrane (Fig. 9.6).

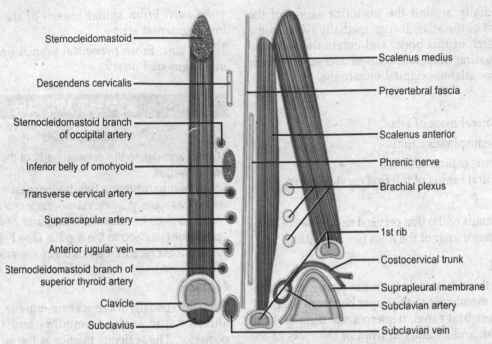

Fig. 9.4: Lateral view of the scalene muscles with a few related structures

Labels (top to bottom, left): Sternocleidomastoid; Descendens cervicalis; Sternocleidomastoid branch of occipital artery; Inferior belly of omohyoid; Transverse cervical artery; Suprascapular artery; Anterior jugular vein; Sternocleidomastoid branch of superior thyroid artery; Clavicle; Subclavius

Labels (right): Scalenus medius; Prevertebral fascia; Scalenus anterior; Phrenic nerve; Brachial plexus; 1st rib; Costocervical trunk; Suprapleural membrane; Subclavian artery; Subclavian vein

Table 9.2: The scalene muscles				
Muscle	Origin	Insertion	Nerve supply	Actions
1. **Scalenus anterior** (Fig. 9.4)	Anterior tubercles of transverse processes of cervical vertebrae 3, 4, 5 and 6	Scalene tubercle and adjoining ridge on the superior surface of the first rib (between subclavian artery and vein)	Ventral rami of nerves C4–C6	a. Anterolateral flexion of cervical spine b. Rotates cervical spine to opposite side c. Elevates the first rib during inspiration d. Stabilises the neck along with other muscles
2. **Scalenus medius** (Fig. 9.3)	a. Posterior tubercles of transverse processes of cervical vertebrae 3, 4, 5, 6, 7 b. Transverse process of axis and sometimes also of the atlas vertebra	Superior surface of the first rib behind the groove for the subclavian artery	Ventral rami of nerves C3–C8	a. Lateral flexion of the cervical spine. b. Elevation of first rib c. Stabilises neck along with other muscles
3. **Scalenus posterior** (Fig. 9.3)	Posterior tubercles of transverse processes of cervical vertebrae 4, 5, 6	Outer surface of the second rib behind the tubercle for the serratus anterior	Ventral rami of nerves C6–C8	a. Lateral flexion of cervical spine b. Elevation of the second rib c. Stabilises neck along with other muscles

The *medial border* of the muscle is related:

a. In its lower part to an inverted V-shaped interval, formed by the diverging borders of the scalenus anterior and the longus colli. This interval contains many important structures as follows:

   i. Vertebral vessels running vertically from the base to the apex of this space.

   ii. Inferior thyroid artery arching medially at the level of the 6th cervical transverse process.

   iii. Sympathetic trunk.

   iv. The first part of the subclavian artery traverses the lower part of the gap.

   v. On the left side, the thoracic duct arches laterally at the level of the seventh cervical transverse process (Fig. 9.5).

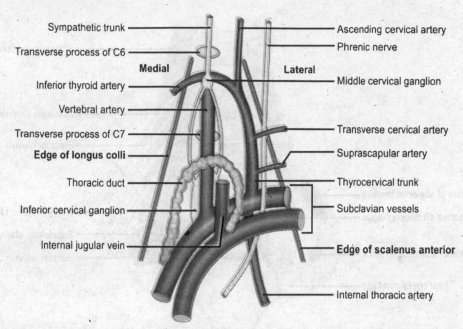

Fig. 9.5: Structures present in the triangular interval between scalenus anterior and the longus colli, i.e. scalenovertebral triangle

vi. The carotid sheath covers all the structures mentioned above.

vii. The sternocleidomastoid covers the carotid sheath (*see* Fig. 8.4).

b. In its upper part, the scalenus anterior is separated from the longus capitis by the ascending cervical artery.

The *lateral border* of the muscle is related to the trunks of the brachial plexus and the subclavian artery which emerges at this border and enter the posterior triangle (Fig. 9.4).

CERVICAL PLEURA

The cervical pleura covers the apex of the lung. It rises into the root of the neck, about 5 cm above the first costal cartilage and 2.5 cm above the medial one-third of the clavicle. The pleural dome is strengthened on its outer surface by the suprapleural membrane so that the root of the neck is not puffed up and down during respiration (*see* Chapter 12, Volume 1).

Relations

Anterior

1 Subclavian artery and its branches
2 Scalenus anterior (Fig. 9.6).

Posterior

Neck of the first rib and the following structures in front of it.

1 Sympathetic trunk (*see* Chapter 13, Volume 1)
2 First posterior intercostal vein

3 Superior intercostal artery
4 The first thoracic nerve.

Lateral

i. Scalenus medius
ii. Lower trunk of the brachial plexus.

Medial

1 Vertebral bodies
2 Oesophagus (Fig. 9.6)
3 Trachea
4 Left recurrent laryngeal nerve
5 Thoracic duct (on left side)
6 Large arteries and veins of the neck.

CERVICAL PLEXUS

FORMATION

The cervical plexus is formed by the ventral rami of the upper four cervical nerves (Fig. 9.7). The rami emerge between the anterior and posterior tubercles of the cervical transverse processes, grooving the costotransverse bars. The four roots are connected with one another to form three loops (Fig. 9.8).

Position and Relations of the Plexus

The plexus is related:

1 *Posteriorly,* to the muscles which arise from the posterior tubercles of the transverse processes, i.e. the levator scapulae and the scalenus medius.

2 *Anteriorly,* to the prevertebral fascia, the internal jugular vein and the sternocleidomastoid.

Head and Neck

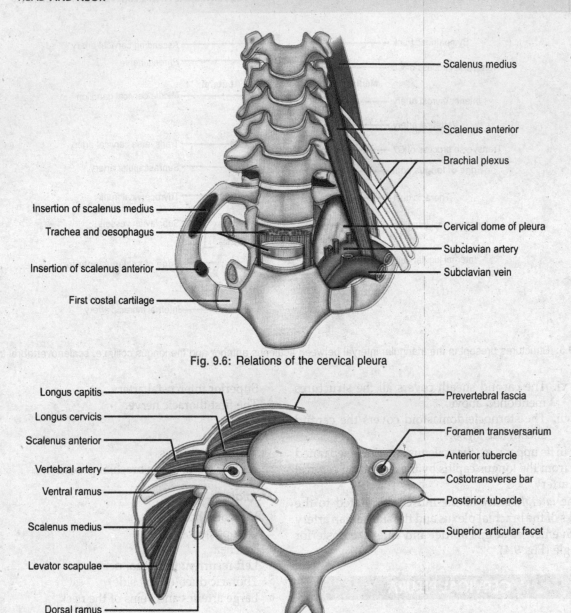

Fig. 9.6: Relations of the cervical pleura

Fig. 9.7: Scheme to show the position of a cervical nerve relative to the muscles of the region

Branches

Superficial (Cutaneous) Branches

1 Lesser occipital (C2)
2 Great auricular (C2, C3)
3 Transverse (anterior) cutaneous nerve of the neck (C2, C3)
4 Supraclavicular (C3, C4)

These are described in Chapter 3.

Deep Branches

Communicating Branches

1 Grey rami pass from the superior cervical ganglion to the roots of C1–C4 nerves.
2 A branch from C1 joins the hypoglossal nerve and carries fibres for supply of the thyrohyoid and

geniohyoid muscles (directly) and the superior belly of the omohyoid through the ansa cervicalis.
3 A branch each from C2, C3 to the sternocleidomastoid and branches from C3 and C4 to the trapezius communicate with the accessory nerve.

Muscular Branches

Muscles supplied solely by cervical plexus:

1 Rectus capitis anterior from C1.
2 Rectus capitis lateralis from C1, C2.
3 Longus capitis from C1 to C3.
4 Lower root of ansa cervicalis (descendens cervicalis) from C2, C3 (to sternohyoid, sternothyroid and inferior belly of omohyoid.

Muscles supplied by cervical plexus along with the brachial plexus or the spinal accessory nerve:

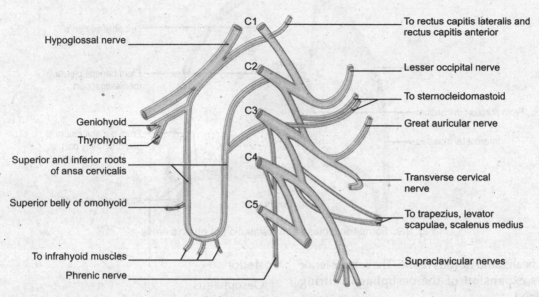

Fig. 9.8: Left cervical plexus and its branches

a. Sternocleidomastoid from C2 to C3 along with accessory nerve (Fig. 9.8).
b. Trapezius from C3 to C4 along with accessory nerve.
c. Levator scapulae from C3 to C5 (dorsal scapular nerve).
d. The diaphragm from phrenic nerve from C3 to C5.
e. Longus colli from C3 to C8.
f. Scalenus medius from C3 to C8.
g. Scalenus anterior from C4 to C6.
h. Scalenus posterior from C6 to C8.

PHRENIC NERVE

This is a mixed nerve carrying motor fibres to the diaphragm and sensory fibres from the diaphragm, pleura, pericardium, and part of the peritoneum (Fig. 9.8).

Origin

Phrenic nerve arises chiefly from the fourth cervical nerve but receives contributions from third and fifth cervical nerves. The contribution from C5 may come directly from the root or indirectly through the nerve to the subclavius. In the latter case, the contribution is known as the *accessory phrenic nerve*.

Course and Relations in the Neck

1 The nerve is formed at the lateral border of the scalenus anterior, opposite the middle of the sternocleidomastoid, at the level of the upper border of the thyroid cartilage.
2 It runs vertically downwards on the anterior surface of the scalenus anterior (Fig. 9.9). Since the muscle is oblique, the nerve appears to cross it obliquely from lateral to medial border. In this part of its course,

the nerve is related anteriorly to the prevertebral fascia, the inferior belly of the omohyoid, the transverse cervical artery, the suprascapular artery, the internal jugular vein, the sternocleidomastoid, and the thoracic duct on left side (Fig. 9.5).
3 After leaving the anterior surface of scalenus anterior, the nerve runs downwards on the cervical pleura behind the commencement of the brachiocephalic vein. Here it crosses the internal thoracic artery (either anteriorly or posteriorly) from lateral to medial side, and enters the thorax behind the first costal cartilage. On the left side, the nerve leaves (crosses) the medial margin of the scalenus anterior at a higher level and crosses in front of the first part of the subclavian artery.

CLINICAL ANATOMY

The accessory phrenic nerve is commonly a branch from the nerve to the subclavius. It lies lateral to the phrenic nerve and descends behind, or sometimes in front of the subclavian vein. It joins the main nerve usually near the first rib, but occasionally the union may even be below the root of the lung.

TRACHEA

The trachea is a noncollapsible, wide tube forming the beginning of the lower respiratory passages. It is kept patent because of the presence of C-shaped cartilaginous 'rings' in its wall. The cartilages are deficient posteriorly, this part of the wall-being made up of

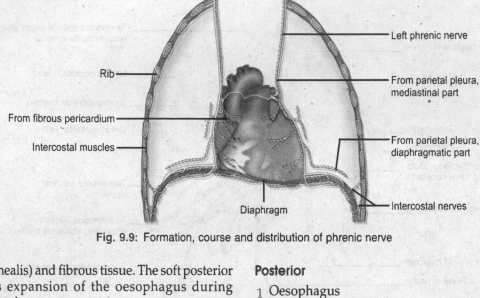

C3
C4
C5

Left phrenic nerve

Rib

From parietal pleura, mediastinal part

From fibrous pericardium

Intercostal muscles

From parietal pleura, diaphragmatic part

Diaphragm

Intercostal nerves

Fig. 9.9: Formation, course and distribution of phrenic nerve

muscle (trachealis) and fibrous tissue. The soft posterior wall allows expansion of the oesophagus during passage of food.

DIMENSIONS

The trachea (Latin *rough air vessel*) is about 10 to 15 cm long. Its upper half lies in the neck and its lower half in the superior mediastinum. The external diameter measures 2 cm in the male and 1.5 cm in the female. The lumen is smaller in the living than in cadavers. It is about 3 mm at 1 year of age, and corresponds to the age in years during childhood, with a maximum of 12 mm at puberty.

CERVICAL PART OF TRACHEA

1 The trachea begins at the lower border of the cricoid cartilage opposite the lower border of vertebra C6. It runs downwards and slightly backwards in front of the oesophagus, follows the curvature of the spine, and enters the thorax in the median plane.
2 In the neck, the trachea is comparatively superficial and has the following relations.

Anterior

1 Isthmus of the thyroid gland covering the second and third tracheal rings (*see* Fig. 8.1).
2 Inferior thyroid veins below the isthmus (*see* Fig. 8.8).
3 Pretracheal fascia enclosing the thyroid and the inferior thyroid veins.
4 Sternohyoid and sternothyroid muscles (*see* Fig. 8.4).
5 Investing layer of the deep cervical fascia and the suprasternal space.
6 The skin and superficial fascia.
7 In children, the left brachiocephalic vein extends into the neck and then lies in front of the trachea.

Posterior

1 Oesophagus
2 Longus colli
3 Recurrent laryngeal nerve in the tracheo-oesophageal groove (*see* Fig. 8.5).

On Each Side

1 The corresponding lobe of the thyroid glands.
2 The common carotid artery within the carotid sheath (*see* Fig. 8.4).

Vessels and Nerves

The trachea is supplied by branches from the inferior thyroid arteries. Its veins drain into the left brachiocephalic vein. Lymphatics drain into the pretracheal and paratracheal nodes.

Parasympathetic nerves (from the vagus through the recurrent laryngeal nerve) are sensory and secretomotor to the mucous membrane, and motor to the trachealis muscle. Sympathetic nerves (from the cervical ganglion) are vasomotor.

CLINICAL ANATOMY

- The trachea may be compressed by pathological enlargements of the thyroid, the thymus, lymph nodes and the aortic arch. This causes dyspnoea, irritative cough, and often a husky voice.
- Tracheostomy is an emergency operation done in cases of laryngeal obstruction (foreign body, diphtheria, carcinoma, etc.). It is commonly done in the retrothyroid region after retracting the isthmus of the thyroid gland.

OESOPHAGUS

The oesophagus is a muscular food passage lying between the trachea and the vertebral column. Normally, its anterior and posterior walls are in contact. The oesophagus expands during the passage of food by pressing into the posterior muscular part of the trachea (*see* Fig. 8.4).

The oesophagus is a downward continuation of the pharynx and begins at the lower border of the cricoid cartilage, opposite the lower border of the body of vertebra C6. It passes downwards behind the trachea, traverses the superior and posterior mediastina of the thorax, and ends by opening into the cardiac end of the stomach in the abdomen. It is about 25 cm long.

The cervical part of the oesophagus is related:

a. *Anteriorly,* to the trachea and to the right and left recurrent laryngeal nerves.

b. *Posteriorly,* to the longus colli muscle and the vertebral column.

c. *On each side,* to the corresponding (*see* Fig. 8.5) lobe of the thyroid gland; and on the left side, to the thoracic duct.

The cervical part of the oesophagus is supplied by the inferior thyroid arteries. Its veins drain into the left brachiocephalic vein. Its lymphatics pass to the deep cervical lymph nodes. The oesophagus is narrowest at its junction with the pharynx, the junction being the narrowest part of the gastrointestinal tract, except for the vermiform appendix.

For thoracic part of oesophagus study, *see* Chapter 20, Volume 1.

CLINICAL ANATOMY

Oesophagus has four natural constrictions. While passing any instrument, one must be careful at these sites (Fig. 9.10).

JOINTS OF THE NECK

Typical Cervical Joints between the Lower Six Cervical Vertebrae

The adjacent vertebrae are connected by several ligaments which are as follows:

1. The *anterior longitudinal ligament* passes from the anterior surface of the body of one vertebra to another. Its upper end reaches the basilar part of the occipital bone (Fig. 9.11).

2. The *posterior longitudinal ligament* is present on the posterior surface of the vertebral bodies within the vertebral canal. Its upper end reaches the body of the axis vertebra beyond which it is continuation the *membrana tectoria* (Fig. 9.11).

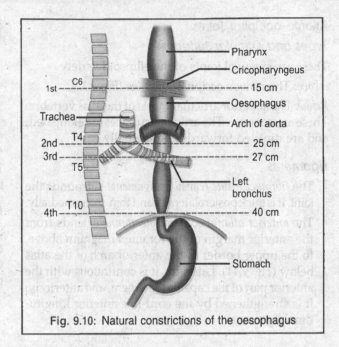

Fig. 9.10: Natural constrictions of the oesophagus

3. The *intertransverse ligaments* connect adjacent transverse processes.

4. The *interspinous ligaments* connect adjacent spines.

5. The *supraspinous ligaments* connect the tips of the spines of vertebrae from the seventh cervical to the sacrum. In the cervical region, they are replaced by the ligamentum nuchae.

6. *Joint between vertebral arches:* Joint between superior and inferior articular processes of adjacent vertebrae is plane joint of synovial variety. The articular processes slope inferiorly to allow rotation of neck. These are also called zygapophyseal/facet joints.

7. The laminae of adjacent vertebrae are united by ligamentum flava, made up of elastic fibres.

The *ligamentum nuchae* is triangular in shape. Its apex lies at the seventh cervical spine and its base at the external occipital crest. Its anterior border is attached to cervical spines, while the posterior border is free and provides attachment to the investing layer of deep cervical fascia. The ligament gives origin to the splenius, rhomboids and trapezius muscles.

Joints between the Atlas, the Axis and the Occipital Bone

1. The atlanto-occipital and the atlantoaxial joints are designed to permit free movements of the head on the neck (vertebral column).

2. The axis vertebra and the occipital bone are connected together by very strong ligaments. Between these two bones, the atlas is held like a washer. The axis of movement between the atlas and skull is transverse, permitting flexion and extension (nodding), whereas the axis of movement between the axis and the atlas is vertical, permitting rotation of the head (Fig. 9.11).

Head and Neck

Atlanto-occipital Joints

Types and Articular Surfaces

These are synovial joints of the ellipsoid variety.

Above: The convex occipital condyles (Fig. 9.12).

Below: The superior articular facets of the atlas vertebra. These are concave. The articular surfaces are elongated, and are directed forwards and medially.

Ligaments

1   The *fibrous capsule (capsular ligament)* surrounds the joint. It is thick posterolaterally and thin anteromedially.

2   The *anterior atlanto-occipital membrane* extends from the anterior margin of the foramen magnum above, to the upper border of the anterior arch of the atlas below (Fig. 9.11). Laterally, it is continuous with the anterior part of the capsular ligament, and anteriorly, it is strengthened by the cord-like anterior longitudinal ligament.

3   The *posterior atlanto-occipital membrane* extends from the posterior margin of the foramen magnum above, to the upper border of the posterior arch of the atlas below. Inferolaterally, it has a free margin which arches over the vertebral artery and the first cervical nerve (*see* Fig. 10.5). Laterally, it is continuous with the posterior part of the capsular ligament.

Arterial and Nerve Supply

The joint is supplied by the vertebral artery and by the first cervical nerve.

Movements

Since these are ellipsoid joints, they permit movements around two axes. Flexion and extension (nodding) occur around a transverse axis. Slight lateral flexion is permitted around an anteroposterior axis.

1   *Flexion* is brought about by the longus capitis and the rectus capitis anterior.

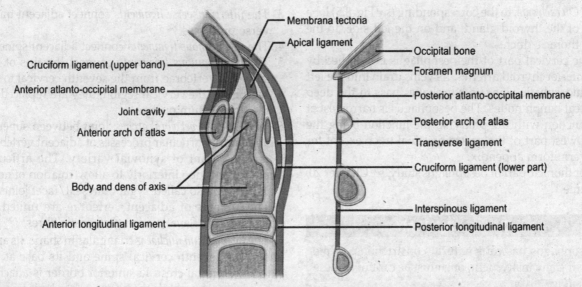

Fig. 9.11: Median section through the foramen magnum and upper two cervical vertebrae showing the ligaments in this region

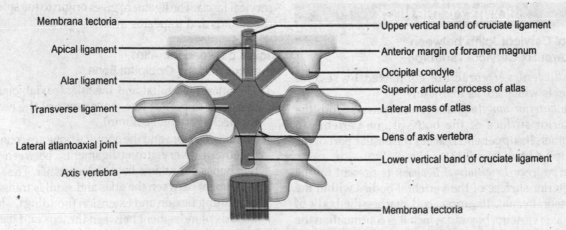

Fig. 9.12: Posterior view of the ligaments connecting the axis with the occipital bone

2 *Extension* is done by the rectus capitis posterior major and minor, the obliquus capitis superior, the semispinalis capitis, the splenius capitis, and the upper part of the trapezius.

3 *Lateral bending* is produced by the rectus capitis lateralis, the semispinalis capitis, the splenius capitis, the sternocleidomastoid, and the trapezius (Fig. 9.13).

Atlantoaxial Joints

Types and Articular Surfaces

These joints comprise:

1 A pair of lateral atlantoaxial joints between the inferior facets of the atlas and the superior facets of the axis. These are plane joints.

2 A median atlantoaxial joint between the dens (odontoid process) and the anterior arch and between dens and transverse ligament of the atlas. It is a pivot joint. The joint has two separate synovial cavities, anterior and posterior (Figs 9.11 and 9.12).

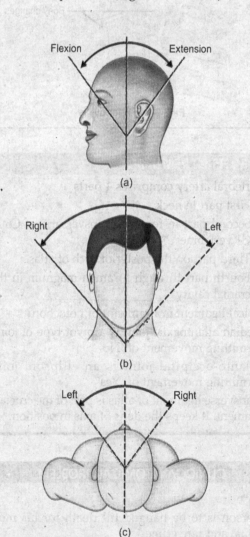

(a)

(b)

(c)

Figs 9.13a to c: Various movements of the neck

Ligaments

The lateral atlantoaxial joints are supported by:

a. A capsular ligament all around.

b. The lateral part of the anterior longitudinal ligament.

c. The ligamentum flavum.

The median atlantoaxial joint is strengthened by the following:

a. The anterior smaller part of the joint between the anterior arch of the atlas and the dens is surrounded by a loose capsular ligament (Fig. 9.11).

b. The posterior larger part of the joint between the dens and transverse ligament (often called a bursa) is often continuous with one of the atlanto-occipital joints. Its main support is the transverse ligament which forms a part of the cruciform ligament of the atlas (Fig. 9.12).

The *transverse ligament* (Fig. 9.12) is attached on each side to the medial surface of the lateral mass of the atlas. In the median plane, its fibres are prolonged upwards to the basiocciput and downwards to the body of the axis, thus forming the *cruciform ligament of the atlas vertebra*. The transverse ligament embraces the narrow neck of the dens, and prevents its dislocation.

Movements

Movements at all three joints are rotatory and take place around a vertical axis. The dens forms a pivot around which the atlas rotates (carrying the skull with it). The movement is limited by the alar ligaments (Figs 9.12 and 9.13a to c).

The rotatory movements are brought about by the obliquus capitis inferior, the rectus capitis posterior major and the splenius capitis of one side (*see* Fig. 10.5), acting with the sternocleidomastoid of the opposite side.

Ligaments Connecting the Axis with the Occipital Bone

These ligaments are the membrana tectoria, the cruciate ligament, the apical ligament of the dens and the alar ligaments. They support both the atlanto-occipital and atlantoaxial joints.

1 The *membrana tectoria* is an upward continuation of the posterior longitudinal ligament. It lies posterior to the transverse ligament. It is attached inferiorly to the posterior surface of the body of the axis and superiorly to the basiocciput (within the foramen magnum) (Fig. 9.11).

2 *Cruciate ligament*: (*see* transverse ligament).

3 The *apical ligament of the dens* extends from the apex of the dens close to the anterior margin of the foramen magnum behind the attachment of the cruciate ligament. It is the continuation of the notochord.

4 The *alar ligament*, one on each side, extends from the upper part of the lateral surface of the dens to the medial surface of the occipital condyles. These are strong ligaments which limit the rotation and flexion of the head. They are relaxed during extension (Fig. 9.12).

CLINICAL ANATOMY

- Death in execution by hanging is due to dislocation of the dens following rupture of the transverse ligament of the dens, which then crushes the spinal cord and medulla. However, hanging can also cause fracture through the axis, or separation of the axis from the third cervical vertebra (Fig. 9.14).
- *Cervical spondylosis.* Injury or degenerative changes of old age may rupture the thin lateral parts of the annulus fibrosus (of the intervertebral disc) resulting in prolapse of the nucleus pulposus. This is known as disc prolapse or spondylosis and may be lateral or median (Fig. 9.15). Although, it is commonest in the lumbar region, it may occur in the lower cervical region. This causes shooting pain along the distribution of the cervical nerve pressed. A direct posterior prolapse may compress the spinal cord.
- Cervical vertebrae may be fractured, or dislocated by a fall on the head with acute flexion of the neck. In the cervical region, the vertebrae can dislocate without any fracture of the articular processes due to their horizontal position.
- Pithing of frog takes place when the cruciate ligament of median atlantoaxial joint ruptures, crushing the vital centres in medulla oblongata, resulting in immediate death. This occurs in judicial hanging as well.
- The degenerative changes or spondylitis may occur in the cervical spine, leading to narrowed intervertebral foramen, causing pressure on the spinal nerves (Fig. 9.16).

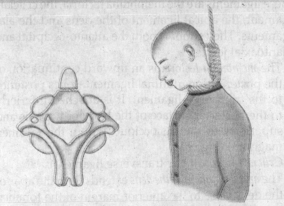

Fig. 9.14: Fracture of the dens during hanging

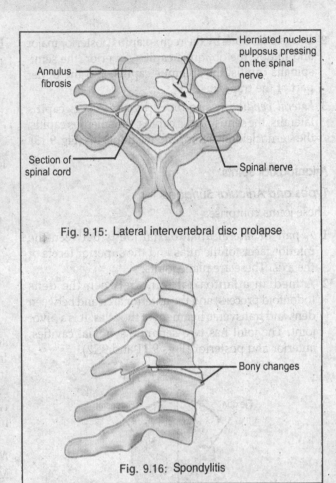

Fig. 9.15: Lateral intervertebral disc prolapse

Fig. 9.16: Spondylitis

FACTS TO REMEMBER

- Vertebral artery comprises 4 parts
  a. First part in neck
  b. Second part in forearm transversaria of C6 to C1 vertebrae
  c. Third part on the posterior arch of atlas.
  d. Fourth part through foramen magnum in the cranial cavity
- Apical ligament is a remnant of notochord
- Median atlantoaxial joint is a pivot type of joint, permitting movement of 'No'
- Atlanto-occipital joint is an ellipsoid joint permitting movement of 'Yes'
- Transverse ligament of atlas is part of the cruciate ligament. It keeps the dens of axis in position.

CLINICOANATOMICAL PROBLEM

Case 1

A person is to be hanged till death for his most unusual and rare crime

- What anatomical changes occur during this procedure?
- Name the ligaments of median atlantoaxial joint.

Ans: Death in execution by hanging is due to dislocation of the dens of the axis vertebra following rupture of the transverse ligament of the dens. Dens all of a sudden is pushed backwards with great force, crushing the lowest part of medulla oblongata which houses the vasomotor centres

The ligaments of atlantoaxial joint are:

- Transverse ligament of dens
- Upper part of vertical band
- Lower part of vertical band

These three parts form cruciform ligament of the atlas vertebra.

There are two joint cavities. The anterior one between the posterior surface of anterior arch of atlas and dens. It is surrounded by loose capsular ligament.

The posterior, larger one is between the dens and the transverse ligament of the dens (Fig. 9.11).

Case 2

A man aged 55 years complained of dysphagia in eating solid and even soft food and liquids. There was a large lymph node felt at the anterior border of sternocleidomastoid muscle. The diagnosis on biopsy was cancer of cervical part of oesophagus.

- How was the large lymph node formed?
- Why did the patient have dysphagia?
- Where can the cancer spread around oesophagus?

Ans: The pain during eating or drinking is due to cancer of the oesophagus. The cancer obliterates increasing part of the lumen, giving rise to pain. The lymphatic drainage of cervical part of oesophagus goes to inferior group of deep cervical lymph nodes. These had metastasized to the lymph node at the anterior border of sternocleidomastoid muscle. Since trachea lies just anterior to oesophagus, the cancer can spread to trachea or any of the principal bronchi. It may even of cause narrowing of trachea or bronchi.

FREQUENTLY ASKED QUESTIONS

1. Describe median atlantoaxial joint. Name the movements which occur here with their muscles.

2. Describe atlanto-occipital joint briefly.

3. Write short notes on/enumerate:
   a. Ligaments connecting axis to the skull
   b. Cruciate ligament
   c. Parts of vertebral artery

MULTIPLE CHOICE QUESTIONS

1. How many synovial cavities are there in median atlantoaxial joint?
   a. One   b. Three
   c. Two   d. Four

2. Which of the following ligaments is the upward continuation of membrana tectoria?
   a. Posterior longitudinal
   b. Ligamentum nuchae
   c. Ligamentum flava
   d. Anterior longitudinal

3. Which ligament mentioned below is chiefly elastic?
   a. Anterior longitudinal
   b. Ligamenta flava

   c. Ligamentum nuchae
   d. Posterior longitudinal

4. Where is the intervertebral disc absent?
   a. Between first and second cervical vertebrae
   b. Between thoracic twelve and first lumbar vertebrae
   c. Between thoracic one and cervical seven vertebrae
   d. Between lumbar five and first sacral vertebrae

5. Which of the following joints do not have a fibrocartilaginous intra-articular disc?
   a. Temporomandibular
   b. Shoulder
   c. Sternoclavicular
   d. Inferior radioulnar

ANSWERS

1. c   2. a   3. b   4. a   5. b

Head and Neck

Back of the Neck

I bend, but do not break

INTRODUCTION

The vertebral column at back provides a median axis for the body (*see* Vol 1—Chap 13; Vol 2—Chap 15; Vol 3—Chap 1). The joints of neck are described in Chap 9. There are big muscles from the sacrum to the skull in different strata which keep the spine straight. The only triangle in the upper most part of back is the suboccipital triangle containing the third part of the vertebral artery, which enters the skull to supply the brain. If it gets pressed, many symptoms appear.

THE MUSCLES

DISSECTION

Extend the incision from external occipital protuberance (i), to the spine of the seventh cervical vertebra. Give a horizontal incision from spine of 7th cervical vertebra or vertebra prominens (iv), till the acromion (v). This will expose the upper part and apex of posterior triangle of neck. Look for the occipital artery at its apex.

Extend the incision from vertebra prominens to spine of lumbar 5 vertebra. Reflect the skin laterally along an oblique line from spine of T12 (ii), till the deltoid tuberosity (iii) (Fig. 10.1).

Close to the median plane in the superficial fascia are seen the greater occipital nerve and occipital artery.

Cut through trapezius muscle vertically at a distance of 2 cm from the median plane. Reflect it laterally and identify the accessory nerve, superficial branch of transverse cervical artery and ventral rami of 3rd and 4th cervical nerves.

Latissimus dorsi has already been exposed by the students dissecting the upper limb. Otherwise extend the incision from T12 spine till L5 spine. Reflect the skin till lateral side of the trunk and define the margins of broad thin latissimus dorsi. This muscle and trapezius form the first layer of muscles.

The second layer comprises splenius muscle, levator scapulae, rhomboid major, rhomboid minor, serratus posterior superior and serratus posterior inferior muscles. The splenius is the highest of these muscles.

Levator scapulae forms part of the muscular floor of the posterior triangle. It is positioned between scalenus medius below and splenius capitis above. Follow its nerve and blood supply from dorsal scapular nerve and deep branch of transverse cervical artery, respectively.

Spinal root of accessory nerve and fibres from C3 and C4 to trapezius muscle lie on the levator scapulae.

Rhomboid minor and major lie on same plane as levator scapulae. Both are supplied by dorsal scapular nerve (C5).

Deep to the two rhomboid muscles is thin aponeurotic serratus posterior superior muscle from spines of C7 and T1–T2 vertebrae to be inserted into 2–5th ribs. Serratus posterior inferior muscle arises from T11 to T12 spines and thoracolumbar fascia and is inserted into 9th–12th ribs.

The third layer is composed of erector spinae or sacrospinalis with its three subdivisions and semispinalis with its three divisions (Figs 10.2a to c).

Erector spinae arises from the dorsal surface of sacrum and ascends up the lumbar region. There it divides into three subdivisions, the medial one is spinalis, inserted into the spines, the intermediate one is longissimus inserted into the transverse processes and the lateral one is iliocostalis, inserted into the ribs. Each of these divisions is made of short parts, fresh slips arising from the area where the lower slips are inserted (Fig. 10.3).

Deep to erector spinae is the semispinalis again made up of three parts: semispinalis thoracis, semispinalis cervicis and semispinalis capitis.

Both these muscles are innervated by the dorsal rami of cervical, thoracic, lumbar and sacral nerves.

Muscles of fourth layer are the multifidus, rotatores, interspinales, intertransversarii and suboccipital muscles (Fig. 10.4).

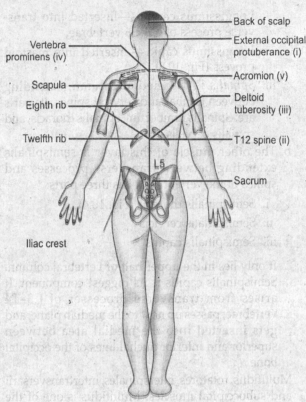

Fig. 10.1: Lines of dissection

Nerve Supply of Skin

The skin of the nape or back of the neck, and of the back of the scalp (Fig. 10.2) is supplied by medial branches of the dorsal rami of C2 the *greater occipital nerve;* C3 the *third occipital nerve.* Each posterior primary ramus divides into a medial and a lateral branch, both of which supply the intrinsic muscles of the back. The medial branch in this region supplies the skin as well. The *dorsal ramus of C1* does not divide into medial and lateral branches, and is distributed only to the muscles bounding the suboccipital triangle.

The *ligamentum nuchae* is a triangular fibrous sheet that separates muscles of the two sides of the neck. It is better developed and is more elastic in quadrupeds in whom, it has to support a heavy head.

MUSCLES OF THE BACK

The *muscles* of the entire back can be grouped into the following four layers from superficial to the deeper plane.

1 Trapezius and latissimus dorsi (*see* Chapter 5, Volume 1).
2 Levator scapulae, rhomboids (two), serratus posterior superior have been studied in Chapter 5, Volume 1. Serratus posterior inferior is mentioned in Chapter 24, Volume 2. Splenius is described briefly here.

Splenius muscles are two in number. These are splenius cervicis and splenius capitis. These cover the deeper muscles like a bandage (Figs 10.2a and b).

Origin: From lower half of ligamentum nuchae and spines of upper 6 thoracic vertebrae. These curve in a half spiral fashion and separate into splenius cervicis and splenius capitis.

Splenius cervicis gets inserted into the posterior tubercles of transverse processes of C1–C4 vertebrae.

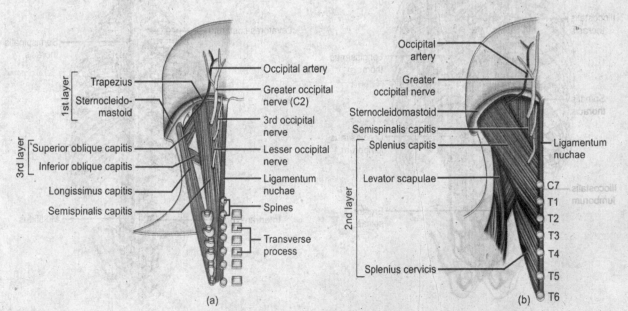

Figs 10.2a and b: Three layers of muscles covering the suboccipital triangle: (a) First and third layers, and (b) second layer of muscles

Splenius capitis forms the floor of the posterior triangle and gets inserted into the mastoid process beneath the sternocleidomastoid muscle (Fig. 10.5). It is supplied by dorsal rami of C1–C6 nerves.

3   a. Erector spinae or sacrospinalis is the true muscle of the back, supplied by posterior rami of the spinal nerves. It extends from the sacrum to the skull (Fig. 10.3).

Origin from the back of sacrum between median and lateral sacral crests, from the dorsal segment of iliac crest and related ligaments. Soon it splits into three columns: Iliocostalis, longissimus, and spinalis:

   i. *Iliocostalis* is the lateral column and comprises iliocostalis lumborum, iliocostalis thoracis and iliocostalis cervicis.

These are short slips and are inserted into angles of the ribs and posterior tubercles of cervical transverse process. Origin of the higher slips is medial to the insertion of the lower slips.

   ii. *Longissimus* is the middle column and is composed of:
Longissimus thoracis—inserted into transverse processes of thoracic vertebrae.

Longissimus cervicis—inserted into transverse process of C2–C6 vertebrae.

Longissimus capitis—inserted into mastoid process (Fig. 10.3).

   iii. *Spinalis* is the medial column, extending between lumbar and cervical spines. Its parts are: Spinalis lumborum, spinalis thoracis, and spinalis cervicis.

b. The other muscle of this layer is semispinalis extending between transverse processes and spines of the vertebrae. It has three parts:

   i. Semispinalis thoracis (Fig. 10.4).

   ii. Semispinalis cervicis

   iii. Semispinalis capitis

It only lies in the upper half of vertebral column. Semispinalis capitis is its biggest component. It arises from transverse processes of C3–T4 vertebrae, passes up next to the median plane, and gets inserted into the medial area between superior and inferior nuchal lines of the occipital bone.

4   Multifidus, rotatores, interspinales, intertransversarii and suboccipital muscles. Multifidus is one of the oblique deep muscles. It arises from mammillary

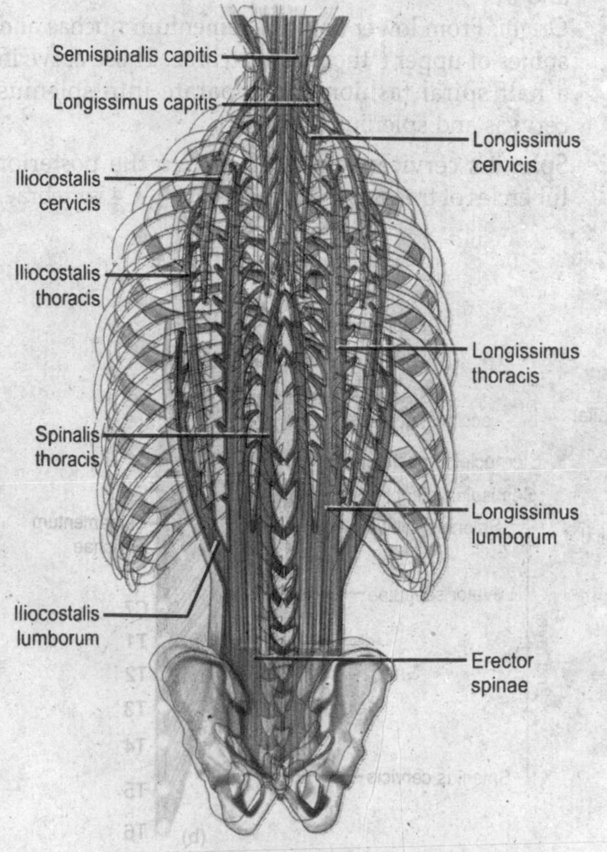

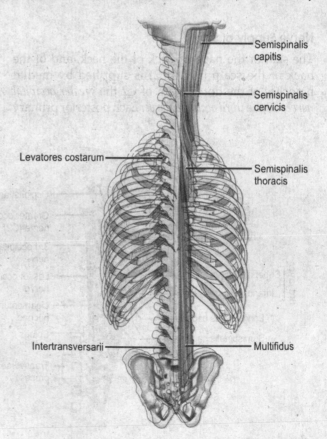

Fig. 10.3: The erector spinae/sacrospinalis muscle with its three columns

Fig. 10.4: Splenius cervicis and capitis; three parts of semispinalis—the multifidus, levator costarum and intertransversarii muscles

process of lumbar vertebrae to be inserted into 2–3 higher spinous processes. Rotatores are the deepest group. These pass from root of transverse process to the root of the spinous process. These are well developed in thoracic region. Interspinales lie between the adjacent spines of the vertebrae. These are better developed in cervical and lumbar regions. Intertransversarii connect the transverse processes of the adjacent vertebrae.

SUBOCCIPITAL TRIANGLE

DISSECTION

It is deep triangle in the area between the occiput and the spine of second cervical (the axis) vertebra. The deepest muscles are the muscles of suboccipital triangle.

Cut the attachments of trapezius from superior nuchal line and reflect it towards the spine of scapula. Cut the splenius capitis from its attachment on the mastoid process and reflect it downwards. Clean the superficial fascia over the semispinalis capitis medially and longissimus capitis laterally. Reflect longissimus capitis downwards from the mastoid process.

Cut through semispinalis capitis and turn it towards lateral side. Define the boundaries and contents of the suboccipital triangle.

Muscle Layers in Neck (Fig. 10.4)

In the *suboccipital region* between the occiput and the spine of the axis vertebra, the four muscular layers are represented by:

- Trapezius.
- Splenius capitis.

- Semispinalis capitis and longissimus capitis.
- The four suboccipital muscles.

The *arteries* found in the back of the neck are:
a. Occipital
b. Deep cervical
c. Third part of the vertebral artery
d. Minute twigs from the second part of the vertebral artery.

The *suboccipital venous plexus* is known for its extensive layout and complex connections.

Suboccipital Muscles

The suboccipital muscles are described in Table 10.1.

The suboccipital triangle is a muscular space situated deep in the suboccipital region.

Exposure of Suboccipital Triangle

In order to expose the triangle, the following layers are reflected (Fig. 10.5).

1 The *skin* is very thick.
2 The *superficial fascia* is fibrous and dense. It contains:
   a. The greater and third occipital nerves.
   b. The terminal part of the occipital artery, with accompanying veins.
3 The fibres of the *trapezius* run downwards and laterally over the triangle. The sternocleidomastoid overlaps the region laterally.
4 The *splenius capitis* runs upwards and laterally for insertion into the mastoid process deep to the sternocleidomastoid.
5 The *semispinalis capitis* runs vertically upwards for insertion into the medial part of the area between the superior and inferior nuchal lines. In the same plane

Muscle	Origin	Insertion	Nerve supply	Actions
Table 10.1: The suboccipital muscles				
1. **Rectus capitis posterior major** (Fig. 10.5)	Spine of axis	Lateral part of the area below the inferior nuchal line	Suboccipital nerve or dorsal ramus C1	1. Mainly postural 2. Acting alone, it turns the chin to the same side 3. Acting together, the two muscles extend the head
2. **Rectus capitis posterior minor** (Fig. 10.5)	Posterior tubercle of atlas	Medial part of the area below the inferior nuchal line	"	1. Mainly postural 2. Extends the head
3. **Obliquus capitis superior** (superior oblique)	Transverse process of atlas	Lateral area between the nuchal lines	"	1. Mainly postural 2. Extends the head 3. Flexes the head laterally
4. **Obliquus capitis inferior** (inferior oblique Fig. 10.5)	Spine of axis	Transverse process of atlas	"	1. Mainly postural 2. Turns chin to the same side

laterally, there lies the *longissimus capitis* which is inserted into the mastoid process deep to the splenius.

Reflection of the semispinalis capitis exposes the *suboccipital triangle*.

Boundaries

Superomedially

Rectus capitis posterior major muscle supplemented by the *rectus capitis posterior minor* (Fig. 10.5).

Superolaterally

Superior oblique capitis muscle.

Inferiorly

Inferior oblique capitis muscle.

Roof

Medially

Dense fibrous tissue covered by the *semispinalis capitis*.

Laterally

Longissimus capitis and occasionally the splenius capitis.

Floor

1 Posterior arch of atlas.
2 Posterior atlanto-occipital membrane.

Contents

1 Third part of vertebral artery (Fig. 10.6).
2 Dorsal ramus of nerve C1—suboccipital nerve.
3 Suboccipital plexus of veins.

Dorsal Ramus of First Cervical Nerve

It emerges between the posterior arch of the atlas and the vertebral artery, and soon breaks up into branches which supply the four suboccipital muscles and the semispinalis capitis. The nerve to the inferior oblique gives off a communicating branch to the greater occipital nerve capitis (Figs 10.5 and 10.6).

Greater Occipital Nerve

It is the large medial branch of the dorsal ramus of the second cervical nerve. It is the *thickest cutaneous nerve* in the body. It winds round the middle of the lower border of the inferior oblique muscle, and runs upwards and medially. It crosses the suboccipital triangle and pierces the semispinalis capitis and trapezius muscles to ramify on the back of the head reaching up to the vertex. It supplies the semispinalis capitis in addition to the scalp (Fig. 10.2a).

Third Occipital Nerve

It is the slender medial branch of the dorsal ramus of the third cervical nerve. After piercing the semispinalis capitis and the trapezius, it ascends medial to the greater occipital nerve. It supplies the skin to the back of the neck up to the external occipital protuberance (Fig. 10.2a).

Vertebral Artery

It is the first and largest branch of the first part of the subclavian artery, destined chiefly to supply the brain. Out of its four parts, only the third part appears in the suboccipital triangle (Figs 10.5 and 10.6). This part

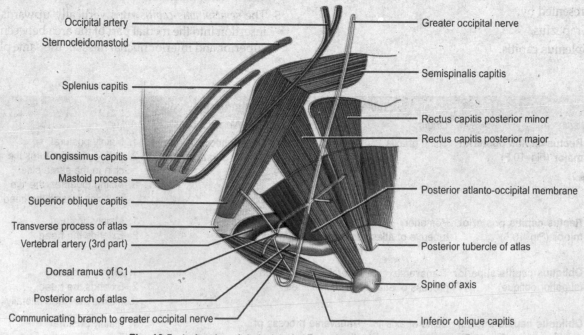

Fig. 10.5: Left suboccipital triangle: Boundaries, floor and contents

Occipital artery
Sternocleidomastoid
Splenius capitis
Longissimus capitis
Mastoid process
Superior oblique capitis
Transverse process of atlas
Vertebral artery (3rd part)
Dorsal ramus of C1
Posterior arch of atlas
Communicating branch to greater occipital nerve

Greater occipital nerve
Semispinalis capitis
Rectus capitis posterior minor
Rectus capitis posterior major
Posterior atlanto-occipital membrane
Posterior tubercle of atlas
Spine of axis
Inferior oblique capitis

Head and Neck

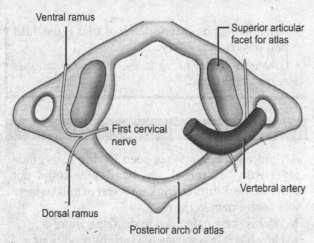

Fig. 10.6: Relationship of the vertebral artery to the atlas vertebra and to the first cervical nerve, as seen from above

appears at the foramen transversarium of the atlas, grooves the atlas, and leaves the triangle by passing deep to the lateral edge of the posterior atlanto-occipital membrane. The artery is separated from the posterior arch of the atlas by the first cervical nerve and its dorsal and ventral rami. For complete description of the vertebral artery, *see* Chapter 9.

Occipital Artery

It arises from the external carotid artery, opposite the origin of the facial artery (Figs 10.2 and 10.5). It runs backwards and upwards deep to the lower border of the posterior belly of the digastric, crossing the carotid sheath, and the accessory and hypoglossal nerves. Next it runs deep to the mastoid process and to the muscles attached to it; the sternocleidomastoid, digastric, splenius capitis and longissimus capitis. The artery then crosses the rectus capitis lateralis, the superior oblique and the semispinalis capitis muscles at the apex of the posterior triangle. Finally, it pierces the trapezius 2.5 cm from the midline and comes to lie along the greater occipital nerve. In the superficial fascia of the scalp, it ha a tortuous course.

Its branches in this region are:

a. Mastoid

b. Meningeal

c. Muscular.

One of the muscular branches is large, it is called the *descending branch* and has superficial and deep branches. The superficial branch anastomoses with the superficial branch of the transverse cervical artery; while the deep branch descends between the semispinalis capitis and cervicis, and anastomoses with the vertebral and deep cervical arteries. It also gives two branches to sternocleidomastoid muscle.

Deep Cervical Artery

It is a branch of the costocervical trunk of the subclavian artery. It passes into the back of the neck just above the neck of the first rib. It ascends deep to the *semispinalis capitis* and anastomoses with the descending branch of the occipital artery (*see* Fig. 8.19).

Suboccipital Plexus of Veins

It lies in and around the suboccipital triangle, and drains the:

1 Muscular veins

2 Occipital veins

3 Internal vertebral venous plexus

4 Condylar emissary vein. It itself drains into the deep cervical and vertebral plexus of veins.

CLINICAL ANATOMY

- Neck rigidity, seen in cases with meningitis, is due to spasm of the extensor muscles. This is caused by irritation of the nerve roots during their passage through the subarachnoid space which is infected. Passive flexion of neck and straight leg raising test cause pain as the nerves are stretched (Figs 10.7a and b).
- Cisternal puncture is done when lumbar puncture fails. The patient either sits up or lies down in the left lateral position. A needle is introduced in the midline above the spine of axis in forward and upward direction parallel to an imaginary line extending from external acoustic meatus to nasion. It passes through the posterior atlanto-occipital membrane between the posterior arch of atlas and the posterior margin of foramen magnum. The needle enters the cerebellomedullary cistern and small amount of CSF is withdrawn.
- Neurosurgeons approach the posterior cranial fossa through this region.

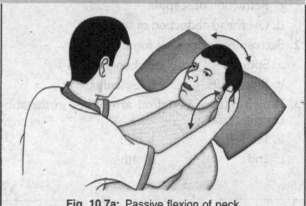

Fig. 10.7a: Passive flexion of neck

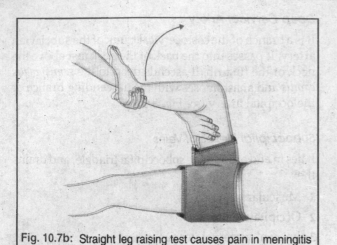
Fig. 10.7b: Straight leg raising test causes pain in meningitis

- Artery lying on posterior arch of atlas is the third part of vertebral artery.
- Greater occipital nerve is the thickest cutaneous nerve of the body.

CLINICOANATOMICAL PROBLEM

A child aged 8 years has been having high grade fever with bad throat. On 4th day he could not move his neck during drinking water or milk as there was severe pain in the neck.
- Why is there pain even in drinking water?
- How has it become such a serious condition?

Ans: Due to bad throat, the infection from pharynx reached middle ear via pharyngotympanic tube, from where it infected the meninges of the brain. This is a serious condition and is called meningitis. The child shows neck rigidity. It is due to spasm of the extensor muscles and is caused by irritation of nerve roots during their passage through subarachnoid space, which is infected.

Passive flexion of neck and straight leg raising test result in pain as the nerves are stretched (Figs 10.7a and b).

FACTS TO REMEMBER

Muscles of the back are disposed in four layers:
- Muscles of 1st and 2nd layers are supplied by nerves of upper limb except trapezius, splenius capitis and splenius cervicis.
- Muscles of 3rd and 4th layers are true muscles of the back, supplied by dorsal primary rami.

FREQUENTLY ASKED QUESTIONS

1. Enumerate the boundaries and contents of the suboccipital triangle. Name the muscles supplied by dorsal ramus of 1st cervical nerve.
2. Name the various parts of sacrospinalis/erector spinae muscle.

3. Write short notes on:
   a. Occipital artery
   b. Meningitis

MULTIPLE CHOICE QUESTIONS

1. Which action is not done by trapezius muscles?
   a. Protraction of scapula
   b. Shrugging of shoulder
   c. Retraction of scapula
   d. Overhead abduction of scapula
2. Sacrospinalis does not form:
   a. Spinalis   b. Longissimus
   c. Iliocostalis   d. Splenius
3. Which part of vertebral artery lies in the suboccipital triangle?
   a. 1st   b. 3rd
   c. 2nd   d. 4th

4. Dorsal ramus of one of the cervical nerves has no cutaneous branch:
   a. 1st   b. 2nd
   c. 3rd   d. 4th
5. Which is the thickest cutaneous nerve of the body?
   a. Greater occipital
   b. Lesser occipital
   c. Great auricular
   d. Third occipital
6. Which of the following cervical nerves is known as suboccipital nerve?
   a. 1st   b. 2nd
   c. 3rd   d. 4th

ANSWERS

1. a   2. d   3. b   4. a   5. a   6. a

Contents of Vertebral Canal

Remember that your patient is a human being like yourself. Your knowledge of anatomy may save his or her life
—Richard Snell

When the vertebrae are put in a sequence, their vertebral foramina lie one below the other forming a continuous canal which is called the *vertebral canal*. This canal contains the three meninges with their spaces and the spinal cord including the cauda equina. The intervertebral foramina are a pair of foramina between the pedicles of the adjacent vertebrae. Each foramen contains dorsal and ventral roots, trunk and dorsal and ventral primary rami of the spinal nerve, and spinal vessels.

REMOVAL OF SPINAL CORD

DISSECTION

Clean the spines and laminae of the entire vertebral column by removing all the muscles attached to them. Trace the dorsal rami of spinal nerves towards the intervertebral foramina. Saw through the spines and laminae of the vertebrae carefully and detach them so that the spinal medulla/spinal cord encased in the meninges becomes visible.

Clean the external surface of dura mater enveloping the spinal cord by removing fat and epidural plexus of veins. Carefully cut through a small part of the dura mater by a fine median incision. Extend this incision above and below. See the delicate arachnoid mater. Incise it. Push the spinal cord to one side and try to identify the ligamentum denticulatum. Define the attachments of the dorsal and ventral nerve roots on the surface of spinal cord and their union to form the trunk of the spinal nerve. Cut the trunk of all spinal nerves on both the sides. Gently pull the spinal cord with cauda equina out from the vertebral canal.

CONTENTS

The vertebral canal contains the following structures from without inwards (Fig. 11.1).

1 Epidural or extradural space.
2 Thick dura mater or pachymeninx.
3 Subdural capillary space.
4 Delicate arachnoid mater.
5 Wide subarachnoid space containing cerebrospinal fluid (CSF).
6 Firm pia mater. The arachnoid and pia together form the leptomeninges.
7 Spinal cord or spinal medulla and the cauda equina.

The spinal cord is considered along with the brain in Chapter 3, Volume 4. The other contents are described below.

Epidural Space

Epidural space lies between the spinal dura mater, and the periosteum with ligaments lining the vertebral canal.
It contains:
a. Loose areolar tissue.
b. Semiliquid fat.

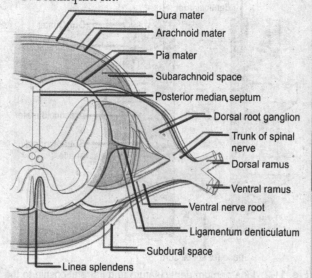

- Dura mater
- Arachnoid mater
- Pia mater
- Subarachnoid space
- Posterior median septum
- Dorsal root ganglion
- Trunk of spinal nerve
- Dorsal ramus
- Ventral ramus
- Ventral nerve root
- Ligamentum denticulatum
- Subdural space
- Linea splendens

Fig. 11.1: Schematic transverse section showing the spinal meninges

c. Spinal arteries on their way to supply the deeper contents.

d. The internal vertebral venous plexus.

The *spinal arteries* arise from different sources at different levels; they enter the vertebral canal through the intervertebral foramina, and supply the spinal cord, the spinal nerve roots, the meninges, the periosteum and ligaments.

Venous blood from the spinal cord drains into the epidural or internal vertebral plexus.

Spinal Dura Mater

Spinal dura mater is a thick, tough fibrous membrane which forms a loose sheath around the spinal cord (Fig. 11.2). It is continuous with the meningeal layer of the cerebral dura mater. The spinal dura extends from the foramen magnum to the lower border of the second sacral vertebra; whereas the spinal cord ends at the lower border of first lumbar vertebra. The dura gives tubular prolongations to the dorsal and ventral nerve roots and to the spinal nerves as they pass through the intervertebral foramina.

Subdural Space

Subdural space is a capillary or potential space between the dura and the arachnoid, containing a thin film of serous fluid. This space permits movements of the dura over the arachnoid. The space is continued for a short distance on to the spinal nerves, and is in free communication with the lymph spaces of the nerves.

Arachnoid Mater

Arachnoid mater is a thin, delicate and transparent membrane that loosely invests the entire central nervous system (Fig. 11.2). Inferiorly, it extends, like

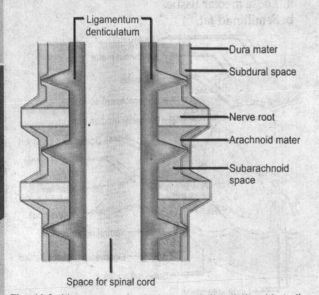

Fig. 11.2: Ligamentum denticulatum and its relationship to the dura mater and to the arachnoid mater

the dura, up to the lower border of the second sacral vertebra. It is adherent to the dura only where some structures pierce the membrane, and where the ligamentum denticulata are attached to the dura mater.

Subarachnoid Space

Subarachnoid space is a wide space between the pia and the arachnoid, filled with cerebrospinal fluid (CSF). It surrounds the brain and spinal cord like a water cushion. The spinal subarachnoid space is wider than the space around the brain. It is widest below the lower end of the spinal cord where it encloses the cauda equina. *Lumbar puncture* is usually done in the lower widest part of the space, between third and fourth lumbar vertebrae.

Spinal Pia Mater

Spinal pia mater is thicker, firmer, and less vascular than the cerebral pia, but both are made up of two layers:

a. An outer *epi-pia* containing larger vessels.

b. An inner *pia-glia or pia-intima* which is in contact with nervous tissue.

Between the two layers, there are many small blood vessels and also cleft like spaces which communicate with the subarachnoid space. The pia mater closely invests the spinal cord, and is continued below the spinal cord as the *filum terminale*.

Posteriorly, the pia is adherent to the posterior median septum of the spinal cord, and is also connected to the arachnoid by a fenestrated *subarachnoid septum*.

Anteriorly, the pia is folded into the anterior median fissure of the spinal cord. It thickens at the mouth of the fissure to form a median, longitudinal glistening band, called the *linea splendens* (Fig. 11.1).

On each side between the ventral and dorsal nerve roots, the pia forms a narrow vertical ridge, called the *ligamentum denticulatum*. This is so called because it gives off a series of triangular tooth-like processes which project from its lateral free border (Fig. 11.3). Each ligament has 21 processes; the first at the level of the foramen magnum, and the last between twelfth thoracic and first lumbar spinal nerves. Each process passes through the arachnoid to the dura between two *adjacent spinal nerves*. The processes suspend the spinal cord in the middle of the subarachnoid space.

The *filum terminale* is a delicate, thread-like structure about 20 cm long. It extends from the apex of the conus medullaris to the dorsum of the first piece of the coccyx. It is composed chiefly of pia mater, although a few nerve fibres rudiments of 2nd and 3rd coccygeal nerves are found adherent to the upper part of its outer surface. The central canal of the spinal cord extends into it for about 5 mm.

The filum terminale is subdivided into a part lying within the dural sheath called the *filum terminale*

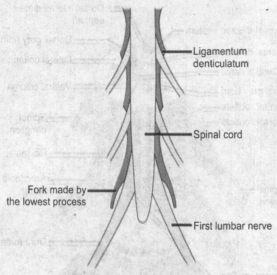

Fig. 11.3: Ligamentum denticulatum

internum; and a part lying outside the dural sheath, below the level of the second sacral vertebra called the *filum terminale externum*. The filum terminale internum is 20 cm long, and the externum is 5 cm long.

Pial sheaths surround the nerve roots crossing the subarachnoid space, and the vessels entering the substance of the spinal cord.

CLINICAL ANATOMY

Leptomeningitis
- Inflammation due to infection of leptomeninges, i.e. pia mater and arachnoid mater is known as *meningitis*. This is commonly tubercular or pyogenic. It is characterized by fever, marked headache, neck rigidity, often accompanied by delirium and convulsions, and a changed biochemistry of CSF. CSF pressure is raised, its proteins and cell content are increased, and sugars and chloride are selectively diminished.
- *Lumbar puncture in adult:* Patient is lying on side with maximally flexed spine. A line is taken between highest points of iliac spine at L4 level. Skin locally anaesthetized, and lumbar puncture needle with trocar inserted carefully between L3 and L4 spines. Needle courses through skin fat, supraspinous and interspinous ligaments, ligamentum flava, epidural space, dura, arachnoid, subarachnoid space to release CSF (Fig. 11.4).
- *Lumbar puncture in infant/children:* During 2nd month of life, spinal cord usually reaches L3 level. Lumbar puncture needle is introduced in flexed spine between L4 and L5.
- *Cisternal puncture:* This procedure is rather difficult and dangerous. Cerebellomedullary cistern is approached through posterior atlanto-occipital membrane.
- *Lumbar epidural:* The epidural space is the space between vertebral canal and dura mater. The epidural space is deeper in the midline. The procedure is same as lumbar puncture, the needle should reach only in the epidural space and not deep to it in the dura mater. Epidural space is utilized for giving anaesthesia or analgesia (Fig. 11.5).
- *Caudal epidural:* The needle is passed through sacral hiatus, which lies equidistant from the right and left posterior superior iliac spines. The needle passes through posterior sacrococcygeal ligament and enters the sacral canal. Then the hub of needle is lowered so that it passes along sacral canal. This space lies below S2 (Fig. 11.6).

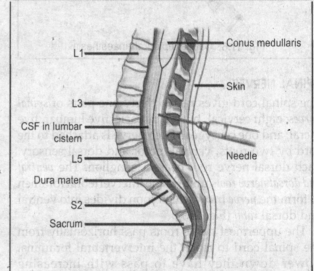

Fig. 11.4: Lumbar puncture in an adult

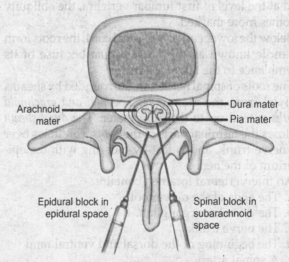

Fig. 11.5: Lumbar epidural anaesthesia and spinal block

Head and Neck

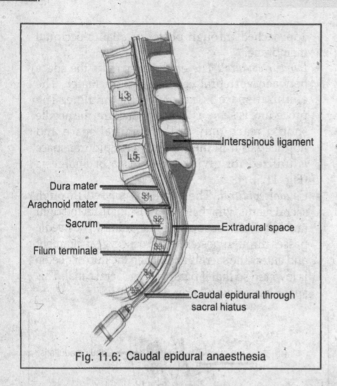

Fig. 11.6: Caudal epidural anaesthesia

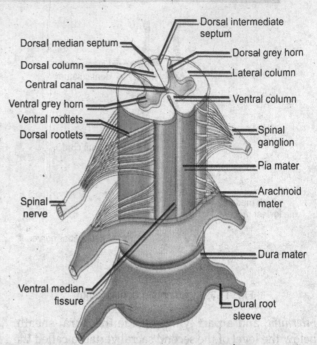

Fig. 11.7: Formation of spinal nerve

SPINAL NERVES

The spinal cord gives rise to thirty-one pairs of *spinal nerves:* eight cervical, twelve thoracic, five lumbar, five sacral, and one coccygeal. Each nerve is attached to the cord by two roots, ventral motor and dorsal sensory. Each dorsal nerve root bears a ganglion. The *ventral and dorsal nerve roots* unite in the intervertebral foramen to form the *nerve trunk* which soon divides into ventral and dorsal *rami* (Fig. 11.7).

The uppermost nerve roots pass horizontally from the spinal cord to reach the intervertebral foramina. Lower down they have to pass with increasing obliquity, as the spinal cord is much shorter than the vertebral column. Below the termination of the spinal cord at the level of first lumbar vertebra, the obliquity becomes more marked.

Below the lower end of the spinal cord, the roots form a bundle known as the *cauda equina* because of its resemblance to the tail of a horse.

The roots of spinal nerves are surrounded by sheaths derived from the meninges. The *pial and arachnoid sheaths* extend up to the dura mater. The *dural sheath* encloses the terminal parts of the roots, continues over the nerve trunk, and is lost by merging with the epineurium of the nerve.

An intervertebral foramen contains:
a. The ends of the nerve roots.
b. The dorsal root ganglion.
c. The nerve trunk.
d. The beginning of the dorsal and ventral rami
e. A spinal artery.
f. An intervertebral vein (Fig. 11.1).

CLINICAL ANATOMY

Vertebral canal
- Compression of the spinal cord by a tumour gives rise to paraplegia or quadriplegia, depending on the level of compression.
- Spinal tumours may arise from dura mater—meningioma, glial cells—glioma, nerve roots—neurofibroma, ependyma–ependymoma, and other tissues. Apart from compression of the spinal cord, the tumour causes obstruction of the subarachnoid space so that pressure of CSF is low below the level of lesion (*Froin's syndrome*). There is yellowish discolouration of CSF below the level of obstruction. CSF reveals high level of protein but the cell content is normal. *Queckenstedt's test* does not show a sudden rise and a sudden fall of CSF pressure by coughing or by brief pressure over the jugular veins. Spinal block can be confirmed either by myelography, CT scan or MRI scan.
- Compression of the cauda equina gives rise to flaccid paraplegia, saddle anaesthesia and sphincter disturbances. This is called the *cauda equina syndrome.*
- Compression of roots of spinal nerves may be caused by prolapse of an intervertebral disc, by osteophytes (formed in osteoarthritis), by a cervical rib, or by an extramedullary tumour. Such compression results in shooting pain along the distribution of the nerve.

VERTEBRAL SYSTEM OF VEINS

The vertebral venous plexus assumes importance in cases of:

1 Carcinoma of the prostate causing secondaries in the vertebral column and the skull.
2 Chronic empyema (collection of pus in the pleural cavity) causing brain abscess by septic emboli.

Anatomy of the Vertebral Venous Plexus

The vertebral venous system is made up of a valveless, complicated network of veins with a longitudinal pattern. It runs parallel to and anastomoses with the superior and inferior venae cavae. This network has three intercommunicating subdivisions (Fig. 11.8).

1 *The epidural plexus:* Lies in the vertebral canal outside the dura mater. The plexus consists of a postcentral and a prelaminar portion. Each portion is drained by two vessels. The plexus drains the structures in the vertebral canal, and is itself drained at regular intervals by segmental veins—vertebral, posterior intercostal, lumbar and lateral sacral.
2 *Plexus within the vertebral bodies:* It drains backwards into the epidural plexus, and anterolaterally into the external vertebral plexus.
3 *External vertebral venous plexus:* It consists of anterior vessels lying in front of the vertebral bodies, and the posterior vessels on the back of the vertebral arches and on adjacent muscles. It is drained by segmental veins.

The suboccipital plexus of veins is a part of the external plexus. It lies in the suboccipital triangle. It receives the occipital veins of the scalp, is connected with the transverse sinus by emissary veins, and drains into the subclavian veins.

Communications and Implications

Valveless vertebral system of veins communicates:
1 Above with the intracranial venous sinuses.
2 Below with the pelvic veins, the portal vein, and the caval system of veins.

The veins are *valveless* and the blood can flow in them in either direction. An increase in intrathoracic or intra-abdominal pressure, brought about by coughing and straining, may cause blood to flow in the plexus away from the heart, either upwards or downwards. Such periodic changes in venous pressure are clinically important because they make possible the spread of tumours or infections. For example, cells from pelvic, abdominal, thoracic and breast tumours may enter the venous system, and may ultimately lodge in the vertebrae, the spinal cord, the skull, or the brain.

The common primary sites of tumours causing secondaries in vertebrae are the breast and the prostate.

FACTS TO REMEMBER

- Spinal cord in adult ends at lower border of lumbar one vertebra
- Spinal dura mater and arachnoid mater extend till second sacral vertebra.
- Spinal pia mater comprises an outer epi-pia and an inner pia-intima.
- Ligamenta denticulata of pia mater are two vertical ridges with 21 tooth-like processes which suspend the spinal cord in the subarachnoid space.
  The lowest or 21st process lies between T12 and L1 spinal nerves.
- Through the vertebral venous plexus, secondaries of prostate or breast can reach up to the cranial cavity.

CLINICOANATOMICAL PROBLEM

A patient suffering from cancer of prostate gland has developed secondaries in the brain
- What route is taken by cancer cells to reach the brain from the prostate gland, a pelvic organ?

Ans: The veins from prostate drain into prostatic venous plexus which communicates with the pelvic veins. These veins send small tributaries through pelvic sacral foramina into the vertebral canal. The vertebral canal lodges vertebral venous plexus which continues up the whole height of the vertebral canal and drains into segmental veins in abdominal cavity, thoracic cavity, in the neck and in basilar venous plexus. Thus, cancer cells "climb" up to reach basilar venous plexus which has connections with cerebral veins. These cells travel through the cerebral veins to settle in brain resulting in secondaries. This plexus is valveless and dangerous.

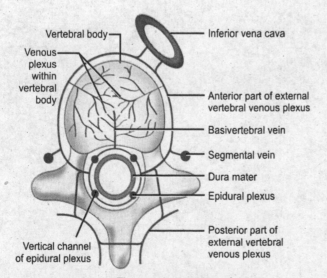

Vertebral body
Inferior vena cava
Venous plexus within vertebral body
Anterior part of external vertebral venous plexus
Basivertebral vein
Segmental vein
Dura mater
Epidural plexus
Posterior part of external vertebral venous plexus
Vertical channel of epidural plexus

Fig. 11.8: The vertebral system of veins

Head and Neck

FREQUENTLY ASKED QUESTION

1. Write short notes on:
   a. Cauda equina
   b. Ligamentum denticulatum
   c. Filum terminale
   d. Typical spinal nerve
   e. Caudal anaesthesia

MULTIPLE CHOICE QUESTIONS

1. Where does main part of vertebral venous plexus lie?
   a. Subdural space
   b. Epidural space
   c. Subarachnoid space
   d. Outside the vertebrae
2. Contents of thoracic part of vertebral canal are following *except*:
   a. Dura mater
   b. Arachnoid mater
   c. Pia mater
   d. Cauda equina
3. Intervertebral foramen contains all *except*:
   a. Ends of nerve roots
   b. Nerve trunk
   c. Sympathetic ganglion
   d. Spinal artery
4. Subarachnoid space extends till:
   a. S1 vertebra   b. S2 vertebra
   c. L1 vertebra   d. L3 vertebra

ANSWERS

1. b   2. d   3. c   4. b

Cranial Cavity

Happiness is when head, heart and hand work in harmony
—Krishna Garg

INTRODUCTION

Cranial cavity, the highest placed cavity, contains the brain, meninges, venous sinuses, all cranial nerves, four petrosal nerves, parts of internal carotid artery and a part of the vertebral artery besides the special senses. The anterior branch of middle meningeal artery lies at the pterion and is prone to rupture resulting in extra-dural haemorrhage.

CONTAINS OF CRANIAL CAVITY

DISSECTION

Detach the epicranial aponeurosis if not already done laterally till the inferior temporal line. In the region of the temple, detach the temporalis muscle with its over-lying fascia and reflect these downwards over the pinna.

Removal of Skull Cap or Calvaria

Draw a horizontal line across the skull 1 cm above the orbital margins and 1 cm above the inion. Saw through the skull. Be careful in the temporal region as skull is rather thin there. Separate the inner table of skull from the fused endosteum and dura mater.

Removal of the Brain

To remove the brain and its enveloping meninges, the structures leaving or entering the brain through various foramina of the skull have to be carefully detached/incised. Start from the anterior aspect by detaching falx cerebri from the crista galli.

Put 2–3 blocks under the shoulders so that head falls backwards. This will expose the olfactory bulb, which may be lifted from the underlying anterior cranial fossa. Identify optic nerve, internal carotid artery, infundibulum passing towards hypophysis cerebri. Divide all three structures. Cut through the oculomotor and trochlear nerves in relation to free margin of tentorium cerebelli (Fig. 12.1). Divide the attachment of tentorium from the petrous temporal bone.

Identify and divide trigeminal, abducent, facial, and vestibulo-cochlear nerves. Then cut glossopharyngeal, vagus, accessory and hypoglossal nerves. All these nerves have to be cut first on one side and then on the other side. Lastly identify the two vertebral arteries entering the skull through foramen magnum on each side of the spinal medulla. With a sharp knife cut through these structures. Thus the whole brain with the meninges can be gently removed from the skull. Preserve it in 5% formaldehyde.

Cut through the dura mater on the ventral aspect of brain till the inferolateral borders along the superciliary margin. Pull upwards the fold of dura mater present between the adjacent medial surfaces of cerebral hemispheres. This will be possible till the occipital lobe of brain. Pull backwards a similar but much smaller fold between two lobes of cerebellum, i.e. falx cerebelli.

Separating the cerebrum from the cerebellum is a double fold of dura mater called tentorium cerebelli. Pull it out in a horizontal plane by giving incision along the petrous temporal bone (Fig. 12.1).

Learn about the folds of dura mater, i.e. falx cerebri, tentorium cerebelli, falx cerebelli, diaphragma sellae including trigeminal cave from the specimen with the help of base of skull. Make a paper model of these dural folds for recapitulation.

Contents

The convex upper wall of the cranial cavity is called the *vault*. It is uniform and smooth. The base of the cranial cavity is uneven and presents three cranial fossae (anterior, middle and posterior) lodging the uneven base of the brain (Figs 12.2a to c).

The cranial cavity contains the brain and meninges; the outer dura mater, the middle arachnoid mater, and the inner pia mater. The dura mater is the thickest of the three meninges. It encloses the cranial venous sinuses, and has a distinct blood supply and nerve supply. The dura is separated from the arachnoid by a potential subdural space. The arachnoid is separated from the pia by a wider subarachnoid space filled with cerebrospinal fluid (CSF). The arachnoid, pia, subarachnoid space and CSF are dealt with the brain; the dura is described here.

Cerebral Dura Mater

The dura mater is the outermost, thickest and toughest membrane covering the brain (*dura* = hard) (*mater* = mother).

There are two layers of dura:

a. An outer or *endosteal layer* which serves as an internal periosteum or endosteum or endocranium for the skull bones.

b. An inner or *meningeal layer* which surrounds the brain. The meningeal layer is continuous with the spinal dura mater.

The two layers are fused to each other at all places, except where the cranial venous sinuses are enclosed between them.

Endosteal Layer or Endocranium

1 The endocranium is continuous:

a. With the periosteum lining the outside of the skull or pericranium through the sutures and foramina.

b. With the periosteal lining of the orbit through the superior orbital fissure.

2 It provides sheaths for the cranial nerves, the sheaths fuse with the epineurium outside the skull. Over the optic nerve, the dura forms a sheath which becomes continuous with the sclera.

3 Its outer surface is adherent to the inner surface of the cranial bones by a number of fine fibrous and vascular processes. The adhesion is most marked at the sutures, on the base of the skull and around the foramen magnum.

Meningeal Layer

At places, the meningeal layer of dura mater is folded on itself to form partitions which divide the cranial cavity into compartments which lodge different parts of the brain (Fig. 12.1). The folds are:

- Falx cerebri
- Tentorium cerebelli
- Falx cerebelli
- Diaphragma sellae.

Falx cerebri

The falx cerebri is a large sickle-shaped fold of dura mater occupying the median longitudinal fissure between the two cerebral hemispheres (Fig. 12.1). It has two ends:

1 The *anterior end* is narrow, and is attached to the crista galli.

2 The *posterior end* is broad, and is attached along the median plane to the upper surface of the tentorium cerebelli.

The falx cerebri has two margins:

1 The *upper margin* is convex and is attached to the lips of the sagittal sulcus.

2 The *lower margin* is concave and free.

The falx cerebri has right and left surfaces each of which is related to the medial surface of the corresponding cerebral hemisphere.

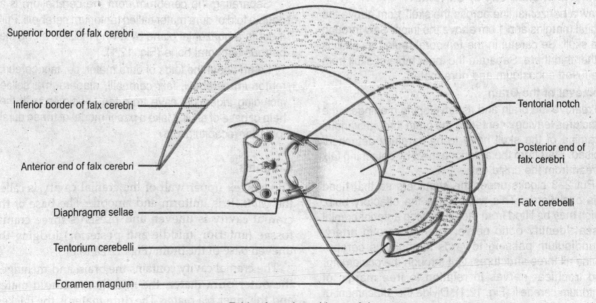

Superior border of falx cerebri

Inferior border of falx cerebri

Anterior end of falx cerebri

Diaphragma sellae

Tentorium cerebelli

Foramen magnum

Tentorial notch

Posterior end of falx cerebri

Falx cerebelli

Fig. 12.1: Folds of meningeal layer of dura mater

Three important venous sinuses are present in relation to this fold. The *superior sagittal sinus* lies along the upper margin; the *inferior sagittal* sinus along the lower margin; and the *straight sinus* along the line of attachment of the falx to the tentorium cerebelli (Figs 12.2a to c).

Tentorium cerebelli

The tentorium cerebelli is a tent-shaped fold of dura mater, forming the roof of the posterior cranial fossa. It separates the cerebellum from the occipital lobes of the cerebrum, and broadly divides the cranial cavity into supratentorial and infratentorial compartments. The infratentorial compartment is the posterior cranial fossa containing the hindbrain and the lower part of the mid-brain.

The tentorium cerebelli has a free margin and an attached margin (Fig. 12.3). The *anterior free margin* is U-shaped and free. The ends of the 'U' are attached anteriorly to the anterior clinoid processes. This margin bounds the *tentorial notch* which is occupied by the midbrain and the anterior part of the superior vermis. The *outer or attached margin* is convex. Posterolaterally, it is attached to the lips of the transverse sulci on the occipital bone, and on the posteroinferior angle of the parietal bone. Anterolaterally, it is attached to the superior border of the petrous temporal bone and to the posterior clinoid processes. Along the attached margin, there are the transverse and superior petrosal venous sinuses.

The *trigeminal* or *Meckel's cave* is a recess of dura mater present in relation to the attached margin of the tentorium. It is formed by evagination of the inferior layer of the tentorium over the trigeminal impression on the petrous temporal bone. It contains the trigeminal ganglion (Fig. 12.4).

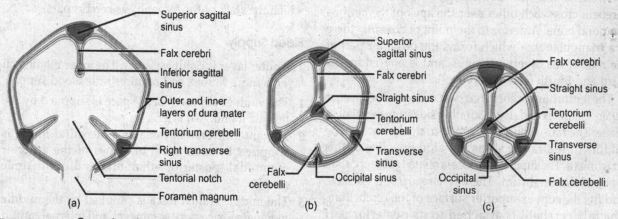

Figs 12.2a to c: Coronal sections through the posterior cranial fossa showing folds of dura mater and the venous sinuses enclosed in them: (a) Section through the tentorial notch (anterior part of the fossa), (b) section through the middle part of the fossa, and (c) section through the posteriormost part

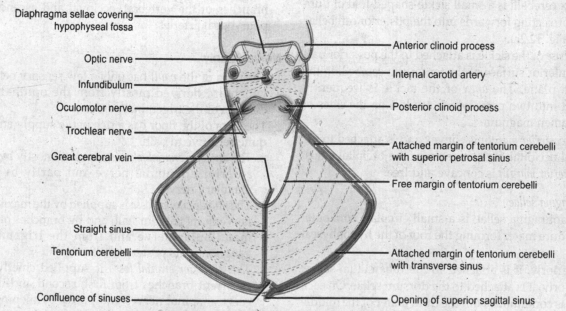

Fig. 12.3: Tentorium cerebelli and diaphragma sellae seen from above

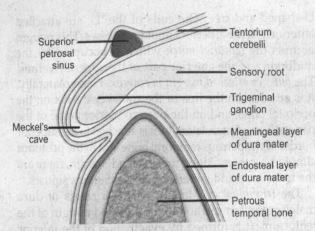

Fig. 12.4: Parasagittal section through the petrous temporal bone and meninges to show the formation of the trigeminal cave

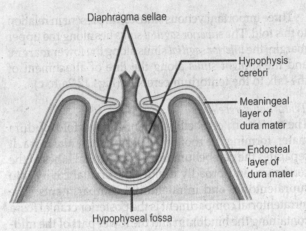

Fig. 12.5: Diaphragma sellae as seen in a sagittal section through the hypophyseal fossa

The free and attached margins of the tentorium cerebelli cross each other near the apex of the petrous temporal bone. Anterior to the point of crossing, there is a triangular area which forms the posterior part of the roof of the cavernous sinus, and is pierced by the third and fourth cranial nerves.

The tentorium cerebelli has two surfaces. The *superior surface* is convex and slopes to either side from the median plane. The falx cerebri is attached to this surface, in the midline; the straight sinus lies along the line of this attachment. The superior surface is related to the occipital lobes of the cerebrum. The *inferior surface* is concave and fits the convex superior surface of the cerebellum. The falx cerebelli is attached to its posterior part (Fig. 12.2c).

Falx cerebelli

The falx cerebelli is a small sickle-shaped fold of dura mater projecting forwards into the posterior cerebellar notch (Fig. 12.2c).

The *base* of the sickle is attached to the posterior part of the inferior surface of the tentorium cerebelli in the median plane. The *apex* of the sickle is frequently divided into two parts which are lost on the sides of the foramen magnum.

The *posterior margin* is convex and is attached to the internal occipital crest. It encloses the occipital sinus. The *anterior margin* is concave and free.

Diaphragma sellae

The diaphragma sellae is a small circular, horizontal fold of dura mater forming the roof of the hypophyseal fossa.

Anteriorly, it is attached to the tuberculum sellae. Posteriorly, it is attached to the dorsum sellae. On each side, it is continuous with the dura mater of the middle cranial fossa (Fig. 12.5).

The diaphragma has a central aperture through which the stalk of the hypophysis cerebri passes.

Blood Supply

The outer layer is richly vascular. The inner meningeal layer is more fibrous and requires little blood supply.

1 The vault or supratentorial space is supplied by the middle meningeal artery.
2 The anterior cranial fossa and the dural lining is supplied by meningeal branches of the anterior ethmoidal, posterior ethmoidal and ophthalmic arteries.
3 The middle cranial fossa is supplied by the middle meningeal, accessory meningeal, and internal carotid arteries; and by meningeal branches of the ascending pharyngeal artery.
4 The posterior cranial fossa is supplied by meningeal branches of the vertebral, occipital and ascending pharyngeal arteries.

Nerve Supply

1 The dura of the *vault* has only a few sensory nerves which are derived mostly from the ophthalmic division of the trigeminal nerve.
2 The dura of the floor has a rich nerve supply and is quite sensitive to pain.
   a. The *anterior cranial fossa* is supplied mostly by the anterior ethmoidal nerve and partly by the maxillary nerve.
   b. The *middle cranial fossa* is supplied by the maxillary nerve in its anterior half, and by branches of the mandibular nerve and from the trigeminal ganglion in its posterior half.
   c. The *posterior cranial fossa* is supplied chiefly by recurrent branches from first, second and third cervical spinal nerves and partly by meningeal branches of the ninth and tenth cranial nerves.

CLINICAL ANATOMY

- *Pain sensitive intracranial structures* are:
  a. The large cranial venous sinuses and their tributaries from the surface of the brain.
  b. Dural arteries.
  c. The dural floor of the anterior and posterior cranial fossae.
  d. Arteries at the base of the brain.
- *Headache* may be caused by:
  a. Dilatation of intracranial arteries.
  b. Dilatation of extracranial arteries.
  c. Traction or distension of intracranial pain sensitive structures.
  d. Infection and inflammation of intracranial and extracranial structures supplied by the sensory cranial and cervical nerves.
- *Extradural and subdural haemorrhages* are both common. An extradural haemorrhage can be distinguished from a subdural haemorrhage because of the following differences.
  a. The extradural haemorrhage is arterial due to injury to middle meningeal artery, whereas subdural haemorrhage is venous in nature.
  b. Symptoms of cerebral compression are late in extradural haemorrhage.
  c. In an extradural haemorrhage, paralysis first appears in the face and then spreads to the lower parts of the body. In a subdural haemorrhage, the progress of paralysis is haphazard.
  d. In an extradural haemorrhage, there is no blood in the CSF, while it is a common feature of subdural haemorrhage.

VENOUS SINUSES OF DURA MATER

These are venous spaces, the walls of which are formed by dura mater. They have an inner lining of endothelium. There is no muscle in their walls. They have no valves.

Venous sinuses receive venous blood from the brain, the meninges, and bones of the skull. Cerebrospinal fluid is poured into some of them.

Cranial venous sinuses communicate with veins outside the skull through *emissary veins*. These communications help to keep the pressure of blood in the sinuses constant (*see* Table 1.1).

There are 23 venous sinuses, of which 8 are paired and 7 are unpaired.

Paired Venous Sinuses

There is one sinus each on right and left side.
1 Cavernous sinus.
2 Superior petrosal sinus (Fig. 12.4).
3 Inferior petrosal sinus.
4 Transverse sinus (Fig. 12.2).
5 Sigmoid sinus.
6 Sphenoparietal sinus.
7 Petrosquamous sinus.
8 Middle meningeal sinus/veins.

Unpaired Venous Sinuses

These are median in position.
1 Superior sagittal sinus (Fig. 12.2).
2 Inferior sagittal sinus.
3 Straight sinus (Fig. 12.3).
4 Occipital sinus.
5 Anterior intercavernous sinus.
6 Posterior intercavernous sinus.
7 Basilar plexus of veins.

CAVERNOUS SINUS

DISSECTION

Define the cavernous sinuses situated on each side of the body of the sphenoid bone. Cut through it between the anterior and posterior ends and locate its contents. Define its connections with the other venous sinuses and veins.

Introduction

Each cavernous sinus is a large venous space situated in the middle cranial fossa, on either side of the body of the sphenoid bone. Its interior is divided into a number of spaces or caverns by trabeculae. The trabeculae are much less conspicuous in the living than in the dead (Fig. 12.6).

The floor and medial wall of the sinus is formed by the endosteal dura mater. The lateral wall, and roof are formed by the meningeal dura mater.

Anteriorly, the sinus extends up to the medial end of the superior orbital fissure and *posteriorly*, up to the apex of the petrous temporal bone. It is about 2 cm long, and 1 cm wide (*see* Fig. 1.18).

Relations

Structures outside the sinus:
1 *Superiorly:* Optic tract, optic chiasma, olfactory tract, internal carotid artery and anterior perforated substance (*see* Fig. 4.1 of Volume 4).
2 *Inferiorly:* Foramen lacerum and the junction of the body and greater wing of the sphenoid bone (*see* Fig. 1.18).
3 *Medially:* Hypophysis cerebri and sphenoidal air sinus (Fig. 12.6).
4 *Laterally:* Temporal lobe with uncus.
5 *Below laterally:* Mandibular nerve
6 *Anteriorly:* Superior orbital fissure and the apex of the orbit.
7 *Posteriorly:* Apex of the petrous temporal and the crus cerebri of the midbrain.

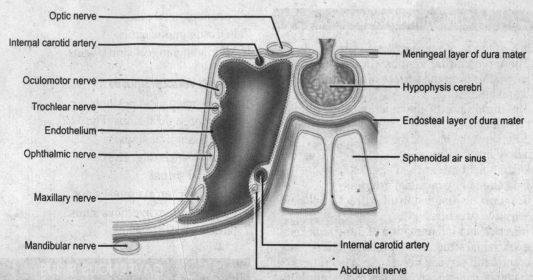

Fig. 12.6: Coronal section through the middle cranial fossa showing the relations of the cavernous sinus

Structures with in the Lateral Wall of the Sinus, from above Downwards

1 *Oculomotor nerve*: In the anterior part of the sinus, it divides into superior and inferior divisions which leave the sinus by passing through the superior orbital fissure.

2 *Trochlear nerve*: In the anterior part of the sinus, it crosses superficial to the oculomotor nerve, and enters the orbit through the superior orbital fissure.

3 *Ophthalmic nerve*: In the anterior part of the sinus, it divides into the lacrimal, frontal and nasociliary nerves (*see* Figs 13.4 and 13.6).

4 *Maxillary nerve*: It leaves the sinus by passing through the foramen rotundum on its way to the pterygopalatine fossa.

5 *Trigeminal ganglion*: The ganglion and its dural cave project into the posterior part of the lateral wall of the sinus (Fig. 12.4).

Structures Passing through the Medial Aspect of the Sinus

a. *Internal carotid artery* with the venous and sympathetic plexus around it.

b. *Abducent nerve*, inferolateral to the internal carotid artery.

The structures in the lateral wall and on the medial aspect of the sinus are separated from blood by the endothelial lining.

Tributaries or Incoming Channels

From the Orbit

1 The superior ophthalmic vein.

2 A branch of the inferior ophthalmic vein or sometimes the vein itself.

3 The central vein of the retina may drain either into the superior ophthalmic vein or into the cavernous sinus (Fig. 12.7).

From the Brain

1 Superficial middle cerebral vein.

2 Inferior cerebral veins from the temporal lobe (Fig. 12.8).

From the Meninges

1 Sphenoparietal sinus.

2 The frontal trunk of the middle meningeal vein may drain either into the pterygoid plexus through the foramen ovale or into the sphenoparietal or cavernous sinus.

Draining Channels or Communications

The cavernous sinus drains:

1 Into the transverse sinus through the superior petrosal sinus.

2 Into the internal jugular vein through the inferior petrosal sinus and through a plexus around the internal carotid artery.

3 Into the pterygoid plexus of veins through the emissary veins passing through the foramen ovale, the foramen lacerum and the emissary sphenoidal foramen (Table 12.1).

4 Into the facial vein through the superior ophthalmic vein.

5 The right and left cavernous sinuses communicate with each other through the anterior and posterior intercavernous sinuses and through the basilar plexus of veins (Fig. 12.8).

All these communications are valveless, and blood can flow through them in either direction.

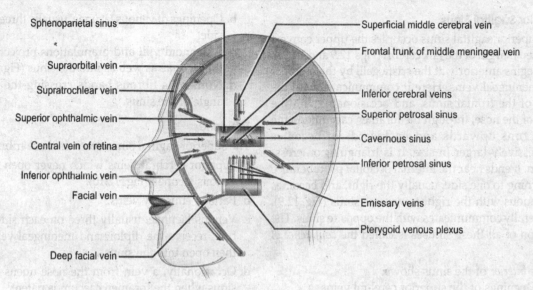

Fig. 12.7: Side view of the tributaries and communications of the cavernous sinus

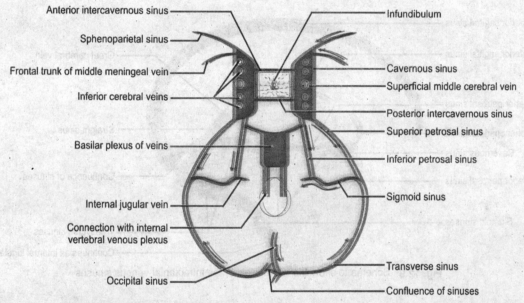

Fig. 12.8: Superior view of the tributaries and communications of the cavernous sinus

Factors Helping Expulsion of Blood from the Sinus

1 Expansile pulsations of the internal carotid artery within the sinus.
2 Gravity.
3 Position of the head.

CLINICAL ANATOMY

• *Thrombosis of the cavernous sinus* may be caused by sepsis in the dangerous area of the face, in nasal cavities, and in paranasal air sinuses. This gives rise to the following symptoms.

a. *Nervous symptoms:*
  – Severe pain in the eye and forehead in the area of distribution of ophthalmic nerve.
  – Involvement of the third, fourth and sixth cranial nerves resulting in paralysis of the muscles supplied.
b. *Venous symptoms:* Marked oedema of eyelids, cornea and root of the nose, with exophthalmos due to congestion of the orbital veins.
• A communication between the cavernous sinus and the internal carotid artery may be produced by head injury. When this happens the eyeball protrudes and pulsates with each heart beat. It is called the *pulsating exophthalmos.*

Superior Sagittal Sinus

The superior sagittal sinus occupies the upper convex, attached margin of the falx cerebri (Figs 12.9 and 12.10).

It begins anteriorly at the crista galli by the union of tiny meningeal veins. Here it communicates with the veins of the frontal sinus, and occasionally with the veins of the nose, through the foramen caecum. As the sinus runs upwards and backwards, it becomes progressively larger in size. It is triangular on cross-section. It ends near the internal occipital protuberance by turning to one side, usually the right, and becomes continuous with the right transverse sinus (Fig. 12.9). It generally communicates with the opposite sinus. The junction of all these sinuses is called the *confluence of sinuses*.

The *interior* of the sinus shows:

a. Openings of the superior cerebral veins.

b. Openings of venous lacunae, usually three on each side.

c. Arachnoid villi and granulations projecting into the lacunae as well as into the sinus (Fig. 12.10).

d. Numerous fibrous bands crossing the inferior angle of the sinus.

Tributaries

The superior sagittal sinus receives these tributaries.

a. Superior cerebral veins which never open into the venous lacunae (Fig. 12.10).

b. Parietal emissary veins.

c. Venous lacunae, usually three on each side which first, receive the diploic and meningeal veins, and then open into the sinus.

d. Occasionally, a vein from the nose opens into the sinus when the foramen caecum is patent.

Fig. 12.9: Scheme to show the lateral view of the intracranial venous sinuses

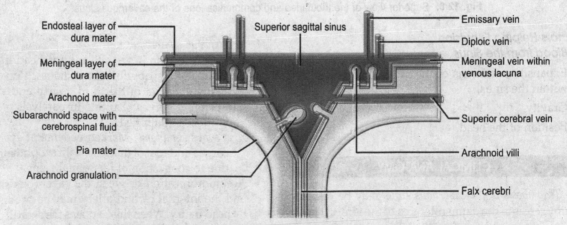

Fig. 12.10: Coronal section through superior sagittal sinus showing arrangement of the meninges, the arachnoid villi and granulations, and the various (emissary, diploic, meningeal and cerebral) veins in its relation

Thrombosis of the superior sagittal sinus may be caused by spread of infection from the nose, scalp and diploe. This gives rise to:

a. A considerable rise in intracranial tension due to defective absorption of CSF.
b. Delirium and sometimes convulsions due to congestion of the superior cerebral veins.
c. Paraplegia of the upper motor neuron type due to bilateral involvement of the paracentral lobules of cerebrum where the lower limbs and perineum are represented.

Inferior Sagittal Sinus

The inferior sagittal sinus, a small channel lies in the posterior two-thirds of the lower, concave free margin of the falx cerebri. It ends by joining the great cerebral vein to form the straight sinus (Fig. 12.9).

Straight Sinus

The straight sinus lies in the median plane within the junction of falx cerebri and the tentorium cerebelli. It is formed anteriorly by the union of the inferior sagittal sinus with the great cerebral vein, and ends at the internal occipital protuberance by continuing as the transverse sinus usually left (Fig. 12.9). In addition to the veins forming it, also receives a few of the superior cerebellar veins.

At the termination of the great cerebral vein into the sinus, there exists a ball valve mechanism, formed by a sinusoidal plexus of blood vessels, which regulates the secretion of CSF.

Transverse Sinus

The transverse sinuses are large sinuses (Fig. 12.8). The right sinus usually larger than the left, is situated in the posterior part of the attached margin of the tentorium cerebelli. The right transverse sinus is usually a continuation of the superior sagittal sinus, and the left sinus a continuation of the straight sinus. Each sinus extends from the internal occipital protuberance to the posteroinferior angle of the parietal bone at the base of mastoid process where it bends downwards and becomes the sigmoid sinus. Its *tributaries* are:

1 Superior petrosal sinus
2 Inferior cerebral veins
3 Inferior cerebellar veins
4 Diploic (posterior temporal) vein
5 Inferior anastomotic vein.

Sigmoid Sinuses

Each sinus, right or left, is the direct continuation of the transverse sinus (Fig. 12.9). It is S-shaped, hence the name. It extends from the posteroinferior angle of the parietal bone to the posterior part of the jugular foramen where it becomes the superior bulb of the internal jugular vein. It grooves the mastoid part of the temporal bone, where *it is separated anteriorly from the mastoid antrum and mastoid air cells by only a thin plate of bone.* Its tributaries are:

1 The mastoid and condylar emissary veins.
2 Cerebellar veins.
3 The internal auditory vein.

• *Thrombosis of the sigmoid sinus* is always secondary to infection in the middle ear or otitis media, or in the mastoid process called mastoiditis.
• During operations on the mastoid process, one should be careful about the sigmoid sinus, so that it is not exposed.
• Spread of infection or thrombosis from the sigmoid and transverse sinuses to the superior sagittal sinus may cause impaired CSF drainage into the latter and may, therefore, lead to the development of hydrocephalus. Such a hydrocephalus associated with sinus thrombosis following ear infection is known as *otitic hydrocephalus.*

Other Sinuses

The *occipital sinus* is small, and lies in the attached margin of the falx cerebelli. It begins near the foramen magnum and ends in the confluence of sinuses (Figs 12.2 and 12.8).

The *sphenoparietal sinuses*, right and left lie along the posterior free margin of the lesser wing of the sphenoid bone, and drain into the anterior part of the cavernous sinus. Each sinus may receive the frontal trunk of the middle meningeal vein (Fig. 12.9).

The *superior petrosal sinuses* lie in the anterior part of the attached margin of the tentorium cerebelli along the upper border of the petrous temporal bone. It drains the cavernous sinus into the transverse sinus (Fig. 12.8).

The *inferior petrosal sinuses* right and left lie in the corresponding petro-occipital fissure, and drain the cavernous sinus into the superior bulb of the internal jugular vein.

The *basilar plexus of veins* lies over the clivus of the skull. It connects the two inferior petrosal sinuses and communicates with the internal vertebral venous plexus.

The *middle meningeal veins* form two main trunks, one frontal or anterior and one parietal or posterior, which

Table 12.1: Emissary veins: Valveless and communicate intracranial with extracranial veins

Sinus	Connection	Veins
Superior sagittal sinus	Parietal emissary vein	Veins of scalp,
	Foramen caecum	nasal veins
	Middle meningeal vein	Pterygoid veins
Transverse sinus	Petrosquamous	External jugular
Sigmoid sinus	Mastoid vein	Posterior auricular
	Hypoglossal vein	IJV
	Posterior condylar vein	Suboccipital vein
Cavernous sinus	Emissary veins	Pterygoid veins
	Veins around ICA	IJV
	Ophthalmic vein	Facial vein
	Inferior petrosal	IJV

ICA: Internal carotid artery; IJV: Internal jugular vein

accompany the two branches of the middle meningeal artery. The *frontal trunk* may end either in the pterygoid plexus through the foramen ovale, or in the spheno-parietal or cavernous sinus. The *parietal trunk* usually ends in the pterygoid plexus through the foramen spinosum. The meningeal veins are nearer to the bone than the arteries, and are, therefore, more liable to injury in fractures of the skull.

The anterior and posterior *intercavernous sinuses* connect the cavernous sinuses. They pass through the diaphragma sellae, one in front and the other behind the infundibulum (Fig. 12.8).

HYPOPHYSIS CEREBRI (PITUITARY GLAND)

DISSECTION

Identify diaphragma sellae over the hypophyseal fossa. Incise it radially and locate the hypophysis cerebri lodged in its fossa. Take it out and examine it in detail with the hand lens (Figs 12.11 and 12.12).

Introduction

The hypophysis cerebri is a small endocrine gland situated in relation to the base of the brain. It is often called the master of the endocrine orchestra because it produces a number of hormones which control the secretions of many other endocrine glands of the body (Fig. 12.11).

The gland lies in the hypophyseal fossa or sella turcica or pituitary fossa. The fossa is roofed by the diaphragma sellae. The stalk of the hypophysis cerebri pierces the diaphragma sellae and is attached above to the floor of the third ventricle.

The gland is oval in shape, and measures 8 mm anteroposteriorly and 12 mm transversely. It weighs about 500 mg.

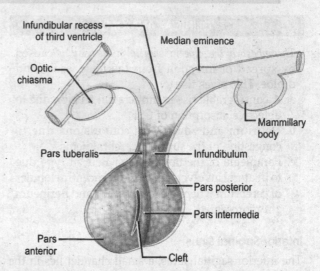

Fig. 12.11: Parts of the hypophysis cerebri as seen in a sagittal section

Relations

Superiorly

1 Diaphragma sellae (Fig. 12.5)
2 Optic chiasma
3 Tubercinerium
4 Infundibular recess of the third ventricle.

Inferiorly

1 Irregular venous channels between the two layers of dura mater lining the floor of the hypophyseal fossa.
2 Hypophyseal fossa.
3 Sphenoidal air sinuses (Fig. 12.6).

On each side

The cavernous sinus with its contents (Fig. 12.6).

Subdivisions/Parts and Development

The gland has two main parts: *Adenohypophysis* and *neurohypophysis* which differ from each other embryologically, morphologically and functionally.

The adenohypophysis develops as an upward growth called the Rathke's pouch from the ectodermal roof of the stomodeum. The neurohypophysis develops as a downward growth from the floor of the diencephalon, and is connected to the hypothalamus by neural pathways. Further subdivisions of each part are given below.

Adenohypophysis

1 *Anterior lobe* or *pars anterior, pars distalis, or pars glandularis:* This is the largest part of the gland (Fig. 12.11).
2 *Intermediate lobe* or *pars intermedia:* This is in the form of a thin strip which is separated from the anterior lobe by an intraglandular cleft, a remnant of the lumen of Rathke's pouch.

3 *Tuberal lobe* or *pars tuberalis:* It is an upward extension of the anterior lobe that surrounds and forms part of the infundibulum.

Neurohypophysis

1 *Posterior lobe* or *neural lobe, pars posterior:* It is smaller than the anterior lobe and lies in the posterior concavity of the larger anterior lobe.

2 *Infundibular stem,* which contains the neural connections of the posterior lobe with the hypothalamus.

3 *Median eminence* of the tubercinerium which is continuous with the infundibular stem.

Arterial Supply

The hypophysis cerebri is supplied by the following branches of the internal carotid artery.

1 One superior hypophyseal artery on each side (Fig. 12.12a).

2 One inferior hypophyseal artery on each side.

Each superior hypophyseal artery supplies:

a. Ventral part of the hypothalamus.

b. Upper part of the infundibulum.

c. Lower part of the infundibulum through a separate long descending branch, called the trabecular artery.

Each inferior hypophyseal artery divides into medial and lateral branches which join one another to form an arterial ring around the posterior lobe. Branches from this ring supply the posterior lobe and also anastomose with branches from the superior hypophyseal artery.

The anterior lobe or pars distalis is supplied exclusively by *portal vessels* arising from capillary tufts formed by the superior hypophyseal arteries (Fig. 12.12). The long portal vessels drain the median eminence and the upper infundibulum, and the short portal vessels drain the lower infundibulum. The portal vessels are of great functional importance because they carry the *hormone releasing factors* from the hypothalamus to the anterior lobe where they control the secretory cycles of different glandular cells.

Venous Drainage

Short veins emerge on the surface of the gland and drain into neighbouring dural venous sinuses. The hormones pass out of the gland through the venous blood, and are carried to their target cells.

Histology

Anterior Lobe (Fig. 12.12b)

Chromophilic cells 50%

1 *Acidophils/alpha cells;* about 43%

  a. Somatotrophs: Secrete growth hormone (STH, GH).

  b. Mammotrophs (prolactin cells): Secrete lactogenic hormone.

2 *Basophils/beta cells,* about 7% of cells

  a. Thyrotrophs: Secrete thyroid stimulating hormone (TSH).

  b. Corticotrophs: Secrete adrenocorticotrophic hormone (ACTH).

  c. Gonadotrophs: Secrete follicle stimulating hormone (FSH).

  d. Luteotrophs: Secrete luteinising hormone (LH).

Chromophobic cells 50% represent the non-secretory phase of the other cell types, or their precursors.

Intermediate Lobe

It is made up of numerous basophil cells, and chromophobe cells surrounding masses of colloid material. It secretes the melanocyte stimulating hormone (MSH).

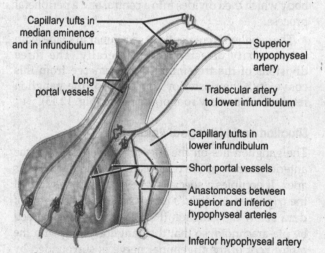

Fig. 12.12a: Arterial supply of the hypophysis cerebri. Note that the neurohypophysis is supplied by the superior and inferior hypophyseal arteries, and the adenohypophysis, exclusively by the portal vessels

Labels: Capillary tufts in median eminence and in infundibulum; Long portal vessels; Superior hypophyseal artery; Trabecular artery to lower infundibulum; Capillary tufts in lower infundibulum; Short portal vessels; Anastomoses between superior and inferior hypophyseal arteries; Inferior hypophyseal artery

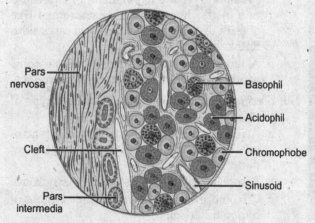

Labels: Pars nervosa; Basophil; Acidophil; Cleft; Chromophobe; Sinusoid; Pars intermedia

- Pars anterior contains acidophil, basophil and chromophobe cells
- Pars intermedia contains vesicles
- Pars posterior contains nerve fibres and pituicytes

Fig. 12.12b: Histology of hypophysis cerebri

Head and Neck

Posterior Lobe

It is composed of:

1 A large number of nonmyelinated fibres hypothalamo-hypophyseal tract.
2 Modified neurological cells, called *pituicytes*. They have many dendrites which terminate on or near the sinusoids (Fig. 12.12b).

Hypothalamo-hypophyseal portal system

The hypothalamo-hypophyseal tract begins in the preoptic and paraventricular nuclei of the hypothalamus. Its short fibres terminate in relation to capillary tufts of portal vessels, providing the possibility for a neural control of the secretory activity of the anterior lobe. The long fibres of the neurosecretory tract pass to the posterior lobe and terminate near vascular sinusoids.

The hormones related to the posterior lobe are:

a. *Vasopressin* antidiuretic hormone (ADH) which acts on kidney tubules.
b. *Oxytocin* which promotes contraction of the uterine and mammary smooth muscle.

These hormones are actually secreted by the hypothalamus, from where these are transported through the hypothalamo-hypophyseal tract to the posterior lobe of the gland.

CLINICAL ANATOMY

Pituitary tumours give rise to two main categories of symptoms:

A. *General symptoms* due to pressure over surrounding structures:

a. The sella turcica is enlarged in size.
b. Pressure over the central part of optic chiasma causes bitemporal hemianopia (Fig. 12.13).
c. Pressure over the hypothalamus may cause one of the hypothalamic syndromes like obesity of Frolich's syndrome in cases with Rathke's pouch tumours.
d. A large tumour may press upon the third ventricle, causing a rise in intracranial pressure.

B. *Specific symptoms* depending on the cell type of the tumour.

a. Acidophil or eosinophil adenoma causes acromegaly in adults and gigantism in younger patients.
b. Basophil adenoma causes Cushing's syndrome.
c. Chromophobe adenoma causes effects of hypopituitarism.
d. Posterior lobe damage causes diabetes insipidus, although the lesion in these cases usually lies in the hypothalamus.

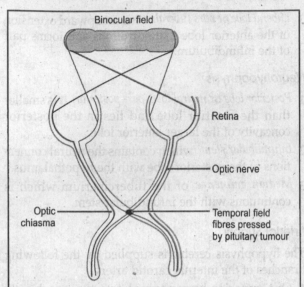

Fig. 12.13: Bitemporal hemianopia due to pressure of pituitary tumour on the central part of optic chiasma

---

TRIGEMINAL GANGLION

DISSECTION

Identify trigeminal ganglion situated on the anterior surface of petrous temporal bone near its apex. Define the three branches emerging from its convex anterior surface.

Introduction

This is the *sensory ganglion* of the fifth cranial nerve. It is homologous with the dorsal nerve root ganglia of spinal nerves. All such ganglia are made up of pseudounipolar nerve cells, with a 'T'-shaped arrangement of their process; one process arises from the cell body which then divides into a central and a peripheral process.

The ganglion is crescentic or semilunar in shape, with its convexity directed anterolaterally. The three divisions of the trigeminal nerve emerge from this convexity. The posterior concavity of the ganglion receives the sensory root of the nerve (Fig. 12.13).

Situation and Meningeal Relations

The ganglion lies on the *trigeminal impression*, on the anterior surface of the petrous temporal bone near its apex. It occupies a special space of dura mater, called the *trigeminal or Meckel's cave*. There are two layers of dura below the ganglion (Fig. 12.4). The cave is lined by pia-arachnoid, so that the ganglion along with the motor root of the trigeminal nerve is surrounded by CSF. The ganglion lies at a depth of about 5 cm from the preauricular point.

Relations

Medially

1 Internal carotid artery.
2 Posterior part of cavernous sinus.

Laterally

Middle meningeal artery.

Superiorly

Parahippocampal gyrus.

Inferiorly

1 Motor root of trigeminal nerve.
2 Greater petrosal nerve (Fig. 12.14).
3 Apex of the petrous temporal bone.
4 The foramen lacerum.

Associated Root and Branches

The central processes of the ganglion cells form the large *sensory root* of the trigeminal nerve which is attached to pons at its junction with the middle cerebellar peduncle.

The peripheral processes of the ganglion cells form three divisions of the trigeminal nerve, namely the *ophthalmic, maxillary and mandibular*.

The small *motor root* of the trigeminal nerve is attached to the pons superomedial to the sensory root. It passes under the ganglion from its medial to the lateral side, and joins the mandibular nerve at the foramen ovale.

Blood Supply

The ganglion is supplied by twigs from:

1 Internal carotid
2 Middle meningeal

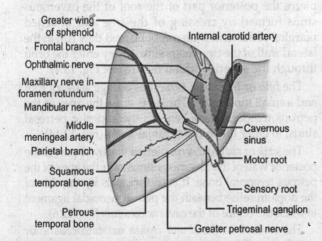

Fig. 12.14: Superior view of the middle cranial fossa showing some of its contents

3 Accessory meningeal arteries
4 By the meningeal branch of the ascending pharyngeal artery.

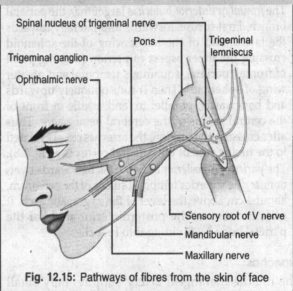

Fig. 12.15: Pathways of fibres from the skin of face

MIDDLE MENINGEAL ARTERY

DISSECTION

Dissect the middle meningeal artery which enters the skull through foramen spinosum. It is an important artery for the supply of endocranium, inner table of skull and diploe. Examine the other structures seen in cranial fossae after removal of brain. These are the cranial nerves, internal carotid artery, petrosal nerves and fourth part of vertebral artery.

Introduction

The middle meningeal artery is important to the surgeon because this artery is the commonest source of extradural haemorrhage, which is an acute surgical emergency (Fig. 12.14).

Origin

The artery is a branch of the first part of the maxillary artery, given off in the infratemporal fossa (*see* Figs 6.6 and 6.7).

Course and Relations

1 In the infratemporal fossa, the artery runs upwards and medially deep to the lateral pterygoid muscle and superficial to the sphenomandibular ligament. Here it passes through a loop formed by the two roots of the auriculotemporal nerve (see Fig. 6.15).

2 It enters the middle cranial fossa through the foramen spinosum (Fig. 12.14).

3 In the middle cranial fossa, the artery has an extradural course, but the middle meningeal veins are closer to the bone than the artery. Here the artery runs forwards and laterally for a variable distance, grooving the squamous temporal bone, and divides into a frontal and parietal branch (Fig. 12.14).

4 The *frontal* or *anterior branch* is larger than the parietal branch. First it runs forwards and laterally towards the lateral end of the lesser wing of the sphenoid crossing the inner aspect of pterion (meeting point of frontal, parietal, squamous temporal and greater wing of sphenoid). Then it runs obliquely upwards and backwards, parallel to, and a little in front of the central sulcus of the cerebral hemisphere. Thus after crossing the pterion, the artery is closely related to the motor area of the cerebral cortex (see Fig. 1.8).

5 The *parietal* or *posterior branch* runs backwards over, or near, the superior temporal sulcus of the cerebrum, about 4 cm above the level of the zygomatic arch. It ends in front of the posteroinferior angle of the parietal bone by dividing into branches.

Branches

The middle meningeal artery supplies only small branches to the dura mater. It is predominantly a periosteal artery supplying bone and red bone marrow in the diploe.

Within the cranial cavity, it gives off:

a. The *ganglionic branches* to the trigeminal ganglion.
b. A *petrosal branch* to the hiatus for the greater petrosal nerve.
c. A *superior tympanic branch* to the tensor tympani.
d. *Temporal branches* to the temporal fossa.
e. *Anastomotic branch* that enters the orbit and anastomoses with the lacrimal artery.

CLINICAL ANATOMY

• The middle meningeal artery is of great surgical importance because it can be torn in head injuries resulting in *extradural haemorrhage. The frontal* or *anterior branch* is commonly involved. The haematoma presses on the motor area, giving rise to hemiplegia of the opposite side. The anterior division can be approached surgically by making a hole in the skull over the pterion, 4 cm above the midpoint of the zygomatic arch (see Fig. 1.8).

• Rarely, the parietal or posterior branch is implicated, causing contralateral deafness. In this case, the hole is made at a point 4 cm above and 4 cm behind the external acoustic meatus.

OTHER STRUCTURES SEEN IN CRANIAL FOSSAE AFTER REMOVAL OF BRAIN

DISSECTION

Following structures are seen in the anterior cranial fossa.

Crista galli, cribriform plate of ethmoid, orbital part of frontal bone, lesser wing of sphenoid.

Following structures are seen in the middle cranial fossa: Middle meningeal vessels, diaphragma sellae pierced by infundibulum, oculomotor nerves, internal carotid arteries, optic nerve, posterior cerebral artery, great cerebral vein.

Following structures are seen in the posterior cranial fossa: Facial, vestibulocochlear, glossopharyngeal, vagus, accessory, hypoglossal nerves, vertebral arteries, spinal root of accessory nerve.

Various Structures

The structures seen after removal of the brain are: 12 cranial nerves, cavernous part of internal carotid artery, four petrosal nerves and fourth part of the vertebral artery.

Cranial Nerves

The *first* or *olfactory nerve* is seen in the form of 15 to 20 filaments on each side that pierce the cribriform plate of the ethmoid bone (Chapter 4, Volume 4).

The *second* or *optic nerve* passes through the optic canal with the ophthalmic artery.

The *third* or *oculomotor* and *fourth* or *trochlear nerves* pierce the posterior part of the roof of the cavernous sinus formed by crossing of the free and attached margins of the tentorium cerebelli; next they run in the lateral wall of the cavernous sinus. They enter the orbit through the superior orbital fissure (see Fig. 13.4).

The *fifth* or *trigeminal nerve*, has a large sensory root and a small motor root. The roots cross the apex of the petrous temporal bone beneath the superior petrosal sinus, to enter the middle cranial fossa (Fig. 12.14).

The *sixth* or *abducent nerve* pierces the lower part of posterior wall of the cavernous sinus near the apex of petrous temporal bone. It runs forwards by the side of the dorsum sellae beneath the petrosphenoidal ligament to reach the centre of the cavernous sinus (Fig. 12.6).

The *seventh* or *facial* and *eighth* or *statoacoustic* or vestibulocochlear nerves pass through the internal acoustic meatus with the labyrinthine vessels.

The *ninth* or *glossopharyngeal, tenth* or *vagus and eleventh* or *accessory nerves* pierce the dura mater at the jugular foramen and pass out through it. The *glossopharyngeal* nerve is enclosed in a separate sheath of dura mater, while vagus and accessory nerves are enclosed in one sheath. The spinal part of the accessory nerve first enters the posterior cranial fossa through the foramen magnum, and then passes out through the jugular foramen along with cranial part.

The two parts of the *twelfth or hypoglossal nerve* pierce the dura mater separately opposite the hypoglossal canal and then pass out through it.

Internal Carotid Artery

Internal carotid artery begins in the neck as one of the terminal branches of the common carotid artery at the level of the upper border of the thyroid cartilage. Its course is divided into the four parts (Fig. 12.16). These are:

Cervical part
In the neck, it lies within the carotid sheath. This part gives no branches (*see* Fig. 3.8).

Petrous part
Within the carotid canal situated in petrous part of the temporal bone. It gives caroticotympanic branches and artery of pterygoid canal (Fig. 12.16).

Cavernous part
Within the cavernous sinus (Fig. 12.6). This part of the artery gives off:
1 Cavernous branches to the trigeminal ganglion.
2 The superior and inferior hypophyseal branches to the hypophysis cerebri.

Cerebral part
This part lies at the base of the brain after emerging from the cavernous sinus. It gives off the following arteries:
1 Ophthalmic
2 Anterior cerebral
3 Middle cerebral
4 Posterior communicating.
5 Anterior choroidal.

Of these, the ophthalmic artery supplies structures in the orbit; while the others supply the brain.

The curvatures of the petrous, cavernous and cerebral parts of the internal carotid artery together form an S-shaped figure, the carotid siphon of angiograms.

Petrosal Nerves

1 The *greater petrosal nerve* (Fig. 12.14) carries gustatory and parasympathetic fibres. It arises from the geniculate ganglion of the facial nerve, and enters the middle cranial fossa through the hiatus for the greater petrosal nerve on the anterior surface of the petrous temporal bone. It proceeds towards the foramen lacerum, where it joins the deep petrosal nerve which carries sympathetic fibres to form the nerve of the pterygoid canal (*see* Table A.2).

The nerve of the pterygoid canal passes through the pterygoid canal to reach the pterygopalatine ganglion. The parasympathetic fibres relay in this ganglion. Postganglionic parasympathetic fibres arising in the ganglion ultimately supply the lacrimal gland and the mucosal glands of the nose, palate and

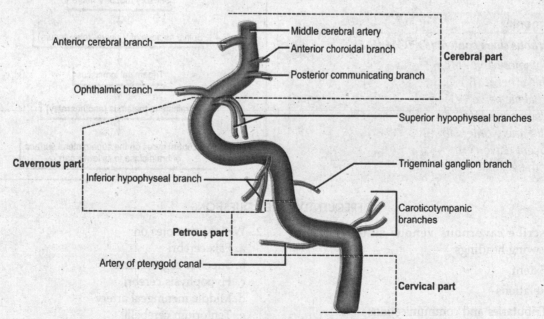

Fig. 12.16: Various parts of internal carotid artery

pharynx (*see* Fig. 15.16b). The gustatory or taste fibres do not relay in the ganglion and are distributed to the palate.

2   The *deep petrosal nerve*, sympathetic in nature, is a branch of the sympathetic plexus around the internal carotid artery. It contains postganglionic fibres from the superior cervical sympathetic ganglion. The nerve joins the greater petrosal nerve to form the nerve of the pterygoid canal. The sympathetic fibres are distributed through the branches of the pterygopalatine ganglion (*see* Table A.2 in Appendix).

3   The *lesser petrosal nerve*, parasympathetic in nature, is a branch of the tympanic plexus, deriving its preganglionic parasympathetic fibres from the tympanic branch of the glossopharyngeal nerve. It emerges through the hiatus for the lesser petrosal nerve, situated just lateral to the hiatus for the greater petrosal nerve, passes out of the skull through the foramen ovale, and ends in the otic ganglion (*see* Fig. 6.17). Postganglionic fibres arising in the ganglion supply the parotid gland through the auriculotemporal nerve (*see* Table A.2 in Appendix).

4   The *external petrosal nerve*, sympathetic in nature is an inconstant branch from the sympathetic plexus around the middle meningeal artery to the geniculate ganglion of the facial nerve.

Fourth Part of the Vertebral Artery

It enters the posterior cranial fossa through the foramen magnum after piercing the dura mater near the skull. It has been studied in Chapter 9.

Mnemonics

Cavernous sinus contents O TOM CAT

Oculomotor nerve (III)
Trochlear nerve (IV)
Ophthalmic nerve (V1)
Maxillary nerve (V2)
Carotid artery (internal)
Abducent nerve (VI)
T: Nothing

FACTS TO REMEMBER

- Meningeal layer of dura mater forms falx cerebri and falx cerebelli in sagittal plane and tentorium cerebelli and diaphragma sellae in horizontal plane.
- Only spinal ganglia present in the cranial cavity is the trigeminal ganglion.
- Only mixed branch of trigeminal is the mandibular branch. The other two are purely sensory.
- Anterior branch of middle meningeal artery lies on the inner aspect of *pterion* and is liable to injury, leading to extradural haemorrhage.

CLINICOANATOMICAL PROBLEM

A young person complains of a little painful papules on the right side of forehead along a nerve on the right side. There is redness of the eyes with severe pain.
- What is the diagnosis?
- Trace the pathway of pain impulses

Ans: The diagnosis is 'herpes zoster'.

The pathway of pain impulses is shown in Flowchart 12.1.

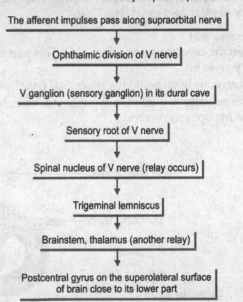

Flowchart 12.1: Pathway of pain impulses

The afferent impulses pass along supraorbital nerve
↓
Ophthalmic division of V nerve
↓
V ganglion (sensory ganglion) in its dural cave
↓
Sensory root of V nerve
↓
Spinal nucleus of V nerve (relay occurs)
↓
Trigeminal lemniscus
↓
Brainstem, thalamus (another relay)
↓
Postcentral gyrus on the superolateral surface of brain close to its lower part

FREQUENTLY ASKED QUESTIONS

1. Describe cavernous venous sinus under the following headings:
    a. Extent
    b. Relations
    c. Tributaries and communications
    d. Clinical anatomy

2. Write short notes on:
    a. Falx cerebri
    b. Superior sagittal sinus
    c. Hypophysis cerebri
    d. Middle meningeal artery
    e. Tentorium cerebelli
    f. Trigeminal ganglion

MULTIPLE CHOICE QUESTIONS

1. One of the following structures is not related to cavernous sinus:
   a. Trochlear nerve
   b. Oculomotor nerve
   c. Optic nerve
   d. Ophthalmic nerve

2. Which is true about cavernous sinus?
   a. Oculomotor nerve in medial wall
   b. Trochlear nerve on medial wall
   c. Optic tract inferiorly
   d. Drains into transverse sinus

3. What is the correct position of VI nerve in relation to internal carotid artery in cavernous sinus?
   a. Medial
   b. Lateral
   c. Inferolateral
   d. Posterior

4. If III, IV, VI and ophthalmic nerves are paralysed the infection is localised to:
   a. Brain stem
   b. Base of skull
   c. Cavernous sinus
   d. Apex of orbit

5. Which is not a part of internal carotid artery?
   a. Cervical
   b. Petrous
   c. Cerebral
   d. Ophthalmic

6. Rupture of which commonly injured artery causes extradural haemorrhage:
   a. Trunk of middle meningeal artery
   b. Anterior branch of middle meningeal artery
   c. Posterior branch of middle meningeal artery
   d. None of the above

7. Which of the petrosal nerve carries preganglionic fibres to the otic ganglion?
   a. Greater
   b. Deep
   c. Lesser
   d. External

8. Arachnoid villi drain into which of the following sinuses?
   a. Transverse
   b. Straight
   c. Superior sagittal
   d. Sigmoid

ANSWERS

1. c	2. d	3. c	4. c	5. d	6. b	7. c	8. c

Contents of the Orbit

My heart leaps up when I behold a rainbow in the sky
—William Wordsworth

INTRODUCTION

The orbits are bony cavities lodging the eyeballs, extraocular muscles, nerves, blood vessels and lacrimal gland. Out of 12 pairs of cranial nerves; II, III, IV, VI, a part of V, and some sympathetic fibres are dedicated to the contents of orbit only. Nature has provided orbit for the safety of the eyeball. We must also try and look after our orbits and their contents.

ORBITS

DISSECTION

Strip the endosteum from the floor of the anterior cranial fossa. Gently break the orbital plate of frontal bone forming the roof of the orbit and remove it in pieces so that orbital periosteum is clearly visible. Medially, the ethmoidal vessels and nerves should be preserved. Posteriorly, identify the optic canal and superior orbital fissure and structures traversing these. Define the orbital fascia and fascial sheath of eyeball.

Divide the orbital periosteum along the middle of the orbit anteroposteriorly. Cut through it horizontally close to anterior margin of orbit.

Features

The orbits are pyramidal cavities, situated one on each side of the root of the nose. They provide sockets for rotatory movements of the eyeball. The long axis of the each orbit passes backwards and medially. The medial walls are parallel to each other at a distance of 2.5 cm but the lateral walls are set at right angles to each other (see Fig. 1.19).

Contents

1 *Eyeball:* Eyeball occupies anterior one-third of orbit. It is described in Chapter 19.
2 *Fascia:* Orbital and bulbar.

3 *Muscles:* Extraocular and intraocular.
4 *Vessels:* Ophthalmic artery, superior and inferior ophthalmic veins, and lymphatics.
5 *Nerves:* Optic, oculomotor, trochlear and abducent; branches of ophthalmic and maxillary nerves, and sympathetic nerves.
6 *Lacrimal gland:* It has already been studied in Chapter 2.
7 *Orbital fat.*

Visual Axis and Orbital Axis

Axis passing through centres of anterior and posterior poles of the eyeball is known as visual axis. It makes an angle of 20–25° with the orbital axis (see Fig. 1.19), i.e. line passing through optic canal and centre of base of orbit, i.e. opening on the face.

Orbital Fascia or Periorbita

It forms the *periosteum* of the bony orbit. Due to the loose connection to bone, it can be easily stripped. Posteriorly, it is continuous with the dura mater and with the sheath of the optic nerve. Anteriorly, it is continuous with the periosteum lining the bones around the orbital margin (Fig. 13.1).

There is a gap in the periorbita over the inferior orbital fissure. This gap is bridged by connective tissue with some smooth muscle fibres in it. These fibres constitute the orbitalis muscle.

a. At the upper and lower margins of the orbit, the orbital fascia sends off flap-like continuations into the eyelids. These extensions form the *orbital septum*.
b. A process of the fascia holds the fibrous pulley of the tendon of the superior oblique muscle in place.
c. Another process forms the *lacrimal fascia* which bridges the lacrimal groove.

Fascial Sheath of Eyeball or Bulbar Fascia

1 *Tenon's capsule* forms a thin, loose membranous sheath around the eyeball, extending from the optic

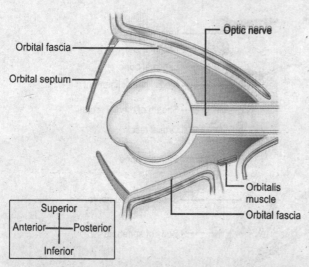

Fig. 13.1: Orbital fascia and fascial sheath of the eyeball as seen in a parasagittal section

nerve to the sclerocorneal junction or limbus. It is separated from the sclera by the episcleral space which is traversed by delicate fibrous bands. The eyeball can freely move within this sheath.

2 The *sheath* is pierced by:
  a. Tendons of the various extraocular muscles.
  b. Ciliary vessels and nerves around the entrance of the optic nerve.

3 The sheath gives off a number of expansions.
  a. A *tubular sheath* covers each orbital muscle.
  b. The *medial check ligament* is a strong triangular expansion from the sheath of the medial rectus muscle; it is attached to the lacrimal bone.
  c. The *lateral check ligament* is a strong triangular expansion from the sheath of the lateral rectus muscle; it is attached to the zygomatic bone (Fig. 13.2).

4 The lower part of Tenon's capsule is thickened, and is named the *suspensory ligament of the eye* or the *suspensory ligament of Lockwood* (Fig. 13.3). It is expanded in the centre and narrow at its extremities, and is slung like a hammock below the eyeball. It is formed by union of the margins of the sheaths of the inferior rectus and the inferior oblique muscles with the medial and lateral check ligaments.

EXTRAOCULAR MUSCLES

DISSECTION

Identify and preserve the trochlear nerve entering the superior oblique muscle in the superomedial angle of the orbit. Find the frontal nerve lying in the midline on the levator palpebrae superioris. It divides into two terminal divisions in the anterior part of orbit.

Beneath the levator palpebrae superioris is the superior rectus muscle. The upper division of oculomotor nerve lies between these two muscles, supplying both of them. Along the lateral wall of the orbit look for lacrimal nerve and artery to reach the superolateral corner of the orbit.

Follow the tendon of superior oblique muscle passing superolaterally beneath the superior rectus to be inserted into sclera behind the equator. After identification, divide frontal nerve, levator palpebrae superioris and superior rectus in the middle of the orbit and reflect them apart. Identify the optic nerve and other structures crossing it. These are nasociliary nerve, ophthalmic artery and superior ophthalmic vein. With the optic nerve find two long ciliary nerves and 12–20 short ciliary nerves are seen. Remove the orbital fat and look carefully in the posterior part of the interval between the optic nerve and lateral rectus muscle along the lateral wall of the orbit and identify the pin head sized ciliary ganglion. Trace the roots connecting it to the nasociliary nerve and nerve to inferior oblique muscle.

Lastly, identify the abducent nerve closely adherent to the medial surface of lateral rectus muscle.

Incise the inferior fornix of conjunctiva and palpebral fascia. Elevate the eyeball and remove the fat and fascia to identify the origin of inferior oblique muscle from the floor of the orbit anteriorly.

Identify the levator palpebrae superioris and superior rectus above the eyeball, superior oblique superomedially, medial rectus medially, lateral rectus laterally, and inferior rectus inferiorly.

The voluntary muscles are miniature ribbon muscles, having short tendons of origin and long tendons of insertion.

Voluntary Muscles

1 Four recti:
  a. Superior rectus.
  b. Inferior rectus.
  c. Medial rectus.
  d. Lateral rectus.

2 Two obliques:
  a. Superior oblique.
  b. Inferior oblique.

3 The levator palpebrae superioris elevates the upper eyelid.

Involuntary Muscles

1 The superior tarsal muscle is the deeper portion of the levator palpebrae superioris. It is inserted on the upper margin of the superior tarsus. It elevates the upper eyelid.

Head and Neck

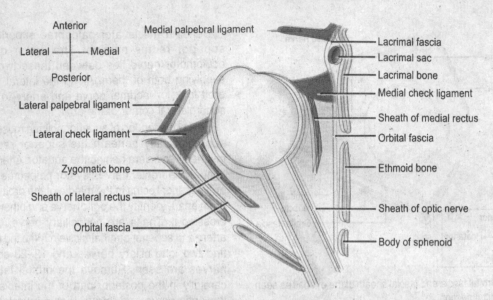

Fig. 13.2: Orbital fascia and fascial sheath of the eyeball as seen in transverse section

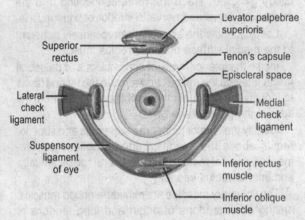

Fig. 13.3: Fascial sheath of the eyeball as seen in coronal section

2 The inferior tarsal muscle extends from the fascial sheath of the inferior rectus and inferior oblique to the lower margin of the inferior tarsus. It possibly depresses the lower eyelid.

3 The orbitalis bridges the inferior orbital fissure. Its action is uncertain (Fig. 13.1).

Voluntary Muscles

Origin

1 The four recti arise from a *common annular tendon* or *tendinous ring* of zinn. The ring is attached to the middle part of superior orbital fissure (Fig. 13.4). The lateral rectus has an additional small tendinous head which arises from the orbital surface of the

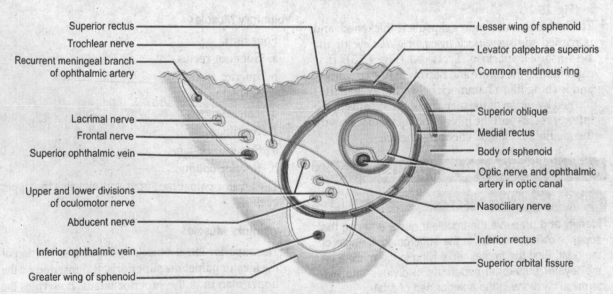

Fig. 13.4: Apical part of the orbit showing the origins of the extraocular muscles, the common tendinous ring and the structures passing through superior orbital fissure

greater wing of the sphenoid bone lateral to the tendinous ring. Through the gap between the two heads abducent nerve passes.

2 The superior oblique arises from the undersurface of lesser wing of the sphenoid, superomedial to the optic canal.

3 The inferior oblique arises from the orbital surface of the maxilla, lateral to the lacrimal groove. The muscle is situated near the anterior margin of the orbit.

4 The levator palpebrae superioris arises from the orbital surface of the lesser wing of the sphenoid bone, anterosuperior to the optic canal and to the origin of the superior rectus.

Insertion

1 The recti are inserted into the sclera, a little posterior to the limbus (corneo-scleral junction). The average distances of the insertions from the cornea are: superior 7.7 mm; inferior 6.5 mm, medial 5.5 mm; lateral 6.9 mm (Fig. 13.5).

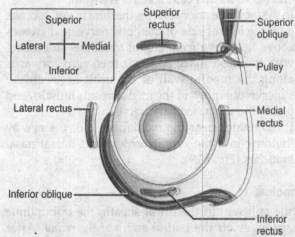

Fig. 13.5: Scheme to show the insertion of the oblique muscles of the eyeball

2 The tendon of the superior oblique passes through a fibrocartilaginous pulley attached to the trochlear fossa of the frontal bone. The tendon then passes laterally, downwards and backward below the superior rectus. It is inserted into the sclera behind the equator of the eyeball, between the superior rectus and the lateral rectus.

3 The inferior oblique is fleshy throughout. It passes laterally, upwards and backwards below the inferior rectus and then deep to the lateral rectus. The inferior oblique is inserted close to the superior oblique a little below and posterior to the latter.

4 The flat tendon of the levator splits into a superior or voluntary and an inferior or involuntary lamellae. Superior lamella of the levator is inserted into the anterior surface of the superior tarsus, and into the skin of the upper eyelid. The inferior lamella (smooth part) is inserted into the upper margin of the superior tarsus (see Fig. 2.21b) and into superior conjunctival fornix.

Nerve Supply

1 The superior oblique is supplied by the IV cranial or trochlear nerve (SO4) (Fig. 13.6).

2 The lateral rectus is supplied by the VI cranial or abducent nerve (LR6).

3 The remaining five extraocular muscles; superior, inferior and medial recti; inferior oblique and part of levator palpebrae superioris are all supplied by the III cranial or oculomotor nerve.

Actions

1 The *movements of the eyeball* are as follows.
  a. *Around a transverse axis*
   • Upward rotation or elevation (33°).
   • Downwards rotation or depression (33°).

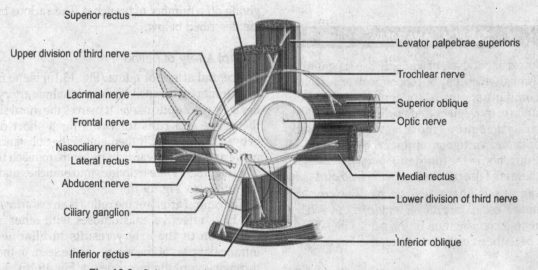

Fig. 13.6: Scheme to show the nerve supply of the extraocular muscles

b. *Around a vertical axis*
- Medial rotation or adduction (50°).
- Lateral rotation or abduction (50°).

c. *Around an anteroposterior axis*
- Intorsion
- Extorsion.

The rotatory movements of the eyeball upwards, downwards, medially or laterally, are defined in terms of the direction of movement of the centre of the pupil. The torsions are defined in terms of the direction of movement of the upper margin of the pupil at 12 o'clock position.

d. The movements given above can take place in various combinations.

2 *Actions of individual muscles* shown in Fig. 13.7a and Table 13.1.

3 *Single* or *pure movements* are produced by combined actions of muscles. Similar actions get added together, while opposing actions cancel each other enabling pure movements (Fig. 13.7b).

a. *Upward rotation or elevation:* By the superior rectus and the inferior oblique.

b. *Downward rotation or depression:* By the inferior rectus and the superior oblique.

c. *Medial rotation or adduction:* By the medial rectus, the superior rectus and the inferior rectus.

d. *Lateral rotation or abduction:* By the lateral rectus, the superior oblique and the inferior oblique.

e. *Intorsion:* By the superior oblique and the superior rectus.

f. *Extorsion:* By the inferior oblique and the inferior rectus.

4 *Combined movements of the eyes*

Normally, movements of the two eyes are harmoniously coordinated. Such coordinated movements of both eyes are called *conjugate ocular movements* (Fig. 13.7c).

CLINICAL ANATOMY

- Weakness or paralysis of a muscle causes squint or strabismus, which may be concomitant or paralytic. Concomitant squint is congenital; there is no limitation of movement, and no diplopia (Fig. 13.8). In paralytic squint, movements are limited, diplopia and vertigo are present, head is turned in the direction of the function of paralysed muscle, and there is a false orientation of the field of vision.
- Nystagmus is characterized by involuntary, rhythmical oscillatory movements of the eyes. This is due to incoordination of the ocular muscles. It may be either vestibular or cerebellar, or even congenital.

VESSELS OF THE ORBIT

DISSECTION

Trace the ophthalmic artery after it was seen to cross over the optic nerve along with nasociliary nerve and superior ophthalmic vein. Identify its branches especially the central artery of the retina which is an 'end artery'.

OPHTHALMIC ARTERY

Origin

The ophthalmic artery is a branch of the cerebral part of the internal carotid artery, given off medial to the anterior clinoid process close to the optic canal (Figs 13.9 and 13.10).

Course and Relations

1 The artery enters the orbit through the optic canal, lying inferolateral to the optic nerve. Both the artery and nerve lie in a common dural sheath.

2 In the orbit, the artery pierces the dura mater, ascends over the lateral side of the optic nerve, and crosses above the nerve from lateral to medial side along with the nasociliary nerve. It then runs forwards along the medial wall of the orbit between the superior oblique and the medial rectus muscles and parallel to the nasociliary nerve.

3 It terminates near the medial angle of the eye by dividing into the supratrochlear and dorsal nasal branches (Fig. 13.9).

Branches

While still within the dural sheath, the ophthalmic artery gives off the *central artery of the retina*. After piercing the dura mater, it gives off a large lacrimal branch that runs along the lateral wall of the orbit. The main artery runs towards the medial wall of the orbit giving off a number of branches. The various branches are described below.

Central Artery of Retina

The central artery of retina (Fig. 13.10) is the first and most important branch of the ophthalmic artery. It first lies below the optic nerve. It pierces the dural sheath of the nerve and runs forwards for a short distance between these two. It then enters the substance of the nerve and runs forwards in its centre to reach the optic disc (Fig. 13.9). Here it divides into branches that supply the retina (*see* Fig. 19.10).

The central artery of the retina is an *end artery*. It does not have effective anastomoses with other arteries. Occlusion of the artery results in blindness. The intraocular part of the artery can be seen, in the living, through an ophthalmoscope (*see* Fig. 19.16).

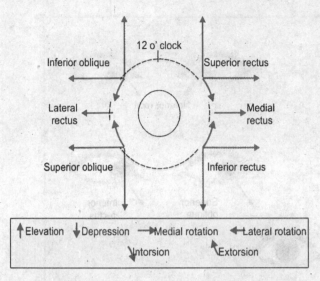

Fig. 13.7a: Scheme to show the actions of the extraocular muscles

Branches Arising from the Lacrimal Artery

1 Branches are given to the lacrimal gland.
2 Two zygomatic branches enter canals in the zygomatic bone. One branch appears on the face through the zygomaticofacial foramen. The other appears on the temporal surface of the bone through the zygomaticotemporal foramen.
3 Lateral palpebral branches supply the eyelids.
4 A recurrent meningeal branch runs backwards to enter the middle cranial fossa through the superior orbital fissure.
5 Muscular branches supply the muscles of the orbit.

Branches Arising from the Main Trunk

1 The posterior (long and short) ciliary arteries supply chiefly the choroid and iris. The eyeball is also supplied through anterior ciliary branches which are

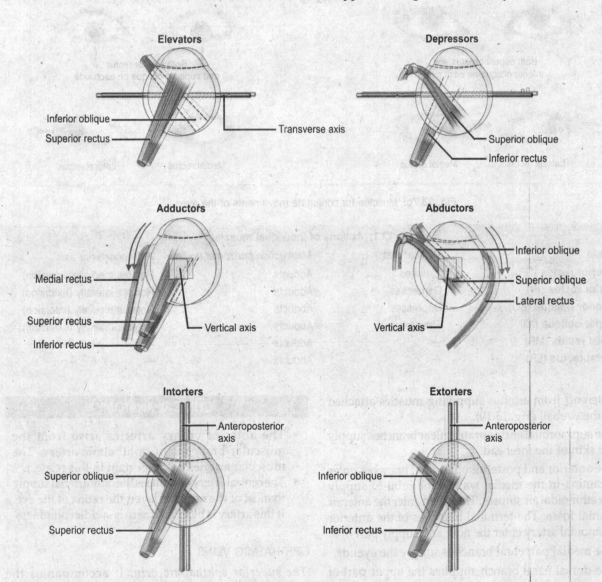

Fig. 13.7b: Single movement of the eye

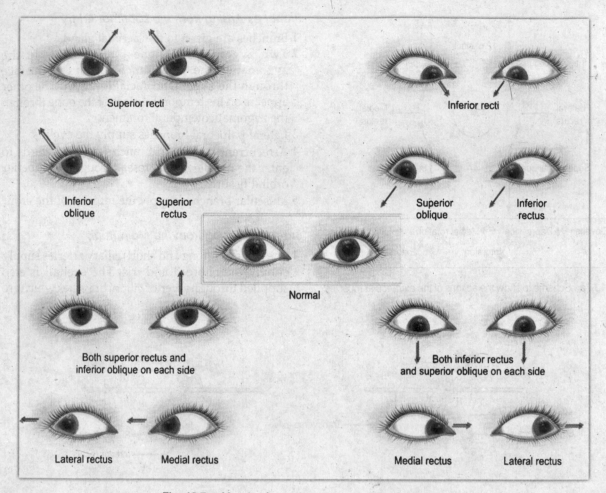

Fig. 13.7c: Muscles for conjugate movements of the eyes

Table 13.1: Actions of individual muscles

Muscle	Vertical axis	Main action horizontal axis	Anteroposterior axis
Superior rectus (SR)	Elevates	Adducts	Rotates medially (intorsion)
Inferior rectus (IR)	Depresses	Adducts	Rotates laterally (extorsion)
Superior oblique (SO)	Depresses	Abducts	Rotates medially (intorsion)
Inferior oblique (IO)	Elevates	Abducts	Rotates laterally (extorsion)
Medial rectus (MR)	—	Adducts	—
Lateral rectus (LR)	—	Abducts	—

given off from arteries supplying muscles attached to the eyeball (Fig. 13.10).

2 The supraorbital and supratrochlear branches supply the skin of the forehead.

3 The anterior and posterior ethmoidal branches enter foramina in the medial wall of the orbit to supply the ethmoidal air sinuses. They then enter the anterior cranial fossa. The terminal branches of the anterior ethmoidal artery enter the nose and supply part of it.

4 The medial palpebral branches supply the eyelids.

5 The dorsal nasal branch supplies the upper part of the nose.

CLINICAL ANATOMY

- The anterior ciliary arteries arise from the muscular branches of ophthalmic artery. The muscular arteries are important in this respect.
- The central artery of retina is the only arterial supply to most of the nervous layer, the retina of the eye. If this artery is blocked, there is sudden blindness.

OPHTHALMIC VEINS

The superior ophthalmic vein: It accompanies the ophthalmic artery. It lies above the optic nerve. It

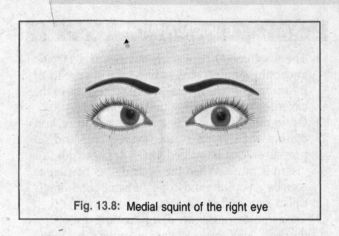

Fig. 13.8: Medial squint of the right eye

receives tributaries corresponding to the branches of the artery, passes through the superior orbital fissure, and drains into the cavernous sinus. It communicates anteriorly with the supraorbital and angular veins (*see* Fig. 2.6).

The inferior ophthalmic vein: It runs below the optic nerve. It receives tributaries from the lacrimal sac, the lower orbital muscles, and the eyelids, and ends either by joining the superior ophthalmic vein or drains directly into the cavernous sinus. It communicates with the pterygoid plexus of veins by small veins passing through the inferior orbital fissure.

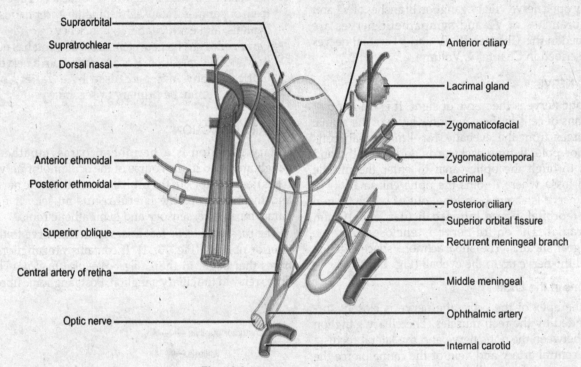

Fig. 13.9: The arteries of the eyeball

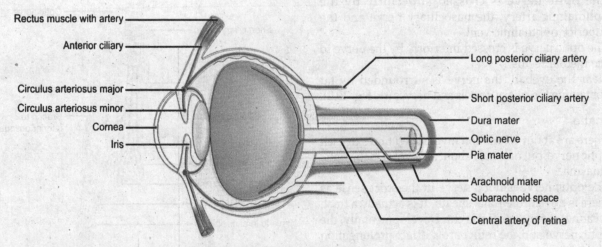

Fig. 13.10: Branches of ophthalmic artery

Head and Neck

Lymphatics of the Orbit

The lymphatics drain into the preauricular parotid lymph nodes (*see* Fig. 2.25).

NERVES OF THE ORBIT

These are:
1 Optic II
2 Ciliary ganglion
3 Oculomotor (III) and trochlear (IV)
4 Branches of ophthalmic (V1) and maxillary divisions (V2) of the trigeminal
5 Abducent (VI)
6 Sympathetic nerves.

Only optic nerve, ciliary ganglion branches of V1 and some branches of V2 and sympathetic nerves are described in this Chapter. III, IV and VI cranial nerves are described in Chapter 4, Volume 4.

OPTIC NERVE

The optic nerve is the nerve of sight. It is made up of the axons of cells in the ganglionic layer of the retina. It emerges from the eyeball 3 or 4 mm nasal to its posterior pole. It runs backwards and medially, and passes through the optic canal to enter the middle cranial fossa where it joins the optic chiasma.

The nerve is about 4 cm long, out of which 25 mm are intraorbital, 5 mm intracanalicular, and 10 mm intracranial. The entire nerve is enclosed in three meningeal sheaths. The subarachnoid space extends around the nerve up to the eyeball (Fig. 13.10).

Relations in the Orbit

1 At the apex of the orbit, the nerve is closely surrounded by the recti muscles. The ciliary ganglion lies between the optic nerve and the lateral rectus.
2 The central artery and vein of the retina pierce the optic nerve inferomedially about 1.25 cm behind the eyeball (Fig. 13.9).
3 The optic nerve is crossed superiorly by the ophthalmic artery, the nasociliary nerve and the superior ophthalmic vein.
4 The optic nerve is crossed inferiorly by the nerve to the medial rectus.
5 Near the eyeball, the nerve is surrounded by fat containing the ciliary vessels and nerves (*see* Fig. 19.2).

Structure

1 There are about 1.2 million myelinated fibres in each optic nerve, out of which about 53% cross in the optic chiasma.
2 The optic nerve is not a nerve in the strict sense as there is no neurolemmal sheath. It is actually a tract. It cannot regenerate if it is cut. Developmentally, the optic nerve and the retina are a direct prolongation of the brain.

CLINICAL ANATOMY

- The anastomoses between tributaries of facial vein and ophthalmic veins may result in spread of infection from the orbital and nasal regions to the cavernous sinus leading to its thrombosis.
- Optic neuritis is characterized by pain in and behind the eye on ocular movements and on pressure. The papilloedema is less but loss of vision is more. When the optic disc is normal as seen by an ophthalmoscope the same condition is called retrobulbar neuritis.
  The common causes are demyelinating diseases of the central nervous system, any septic focus in the teeth or paranasal sinuses, meningitis, encephalitis, syphilis, and even vitamin B deficiency.
- Optic nerve has no neurilemma sheath, and has no power of regeneration. It is a tract and not a nerve.
- Optic atrophy may be caused by a variety of diseases. It may be primary or secondary.

CILIARY GANGLION

Ciliary ganglion is a peripheral parasympathetic ganglion placed in the course of the oculomotor nerve. It lies near the apex of the orbit between the optic nerve and the tendon of the lateral rectus muscle. It has parasympathetic, sensory and sympathetic roots.

The *parasympathetic root* arises from the nerve to the inferior oblique (Fig. 13.11). It contains preganglionic fibres that begin in the *Edinger-Westphal nucleus*. The fibres relay in the ciliary ganglion. Postganglionic fibres

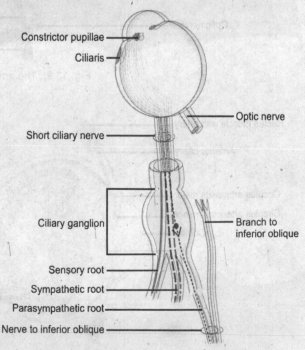

Constrictor pupillae
Ciliaris
Optic nerve
Short ciliary nerve
Ciliary ganglion
Branch to inferior oblique
Sensory root
Sympathetic root
Parasympathetic root
Nerve to inferior oblique

Fig. 13.11: Roots and branches of ciliary ganglion

arising in the ganglion pass through the short ciliary nerves and supply the sphincter pupillae and the ciliaris muscle (*see* Table 1.3). These intraocular muscles are used in accommodation.

The *sensory root* comes from the nasociliary nerve. It contains sensory fibres for the eyeball. The fibres do not relay in the ganglion (Fig. 13.11).

The *sympathetic root* is a branch from the internal carotid plexus. It contains postganglionic fibres arising in the superior cervical ganglion (preganglionic fibres reach the ganglion from lateral horn of T1 spinal segment) which pass along internal carotid, ophthalmic and long ciliary arteries. They pass out of the ciliary ganglion without relay in the short ciliary nerves to supply the blood vessels of the eyeball. They also supply the dilator pupillae.

Branches

The ganglion gives off 8 to 10 short ciliary nerves which divide into 15 to 20 branches, and then pierce the sclera around the entrance of the optic nerve. They contain fibres from all the three roots of the ganglion.

BRANCHES OF OPHTHALMIC DIVISION OF TRIGEMINAL NERVE

Following are the branches of ophthalmic division of trigeminal nerve.

1 Frontal   Supratrochlear
                Supraorbital
2 Nasociliary   Branch to ciliary ganglion
                2–3 long ciliary nerves

                Posterior ethmoidal
                Infratrochlear
                Anterior ethmoidal
3 Lacrimal   Branch to the upper eyelid and secretomotor fibres to lacrimal gland.

Lacrimal Nerve

This is the smallest of the three terminal branches of ophthalmic nerve (Fig. 13.12a). It enters the orbit through lateral part of superior orbital fissure and runs forwards along the upper border of lateral rectus muscle, in company with lacrimal artery. Anteriorly, it receives communication from zygomaticotemporal nerve, passes deep to the lacrimal gland, and ends in the lateral part of the upper eyelid.

The lacrimal nerve supplies the lacrimal gland, the conjunctiva and the upper eyelid. Its own fibres to the gland are sensory. The secretomotor fibres to the gland come from the greater petrosal nerve through its communication with the zygomaticotemporal nerve (*see* Table 1.3).

Frontal Nerve

This is the largest of the three terminal branches of the ophthalmic nerve (Figs 13.12a and b). It begins in the lateral wall of the anterior part of the cavernous sinus. It enters the orbit through the lateral part of the superior orbital fissure, and runs forwards on the superior surface of the levator palpebrae superioris. At the middle of the orbit, it divides into a small supratrochlear branch and a large supraorbital branch.

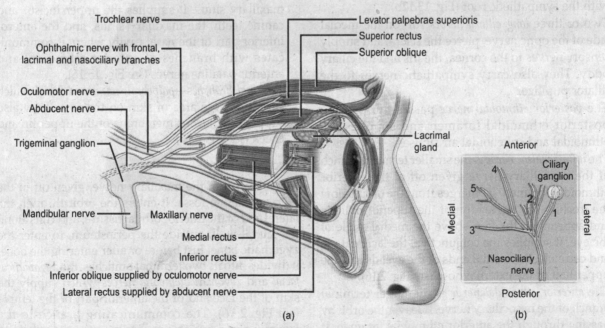

Figs 13.12a and b: (a) Branches of right ophthalmic nerve including III, IV, VI cranial nerves and the extraocular muscles, and (b) branches of nasociliary: (1) Branch to ciliary ganglion, (2) long ciliary, (3) posterior ethmoidal, (4) infratrochlear, and (5) anterior ethmoidal

The *supratrochlear nerve* emerges from the orbit above the trochlea about one finger breadth from the median plane. It supplies the conjunctiva, the upper eyelid, and a small area of the skin of the forehead above the root of the nose (*see* Figs 2.5 and 2.16).

The *supraorbital nerve* emerges from the orbit through the supraorbital notch or foramen about two fingers breadth from the median plane. It divides into medial and lateral branches which runs upwards over the forehead and scalp. It supplies the conjunctiva, the central part of the upper eyelid, the *frontal air sinus* and the skin of the forehead and scalp up to the vertex, or even up to the lambdoid suture.

Nasociliary Nerve

This is one of the terminal branches of the ophthalmic division of the trigeminal nerve (Fig. 13.12b). It begins in the lateral wall of the anterior part of the cavernous sinus. It enters the orbit through the middle part of the superior orbital fissure between the two divisions of the oculomotor nerve (Fig. 13.4). It crosses above the optic nerve from lateral to medial side along with ophthalmic artery and runs along the medial wall of the orbit between the superior oblique and the medial rectus. It ends at the anterior ethmoidal foramen by dividing into the infratrochlear and anterior ethmoidal nerves. Its branches are as follows.

1 A *communicating branch to the ciliary ganglion* forms the sensory root of the ganglion. It is often mixed with the sympathetic root (Fig. 13.12b).

2 Two or three *long ciliary nerves* run on the medial side of the optic nerve, pierce the sclera, and supply sensory nerves to the cornea, the iris and the ciliary body. They also carry sympathetic nerves to the dilator pupillae.

3 The *posterior ethmoidal nerve* passes through the posterior ethmoidal foramen and supplies the ethmoidal and sphenoidal air sinuses.

4 The *infratrochlear nerve* is the smaller terminal branch of the nasociliary nerve given off at the anterior ethmoidal foramen. It emerges from the orbit below the trochlea for the tendon of the superior oblique and appears on the face above the medial angle of the eye. It supplies the conjunctiva, the lacrimal sac and caruncle, the medial ends of the eyelids and the upper half of the external nose (*see* Fig. 2.16).

5 The *anterior ethmoidal nerve* is the larger terminal branch of the nasociliary nerve. It leaves the orbit by passing through the anterior ethmoidal foramen. It appears, for a very short distance, in the anterior cranial fossa, above the cribriform plate of the ethmoid bone. It then descends into the nose through a slit at the side of the anterior part of the crista galli. In the nasal cavity, it lies deep to the nasal bone. It gives off two *internal nasal branches*, medial and lateral to the mucosa of the nose. Finally, it emerges at the lower border of the nasal bone as the *external nasal nerve* which supplies the skin of the lower half of the nose.

SOME BRANCHES OF MAXILLARY DIVISION OF THE TRIGEMINAL NERVE

Infraorbital Nerve

It is the continuation of the maxillary nerve. It enters the orbit through the *inferior orbital fissure*. It then runs forwards on the floor of the orbit or the roof of the maxillary sinus, at first in the *infraorbital groove* and then in the *infraorbital canal* remaining outside the periosteum of the orbit. It emerges on the face through the *infraorbital foramen* and terminates by dividing into palpebral, nasal and labial branches (*see* Fig. 2.16). The nerve is accompanied by the infraorbital branch of the third part of the maxillary artery and the accompanying vein.

Branches

1 The *middle superior alveolar nerve* arises in the infra-orbital groove, runs in the lateral wall of the maxillary sinus, and supplies the upper premolar teeth.

2 The *anterior superior alveolar nerve* arises in the infraorbital canal, and runs in a sinuous canal having a complicated course in the anterior wall of the maxillary sinus. It supplies the upper incisor and canine teeth, the maxillary sinus, and the antero-inferior part of the nasal cavity where it communicates with branches of anterior ethmoidal and anterior palatine nerves (*see* Fig. 15.16).

3 *Terminal branches—palpebral, nasal and labial* which supply a large area of skin on the face. They also supply the mucous membrane of the upper lip and cheek (*see* Fig. 2.16).

Zygomatic Nerve

It is a branch of the maxillary nerve, given off in the pterygopalatine fossa. It enters the orbit through the lateral end of the inferior orbital fissure, and runs along the lateral wall, outside the periosteum, to enter the zygomatic bone. Just before or after entering the bone, it divides into its two terminal branches, the *zygomatico-facial* and *zygomaticotemporal nerves* which supply the skin of the face and of the anterior part of the temple (*see* Fig. 2.16). The communicating branch to the lacrimal nerve, which contains secretomotor fibres to the lacrimal gland, arises from the zygomaticotemporal nerve, and runs in the lateral wall of the orbit (*see* Chapter 2).

SYMPATHETIC NERVES OF THE ORBIT

Sympathetic nerves arise from the internal carotid plexus and enter the orbit through the following sources.

1 The dilator pupillae of the iris is supplied by sympathetic nerves that pass through the ophthalmic nerve, the nasociliary nerve, and its long ciliary branches.

2 Other sympathetic nerves enter the orbit as follows:
   a. A plexus surrounds the ophthalmic artery.
   b. A direct branch from the internal carotid plexus passes through the superior orbital fissure and joins the ciliary ganglion.
   c. Other filaments pass along the oculomotor, trochlear, abducent, and ophthalmic nerves. All these sympathetic nerves are vasomotor in function.

Mnemonics

Extraocular muscles; cranial nerve innervation "LR6SO4 rest 3"

Lateral rectus by **VI**
Superior oblique by **IV**
Rest are by **III** cranial nerve, i.e. levator palpebrae superioris, superior rectus (SR), medial rectus (MR), inferior rectus (IR) and inferior oblique (IO).

FACTS TO REMEMBER

- Levator palpebrae superioris is partly supplied by III nerve and partly by sympathetic fibres
- Central artery of retina is an end artery.
- Nerve supply of extraocular muscles is LR6, SO4, Rest (levator palpebrae sup., SR, MR, IR and IO) by III.

- Edinger-Westphal is the nucleus for the supply of ciliaris muscles and constrictor pupillae muscles. The fibres supply these muscles after relaying in the ciliary ganglion.
- Elevation and depression of the cornea occur around a transverse axis.
- Adduction and abduction of the cornea take place around a vertical axis.
- Intorsion and extorsion occur around an antero-posterior axis.

CLINICOANATOMICAL PROBLEM

A hypertensive and diabetic lady with high cholesterol and lipids develops sudden blindness in her right eye.
- What has caused blindness in this particular case?
- Name the other end arteries in the body.

Ans: Hypertension cause atheromatous changes in the arteries. Most of the nervous layers of retina are supplied by a single "end artery" with no anastomoses with any other artery. This artery is also vulnerable to blockage due to various changes in blood chemistry. If it gets blocked, the result is blindness of that eye.

Other end arteries are:
- Labyrinthine artery for the inner ear
- Coronary arteries are functional end arteries though these do anastomose
- Central branches of cerebral arteries
- Segmental branches of the kidney and spleen

FREQUENTLY ASKED QUESTIONS

1. Describe extraocular muscles under the following headings:
   a. Origin   b. Insertion
   c. Actions   d. Nerve supply
   e. Clinical importance

2. Write short notes on:
   a. Ciliary ganglion
   b. Levator palpebrae superioris
   c. Ophthalmic artery
   d. Actions of oblique muscles

MULTIPLE CHOICE QUESTIONS

1. Which nucleus is related to ciliary ganglion?
   a. Superior salivatory
   b. Lacrimatory
   c. Inferior salivatory
   d. Edinger-Westphal

2. Ophthalmic artery is a branch of which of the following arteries?
   a. Internal carotid
   b. External carotid
   c. Maxillary
   d. Vertebral

3. Supraorbital artery is a branch of:
   a. Maxillary
   b. External carotid
   c. Ophthalmic
   d. Internal carotid

4. Which of the following is true about ocular muscles?
   a. Medial rectus is supplied by III nerve
   b. Superior oblique turns the centre of cornea upwards and laterally
   c. Inferior oblique arises from medial wall of the orbit
   d. Lateral rectus is supplied by IV nerve

5. Which nerve does not transverse the middle part of superior orbital fissure?
   a. Two divisions of III nerve
   b. Frontal nerve
   c. VI nerve
   d. Nasociliary nerve

6. Which out of the following arteries is an end-artery?
   a. Lacrimal artery
   b. Zygomaticotemporal
   c. Central artery of retina
   d. Anterior ethmoidal artery

ANSWERS					
1. d	2. a	3. c	4. a	5. b	6. c

Mouth and Pharynx

At times it is better to keep your mouth shut and let people wonder if you are a fool than to open it and remove all their doubts

—James Sinclair

ORAL CAVITY

Oral cavity is used for ingestion of food and fluids. It is continued posteriorly into the oropharynx, the middle part of the muscular pharynx. In its upper part, opens the posterior part of the nasal cavity and the inlet of larynx opens into its lower part. Roof of oral cavity is formed by the hard and the soft palates. Tongue is the biggest occupant of the oral cavity, described in Chapter 17. The cavity also contains thirty-two teeth in an adult.

IDENTIFICATION

Identify the structures in your own oral cavity. These are the vestibule, lips, cheeks, oral cavity proper and teeth.

Divisions

The oral or mouth cavity is divided into an outer, smaller portion, the vestibule, and an inner larger part, the oral cavity proper.

Vestibule

1 The vestibule of the mouth is a narrow space *bounded* externally by the lips and cheeks, and internally, by the teeth and gums (Fig. 14.1).
2 It *communicates*:
   a. With the exterior through the oral fissure.
   b. With the mouth open, it communicates freely with the oral cavity proper. Even when the teeth are occluded a small communication remains behind the third molar tooth.
3 The *parotid duct* opens on the inner surface of the cheek opposite the crown of the upper second molar tooth (Fig. 14.1). Numerous *labial and buccal glands* (mucous) situated in the submucosa of the lips and cheeks open into the vestibule. Four or five *molar glands* (mucous), situated on the buccopharyngeal fascia also open into the vestibule.

4 Except for the teeth, the entire vestibule is lined by mucous membrane. The mucous membrane forms median folds that pass from the lips to the gums, and are called the *frenula of the lips*.

CLINICAL ANATOMY

- The papilla of the parotid duct in the vestibule of the mouth provides access to the parotid duct for the injection of the radio-opaque dye to locate calculi in the duct system or the gland (Fig. 14.1).
- Koplik's spots are seen as white pin point spots around the opening of the parotid duct in measles. These are diagnostic of the disease.

Lips

1 The lips are fleshy folds lined externally by skin and internally by mucous membrane. The *mucocutaneous junction* lines the 'edge' of the lip, part of the mucosal surface is also normally seen.
2 Each lip is *composed* of:
   a. Skin.
   b. Superficial fascia.
   c. The orbicularis oris muscle.
   d. The submucosa, containing mucous labial glands and blood vessels.
   e. Mucous membrane.
3 The lips bound the *oral fissure*. They meet laterally at the angles of the mouth. The inner surface of each lip is supported by a *frenulum* which ties it to the gum. Philtrum is a median vertical groove on the outer surface of the upper lip.
4 *Lymphatics* of the central part of the lower lip drain to the submental nodes; the lymphatics from the rest of the lower lip pass to the submandibular nodes.

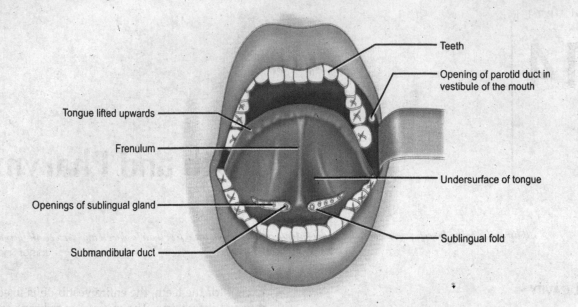

Fig. 14.1: Interior of the mouth cavity

Cheeks (Buccae)

1 The cheeks are fleshy flaps, forming a large part of each side of the face. They are continuous in front with the lips, and the junction is indicated by the *nasolabial sulcus* (*furrow*) which extends from the side of the nose to the angle of the mouth.

2 Each cheek is *composed of*:
   a. Skin.
   b. Superficial fascia containing some facial muscles; the parotid duct, mucous molar glands, vessels and nerves.
   c. The buccinator covered by buccopharyngeal fascia and pierced by the parotid duct.
   d. Submucosa, with mucous buccal glands.
   e. Mucous membrane.

3 The *buccal pad of fat* is best developed in infants. It lies on the buccinator partly deep to the masseter and partly in front of it.

4 The *lymphatics* of the cheek drain chiefly into the submandibular and preauricular nodes, and partly also to the buccal and mandibular nodes.

Oral Cavity Proper

1 It is *bounded* anterolaterally by the teeth, the gums and the alveolar arches of the jaws. The roof is formed by the hard palate and the soft palate. The *floor* is occupied by the tongue posteriorly, and presents the sublingual region anteriorly, below the tip of the tongue. Posteriorly, the cavity communicates with the pharynx through the *oropharyngeal isthmus* (*isthmus of fauces*) which is bounded superiorly by the soft palate, inferiorly by the tongue, and on each side by the palatoglossal arches.

2 The sublingual region presents the following features:
   a. In the median plane, there is a fold of mucosa passing from the inferior aspect of the tongue to the floor of the mouth. This is the *frenulum* of the tongue (*see* Fig. 17.2).
   b. On each side of the frenulum, there is a *sublingual papilla*. On the summit of this papilla, there is the opening of submandibular duct.
   c. Running laterally and backwards from the *sublingual papilla*, there is the sublingual fold which overlies the sublingual gland. A few sublingual ducts open on the edge of this fold.

3 *Lymphatics* from the anterior part of the floor of the mouth pass to the submental nodes. Those from the hard palate and soft palate pass to the retro-pharyngeal and upper deep cervical nodes. The gums and the rest of the floor drain into the submandibular nodes.

Gums (Gingivae)

1 The gums are the soft tissues which envelop the alveolar processes of the upper and lower jaws and surround the necks of the teeth. These are composed of dense fibrous tissue covered by stratified squamous epithelium.

2 Each gum has two parts:
   a. The free part surrounds the neck of the tooth like a collar.
   b. The *attached part* is firmly fixed to the alveolar arch of the jaw. The fibrous tissue of the gum is continuous with the periosteum lining the alveoli (periodontal membrane).

3 Nerve supply of gums is shown in Table 14.1.

Table 14.1: Nerve supply of gums

Upper gums	Nerve supply
Labial side (Fig. 14.4)	Posterior, middle and anterior superior alveolar nerves (V2)
Lingual side (see Figs 15.16)	Anterior palatine and nasopalatine nerves (from pterygopalatine ganglion)
Lower gums	
Labial side	Buccal branch of mandibular and incisive branch of mental nerve (V3)
Lingual side	Lingual nerve (V3)

3 *Lymphatics* of the upper gums pass to the submandibular nodes. The anterior part of the lower gums drains into the submental nodes, whereas the posterior part drains into the submandibular nodes.

CLINICAL ANATOMY

Ludwig's angina is the cellulitis of the floor of the mouth. The tongue is forced upwards leading to swelling both below the chin and within the mouth. The disease is usually caused due to a carious molar tooth.

Teeth

The teeth form part of the masticatory apparatus and are fixed to the jaws. In man, the teeth are replaced only once *(diphyodont)* in contrast with non-mammallian vertebrates where teeth are constantly replaced throughout life *(polyphyodont)*. The teeth of the first set (dentition) are known as *milk,* or *deciduous teeth,* and the second set, as *permanent teeth.*

The deciduous teeth are 20 in number. In each half of each jaw, there are two incisors, one canine, and two molars.

The permanent teeth are 32 in number, and consist of two incisors (Latin *to cut*) one canine (Latin *dog*) two premolars (Latin *millstone*) and three molars in each half of each jaw.

Parts of a Tooth

Each tooth has three parts:
1 A *crown*, projecting above or below the gum.
2 A *root*, embedded in the jaw beneath the gum.
3 A *neck*, between the crown and root and surrounded by the gum (Fig. 14.2).

Structure

Structurally, each tooth is composed of:
1 The pulp in the centre
2 The dentine surrounding the pulp.

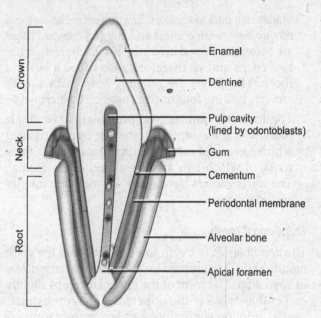

Fig. 14.2: Parts of a tooth

3 The enamel covering the projecting part of dentine, or crown.
4 The cementum surrounding the embedded part of the dentine.
5 The periodontal membrane.

The *pulp* is loose fibrous tissue containing vessels, nerves and lymphatics, all of which enter the pulp cavity through the apical foramen. The pulp is covered by a layer of tall columnar cells, known as *odontoblasts* which are capable of replacing dentine any time in life.

The *dentine* is a calcified material containing spiral tubules radiating from the pulp cavity. Each tubule is occupied by a protoplasmic process from one of the odontoblasts. The calcium and organic matter are in the same proportion as in bone.

The *enamel* is the hardest substance in the body. It is made up of crystalline prisms lying roughly at right angles to the surface of the tooth.

The *cementum* resembles bone in structure, but like enamel and dentine there is neither any blood supply nor any nerve supply. Over the neck, the cementum commonly overlaps the cervical end of enamel; or, less commonly, it may just meet the enamel. Rarely, it stops short of the enamel (10%) leaving the cervical dentine covered only by gum.

The *periodontal membrane (ligament)* holds the root in its socket. This membrane acts as a periosteum to both the cementum as well as the bony socket.

Form and Function (Crowns and Roots)

1 The shape of a tooth is adapted to its function. The *incisors are cutting teeth,* with chisel-like crowns. The upper and lower incisors overlap each other like the

blades of a pair of scissors. *The canines are holding and tearing teeth*, with conical and rugged crowns. These are better developed in carnivores. Each *premolar* has two cusps and is, therefore, also called a *bicuspid* tooth. The *molars are grinding teeth*, with square crowns, bearing four or five cusps on their crowns.

2 The incisors, canines and premolars have single roots, with the exception of the first upper premolar which has a bifid root. The upper molars have three roots, of which two are lateral and one is medial. The lower molars have only two roots, an anterior and a posterior.

Eruption of Teeth

The *deciduous teeth* begin to erupt at about the sixth month, and all get erupted by the end of the second year or soon after. The teeth of the lower jaw erupt slightly earlier than those of the upper jaw. The approximate ages of eruption of deciduous and permanent teeth are given in Table 14.2 and Figs 14.3a and b. Blood supply of teeth—both upper and lower are supplied by branches of maxillary artery.

Nerve Supply of Teeth

The pulp and periodontal membrane have the same nerve supply which is as follows:

The *upper teeth* are supplied by the posterior superior alveolar, middle superior alveolar, and the anterior superior alveolar nerves (maxillary nerve).

The *lower teeth* are supplied by the inferior alveolar nerve (mandibular nerve) (Fig. 14.4).

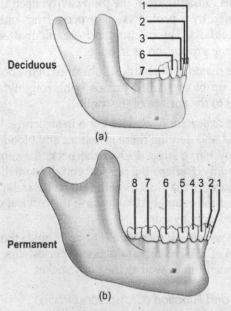

Figs 14.3a and b: Deciduous and permanent teeth. (1) Central incisor, (2) lateral incisor, (3) canine, (4) 1st premolar, (5) 2nd premolar, (6) 1st molar, (7) 2nd molar, and (8) 3rd molar

Table 14.2: Usual time of eruption of teeth and time of shedding of deciduous teeth

Tooth	Eruption time	Shedding time
Deciduous (Fig. 14.2a)		
Medial incisor	6–8 months	6–7 years
Lateral incisor	8–10 months	7–8 years
First molar	12–16 months	8–9 years
Canine	16–20 months	10–12 years
Second molar	20–24 months	10–12 years
Permanent (Fig. 14.2b)		
First molar	6–7 years	
Medial incisor	7–8 years	
Lateral incisor	8–9 years	
First premolar	10–11 years	
Second premolar	11–12 years	
Canine	12–13 years	
Second molar	13–14 years	
Third molar	17–25 years	

STAGES OF DEVELOPMENT OF DECIDUOUS TEETH

1 By 6th week of development, the epithelium covering the convex border of alveolar process of upper and lower jaws become thickened to form C-shaped dental lamina, which projects into the underlying mesoderm.

2 Dental laminae of upper and lower jaws develop 10 centres of proliferation from which dental buds grow into underlying mesenchyme. This is the *bud stage* (Figs 14.5a and b)

3 The deeper enlarged parts of the tooth bud is called *enamel organ*.

4 The enamel organ of dental bud is invaginated by mesenchyme of dental papilla making it cap-shaped. This is the *cap stage* (Fig. 14.5c).

The dental papilla together with enamel organ is known as the tooth germ. The cell of enamel organ adjacent to dental papilla cells get columnar and are known as *ameloblasts*.

The mesenchymal cells now arrange themselves along the ameloblasts and are called odontoblasts. The two cell layers are separated by a basement membrane. The rest of the mesenchymal cells form the "pulp of the tooth". This is the *bell stage* (Fig. 14.5d).

Now ameloblasts lay enamel on the outer aspect, while odontoblasts lay dentine on the inner aspect. Later ameloblasts disappear while odontoblasts remain.

The root of the tooth is formed by laying down of layers of dentine, narrowing the pulp space to a canal for the passage of nerve and blood vessels only (Fig. 14.5e). The dentine in the root is covered by mesenchymal cells which differentiate into cementoblasts for laying down the cementum. Outside, this is the periodontal ligament connecting root to the socket in the bone.

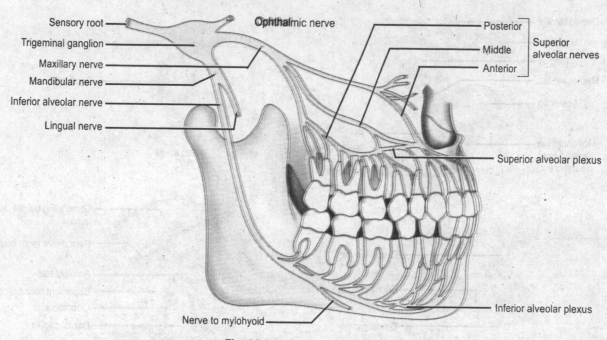

Fig. 14.4: Nerve supply of teeth

Ectoderm forms enamel of tooth. Neural crest cells form dentine, dental pulp, cementum and periodontal ligament.

Formation of permanent teeth: These develop from the dental buds arising from the dental lamina and lie on the medial side of each developing milk tooth.

CLINICAL ANATOMY

- Being the hardest and chemically the most stable tissues in the body, the teeth are selectively preserved after death and may be fossilized. Because of this, the teeth are very helpful in medicolegal practice for identification of otherwise unrecognizable dead bodies. The teeth also provide by far the best data to study evolutionary changes and the relationship between ontogeny and phylogeny.

- In scurvy (caused by deficiency of vitamin C), the gums are swollen and spongy, and bleed on touch. In gingivitis, the edges of the gums are red and bleed easily.

- Improper oral hygiene may cause gingivitis and suppuration with pocket formation between the teeth and gums. This results in a chronic pus discharge at the margin of the gums. The condition is known as *pyorrhoea alveolaris* (chronic periodontitis). Pyorrhoea is common cause of foul breath for which the patient hardly ever consults a dentist because the condition is painless.

- Decalcification of enamel and dentine with consequent softening and gradual destruction of the tooth is known as *dental caries*. A caries tooth is tender on mastication.

- Infection of apex of root (apical abscess) occurs only when the pulp is dead. The condition can be recognized in a good radiograph.

- Irregular dentition is common in rickets and the upper permanent incisors may be notched, the notching corresponds to a small segment of a large circle. Even in congenital syphilis, the same teeth are notched, but the notching corresponds to a large segment of a small circle (*Hutchinson's teeth*).

- The third molar teeth also called *wisdom teeth* usually erupt between 18 and 20 years. These may not erupt normally due to less space and may get impacted causing enormous pain.

- Time of eruption of the teeth helps in assessing the age of the person.

- The upper canine teeth are called as the "eye teeth" as these have long roots which reach up to the medial angle of the eye. Infection of these roots may spread in the facial vein and even lead to thrombosis of the cavernous sinus.

- The upper teeth need separate injections of the anaesthetic on both the buccal and palatal surfaces of the maxillary process just distal to the tooth. The thin layer of bone permits rapid diffusion of the drug up to the tooth.

Head and Neck

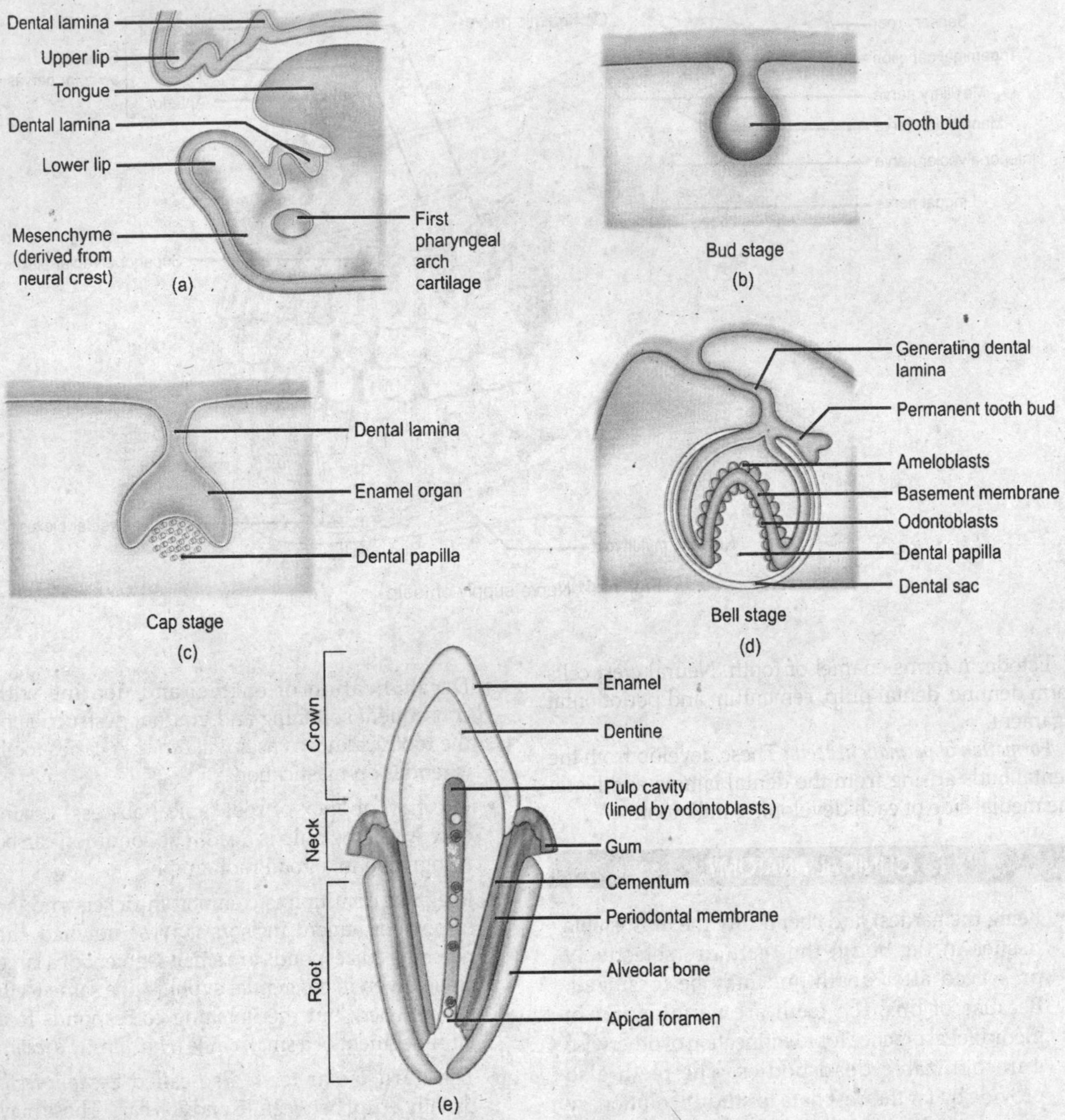

Figs 14.5a to e: Development of tooth

HARD AND SOFT PALATES

DISSECTION

Cut through the centre of the frontal bone, internasal suture, intermaxillary sutures, chin, hyoid bone, thyroid, cricoid and tracheal cartilages; carry the incision through the septum of nose, nasopharynx, tongue, and both the palates.

Cut through the centre of the remaining occipital bone and cervical vertebrae. This will complete the *sagittal section of head and neck*.

Hard palate: Strip the mucoperiosteum of hard palate.
Soft palate: Remove the mucous membrane of the soft palate in order to identify its muscles. Also remove the mucous membrane over palatoglossal and palatopharyngeal arches and salpingopharyngeal fold to visualise the subjacent muscles.

HARD PALATE

It is a partition between the nasal and oral cavities. Its anterior two-thirds are formed by the palatine processes of the maxillae; and its posterior one-third by the horizontal plates of the palatine bones (Fig. 14.6).

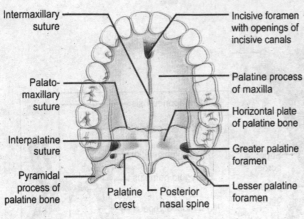

Fig. 14.6: Hard palate

The *anterolateral margins* of the palate are continuous with the alveolar arches and gums.

The *posterior margin* gives attachment to the soft palate.

The *superior surface* forms the floor of the nose.

The *inferior surface* forms the roof of the oral cavity.

Vessels and Nerves

Arteries: Greater palatine branch of maxillary artery (*see* Figs 6.6 and 6.7).

Veins: Drain into the pterygoid plexus of veins.

Nerves: Greater palatine and nasopalatine branches of the pterygopalatine ganglion suspended by the maxillary nerve.

Lymphatics: The lymphatics drain mostly to the upper deep cervical nodes and partly to the retropharyngeal nodes.

SOFT PALATE

It is a movable, muscular fold, suspended from the posterior border of the hard palate.

It separates the nasopharynx from the oropharynx, the crossroads between the food and air passages (Fig. 14.7).

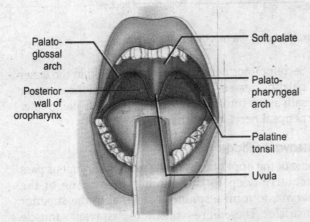

Fig. 14.7: Soft palate with palatine tonsils

The soft palate has two surfaces, anterior and posterior; and two borders, superior and inferior.

The *anterior (oral) surface* is concave and is marked by a median raphe.

The posterior surface is convex, and is continuous superiorly with the floor of the nasal cavity.

The *superior border* is attached to the posterior border of the hard palate, blending on each side with the pharynx (Figs 14.9a and b).

The inferior border is free and bounds the pharyngeal isthmus. From its middle, there hangs a conical projection, called the uvula (Fig. 14.7). From each side of the base of the uvula (Latin *small grape*) two curved folds of mucous membrane extend laterally and downwards. The anterior fold is called the *palatoglossal arch* or anterior pillar of fauces. It contains the palatoglossus muscle and reaches the side of the tongue at the junction of its oral and pharyngeal parts. This fold forms the lateral boundary of the oropharyngeal isthmus or isthmus of fauces. The posterior fold is called the *palatopharyngeal* arch or posterior pillar of fauces. It contains the palatopharyngeus muscle. It forms the posterior boundary of the tonsillar fossa, and merges inferiorly with the lateral wall of the pharynx.

Structure

The soft palate is a fold of mucous membrane containing the following parts:

- The palatine aponeurosis which is the flattened tendon of the tensor veli palatini forms the fibrous basis of the palate. Near the median plane, the aponeurosis splits to enclose the musculus uvulae.
- The levator veli palatini and the palatopharyngeus lie on the superior surface of the palatine aponeurosis.
- The palatoglossus lies on the inferior or anterior surface of the palatine aponeurosis.
- Numerous mucous glands, and some taste buds are present.

Muscles of the Soft Palate

They are as follows:

1 Tensor palati (tensor veli palatini) (Figs 14.8a and b).
2 Levator palati (levator veli palatini).
3 Musculus uvulae.
4 Palatoglossus.
5 Palatopharyngeus (Fig. 14.14).
   Details of the muscles are given in Table 14.3.

Nerve Supply

1 Motor nerves. All muscles of the soft palate except the tensor veli palatini are supplied by the pharyngeal plexus. The fibres of this plexus are derived from the cranial part of the accessory nerve through the vagus. The tensor veli palatini is supplied by the mandibular nerve.

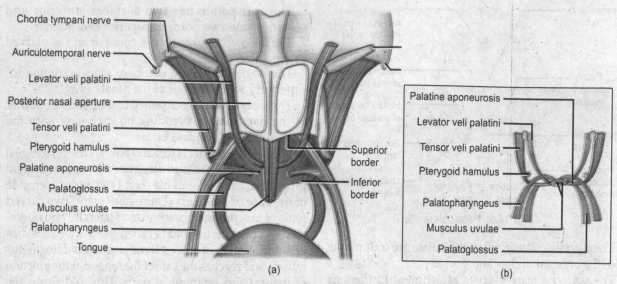

Figs 14.8a and b: (a) Attachment of the muscles of the soft palate, and (b) muscles of soft palate

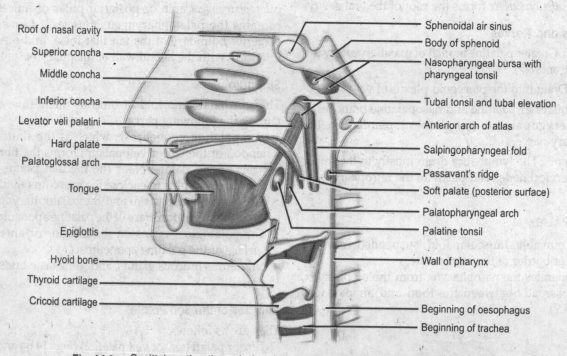

Fig. 14.9a: Sagittal section through the pharynx, the nose, the mouth and the larynx

2 General sensory nerves are derived from:
   a. The middle and posterior lesser palatine nerves, which are branches of the maxillary nerve through the pterygopalatine ganglion (*see* Fig. 15.16).
   b. The glossopharyngeal nerve.
3 Special sensory or gustatory nerves carrying taste sensations from the oral surface are contained in the lesser palatine nerves. The fibres travel through the greater petrosal nerve to the geniculate ganglion of the facial nerve and from there to the nucleus of the tractus solitarius.(Flowchart 14.1).

4 Secretomotor nerves are also contained in the lesser palatine nerves. They are derived from the superior salivatory nucleus and travel through the greater petrosal nerve (Flowchart 14.2).

Passavant's Ridge

Some of the upper fibres of the palatopharyngeus pass circularly deep to the mucous membrane of the pharynx, to form a sphincter internal to the superior constrictor. These fibres constitute Passavant's muscle which on contraction raises a ridge called the

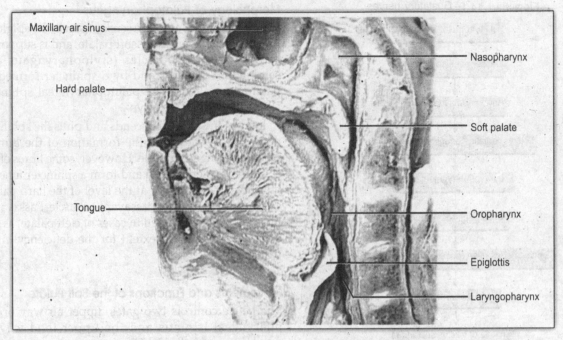

Fig. 14.9b: Sagittal section of pharynx

Labels: Maxillary air sinus, Hard palate, Tongue, Nasopharynx, Soft palate, Oropharynx, Epiglottis, Laryngopharynx

Table 14.3: Muscles of the soft palate

Muscle	Origin	Insertion	Actions
1. **Tensor veli palatini** This is a thin, triangular muscle (Fig. 14.8)	a. Lateral side of auditory tube b. Adjoining part of the base of the skull (greater wing and scaphoid fossa of sphenoid bone)	Muscle descends, converges to form a delicate tendon which winds round the pterygoid hamulus, passes through the origin of the buccinator, and flattens out to form the palatine aponeurosis. Aponeurosis is attached to: a. Posterior border of hard palate b. Inferior surface of palate behind the palatine crest	a. Tightens the soft palate, chiefly the anterior part b. Opens the auditory tube to equalize air pressure between the middle ear and the nasopharynx
2. **Levator veli palatini** This is a cylindrical muscle that lies deep to the tensor veli palatini	a. Inferior aspect of auditory tube b. Adjoining part of inferior surface of petrous temporal bone	Muscle enters the pharynx by passing over the upper concave margin of the superior constrictor, runs downwards and medially and spreads out in the soft palate. It is inserted into the upper surface of the palatine aponeurosis	a. Elevates soft palate and closes the pharyngeal isthmus b. Opens the auditory tube-like the tensor veli palatini
3. **Musculus uvulae** This is a longitudinal strip placed on each side of the median plane, within the palatine aponeurosis	a. Posterior nasal spine b. Palatine aponeurosis	Mucous membrane of uvula	Pulls up the uvula
4. **Palatoglossus**	Oral surface of palatine aponeurosis	Descends in the palatoglossal arch, to the side of the tongue at the junction of its oral and pharyngeal parts	Pulls up the root of the tongue, approximates the palatoglossal arches, and thus closes the oropharyngeal isthmus
5. **Palatopharyngeus** It consists of two fasciculi that are separated by the levator veli palatini (also *see* Passavant's ridge)	a. Anterior fasciculus from posterior border of hard palate b. Posterior fasciculus: from the palatine aponeurosis	Descends in the palatopharyngeal arch and spreads out to form the greater part of longitudinal muscle coat of pharynx. It is inserted into: a. Posterior border of the lamina of the thyroid cartilage b. Wall of the pharynx and its median raphe	Pulls up the wall of the pharynx and shortens, it during swallowing

Flowchart 14.1: Gustatory nerves

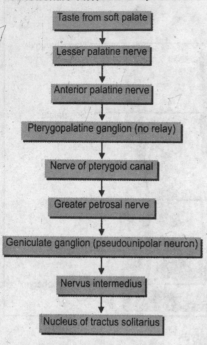

Taste from soft palate

↓

Lesser palatine nerve

↓

Anterior palatine nerve

↓

Pterygopalatine ganglion (no relay)

↓

Nerve of pterygoid canal

↓

Greater petrosal nerve

↓

Geniculate ganglion (pseudounipolar neuron)

↓

Nervus intermedius

↓

Nucleus of tractus solitarius

Flowchart 14.2: Secretomotor nerves

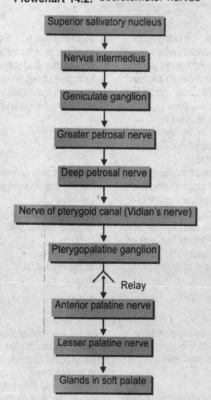

Superior salivatory nucleus

↓

Nervus intermedius

↓

Geniculate ganglion

↓

Greater petrosal nerve

↓

Deep petrosal nerve

↓

Nerve of pterygoid canal (Vidian's nerve)

↓

Pterygopalatine ganglion

↓ Relay

Anterior palatine nerve

↓

Lesser palatine nerve

↓

Glands in soft palate

Passavant's ridge on the posterior wall of the nasopharynx. When the soft palate is elevated it comes in contact with this ridge, the two together closing the pharyngeal isthmus between the nasopharynx and the

Morphology of Palatopharyngeus

In mammals with an acute sense of smell, the epiglottis lies above the level of the soft palate, and is supported by two vertical muscles (stylopharyngeus and salpingopharyngeus) and by a sphincter formed by palatopharyngeus. The palatopharyngeal sphincter clasps the inlet of the larynx.

In man, the larynx descends and pulls the sphincter downwards leading to the formation of the human palatopharyngeus muscle. However, some fibres of the sphincter are left behind and form a sphincter inner to the superior constrictor at the level of the hard palate. These fibres constitute Passavant's muscle. Passavant's muscle is best developed in cases of cleft palate, as this compensates to some extent for the deficiency in the palate.

Movements and Functions of the Soft Palate

The palate controls two gates, upper air way or the pharyngeal isthmus and the upper food way or oropharyngeal isthmus. The upper air way crosses the upper food way (Fig. 14.10). The soft palate can completely close them, or can regulate their sizes according to requirements. Through these movements, the soft palate plays an important role in chewing, swallowing, speech, coughing, sneezing, etc. A few specific roles are given below.

1 It isolates the mouth from the oropharynx during chewing, so that breathing is unaffected.

2 It separates the oropharynx from the nasopharynx by locking Passavant's ridge during the second stage of swallowing, so that food does not enter the nose.

3 By varying the degree of closure of the pharyngeal isthmus, the quality of voice can be modified and various consonants are correctly pronounced.

4 During sneezing, the blast of air is appropriately divided and directed through the nasal and oral cavities without damaging the narrow nose. Similarly during coughing, it directs air and sputum into the mouth and not into the nose (Fig. 14.10).

Blood Supply

Arteries

1 Greater palatine branch of maxillary artery (*see* Fig. 6.6).

2 Ascending palatine branch of facial artery.

3 Palatine branch of ascending pharyngeal artery (Fig. 14.16).

Veins

They pass to the pterygoid and tonsillar plexuses of veins.

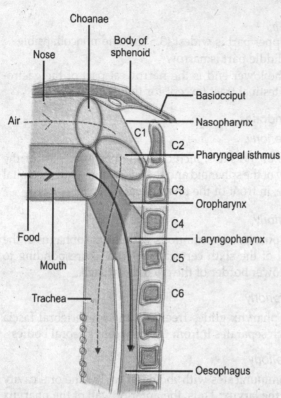

Fig. 14.10: Crossing of upper airway and upper food passages

Lymphatics
Drain into the upper deep cervical and retropharyngeal lymph nodes.

DEVELOPMENT OF PALATE

The premaxilla or primitive palate carrying upper four incisor teeth is formed by the fusion of medial nasal folds, which are folds of frontonasal process.

The rest of the palate is formed by the shelf-like palatine processes of maxilla and horizontal plates of palatine bone. Most of the palate gets ossified to form the hard palate. The unossified posterior part of fused palatal processes forms the soft palate.

STRUCTURE

Soft palate comprises epithelium, connective tissue and muscles. Epithelium is from the ectoderm of maxillary process. The muscles are derived from 1st, 4th and 6th branchial arches and accordingly are innervated by mandibular and vagoaccessory complex.

CLINICAL ANATOMY

• Cleft palate is a congenital defect caused by non-fusion of the right and left palatal processes. It may be of different degrees. In the least severe type, the defect is confined to the soft palate. In the most

severe cases, the cleft in the palate is continuous with harelip (Fig. 14.11).

• Paralysis of the soft palate in lesions of the vagus nerve produces:
  a. Nasal regurgitation of liquids
  b. Nasal twang in voice
  c. Flattening of the palatal arch
  d. Deviation of uvula to normal side (Fig. 14.12).

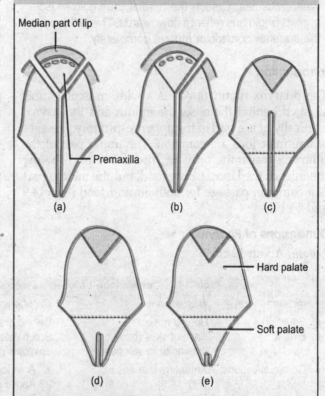

Figs 14.11a to e: Types of congenital cleft palate: (a) Bilateral complete, (b) unilateral complete cleft palate, (c) partial midline cleft, (d) cleft of soft palate, and (e) bifid uvula

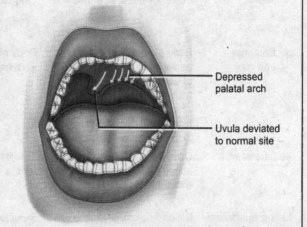

Fig. 14.12: Uvula deviated to right side in paralysis of left vagus nerve

PHARYNX

Identify the structures in the interior of three parts of pharynx, i.e. nasopharynx, oropharynx and laryngopharynx. Clean the surfaces of buccinator muscle and adjoining superior constrictor muscles by removing connective tissue and buccopharyngeal fascia over these muscles. Detach the medial pterygoid muscle from its origin and reflect it downwards. This will expose the superior constrictor muscle completely.

Introduction

The pharynx (Latin *throat*) is a wide muscular tube, situated behind the nose, the mouth and the larynx. Clinically, it is a part of the upper respiratory passages where infections are common. The upper part of the pharynx transmits only air, the lower part (below the inlet of the larynx), only food, but the middle part is a common passage for both air and food (Figs 14.9 and 14.10).

Dimensions of Pharynx

Length: About 12 cm.

Width:
1 Upper part is widest (3.5 cm) and noncollapsible
2 Middle part is narrow
3 The lower end is the narrowest part of the gastro-intestinal tract (except for the vermiform).

Boundaries

Superiorly

Base of the skull, including the posterior part of the body of the sphenoid and the basilar part of the occipital bone, in front of the pharyngeal tubercle.

Inferiorly

The pharynx is continuous with the oesophagus at the level of the sixth cervical vertebra, corresponding to the lower border of the cricoid cartilage.

Posteriorly

The pharynx glides freely on the prevertebral fascia which separates it from the cervical vertebral bodies.

Anteriorly

It communicates with the nasal cavity, the oral cavity and the larynx. Thus, the anterior wall of the pharynx is incomplete.

Table 14.4: Comparison between nasopharynx, oropharynx and laryngopharynx			
Particulars	Nasopharynx	Oropharynx	Laryngopharynx
a. Situation	Behind nose	Behind oral cavity	Behind larynx
b. Extent	Base of skull (body of sphenoid) to soft palate	Soft palate to upper border of epiglottis (Fig. 14.9)	Upper border of epiglottis to lower border of cricoid cartilage
c. Communications	Anteriorly with nose (Fig. 14.9) Below with oropharynx	1. Anteriorly with oral cavity 2. Above with nasopharynx 3. Below with laryngopharynx	Inferiorly with oesophagus Anteriorly with larynx (Fig.14.9) Above with oropharynx
d. Nerve supply	Pharyngeal branches of pterygopalatine ganglion	IX and X nerves	IX and X nerves
e. Relations:			
i. Anterior	Posterior nasal aperture	Oral cavity	1. Inlet of larynx 2. Posterior surface of cricoid cartilage 3. Arytenoid cartilage
ii. Posterior and roof	Body of sphenoid bone and basiocciput and anterior arch of atlas. Presence of: a. Nasopharyngeal tonsil prominent in children b. Nasopharyngeal bursa—mucus diverticulum	Body of second and third cervical vertebrae	Fourth and fifth cervical vertebrae
iii. Lateral wall	Opening of auditory tube above tube is tubal elevation with tubal tonsil	Tonsillar fossa containing palatine tonsils	Piriform fossa on each side of inlet of larynx, bounded by aryepiglottic fold medially and thyroid cartilage laterally.
f. Lining epithelium	Ciliated columnar epithelium	Stratified squamous nonkeratinised epithelium	Stratified squamous nonkeratinised epithelium
g. Function	Passage for air (respiratory function)	Passage for air and food	Passage for food

On each side

1 The pharynx is attached to:
   a. Medial pterygoid plate
   b. Pterygomandibular raphe
   c. Mandible
   d. Tongue
   e. Hyoid bone
   f. Thyroid and cricoid cartilages.
2 It communicates on each side with the middle ear cavity through the auditory tube.
3 The pharynx is related on either side to:
   a. The styloid process and the muscles attached to it.
   b. The common carotid, internal carotid, and external carotid arteries, and the cranial nerves related to them.

Parts of the Pharynx

The cavity of the pharynx is divided into:
1 The nasal part—nasopharynx (Fig. 14.9)
2 The oral part—oropharynx (Table 14.3)
3 The laryngeal part—laryngopharynx (Fig. 14.18).

Comparison between nosopharynx, oropharynx and laryngopharynx shown in Table 14.4.

WALDEYER'S LYMPHATIC RING

In relation to the naso-oropharyngeal isthmus, there are several aggregations of lymphoid tissue that constitute Waldeyer's lymphatic ring (Fig. 14.13). The most important aggregations are the right and left palatine tonsils usually referred to simply as the tonsils. Posteriorly and above, there is the nasopharyngeal tonsil; laterally and above, there are the tubal tonsils, and inferiorly, there is the lingual tonsil over the posterior part of the dorsum of the tongue.

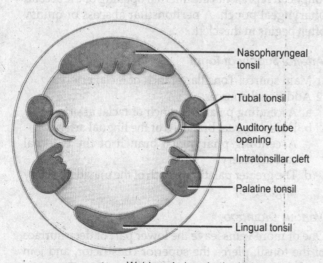

Fig. 14.13: Waldeyer's lymphatic ring

(labels: Nasopharyngeal tonsil; Tubal tonsil; Auditory tube opening; Intratonsillar cleft; Palatine tonsil; Lingual tonsil)

Palatine Tonsil (the Tonsil)

Features

The palatine tonsil (Latin *swelling*) occupies the tonsillar sinus or fossa between the palatoglossal and palatopharyngeal arches (Figs 14.7, 14.13 and 14.14). It can be seen through the mouth.

The tonsil is almond-shaped. It has two surfaces, medial and lateral; two borders, anterior and posterior and two poles, upper and lower.

The *medial surface* is covered by stratified squamous epithelium continuous with that of the mouth. This surface has 12 to 15 crypts. The largest of these is called the *intratonsillar cleft* (Fig. 14.13).

The *lateral surface* is covered by a sheet of fascia which forms the hemicapsule of the tonsil. The capsule is an extension of the pharyngobasilar fascia. It is only loosely attached to the muscular wall of the pharynx, formed here by the superior constrictor and by the styloglossus, but anteroinferiorly the capsule is firmly adherent to the side of the tongue (suspensory ligament of tonsil) just in front of the insertion of the palatoglossus and the palatopharyngeus muscle. This firm attachment keeps the tonsil in place during swallowing.

The tonsillar artery enters the tonsil by piercing the superior constrictor just behind the firm attachment (Fig. 14.15).

The palatine vein or external palatine or paratonsillar vein descends from the palate in the loose areolar tissue on the lateral surface of the capsule, and crosses the tonsil before piercing the wall of the pharynx. The vein may be injured during removal of the tonsil or tonsillectomy (Fig. 14.15).

The bed of the tonsil is formed from within outwards by:
   a. The pharyngobasilar fascia (Fig. 14.14).
   b. The superior constrictor and palatopharyngeus muscles.
   c. The buccopharyngeal fascia.
   d. In the lower part, the styloglossus.
   e. The glossopharyngeal nerve.

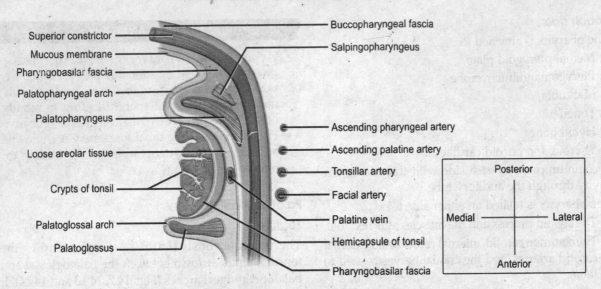

Fig. 14.14: Horizontal section through the tonsil showing its deep relations

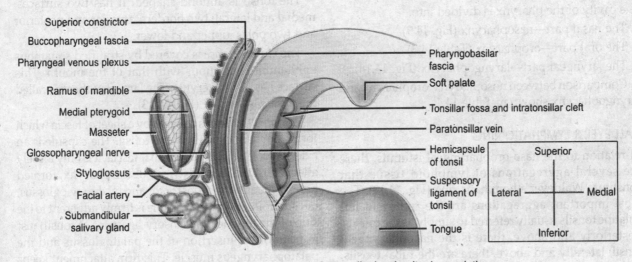

Fig. 14.15: Vertical section through the tonsil, showing its deep relations

Still more laterally, there are the facial artery with its tonsillar and ascending palatine branches. The internal carotid artery is 2.5 cm posterolateral to the tonsil.

The *anterior border* is related to the palatoglossal arch with its muscle (Fig. 14.7).

The *posterior border* is related to the palatopharyngeal arch with its muscle.

The *upper pole* is related to the soft palate, and the *lower pole*, to the tongue (Fig. 14.15).

The *plica triangularis* is a triangular vestigial fold of mucous membrane covering the anteroinferior part of the tonsil. The *plica semilunaris* is a similar semilunar fold that may cross the upper part of the tonsillar sinus.

The *intratonsillar cleft* is the largest crypt of the tonsil. It is present in its upper part (Fig. 14.13). It is sometimes wrongly named the supratonsillar fossa. The mouth of cleft is semilunar in shape and parallel to dorsum of tongue. It represents the internal opening of the second pharyngeal pouch. A peritonsillar abscess or quinsy often begins in this cleft.

Arterial Supply of Tonsil

1 Main source: Tonsillar branch of facial artery.
2 Additional sources:
   a. Ascending palatine branch of facial artery.
   b. Dorsal lingual branches of the lingual artery.
   c. Ascending pharyngeal branch of the external carotid artery.
   d. The greater palatine branch of the maxillary artery (Fig. 14.16).

Venous Drainage

One or more veins leave the lower part of deep surface of the tonsil, pierce the superior constrictor, and join the palatine, pharyngeal, or facial veins.

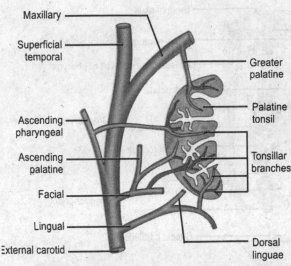

Fig. 14.16: Arterial supply of the palatine tonsil

Lymphatic Drainage

Lymphatics pass to jugulodigastric node (*see* Fig. 8.28). There are no afferent lymphatics to the tonsil.

Nerve Supply

Glossopharyngeal and lesser palatine nerves.

HISTOLOGY

The palatine tonsil is situated at the oropharyngeal isthmus. Its oral aspect is covered with stratified squamous nonkeratinised epithelium, which dips into the underlying tissue to form the crypts. The lymphocytes lie on the sides of the crypts in the form of nodules. The structure of tonsil is not differentiated into cortex and medulla (Fig. 14.17).

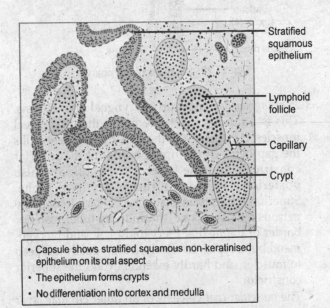

- Capsule shows stratified squamous non-keratinised epithelium on its oral aspect
- The epithelium forms crypts
- No differentiation into cortex and medulla

Fig. 14.17: Histology of palatine tonsil

DEVELOPMENT

The tonsil develops from endoderm of ventral part of second pharyngeal pouch. Some part persists as the intratonsillar cleft. The lymphocytes are mesodermal in origin.

CLINICAL ANATOMY

- The tonsils are large in children. They retrogress after puberty.
- The tonsils are frequently sites of infection, specially in children. Infection may spread to surrounding tissue forming a peritonsillar abscess.
- Enlarged and infected tonsils often require surgical removal. The operation is called *tonsillectomy*. A knowledge of the relationship of the tonsil is of importance to the surgeon.
- Tonsillectomy is usually done by the guillotine method. Haemorrhage after tonsillectomy is checked by removal of clot from the raw tonsillar bed. This is to be compared with the method for checking postpartum haemorrhage from the uterus. These are the only two organs in the body where bleeding is checked by removal of clots. In other parts of the body, clot formation is encouraged.
- Tonsillitis may cause referred pain in the ear as glossopharyngeal nerve supplies both these areas.
- Suppuration in the peritonsillar area is called *quinsy*. A peritonsillar abscess is drained by making an incision in the most prominent point of the abscess.
- Tonsils are often sites of a septic focus. Such a focus can lead to serious disease like pulmonary tuberculosis, meningitis, etc. and is often the cause of general ill health.

Laryngeal Part of Pharynx (Laryngopharynx)

This is the lower part of the pharynx situated behind the larynx. It extends from the upper border of the epiglottis to the lower border of the cricoid cartilage.

The *anterior wall* presents:

a. The inlet of the larynx.

b. The posterior surfaces of the cricoid and arytenoid cartilages.

The *posterior wall* is supported mainly by the fourth and fifth cervical vertebrae, and partly by the third and sixth vertebrae. In this region, the posterior wall of the pharynx is formed by the superior, middle and inferior constrictors of the pharynx.

Head and Neck

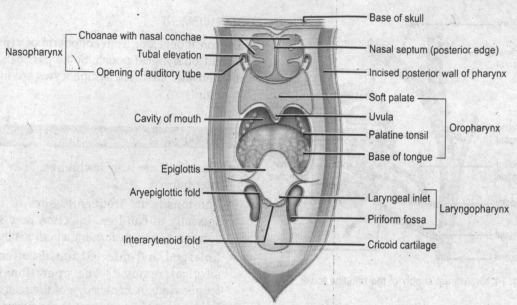

Fig. 14.18: The three regions of the pharynx

The *lateral wall* presents a depression called the *piriform fossa*, one on each side of the inlet of the larynx (Fig. 14.18). The fossa is bounded medially by the aryepiglottic fold, and laterally by the thyroid cartilage and the thyrohyoid membrane. Beneath the mucosa of fossa, there lies the internal laryngeal nerve. Removal of foreign bodies from the piriform fossa may damage the internal laryngeal nerve, leading to anaesthesia in the supraglottic part of the larynx (Fig. 14.19).

Structure of Pharynx

The wall of the pharynx is composed of the following five layers (Fig. 14.20) from within outwards.

1 *Mucosa*

2 *Submucosa*

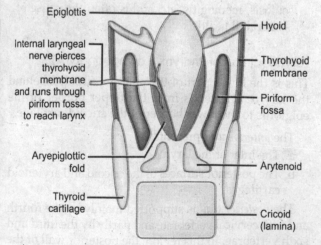

Fig. 14.19: Posterior view of the piriform fossa after removal of the tongue: Internal laryngeal nerve is shown only on left side

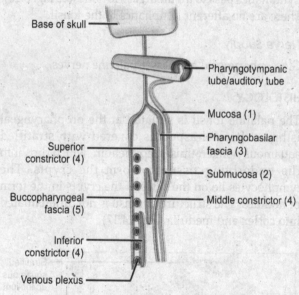

Fig. 14.20: Structure of the pharynx

3 *Pharyngobasilar fascia* or pharyngeal aponeurosis. This is a fibrous sheet internal to the pharyngeal muscles. It is thickest in the upper part where it fills the gap between the upper border of the superior constrictor and the base of the skull, and also posteriorly where it forms pharyngeal raphe. Superiorly, the fascia is attached to basiocciput, the petrous temporal bone, the auditory tube, posterior border of the medial pterygoid plate, and pterygo-mandibular raphe. Inferiorly, it is gradually lost deep to muscles, and hardly extend beyond the superior constrictor.

4 The *muscular coat* consists of an outer circular layer made up of the three constrictors (*superior, middle* and

inferior) and an inner longitudinal layer made up of the stylopharyngeus, the salpingopharyngeus and the palatopharyngeus muscles. These muscles are described later.

5 The *buccopharyngeal fascia* covers the outer surface of the constrictors of the pharynx and extends forwards across the pterygomandibular raphe to cover the buccinator. Like the pharyngobasilar fascia, the buccopharyngeal fascia is best developed in the upper part of the pharynx.

Between the buccopharyngeal fascia, and the muscular coat there are the pharyngeal plexuses of veins and nerves (Fig. 14.20).

Muscles of the Pharynx

Preliminary Remarks about the Constrictors of the Pharynx

The muscular basis of the wall of the pharynx is formed mainly by the three pairs of constrictors—superior, middle and inferior. The origins of the constrictors are situated anteriorly in relation to the posterior openings of the nose, the mouth and the larynx. From here their fibres pass into the lateral and posterior walls of the pharynx, the fibres of the two sides meeting in the mid line in a fibrous raphe.

The three constrictors are so arranged that the inferior overlaps middle which in turn overlaps the superior. The fibres of the superior constrictor reach the base of skull posteriorly, in the middle line. On the sides, however, there is a gap between the base of the skull and the upper edge of the superior constrictor. This gap is closed by the pharyngobasilar fascia which is thickened in this situation (Fig. 14.21). The lower edge of the inferior constrictor becomes continuous with the circular muscle of the oesophagus. These muscles develop from IV and VI pharyngeal arch (*see* Table A.5 in Appendix).

Origin of Constrictors

1 The *superior constrictor* takes origin (Fig. 14.21) from the following (from above downwards):

   a. Pterygoid hamulus (pterygopharyngeus).

   b. Pterygomandibular raphe (buccopharyngeus).

   c. Medial surface of the mandible at the posterior end of the mylohyoid line, i.e. near the lower attachment of the pterygomandibular raphe (*see* Fig. 1.25) (mylopharyngeus).

   d. Side of posterior part of tongue (glossopharyngeus).

2 The *middle constrictor* takes origin from:

   a. The lower part of the stylohyoid ligament

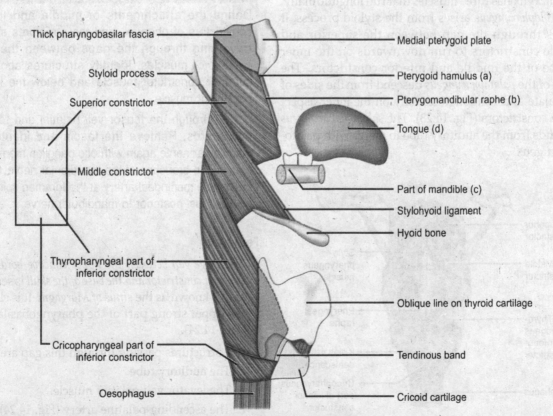

Fig. 14.21: Origin of the constrictors of the pharynx

Thick pharyngobasilar fascia
Styloid process
Superior constrictor
Middle constrictor
Thyropharyngeal part of inferior constrictor
Cricopharyngeal part of inferior constrictor
Oesophagus

Medial pterygoid plate
Pterygoid hamulus (a)
Pterygomandibular raphe (b)
Tongue (d)
Part of mandible (c)
Stylohyoid ligament
Hyoid bone
Oblique line on thyroid cartilage
Tendinous band
Cricoid cartilage

b. Lesser cornua of hyoid bone

c. Upper border of the greater cornua of the hyoid bone (see Fig. 1.47).

3 The *inferior constrictor* consists of two parts. One part the *thyropharyngeus* arises from the thyroid cartilage. The other part the *cricopharyngeus* arises from the cricoid cartilage.

The thyropharyngeus arises from:

a. The oblique line on the lamina of thyroid cartilage, including the inferior tubercle (Fig. 14.21).

b. A tendinous band that crosses the cricothyroid muscle and is attached above to the inferior tubercle of the thyroid cartilage.

c. The inferior cornua of the thyroid cartilage.

The cricopharyngeus arises from the cricoid cartilage behind the origin of the cricothyroid muscle.

Insertion of Constrictors

All the constrictors of the pharynx are inserted into a median raphe on the posterior wall of the pharynx. The upper end of the raphe reaches the base of the skull where it is attached to the pharyngeal tubercle on the basilar part of the occipital bone (Fig. 14.22).

Longitudinal Muscle Coat

The pharynx has three muscles that run longitudinally. The *stylopharyngeus* arises from the styloid process. It passes through the gap between the superior and middle constrictors to run downwards on the inner surface of the middle and inferior constrictors. The fibres of the *palatopharyngeus* descend from the sides of the palate and run longitudinally on the inner aspect of the constrictors (Fig. 14.23). The *salpingopharyngeus* descends from the auditory tube to merge with palatopharyngeus.

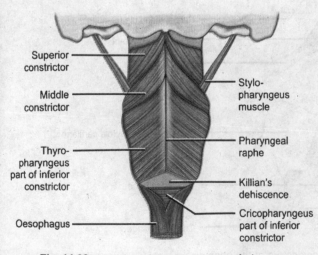

Fig. 14.22: Insertion of the constrictors of pharynx

Labels: Superior constrictor, Middle constrictor, Thyro-pharyngeus part of inferior constrictor, Oesophagus, Stylo-pharyngeus muscle, Pharyngeal raphe, Killian's dehiscence, Cricopharyngeus part of inferior constrictor

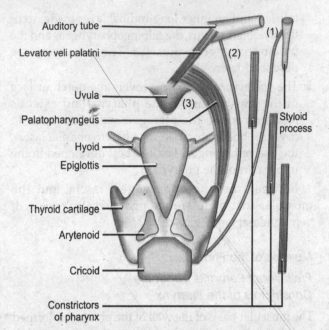

Fig. 14.23: Longitudinal muscles of pharynx: (1) Stylopharyngeus, (2) salpingopharyngeus, and (3) palatopharyngeus

Labels: Auditory tube, Levator veli palatini, Uvula, Palatopharyngeus, Hyoid, Epiglottis, Thyroid cartilage, Arytenoid, Cricoid, Constrictors of pharynx, Styloid process

---

STRUCTURES IN BETWEEN PHARYNGEAL MUSCLES

DISSECTION

Define the attachments of middle and inferior constrictors of pharynx, and the structures situated traversing through the gaps between the three constrictor muscles. Identify structures above the superior constrictor muscle and below the inferior constrictor muscle.

Cut through the tensor veli palatini and reflect it downwards. Remove the fascia and identify the mandibular nerve again with otic ganglion medial to it. Identify the branches of the mandibular nerve. Locate the middle meningeal artery at the foramen spinosum, as it lies just posterior to mandibular nerve.

Features

1 The *large gap between the upper concave border of the superior constrictor and the base of the skull* is semilunar and is known as the *sinus of Morgagni*. It is closed by the upper strong part of the pharyngobasilar fascia (Fig. 14.24).

The structures passing through this gap are:

a. The auditory tube.

b. The levator veli palatini muscle.

c. The ascending palatine artery (Fig. 14.24).

d. Palatine branch of ascending pharyngeal artery.

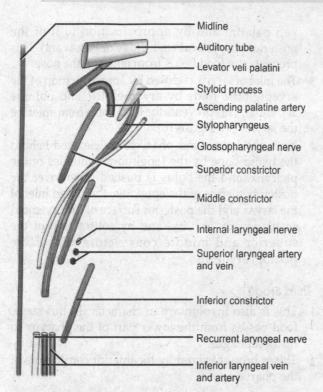

Fig. 14.24: Schematic coronal section through the pharynx, showing the gaps between pharyngeal muscles and the structures related to them

2 The structures passing through the *gap between the superior and middle constrictors* are: The stylopharyngeus muscle and the glossopharyngeal nerve.

3 The internal laryngeal nerve and the superior laryngeal vessels pierce the thyrohyoid membrane in the *gap between the middle and inferior constrictors*.

4 The recurrent laryngeal nerve and the inferior laryngeal vessels pass through the *gap between the lower border of the inferior constrictor and the oesophagus*.

Killian's Dehiscence

In the posterior wall of the pharynx, the lower part of the thyropharyngeus is a single sheet of muscle, not overlapped internally by the superior and middle constrictors. This weak part lies below the level of the vocal folds or upper border of the cricoid lamina and is limited inferiorly by the thick cricopharyngeal sphincter. This area is known as *Killian's dehiscence*. Pharyngeal diverticula are formed by outpouching of the dehiscence (Figs 14.25a and b). Such diverticula are normal in the pig. Pharyngeal diverticula are often attributed to neuromuscular incoordination in this region which may be due to the fact that different nerves supply the two parts of the inferior constrictor (Fig. 14.21). The propulsive thyropharyngeus is supplied by the pharyngeal plexus, and sphincteric cricopharyngeus, by the

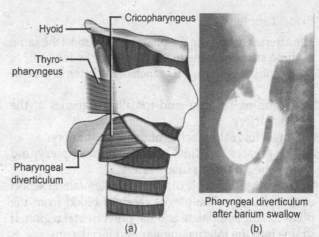

Figs 14.25a and b: (a) Pharyngeal diverticulum, and (b) pharyngeal diverticulum after barium swallow

recurrent laryngeal nerve. If the cricopharyngeus fails to relax when the thyropharyngeus contracts, the bolus of food is pushed backwards, and tends to produce a diverticulum.

Nerve Supply

The pharynx is supplied by the pharyngeal plexus of nerves which lies chiefly on the middle constrictor. The plexus is formed by:

1 The pharyngeal branch of the vagus carrying fibres of the cranial accessory nerve.

2 The pharyngeal branches of the glossopharyngeal nerve.

3 The pharyngeal branches of the superior cervical sympathetic ganglion.

Motor fibres are derived from the cranial accessory nerve through the branches of the vagus. They supply all muscles of pharynx, except the stylopharyngeus which is supplied by the glossopharyngeal nerve.

The inferior constrictor receives an additional supply from the external and recurrent laryngeal nerves.

Sensory fibres or general visceral afferent from the pharynx travel mostly through the glossopharyngeal nerve, and partly through the vagus. However, the nasopharynx is supplied by the maxillary nerve through the pterygopalatine ganglion; and the soft palate and tonsil, by the lesser palatine and glossopharyngeal nerves.

Taste sensations from the vallecula and epiglottic area pass through the internal laryngeal branch of the vagus.

The parasympathetic *secretomotor* fibres to the pharynx are derived from the lesser palatine branches of the pterygopalatine ganglion (*see* Fig. 15.15)

Blood Supply

The arteries supplying the pharynx are almost the same as those supplying the tonsil. These are as follows:

1 Ascending pharyngeal branch of the external carotid artery.
2 Ascending palatine and tonsillar branches of the facial artery.
3 Dorsal lingual branches of the lingual artery.
4 The greater palatine, pharyngeal and pterygoid branches of the maxillary artery.

The veins form a plexus on the posterolateral aspect of the pharynx. The plexus receives blood from the pharynx, the soft palate and the prevertebral region. It drains into the internal jugular and facial veins.

Lymphatic Drainage

Lymph from the pharynx drains into the retro-pharyngeal and deep cervical lymph nodes.

CLINICAL ANATOMY

- Difficulty in swallowing is known as dysphagia.
- *Pharyngeal diverticulum:* Read Killian's dehiscence (Fig. 14.25a).

Deglutition (Swallowing)

Swallowing of food occurs in three stages described below. Muscles of pharynx act during swallowing.

First Stage

1 This stage is voluntary in character.
2 The anterior part of the tongue is raised and pressed against the hard palate by the intrinsic muscles of the tongue, especially the superior longitudinal and transverse muscles. The movement takes place from anterior to the posterior side. This pushes the food bolus (Greek *lump*) into the posterior part of the oral cavity.
3 The soft palate closes down on to the back of the tongue, and helps to form the bolus.
4 Next, the hyoid bone is moved upwards and forwards by the suprahyoid muscles. The posterior part of the tongue is elevated upwards and backwards by the styloglossi; and the palatoglossal arches are approximated by the palatoglossi. This pushes the bolus through the oropharyngeal isthmus to the oropharynx, and the second stage begins.

Second Stage

1 It is involuntary in character. During this stage, the food is pushed from the oropharynx to the lower part of the laryngopharynx.
2 The nasopharyngeal isthmus is closed by elevation of the soft palate by levator veli palatini and tensor veli palatini and by approximation to it of the posterior pharyngeal wall (ridge of Passavant). This prevents the food bolus from entering the nose.
3 The inlet of larynx is closed by approximation of the aryepiglottic folds by aryepiglottic and oblique arytenoid. This prevents the food bolus from entering the larynx (*see* Fig. 16.10).
4 Next, the larynx and pharynx are elevated behind the hyoid bone by the longitudinal muscles of the pharynx, and the bolus is pushed down over the posterior surface of the epiglottis, the closed inlet of the larynx and the posterior surface of the arytenoid cartilages, by gravity, and by contraction of the superior and middle constrictors and of the palatopharyngeus.

Third Stage

1 This is also involuntary in character. In this stage, food passes from the lower part of the pharynx to the oesophagus.
2 This is brought about by the inferior constrictors of the pharynx.

DEVELOPMENT

The primitive gut extends from the buccopharyngeal membrane cranially, to the cloacal membrane caudally. It is divided into four parts—the pharynx, the foregut, the midgut and the hindgut. The pharynx extends from buccopharyngeal membrane to the tracheo-bronchial diverticulum. It is divided into upper part, the nasopharynx; middle part, the oropharynx; and the lower part, the laryngopharynx.

AUDITORY TUBE

Auditory tube is also known as the pharyngotympanic tube or the eustachian tube.

The auditory tube is a trumpet-shaped channel which connects the middle ear cavity with the nasopharynx. It is about 4 cm long, and is directed downwards, forwards and medially. It forms an angle of 45 degrees with the sagittal plane and 30 degrees with the horizontal plane. The tube is divided into bony and cartilaginous parts (Fig. 14.26).

BONY PART

The bony part forms the posterior and lateral one-third of the tube. It is 12 mm long, and lies in the petrous temporal bone near the tympanic plate. Its lateral end is wide and opens on the anterior wall of the middle ear cavity. The medial end is narrow (isthmus) and is jagged for attachment of the cartilaginous part. The lumen of the tube is oblong being widest from side to side.

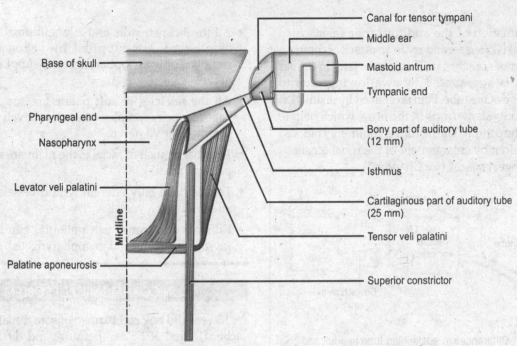

Fig. 14.26: Scheme showing anatomy of auditory tube

Relations

1 *Superior:* Canal for the tensor tympani (*see* Fig. 18.13).

2 *Medial:* Carotid canal.

3 *Lateral:* Chorda tympani, spine of sphenoid, auriculo-temporal nerve (Fig. 14.8) and the temporomandi-bular joint.

CARTILAGINOUS PART

The cartilaginous part forms the anterior and medial two-thirds of the tube. It is 25 mm long, and lies in the sulcus tubae, a groove between the greater wing of the sphenoid and the apex of the petrous temporal.

It is made up of a triangular plate of cartilage which is curled to form the superior and medial walls of the tube. The lateral wall and floor are completed by a fibrous membrane. The apex of the plate is attached to the medial end of the bony part. The base is free and forms the tubal elevation in the nasopharynx (Fig. 14.9).

Relations

1 *Anterolaterally:* Tensor veli palatini, mandibular nerve and its branches, otic ganglion, chorda tympani, middle meningeal artery and medial pterygoid plate (*see* Fig. 6.17).

2 *Posteromedially:* Petrous temporal and levator veli palatini.

3 The levator veli palatini is attached to its inferior surface, and the salpingopharyngeus to lower part near the pharyngeal opening.

Vascular Supply

The arterial supply of the tube is derived from the ascending pharyngeal and middle meningeal arteries and the artery of the pterygoid canal.

The veins drain into the pharyngeal and pterygoid plexuses of veins. Lymphatics pass to the retro-pharyngeal nodes.

Nerve Supply

1 At the ostium, by the pharyngeal branch of the pterygo-palatine ganglion suspended by the maxillary nerve.

2 Cartilaginous part, by the nervus spinosus branch of mandibular nerve.

3 Bony part, by the tympanic plexus formed by glosso-pharyngeal nerve.

Function

The tube provides a communication of the middle ear cavity with the exterior, thus ensuring equal air pressure on both sides of the tympanic membrane.

The tube is usually closed. It opens during swallowing, yawning and sneezing, by the actions of the tensor and levator veli palatini muscles.

CLINICAL ANATOMY

- Infections may pass from the throat to the middle ear through the auditory tube. This is more common in children because the tube is shorter, wider and straighter in them (Fig. 14.27).

Head and Neck

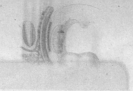

- Inflammation of the auditory tube (eustachian catarrh) is often secondary to an attack of common cold, or of sore throat. This causes pain in the ear which is aggravated by swallowing, due to blockage of the tube. Pain is relieved by instillation of decongestant drops in the nose, which help to open the ostium. The ostium is commonly blocked in children by enlargement of the tubal tonsil.
- Pharyngeal spaces (*see* Chapter 3).

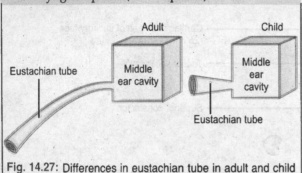

Fig. 14.27: Differences in eustachian tube in adult and child

Mnemonics

Tonsils: The four types "PPLT (people) have tonsils"

Pharyngeal
Palatine
Lingual
Tubal

FACTS TO REMEMBER

- Both the maxillary and mandibular teeth are supplied by the branches of maxillary artery only.
- Upper teeth are supplied by branches of maxillary nerve.
- Lower teeth are supplied by branches of mandibular nerve.
- Waldeyer's ring consists of lingual tonsil, palatine tonsils, tubal tonsils and nasopharyngeal tonsils.

- All the 3 constrictors and 2 longitudinal muscles of pharynx are supplied by vagoaccessory complex, only stylopharyngeus is supplied by IX nerve.
- All the muscles of soft palate are supplied by vagoaccessory complex except tensor veli palatini, supplied by V3 nerve.
- Tonsillar branch of facial is the main artery of the palatine tonsil.
- Tonsils have only efferent lymph vessels but no afferent lymph vessel.
- Killian's dehiscence is a potential gap between thyropharyngeus and cricopharyngeus.

CLINICOANATOMICAL PROBLEM

A 12-year-old boy complained of sore throat and ear ache. He had 102°F temperature and difficulty in swallowing. He was also a mouth breather.
- What is Waldeyer's lymphatic ring?
- Explain the basis of boy's earache.
- What lymph node would likely to be swollen and tender?

Ans: Major collections of lymphoid tissue at the oropharyngeal junction are called the tonsils. These lie in a ring form called the Waldeyer's lymphatic ring. The components of this ring are lingual tonsil anteriorly, palatine tonsil laterally, tubal tonsil posterolaterally and pharyngeal tonsil posteriorly.

The earache may be due to infection of the throat reaching the middle ear. The pharyngotympanic tube from the region of nasopharynx communicates with the anterior wall of the middle ear cavity carrying the infection from pharynx to the ear causing the ear ache IX nerve supplies both the pharynx and the middle ear. So the pain of pharynx is referred to the ear.

The jugulodigastric lymph node belonging to upper group of deep cervical group is most likely to be tender and swollen, as the lymphatics from the tonsil, penetrate the wall of the pharynx to reach these lymph nodes.

FREQUENTLY ASKED QUESTIONS

1. Describe the nerve supply and actions of the muscles of soft palate. Add a note on its development including congenital anomalies.
2. Enumerate the components of Waldeyer's ring. Describe the palatine tonsil in detail. Add a note on its clinical importance.
3. Describe the attachments of the constrictor muscles of pharynx. Enumerate the structures lying in between these constrictor muscles.
4. Enumerate the length, parts, extent, relations and functions of auditory tube

MULTIPLE CHOICE QUESTIONS

1. The communication between vestibule and oral cavity proper lies:
   a. Behind 1st molar tooth
   b. Behind 2nd molar tooth
   c. Behind 3rd molar tooth
   d. No communication

2. The joint between tooth and gum is:
   a. Syndesmosis
   b. Gomphosis
   c. Sutures
   d. Primary cartilaginous joint

3. The first permanent tooth to erupt is:
   a. First molar
   b. First premolar
   c. Second molar
   d. Canine

4. Most of muscles of soft palate are supplied by vagoaccessory complex *except*:
   a. Levator veli palatini
   b. Tensor veli palatini
   c. Palatoglossus
   d. Musculus uvulae

5. Which one of the following is not a component of Waldeyer's ring?
   a. Tubal tonsil
   b. Pharyngeal tonsil
   c. Palatine tonsil
   d. Submental lymph nodes

6. Which of the following structures does not form bed of the tonsil?
   a. Superior constrictor
   b. Pharyngobasilar fascia
   c. Buccinator muscle
   d. Buccopharyngeal fascia

7. Which one of the following muscles of pharynx is not supplied by vagoaccessory complex?
   a. Superior constrictor
   b. Stylopharyngeus
   c. Palatopharyngeus
   d. Salpingopharyngeus

8. Which walls of cartilaginous part of auditory tube are formed by fibrous membrane?
   a. Lateral wall and floor
   b. Medial wall and floor
   c. Superior wall and medial wall
   d. Superior wall and floor

9. Paralysis of unilateral soft palate results in following effects *except*:
   a. Depressed palatal arch
   b. Uvula deviated to paralysed side
   c. Nasal twang of voice
   d. Nasal regurgitation of liquids

10. Tonsillitis pain is referred to pain in ear as both are supplied by:
    a. Auricular branch of vagus
    b. Glossopharyngeal nerve
    c. Sympathetic fibres
    d. Cranial root of XI nerve

ANSWERS

| 1. c | 2. b | 3. a | 4. b | 5. d | 6. c | 7. b | 8. a | 9. b | 10. b |

Head and Neck

Nose and Paranasal Sinuses

Did God give us flowers and trees and also provide the allergies?

INTRODUCTION

Sense of smell perceived in the upper part of nasal cavity by olfactory nerve rootlets ends in olfactory bulb, which is connected to uncus and also to the dorsal nucleus of vagus in medulla oblongata. Good smell of food, thus stimulates secretion of gastric juice through vagus nerve.

Most of the mucous membrane of the nasal cavity is respiratory and is continuous with various paranasal sinuses. Since nose is the most projecting part of the face, its integrity must be maintained.

Environmental pollution causes inhalation of unwanted gases and particles, leading to frequent attacks of sinusitis, respiratory diseases including asthma.

Nasal mucous membrane is quite vascular. Sometimes picking of the nose may cause bleeding from "Little's area". Bleeding from nose is called *epistaxis*.

NOSE

The nose performs two functions. It is a respiratory passage. It is also the organ of smell. The receptors for smell are placed in the upper one-third of the nasal cavity. This part is lined by olfactory mucosa. The rest of the nasal cavity is lined by respiratory mucosa. The respiratory mucosa is highly vascular and warms the inspired air.

The secretions of numerous serous glands make the air moist; while the secretions of mucous glands trap dust and other particles. Thus the nose acts as an air conditioner where the inspired air is warmed, moistened and cleansed before it is passed on to the delicate lungs.

The *olfactory mucosa* lines the upper one-third of the nasal cavity including the roof formed by cribriform plate and the medial and lateral walls up to the level of the superior concha. It is thin and less vascular than the respiratory mucosa. It contains receptors called olfactory cells.

For descriptive purposes, the nose is divided into two main parts, the external nose and nasal cavity.

EXTERNAL NOSE

Some features of the external nose have been described in Chapter 2, *see* page 59. These are root, dorsum, tip, anterior nares, nasal septum and columella.

The external nose has a skeletal framework that is partly bony and partly cartilaginous. The bones are the nasal bones, which form the bridge of the nose, and the frontal processes of the maxillae. The cartilages are the superior and inferior nasal cartilages, the septal cartilage, and small alar cartilages (Figs 15.1a and b). The skin over the external nose is supplied by the external nasal, infratrochlear and infraorbital nerves (*see* Fig. 2.16).

NASAL CAVITY

The nasal cavity extends from the external nares or nostrils to the posterior nasal apertures, and is subdivided into right and left halves by the nasal septum (Figs 15.2 and 15.4). Each half has a roof, a floor, and medial and lateral walls. Each half measures about 5 cm in height, 5–7 cm in length, and 1.5 cm in width near the floor. The width near the roof is only 1–2 mm.

The *roof* is about 7 cm long and 2 mm wide. It slopes downwards, both in front and behind. The middle horizontal part is formed by the cribriform plate of the ethmoid. The anterior slope is formed by the nasal part of the frontal bone, nasal bone, and the nasal cartilages. The posterior slope is formed by the inferior surface of the body of the sphenoid bone (Fig. 15.5).

The *floor* is about 5 cm long and 1.5 cm wide. It is formed by the palatine process of the maxilla and the

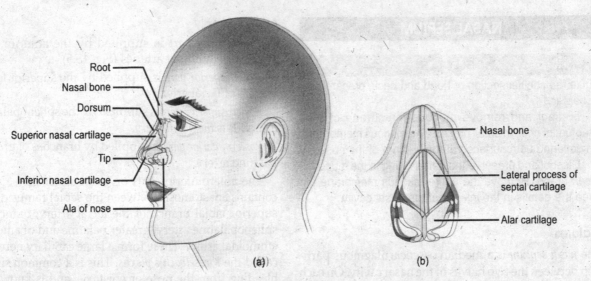

Figs 15.1a and b: (a) Skeleton of the external nose, and (b) anterior view

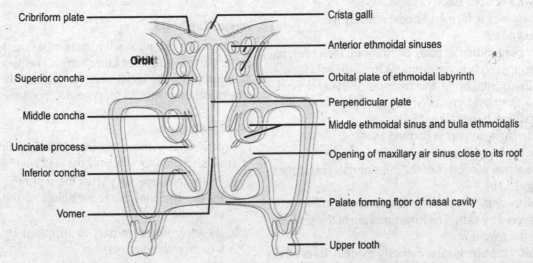

Fig. 15.2: Coronal section through the nasal cavity and the maxillary air sinuses

horizontal plate of the palatine bone. It is concave from side to side and is slightly higher anteriorly than posteriorly (Fig. 15.2).

CLINICAL ANATOMY

- Common cold or rhinitis is the commonest infection of the nose. It may be infective or allergic or both. It commonly occurs during change of the seasons.

- The paranasal air sinuses may get infected from the nose. Maxillary sinusitis is the commonest of such infections.

- The relations of the nose to the anterior cranial fossa through the cribriform plate (Fig. 15.5), and to the lacrimal apparatus through the nasolacrimal duct are important in the spread of infection (*see* Fig. 2.22a).

- Fracture of cribriform plate of ethmoid with tearing off of the meninges may tear the olfactory nerve rootlets. In such cases, CSF may drip from the nasal cavity. It is called CSF rhinorrhoea (Fig. 15.3).

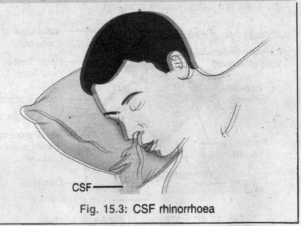

Fig. 15.3: CSF rhinorrhoea

NASAL SEPTUM

Features

The *nasal septum* is a median osseocartilaginous partition between the two halves of the nasal cavity. On each side, it is covered by mucous membrane and forms the medial wall of both nasal cavities.

The *bony part* is formed almost entirely by:
a. The vomer
b. The perpendicular plate of ethmoid. However, its margins receive contributions from the nasal spine of the frontal bone, the rostrum of the sphenoid, and the nasal crests of the nasal, palatine and maxillary bones (Fig. 15.4).

The *cartilaginous part* is formed by:
a. The septal cartilage
b. The septal processes of the inferior nasal cartilages (Fig. 15.1b).

The *cuticular part* or lower end is formed by fibrofatty tissue covered by skin. The lower margin of the septum is called the *columella*.

The nasal septum is rarely strictly median. Its central part is usually *deflected* to one or the other side. The deflection is produced by overgrowth of one or more of the constituent parts.

The septum has:
a. Four borders—superior, inferior, anterior and posterior.
b. Two surfaces—right and left.

Arterial Supply

Anterosuperior part is supplied by the anterior and posterior ethmoidal arteries (Fig. 15.5).

Anteroinferior part is supplied by the superior labial branch of facial artery.

Posterosuperior part is supplied by the sphenopalatine artery. *It is the main artery.*

Posteroinferior part is supplied by branches of greater palatine artery.

The anteroinferior part or vestibule of the septum contains anastomoses between the septal ramus of the superior labial branch of the facial artery, branch of sphenopalatine artery, greater palatine and of anterior ethmoidal artery. These form a large capillary network called the *Kiesselbach's plexus*. This is a common site of bleeding from the nose or epistaxis, and is known as *Little's area*.

Venous Drainage

The veins form a plexus which is more marked in the lower part of septum or Little's area. The plexus drains anteriorly into the facial vein, posteriorly through the sphenopalatine vein to pterygoid venous plexus.

Nerve Supply

1 *General sensory nerves*, arising from trigeminal nerve, are distributed to whole of the septum (Fig. 15.6).
   a. The anterosuperior part of the septum is supplied by the internal nasal branches of the anterior ethmoidal nerve.
   b. Its anteroinferior part is supplied by anterior superior alveolar nerve.
   c. The posterosuperior part is supplied by the medial posterior superior nasal branches of the pterygo-palatine ganglion.

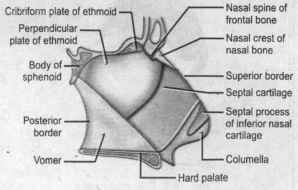

Cribriform plate of ethmoid
Perpendicular plate of ethmoid
Body of sphenoid
Posterior border
Vomer

Nasal spine of frontal bone
Nasal crest of nasal bone
Superior border
Septal cartilage
Septal process of inferior nasal cartilage
Columella
Hard palate

Fig. 15.4: Formation of the nasal septum

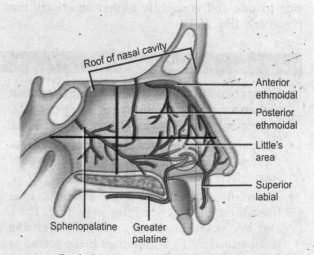

Roof of nasal cavity
Anterior ethmoidal
Posterior ethmoidal
Little's area
Superior labial
Sphenopalatine   Greater palatine

Fig. 15.5: Roof of the nasal cavity and arterial supply of nasal septum

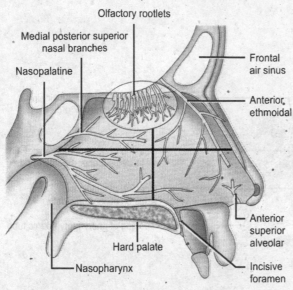

Fig. 15.6: Nerve supply of nasal septum

d. The posteroinferior part is supplied by the naso-palatine branch of the pterygopalatine ganglion. *It is the main nerve.*

2 *Special sensory nerves* or *olfactory* nerves are confined to the upper part or olfactory area.

Lymphatic Drainage

Anterior half to the submandibular nodes.

Posterior half to the retropharyngeal and deep cervical nodes.

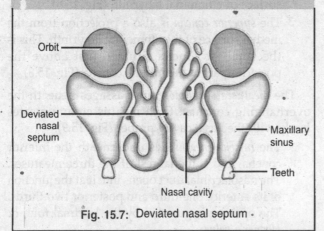

Fig. 15.7: Deviated nasal septum

Features

The lateral wall of the nose is irregular owing to the presence of three shelf-like bony projections called *conchae*. The conchae increase the surface area of the nose for effective air-conditioning of the inspired air (Fig. 15.2).

The lateral wall separates the nose:
a. From the orbit above, with the ethmoidal air sinuses intervening.
b. From the maxillary sinus below.
c. From the lacrimal sac and nasolacrimal duct in front (*see* Fig. 2.22a).

The lateral wall can be subdivided into three parts.
a. A small depressed area in the anterior part is called the vestibule. It is lined by modified skin containing short, stiff, curved hairs called *vibrissae*.
b. The middle part is known as the *atrium* of the middle meatus.
c. The posterior part contains the conchae. Spaces separating the conchae are called meatuses (Fig. 15.8).

The *skeleton of the lateral wall* is partly bony, partly cartilaginous, and partly made up only of soft tissues.

The *bony part* is formed from before backwards by the following bones:
a. Nasal.
b. Frontal process of maxilla (*see* Fig. 1.21).
c. Lacrimal.
d. Labyrinth of ethmoid with superior and middle conchae.
e. Inferior nasal concha, made up of spongy bone only (Fig. 15.8).
f. Perpendicular plate of palatine bone together with its orbital and sphenoidal processes.
g. Medial pterygoid plate.

The *cartilaginous part* is formed by:
a. The superior nasal cartilage (Fig. 15.1).
b. The inferior nasal cartilage.
c. 3 or 4 small cartilages of the ala.

The *cuticular lower part* is formed by fibrofatty tissue covered with skin.

Head and Neck

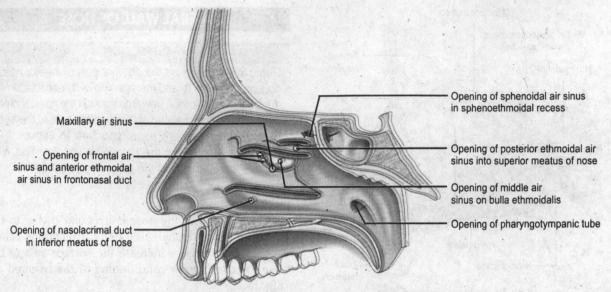

Maxillary air sinus

Opening of frontal air sinus and anterior ethmoidal air sinus in frontonasal duct

Opening of nasolacrimal duct in inferior meatus of nose

Opening of sphenoidal air sinus in sphenoethmoidal recess

Opening of posterior ethmoidal air sinus into superior meatus of nose

Opening of middle air sinus on bulla ethmoidalis

Opening of pharyngotympanic tube

Fig. 15.8: Lateral wall of the nasal cavity seen after removing the conchae

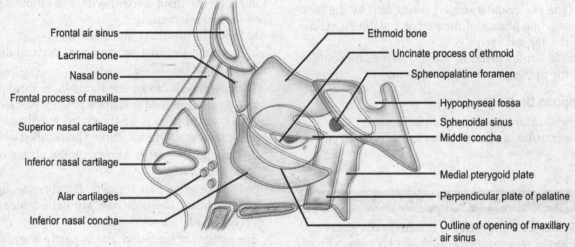

Frontal air sinus

Lacrimal bone

Nasal bone

Frontal process of maxilla

Superior nasal cartilage

Inferior nasal cartilage

Alar cartilages

Inferior nasal concha

Ethmoid bone

Uncinate process of ethmoid

Sphenopalatine foramen

Hypophyseal fossa

Sphenoidal sinus

Middle concha

Medial pterygoid plate

Perpendicular plate of palatine

Outline of opening of maxillary air sinus

Fig. 15.9: Formation of the lateral wall of the nasal cavity

CONCHAE AND MEATUSES

DISSECTION

Trace the nasopalatine nerve till the sphenopalatine foramen. Try to find few nasal branches of the greater palatine nerve.

Gently break the perpendicular plate of palatine bone to expose the greater palatine nerve, branch of the pterygopalatine ganglion. Follow the nerve and its accompanying vessels to the hard palate. Identify the lesser palatine nerves and trace them till the soft palate.

Features

The *nasal conchae* are curved bony projections directed downwards and medially. The following three conchae are usually found:

1 The *inferior concha* (Latin *shell*) is an independent bone.

2 The *middle concha* is a projection from the medial surface of ethmoidal labyrinth (Fig. 15.8).

3 The *superior concha* is also a projection from the medial surface of the ethmoidal labyrinth. This is the smallest concha situated just above the posterior part of the middle concha (Fig. 15.8).

The *meatuses of the nose* are passages beneath the overhanging conchae. Each meatus communicates freely with the nasal cavity proper (Fig. 15.9).

1 The *inferior meatus* lies underneath the inferior concha, and is the largest of the three meatuses. The nasolacrimal duct opens into it at the junction of its anterior one-third and posterior two-thirds. The opening is guarded by the lacrimal fold, or *Hasner's valve.*

2 The *middle meatus* lies underneath the middle concha. It presents the following features:
   a. The *ethmoidal bulla* is a rounded elevation produced by the underlying middle ethmoidal sinuses which open at upper margin of bulla.
   b. The *hiatus semilunaris* is a deep semicircular sulcus below the bulla.
   c. The *infundibulum* is a short passage at the anterior end of the hiatus.
   d. The *opening of frontal air sinus* is seen in the anterior part of hiatus semilunaris (Fig. 15.8).
   e. The *opening of the anterior ethmoidal air sinus* is present behind the opening of frontal air sinus.
   f. The *opening of maxillary air sinus* is located in posterior part of the hiatus semilunaris. It is often represented by two openings.
3 The *superior meatus* lies below the superior concha. This is the shortest and shallowest of the three meatuses. It receives the *openings of the posterior ethmoidal air sinuses*.

The *sphenoethmoidal recess* is a triangular fossa just above the superior concha. It receives the *opening of the sphenoidal air sinus* (Fig. 15.8).

The *atrium of the middle meatus* is a shallow depression just in front of the middle meatus and above the vestibule of the nose. It is limited above by a faint ridge of mucous membrane, the *agger nasi*, which runs forwards and downwards from the upper end of the anterior border of the middle concha (Fig. 15.8).

Arterial Supply

1 The *anterosuperior quadrant* is supplied by the anterior ethmoidal artery assisted by the posterior ethmoidal artery.
2 The *anteroinferior quadrant* is supplied by branches from the facial artery (Fig. 15.10).
3 The *posterosuperior quadrant* is supplied by a few branches of the sphenopalatine artery.
4 The *posteroinferior quadrant* is supplied by branches from greater palatine artery which pierce the perpendicular plate of palatine bone and passes up through the incisive fossa.

Venous Drainage

The veins form a plexus which drains anteriorly into the facial vein; posteriorly, into the pharyngeal plexus of veins; and from the middle part, to the pterygoid plexus of veins.

Nerve Supply

1 *General sensory nerves* derived from the branches of trigeminal nerve are distributed to whole of the lateral wall:
   a. *Anterosuperior quadrant* is supplied by the anterior ethmoidal nerve branch of ophthalmic nerve (Fig. 15.11).
   b. *Anteroinferior quadrant* is supplied by the anterior superior alveolar nerve, branch of infraorbital, continuation of maxillary nerve.
   c. *Posterosuperior quadrant* is supplied by the lateral posterior superior nasal branches from the pterygopalatine ganglion.
   d. *Posteroinferior quadrant* is supplied by the anterior palatine branch from the pterygopalatine ganglion.
2 *Special sensory nerves* or *olfactory nerves* are distributed to the upper part of the lateral wall just below the cribriform plate of the ethmoid up to the superior concha.

Note that the olfactory mucosa lies partly on the lateral wall and partly on the nasal septum.

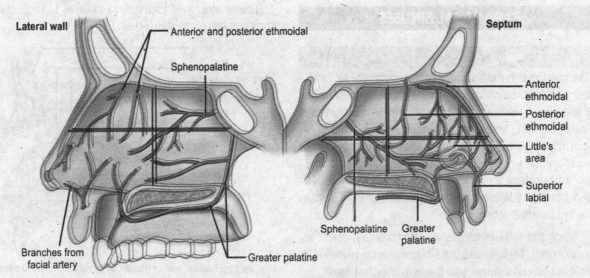

Fig. 15.10: Arteries supplying the lateral wall and septum of the nasal cavity

Lateral wall — Anterior and posterior ethmoidal — Sphenopalatine — Branches from facial artery — Greater palatine

Septum — Anterior ethmoidal — Posterior ethmoidal — Little's area — Superior labial — Sphenopalatine — Greater palatine

Head and Neck

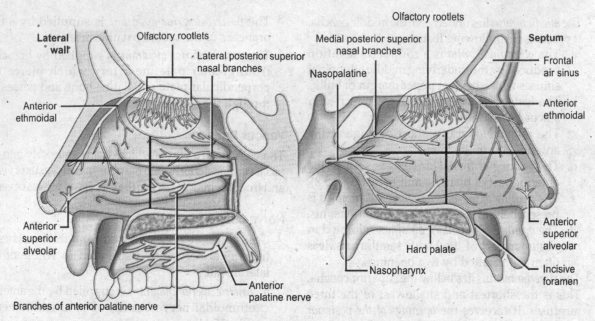

Fig. 15.11: Nerve supply of lateral wall and septum of nasal cavity

Lymphatic Drainage

Lymphatics from the anterior half of the lateral wall pass to the submandibular nodes, and from the posterior half, to the retropharyngeal and upper deep cervical nodes.

CLINICAL ANATOMY

Hypertrophy of the mucosa over the inferior nasal concha is a common feature of allergic rhinitis, which is characterised by sneezing, nasal blockage and excessive watery discharge from the nose.

PARANASAL SINUSES

DISSECTION

Remove the thin medial walls of the ethmoidal air cells, and look for the continuity with the mucous membrane of the nose. Remove the medial wall of maxillary air sinus extending anteriorly from opening of nasolacrimal duct till the greater palatine canal posteriorly. Now maxillary air sinus can be seen. Remove part of the roof of maxillary air sinus so that the maxillary nerve and pterygopalatine ganglion are identifiable in the pterygopalatine fossa.

Trace the infraorbital nerve in infraorbital canal in floor of orbit. Try to locate the sinuous course of anterior superior alveolar nerve into the upper incisor teeth.

Features

Paranasal sinuses are air-filled spaces present within some bones around the nasal cavities. The sinuses are *frontal, maxillary, sphenoidal and ethmoidal*. All of them open into the nasal cavity through its lateral wall (Fig. 15.12). The *function* of the sinuses is to make the skull lighter, warm up and humidify the inspired air. These also add resonance to the voice. In infections of the sinuses or *sinusitis*, the voice is altered.

The sinuses are rudimentary, or even absent at birth. They enlarge rapidly during the ages of 6 to 7 years, i.e. time of eruption of permanent teeth and then after puberty. From birth to adult life, the growth of the sinuses is due to enlargement of the bones; in old age it is due to resorption of the surrounding cancellous bone.

The anatomy of individual sinuses is important as they are frequently infected.

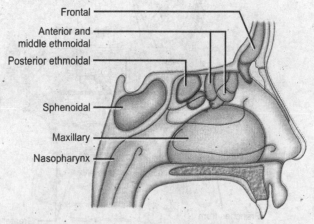

Fig. 15.12: Lateral wall of nasal cavity with location of paranasal sinuses

Frontal Sinus

1 The frontal sinus lies in the frontal bone deep to the superciliary arch. It extends upwards above the medial end of the eyebrow, and backwards into the medial part of the roof of the orbit (Fig. 15.12).

2 It *opens* into the middle meatus of nose at the anterior end of the hiatus semilunaris either through the infundibulum or through the frontonasal duct (Fig. 15.8).

3 The right and left sinuses are usually unequal in size; and rarely one or both may be absent. Their *average* height, width and anteroposterior depth are each about 2.5 cm. The sinuses are better developed in males than in females.

4 They are rudimentary or absent at birth. They are well developed between 7 and 8 years of age, but reach full size only after puberty.

5 *Arterial supply:* Supraorbital artery.

Venous drainage: Into the supraorbital and superior ophthalmic veins.

Lymphatic drainage: To submandibular nodes.

Nerve supply: Supraorbital nerve.

Maxillary Sinus

1 The maxillary sinus lies in the body of the maxilla (Fig. 15.2), and is the largest of all the paranasal sinuses. It is pyramidal in shape, with its base directed medially towards the lateral wall of the nose, and the apex directed laterally in the zygomatic process of the maxilla.

2 It *opens* into the middle meatus of the nose in the lower part of the hiatus semilunaris (Fig. 15.8). *The opening/hiatus is nearer the roof* (Fig. 15.12).

3 In an isolated maxilla, the opening or hiatus of the maxillary sinus is large. However, in the intact skull, the size of opening is reduced to 3 or 4 mm as it is overlapped by the following:

a. From above, by the uncinate process of the ethmoid, and the descending part of lacrimal bone.

b. From below, by the inferior nasal concha.

c. From behind, by the perpendicular plate of the palatine bone (Fig. 15.9). It is further reduced in size by the thick mucosa of nose.

4 The size of sinus is variable. Average measurements are: height—3.5 cm, width—2.5 cm and anteroposterior depth—3.5 cm (Fig. 15.12).

5 Its *roof* is formed by the floor of orbit, and is traversed by the infraorbital nerve. The *floor* is formed by the alveolar process of maxilla, and lies about 1 cm below the level of floor of the nose. The level corresponds to the level of lower border of the ala of nose.

The floor is marked by several conical elevations produced by the roots of upper molar and premolar teeth.

The roots may even penetrate the bony floor to lie beneath the mucous lining. The canine tooth may project into the anterolateral wall.

6 The maxillary sinus is the first paranasal sinus to *develop.*

7 *Arterial supply:* Facial, infraorbital and greater palatine arteries.

Venous drainage into the facial vein and the pterygoid plexus of veins.

Lymphatic drainage into the submandibular nodes.

Nerve supply: Posterior superior alveolar branches from maxillary nerve and anterior and middle superior alveolar branches from infraorbital nerve.

Sphenoidal Sinus

1 The right and left sphenoidal sinuses lie within the body of sphenoid bone (Fig. 15.12). They are separated by a septum. The two sinuses are usually unequal in size. Each sinus opens into the sphenoethmoidal recess of corresponding half of the nasal cavity (Fig. 15.8).

2 Each sinus is related superiorly to the optic chiasma and the hypophysis cerebri; and laterally to the internal carotid artery and the cavernous sinus (*see* Fig. 12.5).

3 *Arterial supply:* Posterior ethmoidal and internal carotid arteries.

Venous drainage: Into pterygoid venous plexus and cavernous sinus.

Lymphatic drainage: To the retropharyngeal nodes.

Nerve supply: Posterior ethmoidal nerve and orbital branches of pterygopalatine ganglion.

Ethmoidal Sinuses

1 Ethmoidal sinuses are numerous small intercommunicating spaces which lie within the labyrinth of the ethmoid bone (Fig. 15.2). They are completed from above by the orbital plate of the frontal bone, from behind by the sphenoidal conchae and the orbital process of the palatine bone, and anteriorly by the lacrimal bone. The sinuses are divided into anterior, middle and posterior groups (Fig. 15.12).

2 The *anterior ethmoidal sinus* is made up of 1 to 11 air cells, opens into the anterior part of the hiatus semilunaris of the nose. It is supplied by the anterior ethmoidal nerve and vessels. Its lymphatics drain into the submandibular nodes.

3 The *middle ethmoidal sinus* consisting of 1 to 7 air cells open into the middle meatus of the nose. It is supplied by the anterior ethmoidal nerve and vessels and the orbital branches of the pterygopalatine ganglion. Lymphatics drain into the submandibular nodes (Fig. 15.8).

4 The *posterior ethmoidal sinus* consisting of 1 to 7 air cells open into the superior meatus of the nose. It is supplied by the posterior ethmoidal nerve and vessels and the orbital branches of the pterygopalatine ganglion. Lymphatics drain into the retropharyngeal nodes.

CLINICAL ANATOMY

- Infection of a sinus is known as sinusitis. It causes headache and persistent, thick, purulent discharge from the nose. Diagnosis is assisted by transillumination and radiography. A diseased sinus is opaque.
- The maxillary sinus is most commonly involved. It may be infected from the nose or from a caries tooth. Drainage of the sinus is difficult because its ostium lies at a higher level than its floor. Hence, the sinus is drained surgically by making an artificial opening near the floor in one of the following two ways:
  - a. Antrum puncture can be done by breaking the lateral wall of the inferior meatus and pushing in fluid and letting it drain through the natural orifice with head in dependent position (Fig. 15.13).
  - b. An opening can be made at the canine fossa through the vestibule of the mouth, deep to the upper lip (Caldwell-Luc operation).
- Carcinoma of the maxillary sinus arises from the mucosal lining. Symptoms depend on the direction of growth.
  - a. Invasion of the orbit causes proptosis and diplopia. If the infraorbital nerve is involved, there is facial pain and anaesthesia of the skin over the maxilla.
  - b. Invasion of the floor may produce a bulging and even ulceration of the palate.
  - c. Forward growth obliterates the canine fossa and produces a swelling of the face.
  - d. Backward growth may involve the palatine nerves and produce severe pain referred to the upper teeth.
  - e. Growth in a medial direction produces nasal obstruction, epistaxis and epiphora.
  - f. Growth in a lateral direction produces a swelling on the face and a palpable mass in the labiogingival groove.
- Frontal sinusitis and ethmoiditis can cause oedema of the lids secondary to infection of the sinuses.
- Pain from ethmoid air sinus may be referred to forehead, as both are supplied by ophthalmic division of trigeminal nerve.

- Pain of maxillary sinusitis may be referred to upper teeth and infraorbital skin as all these are supplied by the maxillary nerve.

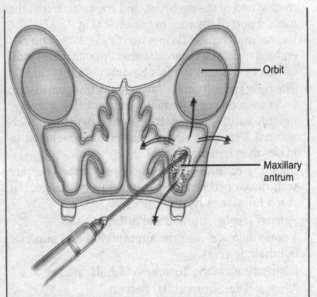

Fig. 15.13: Antrum puncture. Directions to show the invasion of the carcinoma of maxillary sinus

PTERYGOPALATINE FOSSA

This is small pyramidal space situated deeply, below the apex of the orbit (Fig. 15.14).

Boundaries

Study the boundaries on the skull.

Anterior: Superomedial part of the posterior surface of the maxilla.

Posterior: Root of the pterygoid process and adjoining part of the anterior surface of the greater wing of the sphenoid.

Medial: Upper part of the perpendicular plate of the palatine bone. The orbital and sphenoidal processes of the bone also take part.

Lateral: The fossa opens into the infratemporal fossa through the pterygomaxillary fissure.

Superior: Undersurface of the body of sphenoid.

Inferior: Closed by the pyramidal process of the palatine bone in the angle between the maxilla and the pterygoid process.

Communications

Anteriorly: With the orbit through the medial end of the inferior orbital fissure (Fig. 15.14).

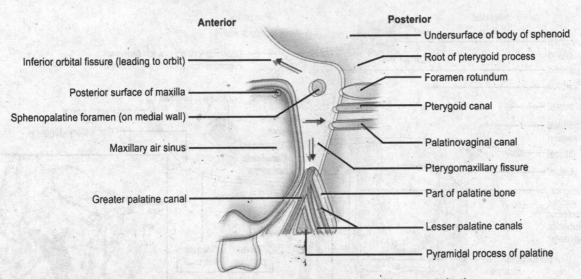

Fig. 15.14: Scheme to show the pterygopalatine fossa and its communications

Labels (anterior, left side):
- Inferior orbital fissure (leading to orbit)
- Posterior surface of maxilla
- Sphenopalatine foramen (on medial wall)
- Maxillary air sinus
- Greater palatine canal

Labels (posterior, right side):
- Undersurface of body of sphenoid
- Root of pterygoid process
- Foramen rotundum
- Pterygoid canal
- Palatinovaginal canal
- Pterygomaxillary fissure
- Part of palatine bone
- Lesser palatine canals
- Pyramidal process of palatine

Posteriorly

1 Middle cranial fossa through the foramen rotundum.
2 Foramen lacerum through the pterygoid canal.
3 Pharynx through the palatinovaginal canal.

Medially: With the nose through sphenopalatine foramen.

Laterally: With the infratemporal fossa through the pterygomaxillary fissure.

Inferiorly: With the oral cavity through the greater and lesser palatine canals.

Contents

1 Third part of the maxillary artery and its branches which bear the same names as the branches of the pterygopalatine ganglia and accompany all of them.
2 Maxillary nerve and its two branches, zygomatic and posterior superior alveolar.
3 Pterygopalatine ganglion and its numerous branches containing fibres of the maxillary nerve mixed with autonomic nerves.

Maxillary Nerve

It arises from the trigeminal ganglion, runs forwards in the lateral wall of the cavernous sinus below the ophthalmic nerve, and leaves the middle cranial fossa by passing through the foramen rotundum (*see* Fig. 12.13). Next, the nerve crosses the upper part of pterygopalatine fossa, beyond which it is continued as the infraorbital nerve.

In the middle cranial fossa, maxillary nerve gives a meningeal branch.

In the pterygopalatine fossa, the nerve is related to the pterygopalatine ganglion, and gives off the ganglionic, posterior superior alveolar and zygomatic nerves.

Ganglionic Branches

The pterygopalatine ganglion is suspended by the ganglionic branches.

Posterior Superior Alveolar Nerve

It enters the posterior surface of the body of the maxilla, and supplies the three upper molar teeth and the adjoining part of the gum.

Zygomatic Nerve

It is a branch of the maxillary nerve, given off in the pterygopalatine fossa. It enters the orbit through the lateral end of the inferior orbital fissure, and runs along the lateral wall, outside the periosteum, to enter the zygomatic bone. Just before or after entering the bone, it divides into two terminal branches, the *zygomaticofacial* and *zygomaticotemporal nerves* which supply the skin of the face and of the anterior part of the temple (*see* Fig. 2.22). The communicating branch to the lacrimal nerve, which contains secretomotor fibres to the lacrimal gland, arises from the zygomaticotemporal nerve, and runs in the lateral wall of the orbit (Fig. 15.15 and inset).

Infraorbital Nerve

It is the continuation of the maxillary nerve. It enters the orbit through the *inferior orbital fissure*. It then runs forwards on the floor of the orbit or the roof of the maxillary sinus, at first in the *infraorbital groove* and then in the *infraorbital canal* remaining outside the periosteum of the orbit. It emerges on the face through the *infraorbital foramen* and terminates by dividing into palpebral, nasal and labial branches. The nerve is accompanied by the infraorbital branch of the third part of the maxillary artery and the accompanying vein (*see* Fig. 2.22).

Head and Neck

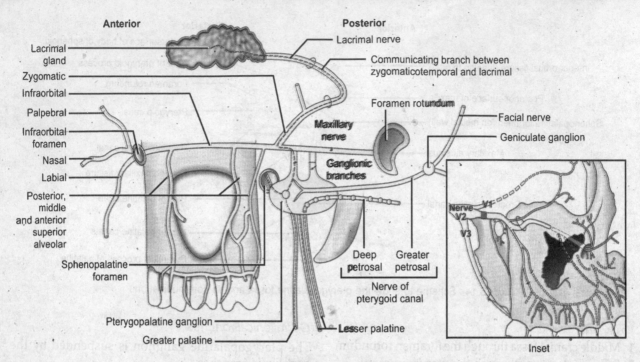

Fig. 15.15: Branches of maxillary nerve with pterygopalatine ganglion

Branches

1 The *middle superior alveolar nerve* arises in the infraorbital groove, runs in the lateral wall of the maxillary sinus, and supplies the upper premolar teeth.

2 The *anterior superior alveolar nerve* arises in the infraorbital canal, and runs in a sinuous canal having a complicated course in the anterior wall of the maxillary sinus. It supplies the upper incisor and canine teeth, the maxillary sinus, and the antero-inferior part of the nasal cavity.

3 *Terminal branches palpebral, nasal and labial* supply a large area of skin on the face. They also supply the mucous membrane of the upper lip and cheek (*see* Fig. 2.22).

PTERYGOPALATINE GANGLION/SPHENO-PALATINE GANGLION/GANGLION OF HAY FEVER/MECKEL'S GANGLION

DISSECTION

Trace the connections, and branches of pterygopalatine ganglion. It is responsible for supplying secretomotor fibres to the glands of nasal cavity, palate, pharynx and the lacrimal gland. It is also called *hay fever ganglion* as inflammation of the ganglion causes allergic sinusitis.

Features

Pterygopalatine is the largest parasympathetic peripheral ganglion. It serves as a relay station for secretomotor fibres to the lacrimal gland and to the mucous glands of the nose, paranasal sinuses, palate and pharynx. Topographically, it is related to the maxillary nerve, but functionally it is connected to facial nerve through its greater petrosal branch.

The flattened ganglion lies in the pterygopalatine fossa just below the maxillary nerve, in front of the pterygoid canal and lateral to the sphenopalatine foramen (Figs 15.15 and 15.16).

Connections

1 The *parasympathetic root* of the ganglion is formed by the nerve of the pterygoid canal. It carries preganglionic fibres that arise from neurons present near the *superior salivatory* and *lacrimatory nuclei*, and pass through the *nervus intermedius*, the *facial nerve*, the *geniculate ganglion*, the *greater petrosal* nerve and the *nerve of the pterygoid canal* to reach the *ganglion*. The fibres relay in the ganglion. Postganglionic fibres arise in the ganglion to supply secretomotor nerves to the lacrimal gland and to the mucous glands of the nose, the paranasal sinuses, the palate and the nasopharynx (Fig. 15.2).

2 The *sympathetic root* is also derived from the nerve of the pterygoid canal. It contains postganglionic fibres arising in the *superior cervical sympathetic ganglion* which pass through the internal carotid plexus, the *deep petrosal nerve* and the *nerve of the*

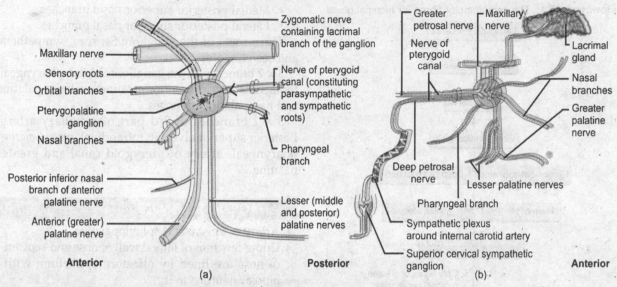

Figs 15.16a and b: (a) Connections of the pterygopalatine ganglion, and (b) roots and branches of pterygopalatine ganglion

pterygoid canal to reach the ganglion. The fibres pass through the ganglion without relay, and supply vasomotor nerves to the mucous membrane of the nose, the paranasal sinuses, the palate and the nasopharynx (*see* Table 1.3).

3 The *sensory roots* come from the maxillary nerve. Its fibres pass through the ganglion without relay. They emerge in the branches (Fig. 15.15) described below.

Branches

The branches of the ganglion are actually branches of the maxillary nerve. They also carry parasympathetic and sympathetic fibres which pass through the ganglion. The branches are:

1 *Orbital branches* pass through the inferior orbital fissure, and supply the periosteum of the orbit, and the orbitalis muscle which is involuntary (Fig. 15.15).

2 *Palatine branches, the greater or anterior palatine nerve* descends through the greater palatine canal, and supplies the hard palate and the labial aspect of the upper gums. The *lesser or middle and posterior palatine nerves* supply the soft palate and the tonsil (Figs 15.16a and b).

3 *Nasal branches* enter the nasal cavity through the sphenopalatine foramen (Fig. 15.15). The *lateral posterior superior nasal branches*, about six in number, supply the posterior parts of the superior and middle conchae (Fig. 15.11).

The *medial posterior superior nasal branches*, two or three in number, supply the posterior part of the roof of the nose and of the nasal septum (Fig. 15.6). The largest of these nerves is known as the *nasopalatine nerve* which descends up to the anterior part of the hard palate through the incisive foramen (Fig. 15.6).

4 The *pharyngeal branch* passes through the palatino-vaginal canal and supplies the part of the nasopharynx behind the auditory tube (Figs 15.16a and b).

5 *Lacrimal branch*: The postganglionic fibres pass back into the maxillary nerve to leave it through its zygomatic nerve and its zygomaticotemporal branch, a communicating branch to lacrimal nerve to supply the secretomotor fibres to the lacrimal gland (Fig. 15.15).

Flowchart 15.1 shows the pathway for secretomotor fibres to lacrimal gland.

CLINICAL ANATOMY

- Trigeminal neuralgia affecting its maxillary branch produces symptoms in the area of its distribution. The nerve can be anaesthetised at the foramen rotundum.
- The pterygopalatine ganglion, if irritated or infected, causes congestion of the glands of palate and nose including the lacrimal gland producing running nose and lacrimation. The condition is called hay fever. The ganglion is called '*ganglion of hay fever*'.
- Maxillary nerve carries the afferent limb fibres of the sneeze reflex as it carries general sensation from the nasal mucous membrane.

SUMMARY OF PTERYGOPALATINE FOSSA

It contains three or multiple of three structures:
Three contents:
- Maxillary nerve
- 3rd part of maxillary artery
- Pterygopalatine ganglion.

Flowchart 15.1: The secretomotor fibres for lacrimal gland

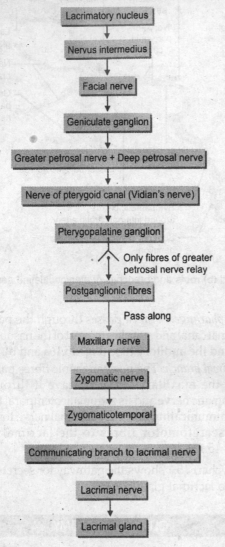

Three names of ganglion:
- Sphenopalatine
- Pterygopalatine
- Ganglion of hay fever/Meckel's ganglion.

Three structures traversing in openings in posterior wall:
- Maxillary nerve through foramen rotundum.
- Nerve of pterygoid canal through pterygoid canal.
- Pharyngeal branch through palatinovaginal canal.

Three structures through inferior orbital fissure:
- Infraorbital nerve.
- Zygomatic nerve.
- Orbital branches of the ganglion.

Three structures through inferior openings:
- One anterior palatine nerve with greater palatine vessels.
- Two posterior palatine nerves including lesser palatine vessels.

Three structures through medial opening:
- Nasopalatine nerve and sphenopalatine vessels.

- Medial posterior superior nasal branches.
- Lateral posterior superior nasal branches.

Three roots of the ganglion: Sensory, sympathetic and secretomotor.

3 × 2 branches of the ganglion: Orbital, pharyngeal, for lacrimal gland, anterior palatine, posterior palatine and nasopalatine branches.

3 × 2 branches of 3rd part of maxillary artery: Posterior superior alveolar, infraorbital, *sphenopalatine*, pharyngeal, artery of pterygoid canal and greater palatine.

FACTS TO REMEMBER

- Artery of epistaxis is sphenopalatine.
- Upper few mm of lateral wall of nose and septum of nose are lined by olfactory epithelium with bipolar neurons in it.
- Most of the nerves and blood vessels to the lateral wall of nose and septum of nose are common. The difference is in their magnitude.
- Maxillary sinusitis is the commonest chronic sinusitis.
- Into the middle meatus of nose drain 4 sets of air sinuses.
- Sinusitis may occur due to air pollution.
- Pterygopalatine ganglion is the ganglion of "hay fever". It gives secretomotor fibres to lacrimal gland, nasal, palatal and pharyngeal gland.
- Pain of maxillary sinusitis is referred to upper teeth; of ethmoidal sinusitis to medial side of orbit and of frontal sinusitis to forehead.

CLINICOANATOMICAL PROBLEM

A child during hot summer months is playing in the park. He picks up his nose, and it starts bleeding
- What is the source of the bleeding?
- Name the arteries supplying septum of the nose.

Ans: The source of the nasal bleeding or epistaxis is injury to the large capillary plexus situated at the anteroinferior part of the septum of nose. It is called Kiesselbach's plexus and the area is also known as Little's area.

The arteries supplying the septum of nose are:
1. Anterior ethmoidal, branch of ophthalmic which is a branch of internal carotid.
2. Superior labial, a branch of facial artery, which in turn is a branch of external carotid artery.
3. Large sphenopalatine artery. This is the continuation of 3rd part of maxillary artery, one of the terminal branches of external carotid artery.
4. Some branches from greater palatine artery, a branch of maxillary artery.

1. Classify paranasal air sinuses. Describe the maxillary air sinus with its clinical importance.
2. Describe the course and branches of maxillary nerve.
3. Write short notes on:
   a. Lateral wall of nose

b. Pterygopalatine ganglion with its roots and branches
c. Nerve supply of lacrimal gland
d. Nerve supply of septum of nose
e. Artery of epistaxis

1. Which of the following is the artery of epistaxis?
   a. Anterior ethmoidal
   b. Greater palatine
   c. Sphenopalatine
   d. Superior labial
2. Which one of the following air sinuses does not drain in the middle meatus of nose?
   a. Anterior ethmoidal
   b. Middle ethmoidal
   c. Posterior ethmoidal
   d. Maxillary
3. Which of the following air sinuses is first to develop?
   a. Maxillary
   b. Ethmoidal
   c. Frontal
   d. Sphenoidal

4. Nerve to pterygoid canal is formed by which nerves?
   a. Greater petrosal and deep petrosal
   b. Lesser petrosal and deep petrosal
   c. Greater petrosal and external petrosal
   d. Lesser petrosal and external petrosal
5. Which air sinus is most commonly infected?
   a. Ethmoidal
   b. Frontal
   c. Maxillary
   d. Sphenoidal
6. What is the length of auditory tube in adult person in mm:
   a. 36
   b. 3.6
   c. 46
   d. 48

1. c   2. c   3. a   4. a   5. c   6. a

Larynx

Always laugh with others, never at them
—Thackery

INTRODUCTION

The larynx (Latin *upper windpipe*) is the organ for production of voice or phonation. It is also an air passage, and acts as a sphincter at the inlet of the lower respiratory passages. The upper respiratory passages include the nose, the nasopharynx and the oropharynx.

Larynx or voice box is well developed in humans. Its capabilities are greatly enhanced by the large "vocalisation area" in the lower part of motor cortex. Our speech is guided and controlled by the cerebral cortex. God has given us two ears and one mouth; to hear more, contemplate and speak less according to time and need.

A man's language is an "index of intellect". One speaks during the expiratory phase of respiration. Larynx is a part of the respiratory system allowing two-way flow of gases. It is kept patent because an adult is breathing about 15 times per minute, unlike the oesophagus which opens at the time of eating or drinking only.

ANATOMY OF LARYNX

DISSECTION

Identify sternothyroid muscle in the sagittal section of head and neck and define its attachments on the thyroid cartilage. Define the attachments of inferior constrictor muscle from both cricoid and thyroid cartilages including the fascia overlying the cricothyroid muscle.

Cut through the inferior constrictor muscle to locate articulation of inferior horn of thyroid cartilage with cricoid cartilage, i.e. cricothyroid joint. Define the median cricothyroid ligament.

Identify thyrohyoid muscle. Remove this muscle to identify thyrohyoid membrane. Identify superior laryngeal vessels and internal laryngeal nerve piercing this membrane.

Identify epiglottis, thyroepiglottic and hyoepiglottic ligaments.

Strip the mucous membrane from the posterior surfaces of arytenoid and cricoid cartilages. Identify posterior cricoarytenoid, transverse arytenoid and oblique arytenoid muscles.

Recurrent laryngeal nerve was seen to enter larynx deep to the inferior constrictor muscle.

Identify cricothyroid muscle, which is the only intrinsic muscle of larynx placed on the external aspect of larynx. Remove the lower half of lamina of thyroid cartilage including the inferior horn of thyroid cartilage. Visualise the thyroarytenoid muscle in the vocal fold.

SITUATION AND EXTENT

The larynx lies in the anterior midline of the neck, extending from the root of the tongue to the trachea. In the adult male, it lies in front of the third to sixth cervical vertebrae, but in children and in the adult female, it lies at a little higher level (at C1 to C4 level) (Figs 16.1a to c).

SIZE

The length of the larynx is 44 mm in males and 36 mm in females. At puberty, the male larynx grows rapidly and becomes larger, seen as prominent angle of thyroid cartilage (Adam's apple); which makes his voice louder and low pitched. The pubertal growth of the female larynx is negligible, and her voice is high pitched. Internal diameter up to 3 yrs, it is 3 mm and adult, it is 12 mm.

CONSTITUTION OF LARYNX

The larynx is made up of a skeletal framework of cartilages. The cartilages are connected by joints, ligaments and membranes; and are moved by a number of muscles. The cavity of the larynx is lined by mucous membrane.

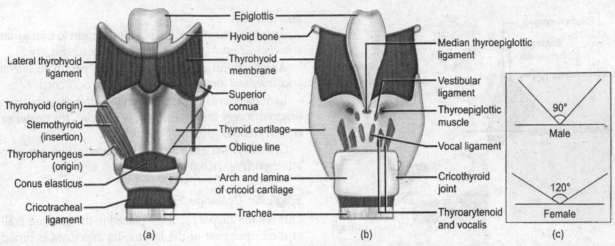

Figs 16.1a to c: Skeleton of the larynx: (a) Anterior view, (b) posterior view, and (c) angle of thyroid laminae in male and female

Cartilages of Larynx

The larynx contains nine cartilages, of which three are unpaired and three are paired.

Unpaired Cartilages

1 Thyroid (Greek *shield-like*)
2 Cricoid (Greek *ring-like*)
3 Epiglottis (Greek *leaf-like*) (Fig. 16.1a)

Paired Cartilages

1 Arytenoid (Greek *cup shaped*) (Fig. 16.1b)
2 Corniculate (Latin *horn shaped*)
3 Cuneiform (Latin *wedge shaped*)

Thyroid Cartilage

This cartilage is V-shaped in cross-section. It consists of right and left laminae (Fig. 16.1a). Each lamina is roughly quadrilateral. The laminae are placed obliquely relative to the midline, their posterior borders are far apart, but the anterior borders approach each other at an angle that is about 90 degrees in the male and about 120 degrees in the female (Fig. 16.1c).

The lower parts of the anterior borders of the right and left laminae fuse and form a median projection called the *laryngeal prominence*. The upper parts of the anterior borders do not meet. They are separated by the *thyroid notch*. The posterior borders are free. They are prolonged upwards and downwards as the superior and inferior cornua or horns. The superior cornua is connected with the greater cornua of the hyoid bone by the lateral *thyrohyoid ligament*.

The inferior cornua articulates with the cricoid cartilage to form the *cricothyroid joint* (Fig. 16.2).

The inferior border of the thyroid cartilage is convex in front and concave behind. In the median plane, it is connected to the cricoid cartilage by the *conus elasticus*.

The *outer surface* of each lamina is marked by an oblique line which extends from the superior thyroid

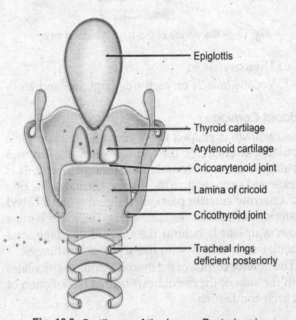

Fig. 16.2: Cartilages of the larynx: Posterior view

tubercle in front of the root of superior cornua to the inferior thyroid tubercle behind the middle of inferior border. The (i) thyrohyoid, (ii) sternothyroid and (iii) thyropharyngeus part of inferior constrictor of pharynx are attached to the oblique line (Fig. 16.1a).

Attachments

Lower border and inferior cornua gives insertion to triangular cricothyroid. Along the posterior border connecting superior and inferior cornua are the insertion of (i) palatopharyngeus, (ii) salpingopharyngeus, (iii) stylopharyngeus (Fig. 16.3).

On inner aspect are attached:
a. Median thyroepiglottic ligament
b. Thyroepiglottic muscle on each side
c. Vestibular fold on each side
d. Vocal fold on each side

Head and Neck

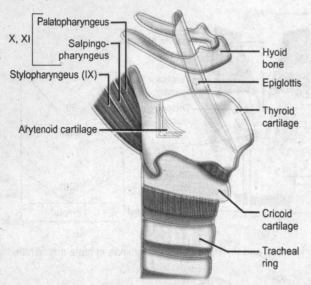

Fig. 16.3: Cartilages of the larynx: Lateral view

e. Thyroarytenoid
f. Vocalis muscle on each side (Figs 16.1 and 16.4).

Cricoid Cartilage

This cartilage is shaped like a ring and is a complete cartilage. It encircles the larynx below the thyroid cartilage and forms foundation stone of larynx. It is thicker and stronger than the thyroid cartilage. The ring has a narrow anterior part called the *arch*, and a broad posterior part, called the *lamina* (Fig. 16.2). The lamina projects upwards behind the thyroid cartilage, and articulates superiorly with the arytenoid cartilages.

The inferior cornua of the thyroid cartilage articulates with the side of the cricoid cartilage at the junction of the arch and lamina.

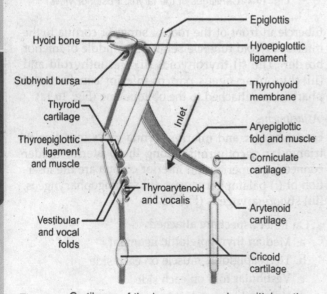

Fig. 16.4: Cartilages of the larynx as seen in sagittal section

Attachments

Anterior part of arch of cricoid gives origin to triangular *cricothyroid muscle*, a tensor of vocal cord (Fig. 16.9).

Anterolateral aspect of arch gives origin to *lateral cricoarytenoid muscle*, an adductor of vocal cord.

Lamina of cricoid cartilage on its outer aspects gives origin to a very important "safety muscle", the posterior cricoarytenoid muscle (Fig. 16.10).

Cricothyroid and quadrate membranes are also attached (Fig. 16.5a).

Epiglottic Cartilage/Epiglottis

This is a *leaf-shaped* cartilage placed in the anterior wall of the upper part of the larynx. Its *upper end* is broad and free, and projects upwards behind the hyoid bone and the tongue (Fig. 16.5b).

The *lower end* or thyroepiglottic ligament is pointed and is attached to the upper part of the angle between the two laminae of the thyroid cartilage (Figs 16.1b and 16.4).

Attachments

The right and left margins of the cartilage provide attachment to the aryepiglottic folds. Its *anterior surface* is connected:

a. To the tongue by a median *glossoepiglottic fold* (*see* Fig. 17.1)
b. To the hyoid bone by the hyoepiglottic ligament (Fig. 16.4). The *posterior surface* is covered with mucous membrane, and presents a tubercle in the lower part (Fig. 16.15).

Thyroepiglottic muscle is attached between thyroid cartilage and margins of epiglottis. It keeps the inlet of larynx patent for breathing.

Aryepiglottic muscle closes inlet during swallowing (Fig. 16.11a).

Arytenoid Cartilage

These are two small *pyramid-shaped* cartilages lying on the upper border of the lamina of the cricoid cartilage. The *apex* of the arytenoid cartilage is curved posteromedially and articulates with the corniculate cartilage. Its *base* is concave and articulates with the lateral part of the upper border of the cricoid lamina. Base is prolonged anteriorly to form the *vocal process*, and laterally to form the *muscular process* (Fig. 16.3). The *surfaces* of the cartilage are anterolateral, medial and posterior (Figs 16.2 to 16.4 and 16.5c).

Attachments

Vocal process: Vocal fold and vocalis muscle is attached.

Above vocal process: Vestibular fold attached.

Muscular process: Posterior aspect gives insertion to posterior cricoarytenoid.

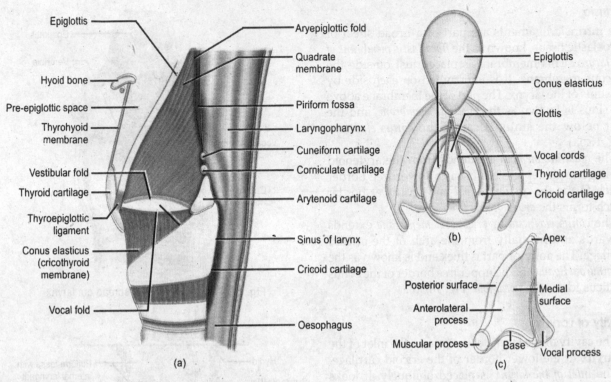

Figs 16.5a and b: (a) Ligaments and membranes of the larynx. Note the quadrate membrane and the conus elasticus, (b) vocal cords and inlet of larynx seen, and (c) arytenoid cartiliage

Anterior aspect gives insertion to lateral crico-arytenoid.

Posterior surface: Transverse arytenoid across the two cartilages.

Between base and apex of arytenoid is *oblique arytenoid* which continues as *aryepiglottic muscle* into two sides of epiglottis.

Quadrangular or quadrate membrane is attached between arytenoid, epiglottis and thyroid cartilages.

Corniculate/Santorini Cartilages

These are two small conical nodules which articulate with the apex of the arytenoid cartilages, and are directed posteromedially. They lie in the posterior parts of the aryepiglottic folds (Fig. 16.5a).

Cuneiform/Wrisberg Cartilages

These are two small rod-shaped pieces of cartilage placed in the aryepiglottic folds just ventral to the corniculate cartilages (Fig. 16.5a).

Histology of Laryngeal Cartilages

The thyroid, cricoid cartilages, and the basal parts of the arytenoid cartilages are made up of the hyaline cartilage. They may ossify after the age of 25 years. The other cartilages of the larynx, e.g. epiglottis, corniculate, cuneiform and processes of the arytenoid are made of the elastic cartilage and do not ossify.

Laryngeal Joints

The *cricothyroid joint* is a *synovial* joint between the inferior cornua of the thyroid cartilage and the side of the cricoid cartilage. It permits rotatory movements around a transverse axis passing through both cricothyroid joints permitting tension and relaxation of vocal cords. There are some gliding movements also in different directions (Fig. 16.2).

The *cricoarytenoid joint* is also a *synovial* joint between the base of the arytenoid cartilage and the upper border of the lamina of the cricoid cartilage. It permits rotatory movements around a vertical axis permitting adduction and abduction of the vocal cords and also gliding movements in all directions (Fig. 16.2).

Laryngeal Ligaments and Membranes
Extrinsic

1 The *thyrohyoid membrane* connects the thyroid cartilage to the hyoid bone. Its median and lateral parts are thickened to form the median and lateral thyrohyoid ligaments (Fig. 16.5). The membrane is pierced by the internal laryngeal nerve, and by the superior laryngeal vessels.

2 The *hyoepiglottic ligament* connects the upper end of the epiglottic cartilage to the hyoid bone (Fig. 16.4).

3 The *cricotracheal ligament* connects the cricoid cartilage to the upper end of the trachea (Fig. 16.1).

Intrinsic

The intrinsic ligaments are part of a broad sheet of fibroelastic tissue, known as the *fibroelastic membrane of the larynx*. This membrane is placed just outside the mucous membrane. It is interrupted on each side by the sinus of the larynx. The part of the membrane above the sinus is known as the *quadrate membrane*, and the part below the sinus is called the *conus elasticus* (Fig. 16.5a).

The *quadrate membrane* extends from the arytenoid cartilage to the epiglottis. It has a lower free border which forms the *vestibular fold* and an upper border which forms the *aryepiglottic fold*.

The *conus elasticus* or *cricovocal membrane* extends upwards and medially from the arch of the cricoid cartilage. The anterior part is thick and is known as the *cricothyroid ligament*. The upper free border of the conus elasticus forms the *vocal fold* (Fig. 16.5b).

Cavity of Larynx

1 The cavity of the larynx extends from the inlet of the larynx to the lower border of the cricoid cartilage. The *inlet of the larynx* is placed obliquely. It looks backwards and upwards, and opens into the laryngopharynx. The inlet is *bounded anteriorly*, by the epiglottis; *posteriorly*, by the interarytenoid fold of mucous membrane; and *on each side*, by the aryepiglottic fold (Fig. 16.5).

Internal diameter: Up to 3 years, 3 mm; every year it increases by 1 mm up to 12 years.

2 Within the cavity of larynx, there are two folds of mucous membrane on each side. The upper fold is the *vestibular fold*, and the lower fold is the *vocal fold*. The space between the right and left vestibular folds is the *rima vestibuli*; and the space between the vocal folds is the *rima glottidis* (Fig. 16.6).

The vocal fold is attached anteriorly to the middle of the angle of the thyroid cartilage on its posterior aspect; and posteriorly to the vocal process of the arytenoid cartilage (Fig. 16.11b).

The rima glottidis is limited posteriorly by an interarytenoid fold of mucous membrane.

The rima, therefore, has an anterior intermembranous part (three-fifth) and a posterior intercartilaginous part (Fig. 16.15a).

The rima is the narrowest part of the larynx. It is longer (23 mm) in males than in females (17 mm).

3 The vestibular and vocal folds divide the cavity of the larynx into three parts.

A. The part above the vestibular fold is called the *vestibule* of the larynx or supraglottis.

B. The part between the vestibular and vocal folds is called the sinus or *ventricle* of the larynx (Fig. 16.6).

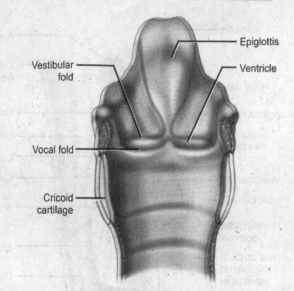

Fig. 16.6: Posterior view of spread out larynx

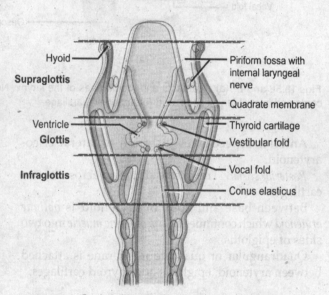

Fig. 16.7: Cavity of larynx and position of piriform fossa

C. The part below the vocal folds is called the *infraglottis* (Fig. 16.7).

The *sinus of Morgagni* or *ventricle of the larynx* is a narrow fusiform cleft between the vestibular and vocal folds. The anterior part of the sinus is prolonged upwards as a diverticulum between the vestibular fold and the lamina of the thyroid cartilage. This extension is known as the *saccule of the larynx*. The saccule contains mucous glands which help to lubricate the vocal folds. It is often called *oil can of larynx*.

Mucous Membrane of Larynx

1 The anterior surface and upper half of the posterior surface of the epiglottis, the upper parts of the aryepiglottic folds, and the vocal folds are lined by the *stratified squamous epithelium*. The rest of the

laryngeal mucous membrane is covered with the *ciliated columnar epithelium.*

2. The mucous membrane is loosely attached to the cartilages of the larynx except over the vocal ligaments and over the posterior surface of the epiglottis where it is thin and firmly adherent.

3. The *mucous glands* are absent over the vocal cords, but are plentiful over the anterior surface of the epiglottis, around the cuneiform cartilages and in the vestibular folds. The glands are scattered over the rest of the larynx.

CLINICAL ANATOMY

- Since the larynx or glottis is the narrowest part of the respiratory passages, foreign bodies are usually lodged here.
- Infection of the larynx is called laryngitis. It is characterized by hoarseness of voice.
- Laryngeal oedema may occur due to a variety of causes. This can cause obstruction to breathing.
- Misuse of the vocal cords may produce nodules on the vocal cords mostly at the junction of anterior one-third and posterior two-thirds. These are called Singer's nodules or Teacher's nodules (Fig. 16.8).
- *Fibreoptic flexible laryngoscopy:* Under local anaesthesia flexible laryngoscope is passed and larynx well visualised.
- *Microlaryngoscopy:* This procedure is performed under operating microscope. Vocal cord tumors and diseases are excised by this method.
- *External examination of larynx:* Head is flexed in sitting position. Examiner stands behind and palpates larynx and neck with finger tips for tumour, swelling, lymphadenitis, etc.
- Speech analysis is also necessary in laryngeal diseases.
- *Foreign body in larynx:* At times fish bones may get impacted in the vallecula or piriform fossa. Often these bones just scratch the mucosa on their way down, and the person gets a feeling of foreign body sensation, due to a dull visceral pain caused by the scratch.
- Piriform fossa lies between quadrate membrane and medial side of thyroid cartilage. It is traversed by internal laryngeal nerve. Piriform fossa is used to smuggle out precious stones, diamonds, etc. It is called *smuggler's fossa* (Fig. 16.7).
- The mucous membrane of the larynx is supplied by X nerve through superior laryngeal or recurrent laryngeal nerves. So laryngeal tumours may also cause referred pain in the ear partly supplied by auricular branch of X nerve.

- Large foreign bodies may block laryngeal inlet leading to suffocation.
- Small foreign bodies may lodge in laryngeal ventricle, cause reflex closure of the glottis and suffocation.
- Inflammation of upper larynx may cause oedema of supraglottis part. It does not extend below vocal cords because mucosa is adherent to vocal ligament.

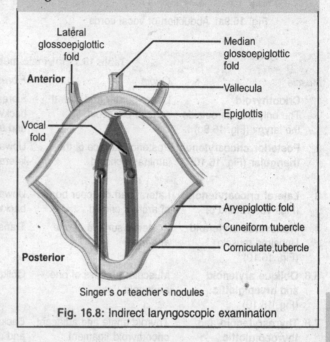

Fig. 16.8: Indirect laryngoscopic examination

Intrinsic Muscles of Larynx

The attachments of intrinsic muscles of larynx are presented in Table 16.1 and their main action shown in Table 16.2.

Nerve Supply

All intrinsic muscles of the larynx are supplied by the recurrent laryngeal nerve except for the cricothyroid which is supplied by the external laryngeal nerve.

Actions

The vocal process and muscular processes move in opposite directions. Any muscle which pulls the muscular process medially, pushes the vocal process laterally, resulting in abduction of vocal cords. This is done by only one pair of muscle, the posterior cricoarytenoid (Fig. 16.9a).

Muscles which pull the muscular process forward and laterally will push the vocal process medially (Fig. 16.9b) causing adduction of vocal cords. This is done by lateral cricoarytenoid and transverse arytenoid.

The cricothyroid causes rocking movement of thyroid forwards and downwards at cricothyroid joints, thus tensing and lengthening the vocal cords (Fig. 16.9c).

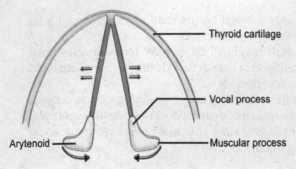

Fig. 16.9a: Abduction of vocal cords

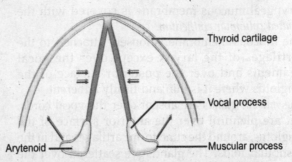

Fig. 16.9b: Adduction of vocal cords

Table 16.1: Intrinsic muscles of the larynx			
Muscle	Origin	Fibres	Insertion
1. **Cricothyroid** The only muscle outside the larynx (Fig. 16.9c)	Lower border and lateral surface of cricoid	Fibres pass backwards and upwards	Inferior cornua and lower border of thyroid cartilage. It is called 'tuning fork of larynx'
2. **Posterior cricoarytenoid triangular** (Fig. 16.10)	Posterior surface of the lamina of cricoid	Upwards and laterally	Posterior aspect of muscular process of arytenoid
3. **Lateral cricoarytenoid** (Figs 16.11a and b)	Lateral part of upper border of arch of cricoid	Upwards and backwards	Anterior aspect of muscular process of arytenoid
4. **Transverse arytenoid** Unpaired muscle (Fig. 16.10)	Posterior surface of one arytenoid	Transverse	Posterior surface of another arytenoid
5,6. **Oblique arytenoid** and **aryepiglottic** (Fig. 16.10)	Muscular process of one arytenoid	Oblique	Apex of the other arytenoid. Some fibres are continued as *aryepiglottic* muscle to the edge of the epiglottis
7,8. **Thyroarytenoid** and **thyroepiglottic** (Figs 16.11a and b)	Thyroid angle and adjacent cricothyroid ligament	Backwards and upwards	Anterolateral surface of arytenoid cartilage. Some of the upper fibres of thyroarytenoid curve upwards into the aryepiglottic fold to reach the edge of epiglottis, known as *thyroepiglottic*
9. **Vocalis** (Fig. 16.12)	Vocal process of arytenoid cartilage	Pass forwards	Vocal ligament and thyroid angle

Table 16.2: Muscles acting on the larynx	
Movement	Muscle
1. Elevation of larynx	Thyrohyoid, mylohyoid
2. Depression of larynx	Sternothyroid, sternohyoid
3. Opening inlet of larynx	Thyroepiglottic
4. Closing inlet of larynx	Aryepiglottic
5. Abductor of vocal cords	Posterior cricoarytenoid only
6. Adductor of vocal cords	Lateral cricoarytenoid transverse and oblique arytenoids
7. Tensor of vocal cords and modulation of voice	Cricothyroid
8. Relaxor of vocal cords	Thyroarytenoid and vocalis

The thyroarytenoid pulls the arytenoid forward, relaxing the vocal cords (Table 16.2 and Fig. 16.11).

a. Muscles which abduct the vocal cords: Only posterior cricoarytenoids (safety muscle of larynx).

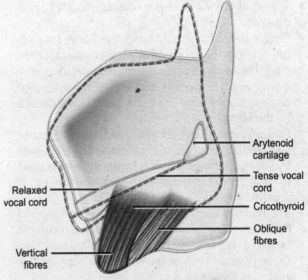

Fig. 16.9c: Cricothyroid muscle

b. Muscles which adduct the vocal cords:
   i. Lateral cricoarytenoids
   ii. Transverse arytenoid
   iii. Cricothyroids (tuning fork of larynx)
   iv. Thyroarytenoids (Figs 16.11a and b).

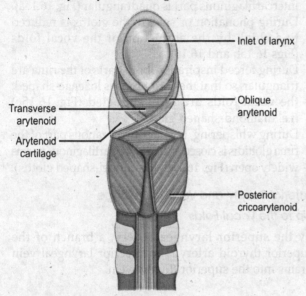

Fig. 16.10: Muscles of larynx: Posterior view

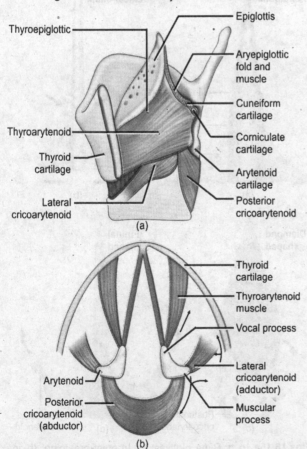

Figs 16.11a and b: Muscles of the larynx: (a) Lateral view, and (b) horizontal view

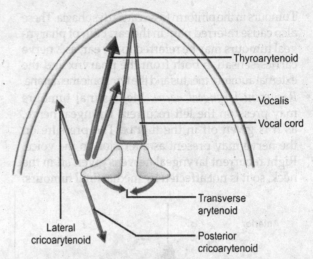

Fig. 16.12: Scheme to show the direction of pull of some intrinsic muscles of the larynx

c. Muscles which tense the vocal cords: Cricothyroids (Fig. 16.9).
d. Muscles which relax the vocal cords:
   i. Thyroarytenoids (Fig. 16.12)
   ii. Vocalis.
e. Muscles which close the inlet of the larynx:
   i. Oblique arytenoids
   ii. Aryepiglottic (Fig. 16.11a).
f. Muscles which open the inlet of larynx: Thyroepiglotticus (Fig. 16.11b).

CLINICAL ANATOMY

- When any foreign object enters the larynx severe protective coughing is excited to expel the object. However, damage to the internal laryngeal nerve produces anaesthesia of the mucous membrane in the supraglottic part of the larynx breaking the reflex arc so that foreign bodies can readily enter it.
- Damage to the external laryngeal nerve causes some weakness of phonation due to loss of the tightening effect of the cricothyroid on the vocal cord.
- When both recurrent laryngeal nerves are interrupted, the vocal cords lie in the cadaveric position in between abduction and adduction and phonation is completely lost. Deep breathing also becomes difficult through the partially opened glottis (Fig. 16.13).
- When only one recurrent laryngeal nerve is paralysed, the opposite vocal cord compensates for it and phonation is possible but there is hoarseness of voice. There is failure of forceful explosive part of voluntary and reflex coughing (Figs 16.14a and b).

- Tumours in the piriform fossa cause dysphagia. These also cause referred pain in the ear. Pain of pharyngeal tumours may be referred to the ear, as X nerve carries sensation both from the pharynx and the external auditory meatus and the tympanic membrane.
- *Recurrent laryngeal nerve:* Mediastinal tumours may press on the left recurrent laryngeal nerve, as it is given off in the thorax. The pressure on the nerve may present as alteration in the voice. Right recurrent laryngeal nerve is given off in the neck, so it is not affected by mediastinal tumours.

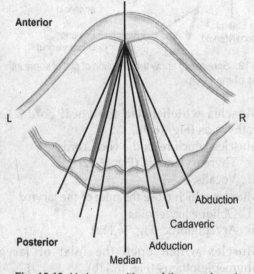

Fig. 16.13: Various positions of the vocal cord

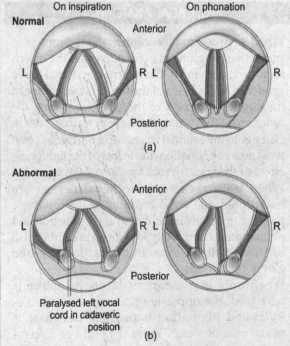

Figs 16.14a and b: Position of vocal cords: (a) Normal, and (b) abnormal conditions

MOVEMENTS OF VOCAL FOLDS

Movements of the vocal folds affect the shape and size of the rima glottidis.

1 During quiet breathing or condition of rest, the intermembranous part of the rima is triangular, and the intercartilaginous part is quadrangular (Fig. 16.15a).
2 During phonation or speech, the glottis is reduced to a chink by the adduction of the vocal folds (Figs 16.15b and 16.16).
3 During forced inspiration, both parts of the rima are triangular, so that the entire rima is lozenge-shaped; the vocal folds are fully abducted (Fig. 16.15c) (i.e. diamond-shaped glottis).
4 During whispering, the intermembranous part of the rima glottidis is closed, but the intercartilaginous part is widely open (Fig. 16.15d) (i.e. funnel-shaped glottis).

Arterial Supply and Venous Drainage

Up to the Vocal Folds

By the superior laryngeal artery, a branch of the superior thyroid artery. The superior laryngeal vein drains into the superior thyroid vein.

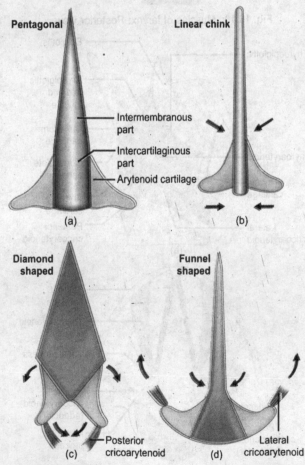

Figs 16.15a to d: Rima glottidis: (a) In quiet breathing, (b) in phonation or speech, (c) during forced inspiration, and (d) during whispering

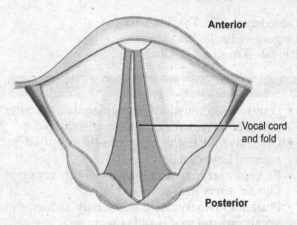

Fig. 16.16: Direct laryngoscopic view of vocal cords in adducted position

Below the Vocal Folds

By the inferior laryngeal artery, a branch of the inferior thyroid artery. The inferior laryngeal vein drains into the inferior thyroid vein.

Nerve Supply

Motor Nerves

Recurrent laryngeal nerve supplies posterior cricoarytenoid, lateral cricoarytenoid, transverse and oblique arytenoid, aryepiglottic, thyroarytenoid, thyroepiglottic muscles. It supplies all intrinsic muscles except cricothyroid.

External laryngeal nerve only supplies cricothyroid muscle.

Sensory Nerves

The internal laryngeal nerve supplies the mucous membrane up to the level of the vocal folds. The recurrent laryngeal nerve supplies it below the level of the vocal folds.

Lymphatic Drainage

Lymphatics from the part above the vocal folds drain along the superior thyroid vessels to the anterosuperior group of deep cervical nodes by piercing thyrohyoid membrane.

Those from the part below the vocal folds drain to the posteroinferior group of deep cervical nodes. A few of them drain into the prelaryngeal nodes by piercing cricothyroid.

CLINICAL ANATOMY

- The larynx can be examined either directly through a laryngoscope (direct laryngoscopy) (Fig. 16.17); or indirectly through a laryngeal mirror (indirect laryngoscopy) (Fig. 16.18).
- By laryngoscopy, one can inspect the base of the tongue, the valleculae, the epiglottis, the aryepiglottic folds, the piriform fossae, the vestibular folds, and the vocal folds.
- Tumours of the vocal cords can be diagnosed early, because there are changes in the voice. Tumours in subglottic area present late so are diagnosed late and have poor prognosis.
- *Laryngotomy:* The needle is inserted in the midline of cricothyroid membrane, below the thyroid prominence. This is done as an emergency procedure (Fig. 16.18).
- Tracheostomy is a permanent procedure. Part of 2nd–4th rings of trachea are removed after incising the isthmus of the thyroid gland.
- If the patient is unconscious, one must remember A: Airway, B: Breathing, C: Circulation in that order. For the patency of airway, pull the tongue out and also endotracheal tube needs to be passed. The tube should be passed between the right and left vocal cords down to the trachea.

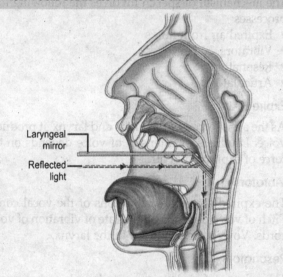

Fig. 16.17: Parts of larynx seen by direct laryngoscopy

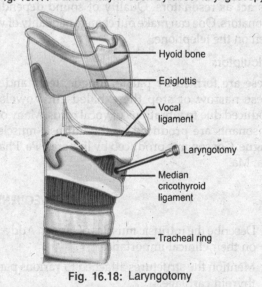

Fig. 16.18: Laryngotomy

INFANT'S LARYNX

Cavity of infant's larynx is short and funnel-shaped.

- Size is one-third of an adult. Lumen is very narrow.
- Position is higher than in adult.
- Epiglottis lies at C2 and during elevation, it reaches C1, so that infant can use nasal airway for breathing while suckling.
- Laryngeal cartilages are softer, more pliable than in adult.
- Thyroid cartilage is shorter and broader.
- Vocal cords are only 4–4.5 mm long, shorter than in childhood and in adult.
- Supraglottic and subglottic mucosa are lax, swelling results in respiratory obstruction.
- One must be careful while giving anaesthesia to an infant (birth to one year).

MECHANISM OF SPEECH

The mechanism of speech involves the following four processes:

- Expired air from lungs
- Vibrators
- Resonators
- Articulators

Expired Air

As the air is forced out of lungs and larynx, it produces voice. Loudness or intensity of voice depends on the force of expiration of air.

Vibrators

The expired air causes vibrations of the vocal cords. Pitch of voice depends on the rate of vibration of vocal cords. Vowels are produced in the larynx.

Resonators

The column of air between vocal cords and nose and lips act as resonators. Quality of sound depends on resonators. One can make out change of quality of voice even on the telephone.

Articulators

These are formed by palate, tongue, teeth and lips. These narrow or stop the exhaled air. Vowels are produced due to vibrations of vocal cards. Many of the consonants are produced by the intrinsic muscles of tongue. Consonants produced by lips are—Pa, Pha, Ba, Bha, Ma

Labiodental—Ta, Tha, Da, Dha, Na
Lingual—Cha, Ja, Jha
Palatal—Ka, Kha, Ga, Gha.

FACTS TO REMEMBER

- Only intrinsic muscle of larynx placed on the outer aspect of laryngeal cartilages is cricothyroid.
- Cricothyroid is the only muscle supplied by external laryngeal nerve.
- External laryngeal nerve runs with superior thyroid artery near the gland
- Posterior cricoarytenoid is the only abductor of vocal cord and so it is a life saving muscle.
- Piriform fossa is called smuggler's fossa as precious stones, etc. can be hidden here.
- The primary function of larynx is to protect the lower respiratory tract. Phonation has developed with evolution and is related to motor speech area of the cerebral cortex.

CLINICOANATOMICAL PROBLEM

Due to a severe infection of the voice box and with high temperature, a patient is not able to speak and breathe at all.

- Paralysis of which muscles causes extreme difficulty in breathing?
- Name the muscles of larynx and their actions.

Ans: Due to infection of the larynx, the branches of recurrent laryngeal nerve supplying posterior cricoarytenoid muscles are infected. Since this pair of muscle is the only abductor of vocal cord, the vocal cords get adducted, resulting in extreme difficulty in breathing. Tracheostomy is the main line of treatment if infection is not controlled.

Movement of larynx	Muscles
Abduction of vocal cord	Posterior cricoarytenoid
Adduction of vocal cord	Lateral cricoarytenoid Transverse arytenoid Oblique arytenoid
Opening inlet of larynx	Thyroepiglottic
Closing inlet of larynx	Aryepiglottic
Tensor of vocal cord	Cricothyroid
Relaxor of vocal cord	Thyroarytenoid

FREQUENTLY ASKED QUESTIONS

1. Describe the intrinsic muscles of larynx. Add a note on their clinical importance.
2. Mention the structures attached to various parts of thyroid cartilage.
3. Write short notes on:
   a. Rima glottidis   b. Epiglottis
   c. Cricoid cartilage   d. Vocal folds
   e. Pyriform fossa

1. Which histological type of cartilage is epiglottis?
   a. Fibrous
   b. Elastic
   c. Hyaline
   d. Fibroelastic

2. Which is the only abductor of the vocal cord?
   a. Lateral cricoarytenoid
   b. Thyroarytenoid
   c. Posterior cricoarytenoid
   d. Thyroepiglottic

3. Recurrent laryngeal nerve supplies all muscles *except:*
   a. Posterior cricoarytenoid
   b. Oblique arytenoids
   c. Lateral cricoarytenoid
   d. Cricothyroid

4. Angle of anterior borders of laminae of thyroid cartilage in adult male is:
   a. 90°
   b. 100°
   c. 80°
   d. 120°

5. Which of the following muscles is not inserted in the posterior border of thyroid cartilage?
   a. Palatopharyngeus b. Salpingopharyngeus
   c. Stylopharyngeus   d. Levator veli palatini

6. Which muscle is not attached to cricoid cartilage?
   a. Cricothyroid
   b. Oblique arytenoid
   c. Lateral cricoarytenoid
   d. Posterior cricoarytenoid

7. Which of the following muscles is the 'safety' muscle of larynx?
   a. Lateral cricoarytenoid
   b. Posterior cricoarytenoid
   c. Oblique arytenoid
   d. Transverse arytenoids

8. Pain of pharyngeal tumours is referred to ear due to which of the following nerves?
   a. IX
   b. X
   c. V
   d. VII

Tongue

Tongue is not steel, yet it cuts

Taste makes waist

INTRODUCTION

The tongue is a muscular organ situated in the floor of the mouth. It is associated with the functions of (i) taste, (ii) speech, (iii) chewing, (iv) deglutition, and (v) cleansing of mouth.

Tongue comprises skeletal muscles which are voluntary. These voluntary muscles start behaving as involuntary in any classroom—funny?

Thanks to the taste buds that the multiple hotels, restaurants, fast food outlets, *chat–pakori* shops, etc. are flourishing. One need not be too fussy about the taste of the food. Nutritionally, it should be balanced and hygienic.

EXTERNAL FEATURES

DISSECTION

In the sagittal section, identify fan-shaped genioglossus muscle. Cut the attachments of buccinator, superior constrictor muscles and the intervening pterygomandibular raphe and reflect these downwards exposing the lateral surface of the tongue. Look at the superior, inferior surfaces of your own tongue with the help of hand lens.

PARTS

The tongue has:

1 A root
2 A tip/ Apex
3 A body, which has:
   a. A curved upper surface or dorsum (Fig. 17.1).
   b. An inferior surface.

The dorsum is divided into oral and pharyngeal parts by a V-shaped, the sulcus terminalis. The inferior surface is confined to the oral part only.

The *root* is attached to the styloid process and soft palate above, and to mandible and the hyoid bone below. Because of these attachments, we are not able to swallow the tongue itself. In between the mandible and hyoid bones, it is related to the geniohyoid and mylohyoid muscles.

The *tip* of the tongue forms the anterior free end which, at rest, lies behind the upper incisor teeth.

The *dorsum* of the tongue (Fig. 17.1) is convex in all directions. It is divided into:

- An *oral part* or anterior two-thirds.
- A *pharyngeal part* or posterior one-third, by a faint V-shaped groove, the *sulcus terminalis*. The two limbs of the 'V' meet at a median pit, named the *foramen caecum*. They run laterally and forwards up to the palatoglossal arches. The foramen caecum represents the site from which the thyroid diverticulum grows down in the embryo. The oral and pharyngeal parts of the tongue differ in their development, topography, structure, and function (Table 17.3).
- Small posteriormost part

1 The *oral or papillary part of the tongue* is placed on the floor of the mouth. Its *margins* are free and in contact with the gums and teeth. Just in front of the palatoglossal arch, each margin shows 4 to 5 vertical folds, named the *foliate papillae*.

The *superior surface* of the oral part shows a median furrow and is covered with papillae which make it rough (Fig. 17.1).

The *inferior surface* is covered with a smooth mucous membrane, which shows a median fold called the *frenulum linguae*.

On either side of the frenulum, there is a prominence produced by the deep lingual veins. More laterally there is a fold called the *plica fimbriata* that is directed forwards and medially towards the tip of the tongue (Fig. 17.2).

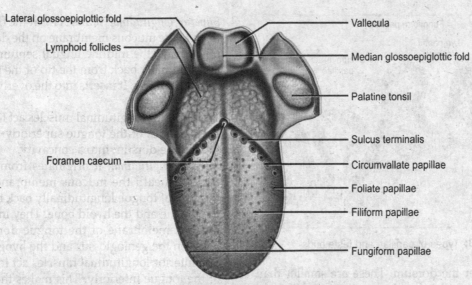

Fig. 17.1: The dorsum of the tongue, epiglottis and palatine tonsil

Labels (Fig. 17.1):
- Lateral glossoepiglottic fold
- Lymphoid follicles
- Foramen caecum
- Vallecula
- Median glossoepiglottic fold
- Palatine tonsil
- Sulcus terminalis
- Circumvallate papillae
- Foliate papillae
- Filiform papillae
- Fungiform papillae

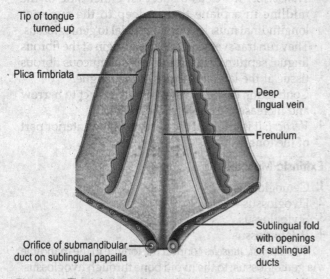

Fig. 17.2: The inferior surface of tongue and the floor of the mouth

Labels (Fig. 17.2):
- Tip of tongue turned up
- Plica fimbriata
- Orifice of submandibular duct on sublingual papailla
- Deep lingual vein
- Frenulum
- Sublingual fold with openings of sublingual ducts

2 The *pharyngeal or lymphoid part of the tongue* lies behind the palatoglossal arches and the sulcus terminalis. Its posterior surface, sometimes called the base of the tongue, forms the anterior wall of the oropharynx. The mucous membrane has no papillae, but has many *lymphoid follicles* that collectively constitute the *lingual tonsil* (Fig. 17.1). Mucous glands are also present.

3 The *posteriormost part of the tongue* is connected to the epiglottis by three-folds of mucous membrane. These are the median glossoepiglottic fold and the right and left lateral glossoepiglottic folds. On either side of the median fold, there is a depression called the *vallecula* (Fig. 17.1). The lateral folds separate the vallecula from the piriform fossa.

CLINICAL ANATOMY

- Glossitis is usually a part of generalized ulceration of the mouth cavity or stomatitis. In certain anaemias, the tongue becomes smooth due to atrophy of the filiform papillae.
- The presence of a rich network of lymphatics and of loose areolar tissue in the substance of tongue is responsible for enormous swelling of tongue in *acute glossitis*. The tongue fills up the mouth cavity and then protrudes out of it.
- The undersurface of the tongue is a good site along with the bulbar conjunctiva for observation of jaundice.
- In unconscious patients, the tongue may fall back and obstruct the air passages. This can be prevented either by lying the patient on one side with head down (the 'tonsil position') or by keeping the tongue out mechanically.
- Lingual tonsil in the posterior one-third of the tongue forms part of Waldeyer's ring (*see* Fig. 14.13).

PAPILLAE OF THE TONGUE

These are projections of mucous membrane or corium which give the anterior two-thirds of the tongue, its characteristic roughness. These are of the following three types (Fig. 17.3).

1 *Vallate* or *circumvallate papillae:* They are large in size 1–2 mm in diameter and are 8–12 in number. They are situated immediately in front of the sulcus terminalis. Each papilla is a cylindrical projection surrounded by a circular sulcus. The walls of the papilla have taste buds.

2 The *fungiform papillae* are numerous near the tip and margins of the tongue, but some of them are also

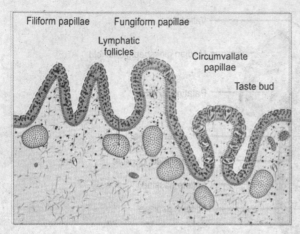

Fig. 17.3: Types of papillae and taste buds

scattered over the dorsum. These are smaller than the vallate papillae but larger than the filiform papillae. Each papilla consists of a narrow pedicle and a large rounded head. They are distinguished by their bright red colour (Fig. 17.3).

3 The *filiform papillae* or *conical papillae* cover the presulcal area of the dorsum of the tongue, and give it a characteristic velvety appearance. They are the smallest and most numerous of the lingual papillae. Each is pointed and covered with keratin; the apex is often split into filamentous processes.

4 Foliate papillae are present at the lateral border just infront of circumvallate papillae. They are leaf shaped.

MUSCLES OF THE TONGUE

A middle fibrous septum divides the tongue into right and left halves. Each half contains four intrinsic and four extrinsic muscles.

Intrinsic Muscles ~ *[handwritten: Does Not attach to bone]*

They occupy the upper part of the tongue, and are attached to the submucous fibrous layer and to the median fibrous septum. They alter the shape of the tongue (Fig. 17.4).

[handwritten at bottom left: Originate and insert within the substance of the tongue]

1 *Superior longitudinal*: It arises from the fibrous tissue deep to the mucous membrane on the dorsum of the tongue and the midline lingual septum. They pass longitudinally back from the tip of the tongue to its root posteriorly. It inserts into the overlying mucous membrane.

The superior longitudinal muscles act to elevate the tip and sides of the tongue superiorly. This shapes the tongue dorsum into a concavity.

2 *Inferior longitudinal*: It originates from the fibrous tissue beneath the mucous membrane stretching from tip of tongue longitudinally back to the root of the tongue and the hyoid bone. They insert into the mucous membrane of the tongue dorsum. It lies between the genioglossus and the hyoglossus.

The inferior longitudinal muscles act to curl the tip of the tongue inferiorly. This makes the dorsum of the tongue convex in shape.

3 *Transverse*: It lies as a sheet on either side of the midline in a plane that is deep to the superior longitudinal muscles but superficial to genioglossus. They run transversely from their origin at the fibrous lingual septum to insert into the submucous fibrous tissue at the lateral margins of the tongue.

Contraction of the transverse muscles act to narrow and increase the depth of the tongue.

4 *Vertical*: It is found at the borders of the anterior part of the tongue.

Extrinsic Muscles

1 Genioglossus
2 Hyoglossus
3 Styloglossus
4 Palatoglossus

The *extrinsic muscles* connect the tongue to the mandible via genioglossus; to the hyoid bone through hyoglossus; to the styloid process via styloglossus, and the palate via palatoglossus. These are described in Table 17.1.

The actions of intrinsic and extrinsic muscles are mentioned in Table 17.2.

Table 17.1: Extrinsic muscles of tongue			
Muscle	*Origin*	*Insertion*	*Actions*
Palatoglossus (Fig. 17.6)	Oral surface of palatine aponeurosis	Descends in the palatoglossal arch to the side of tongue at the junction of oral and pharyngeal parts	Pulls up the root of tongue, approximates the palatoglossal arches and thus closes the oropharyngeal isthmus
Hyoglossus (Fig. 17.6)	Whole length of greater cornua and lateral part of hyoid bone	Side of tongue between styloglossus and inferior longitudinal muscle of tongue	Depresses tongue, makes dorsum convex, retracts the protruded tongue
Styloglossus (Fig. 17.6)	Tip and part of anterior surface of styloid process	Into the side of tongue *[handwritten: Lateral]*	Pulls tongue upwards and backwards, i.e. retracts the tongue
Genioglossus fan-shaped bulky muscle (Fig. 17.5)	Upper genial tubercle of mandible	Upper fibres into the tip of tongue Middle fibres into the dorsum Lower fibres into the hyoid bone	Retracts the tongue Depresses the tongue Pulls the posterior part of tongue forwards and protrudes the tongue. It is a *life-saving muscle*

Table 17.2: Summary of the actions of muscles

Intrinsic muscles	Actions
Superior longitudinal	Shortens the tongue makes its dorsum concave
Inferior longitudinal	Shortens the tongue makes its dorsum convex
Transverse	Makes the tongue narrow and elongated
Vertical (Fig. 17.4)	Makes the tongue broad and flattened
Extrinsic muscles	Actions
Genioglossus (Fig. 17.5)	Protrudes the tongue
Hyoglossus (Fig. 17.6)	Depresses the tongue
Styloglossus (Fig. 17.6)	Retracts the tongue
Palatoglossus	Elevates the tongue

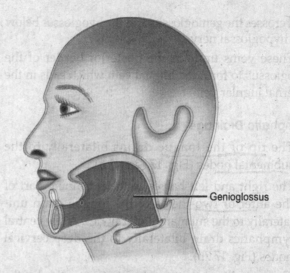

Fig. 17.5: Genioglossus

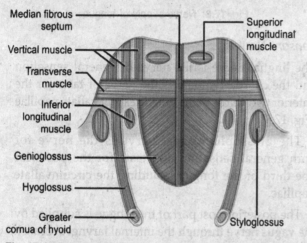

Fig. 17.4: Coronal section of the tongue showing arrangement of the intrinsic muscles and extrinsic muscles

Arterial Supply of Tongue

It is derived from the tortuous *lingual artery*, a branch of the external carotid artery. The root of the tongue is also supplied by the tonsillar artery, a branch of facial artery, and ascending pharyngeal branch of external carotid (Fig. 17.6). *See* Chapter 4 for the course and branches of the lingual artery.

Venous Drainage

The arrangement of the venae comitantes/veins of the tongue is variable. Two venae comitantes accompany the lingual artery, and one vena comitant accompanies the hypoglossal nerve. The deep lingual vein is the largest and principal vein of the tongue. It is visible on the inferior surface of the tongue. It runs backwards

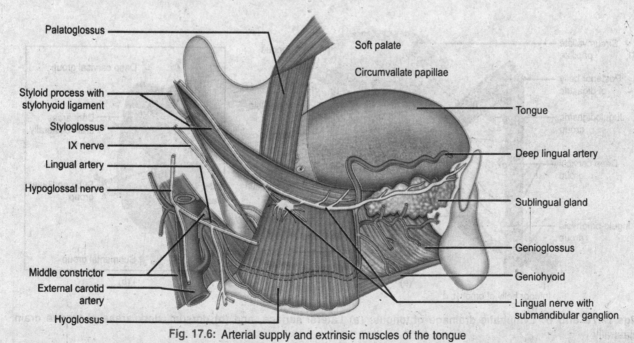

Fig. 17.6: Arterial supply and extrinsic muscles of the tongue

and crosses the genioglossus and the hyoglossus below the hypoglossal nerve.

These veins unite at the posterior border of the hyoglossus to form the lingual vein which ends in the internal jugular vein.

Lymphatic Drainage

1 The tip of the tongue drains bilaterally to the submental nodes (Figs 17.7a and b).

2 The right and left halves of the remaining part of the anterior two-thirds of the tongue drain unilaterally to the submandibular nodes. A few central lymphatics drain bilaterally to the deep cervical nodes (Fig. 17.7b).

3 The posteriormost part and posterior one-third of the tongue drain bilaterally into the upper deep cervical lymph nodes including jugulodigastric nodes.

4 The whole lymph finally drains to the *jugulo-omohyoid nodes. These are known as the lymph nodes of the tongue.*

Nerve Supply

Motor Nerves

All the intrinsic and extrinsic muscles, except the palatoglossus, are supplied by the hypoglossal nerve. The palatoglossus is supplied by the cranial root of the accessory nerve through the pharyngeal plexus.

So seven out of eight muscles are supplied by XII nerve (Fig. 17.8).

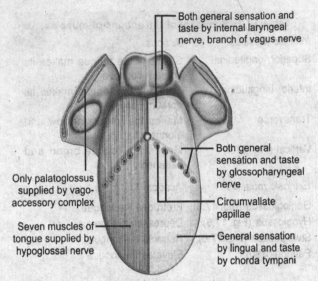

Fig. 17.8: Nerve supply of tongue

Labels: Both general sensation and taste by internal laryngeal nerve, branch of vagus nerve; Only palatoglossus supplied by vago-accessory complex; Seven muscles of tongue supplied by hypoglossal nerve; Both general sensation and taste by glossopharyngeal nerve; Circumvallate papillae; General sensation by lingual and taste by chorda tympani

Sensory Nerves

The lingual nerve is the nerve of general sensation and the chorda tympani is the nerve of taste for the anterior two-thirds of the tongue except vallate papillae (Fig. 17.8).

The glossopharyngeal nerve is the nerve for both general sensation and taste for the posterior one-third of the tongue including the circumvallate papillae.

The posteriormost part of the tongue is supplied by the vagus nerve through the internal laryngeal branch (Table 17.3).

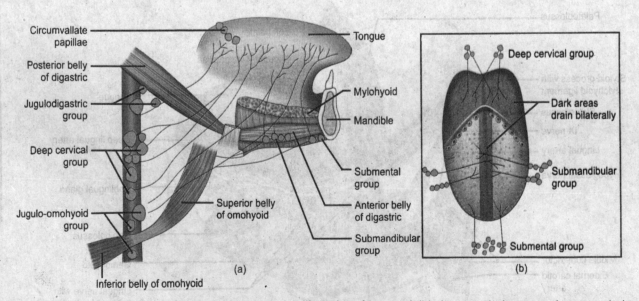

Labels (a): Circumvallate papillae; Posterior belly of digastric; Jugulodigastric group; Deep cervical group; Jugulo-omohyoid group; Inferior belly of omohyoid; Superior belly of omohyoid; Tongue; Mylohyoid; Mandible; Submental group; Anterior belly of digastric; Submandibular group

Labels (b): Deep cervical group; Dark areas drain bilaterally; Submandibular group; Submental group

Figs 17.7a and b: Lymphatic drainage of tongue: (a) Lateral surface, and (b) dorsum, dark areas of tongue drain bilaterally

Table 17.3: Comparison of the parts of the tongue

	Anterior two-thirds	Posterior one-third	Posteriormost part and vallecula
Situation	Lies in mouth cavity	Oropharynx	Oropharynx
Structure	Contains papillae	Contains lymphoid tissue	—
Function	Chewing	Deglutition	Deglutition
Sensory nerve	Lingual (post-trematic branch of 1st arch)	Glossopharyngeal nerve of 3rd arch	Internal laryngeal branch of vagus (nerve of 4th arch)
Sensation of taste	Chorda tympani except circum-vallate papillae (pre-trematic branch of 1st arch)	Glossopharyngeal including the vallate papillae	Internal laryngeal branch of vagus
Development of epithelium from endoderm	Lingual swellings of 1st arch. Tuberculum impar which soon disappears	Third arch which forms large ventral part of hypobranchial eminence	Fourth arch which forms small dorsal part of hypobranchial eminence

Muscles develop from occipital myotomes, so the cranial nerve XII (hypoglossal nerve) supplies all intrinsic and three extrinsic muscles. Only palatoglossus is supplied by cranial root of accessory through pharyngeal plexus and is developed from mesoderm of sixth arch

- Carcinoma of the tongue is quite common. The affected side of the tongue is removed surgically. All the deep cervical lymph nodes are also removed, i.e. block dissection of neck because recurrence of malignant disease occurs in lymph nodes. Carcinoma of the posterior one-third of the tongue is more dangerous due to bilateral lymphatic spread.
- Sorbitrate is taken sublingually for immediate relief from angina pectoris. It is absorbed fast because of rich blood supply of the tongue and bypassing of portal circulation.
- Genioglossus is called the 'safety muscle of the tongue' because if it is paralysed, the tongue will fall back on the oropharynx and block the air passage. During anaesthesia, the tongue is pulled forwards to clear the air passage.
- Genioglossus is the only muscle of the tongue which protrudes it forwards. It is used for testing the integrity of hypoglossal nerve. If hypoglossal nerve of right side is paralysed, the tongue on protrusion will deviate to the right side. Normal left genioglossus will pull the base to left side and apex will get pushed to right side (apex and base lie at opposite ends) (Figs 17.9, 17.10a and b).

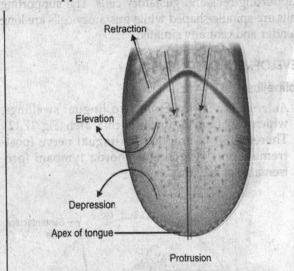

Fig. 17.9: Actions of extrinsic muscles of the tongue

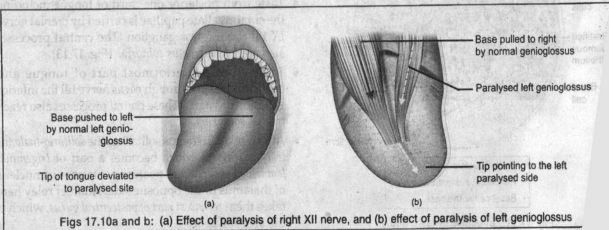

Figs 17.10a and b: (a) Effect of paralysis of right XII nerve, and (b) effect of paralysis of left genioglossus

HISTOLOGY

1. The bulk of the tongue is made up of striated muscles.
2. The *mucous membrane* consists of a layer of connective tissue (corium), lined by stratified squamous epithelium. On the oral part of the dorsum, it is thin, forms papillae (Fig. 17.3), and is adherent to the muscles. On the pharyngeal part of the dorsum, it is very rich in lymphoid follicles. On the inferior surface, it is thin and smooth. Numerous glands, both mucous and serous lie deep to the mucous membrane.
3. *Taste buds* are most numerous on the sides of the circumvallate papillae, and on the walls of the surrounding sulci. Taste buds are numerous over the foliate papillae and over the posterior one-third of the tongue; and sparsely distributed on the fungiform papillae, the soft palate, the epiglottis and the pharynx. There are no taste buds on the mid-dorsal region of the oral part of the tongue (Fig. 17.11).

Structure

There are two types of cells, the sustentacular or supporting cells and gustatory cells. The supporting cells are spindle-shaped while gustatory cells are long, slender and centrally situated.

VELOPMENT OF TONGUE

thelium

nterior two-thirds: From two lingual swellings, hich arise from the first branchial arch (Fig. 17.12). erefore, it is supplied by lingual nerve (postnatic) of 1st arch and chorda tympani (preatic) of 2nd arch.

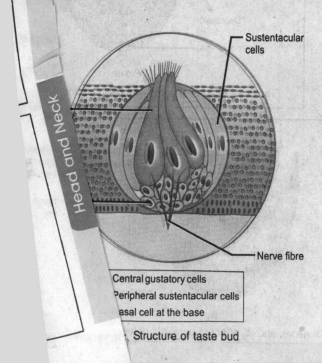

- Sustentacular cells
- Nerve fibre

Central gustatory cells
Peripheral sustentacular cells
asal cell at the base

, Structure of taste bud

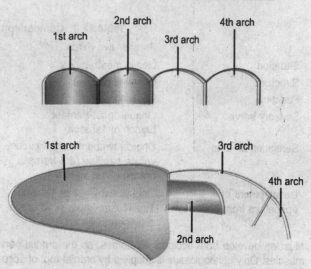

Fig. 17.12: Development of tongue

2. *Posterior one-third:* From cranial large part of the hypobranchial eminence, i.e. from the third arch. Therefore, it is supplied by the glossopharyngeal nerve (Table 17.3).
3. Posteriormost part from the fourth arch. This is supplied by the vagus nerve.

Muscles

The muscles develop from the occipital myotomes which are supplied by the hypoglossal nerve.

Connective Tissue

The connective tissue develops from the local mesenchyme.

TASTE PATHWAY

- The taste from anterior two-thirds of tongue except from vallate papillae is carried by *chorda tympani* branch of facial till the geniculate ganglion. The central processes go to the *tractus solitarius* in the medulla.
- Taste from posterior one-third of tongue including the circumvallate papillae is carried by cranial nerve IX till the inferior ganglion. The central processes also reach the *tractus solitarius* (Fig. 17.13).
- Taste from posteriormost part of tongue and epiglottis travels through *vagus* nerve till the inferior ganglion of vagus. These *central* processes also reach *tractus solitarius*.
- After a relay in tractus solitarius, the *solitario-thalamic tract* is formed which becomes a part of *trigeminal lemniscus* and reaches postero-ventromedial nucleus of thalamus of the opposite side. Another relay here takes them to *lowest part of postcentral gyrus*, which is the area for taste.

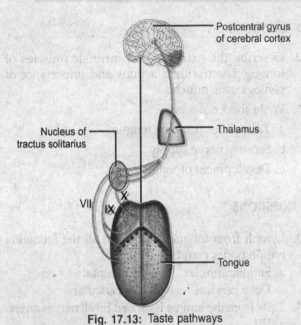

Fig. 17.13: Taste pathways

CLINICAL ANATOMY

- Injury to any part of the pathway causes abnormality in appreciation of taste.
- Referred pain is felt in the ear in diseases of posterior part of the tongue, as ninth and tenth nerves are common supply to both the regions. Other examples of referred pain are seen in Fig. 17.14.

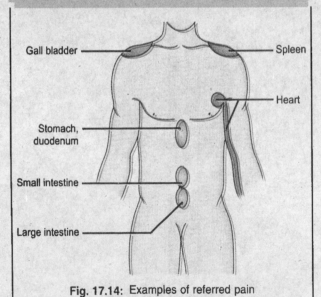

Fig. 17.14: Examples of referred pain

FACTS TO REMEMBER

- All 4 intrinsic muscles of tongue are supplied by XII nerve

- Out of 4 extrinsic muscles of tongue 3 are supplied by XII nerve. Only palatoglossus is supplied by vagoaccessory complex.
- Lingual artery is a tortuous artery as it moves up and down with movements of pharynx
- Tongue is kept in position by its attachment to neighbouring structures through the 4 pairs of extrinsic muscles
- Circumvallate papillae are only 10–12 in number, but have maximum number of taste buds. The taste from here is carried by IX nerve.
- Nerve supply correlates with development. Anterior two-thirds develop from 1st arch, the nerves being lingual and chorda tympani. Chorda tympani is pre-trematic branch of the 1st arch.
- Posterior one-third develops from cranial part of 3rd arch. So it is supplied by IX nerve.
- Posteriormost part develops from 4th arch. So it is supplied by internal laryngeal branch of X.
- Sorbitrate, the drug for prevention of angina is taken sublingually as it reaches the blood very fast, bypassing the portal circulation.
- Genioglossus is the life-saving muscle as it protrudes the tongue forwards.

CLINICOANATOMICAL PROBLEM

A patient is diagnosed as "medial medullary syndrome on right side

- What is the effect on tongue?
- Name the nuclear column to which XII nerve belongs?
- Name the muscles of tongue.

Ans: In medial medullary syndrome, XII nerve, pyramidal fibres and medial lemniscus are damaged due to blockage of anterior spinal artery

a. There is contralateral hemiplegia due to damage to pyramid of medulla oblongata
b. Loss of sense of vibration and position due to damage to medial lemniscus
c. Paralysis of muscles of tongue on the same side due to paralysis of XII nerve. The tip of tongue on protrusion will get protruded to the side of lesion XII nerve belongs to general somatic efferent column (GSE).

Muscles of tongue are intrinsic and extrinsic:

Intrinsic muscle	Extrinsic muscle
Superior longitudinal	Genioglossus
Inferior longitudinal	Hyoglossus
Transverse	Palatoglossus
Vertical	Styloglossus

FREQUENTLY ASKED QUESTIONS

1. Describe tongue under the following headings:
   a. Gross anatomy
   b. Dorsum of tongue
   c. Blood supply and nerve supply
   d. Lymphatic drainage
   e. Clinical anatomy

2. Describe the extrinsic and intrinsic muscles of tongue. Discuss their actions and importance of genioglossus muscle.

3. Write short notes on:
   a. Taste fibres from the tongue
   b. Sensory nerve supply
   c. Development of tongue

MULTIPLE CHOICE QUESTIONS

1. Epithelium of tongue develops from all the following arches *except:*
   a. 1st arch   b. 2nd arch
   c. 3rd arch   d. 4th arch

2. Muscles of tongue are mostly supplied by XII nerve *except:*
   a. Genioglossus
   b. Palatoglossus
   c. Hyoglossus
   d. Styloglossus

3. Lymph from tongue drains into all the following lymph nodes *except:*
   a. Submandibular   b. Submental
   c. Deep cervical   d. Preauricular

4. Taste from the tongue is carried by all nerves *except:*
   a. VII   b. IX
   c. X   d. XI

5. Sensory fibres from tongue is carried by all nerves *except:*
   a. V   b. VIII
   c. IX   d. X

ANSWERS

1. b   2. b   3. d   4. d   5. b

Head and Neck

18

Ear

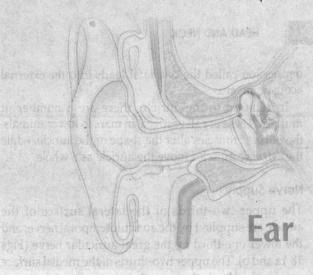

Nature is wonderful. A million years ago PHE didn't know we are going to wear spectacles, yet look at the way she placed our ears
"The ear is an engineering marvel."

INTRODUCTION

Tympanic membrane comprises all the three embryonic layers—outer layer is ectodermal, inner layer is endodermal while middle one is mesodermal in origin. The ossicles of the ear are the only bones fully formed at birth.

One hears with the ears. The centre for hearing is in the temporal lobe of brain above the ear. Reading aloud is a quicker way of memorising, as the ear, temporal lobes and motor speech area are also activated. The labyrinth is also supplied by an "end artery" like the retina.

Noise pollution within the four walls of the homes from the music albums and advertisements emitted from the television sets cause a lot of damage to the cochlear nerves and temporal lobes, besides causing irritation, hypertension and obesity.

The ear is an organ of hearing. It is also concerned in maintaining the equilibrium of the body. It consists of three parts: The external ear, the middle ear and the internal ear.

Features of the Temporal Bone

1 External auditory meatus is for air waves.
2 Internal auditory meatus is for passage of VII, VIII nerves and labyrinthine vessels.
3 Suprameatal triangle is the landmark for mastoid antrum. It is bounded by supramastoid crest, posterosuperior margin of external acoustic meatus and a tangent drawn from the crest to the margin. Mastoid antrum lies about 15 mm deep to the suprameatal triangle in adult (*see* Fig. 1.9b).
4 Tympanic canaliculus lies on the inferior surface of petrous temporal bone between carotid canal and jugular fossa.
5 Petrotympanic fissure gives passage to anterior tympanic artery, anterior ligament of malleus and chorda tympani nerve.

6 Stylomastoid foramen gives passage to posterior tympanic artery for middle ear and facial nerve.
7 Hiatus for greater petrosal nerve gives passage to nerve of the same name and a branch of middle meningeal artery.
8 Tegmen tympani on the anterior face of petrous temporal bone, forms roof of the middle ear, mastoid antrum and canal for tensor tympani muscle.
9 The aqueduct of vestibule opens on posterior aspect of petrous temporal bone. It is plugged by ductus endolymphaticus.
10 Organ of Corti is the end organ for hearing, situated in the cochlear duct.
11 Crista is an end organ in the semicircular canal. These are kinetic balance receptors.
12 Macula are end organs in the utricle and saccule and are static balance receptors.

EXTERNAL EAR

The external ear consists of:
- The auricle or pinna.
- The external acoustic meatus.

AURICLE/PINNA

The auricle is the part seen on the surface. The greater part of it is made up of a single crumpled plate of elastic cartilage which is lined on both sides by skin. It supports the spectacles. However, the lowest part of the auricle is soft and consists only of fibrofatty tissue covered by skin: This part is called the *lobule* for wearing the ear rings. The rest of the auricle is divided into a number of parts. These are helix, antihelix, concha, tragus, scaphoid fossa (*see* Fig. 20.2). In particular, note the large depression called the *concha*; it leads into the external acoustic meatus.

In relation to the auricle, there are a number of muscles. These are all vestigeal in man. In lower animals, the *intrinsic* muscles alter the shape of the auricle, while the *extrinsic* muscles move the auricle as a whole.

Nerve Supply

The upper two-thirds of the lateral surface of the auricle are supplied by the auriculotemporal nerve; and the lower one-third by the great auricular nerve (Figs 18.1a and b). The upper two-thirds of the medial surface are supplied by the lesser occipital nerve; and the lower one-third by the great auricular nerve. The root of the auricle is supplied by the auricular branch of the vagus (Figs 18.1a and b). The auricular muscles are supplied through branches of the facial nerve.

Blood Supply

The blood supply of the auricle is derived from the posterior auricular and superficial temporal arteries (Fig. 18.2). The *lymphatics* drain into the preauricular, and postauricular lymph nodes (Figs 18.1a and b).

EXTERNAL ACOUSTIC MEATUS

DISSECTION

Expose the external auditory meatus by cutting the tragus of the auricle. Put a probe into the external auditory meatus and remove the anterior wall of cartilaginous and bony parts of the external auditory meatus with the scissors. Be slow and careful not to damage the tympanic membrane.

Features

The external auditory meatus conducts sound waves from the concha to the tympanic membrane. The canal is S-shaped. Its outer part is directed medially, forwards and upwards. The middle part is directed medially, backwards and upwards. The inner part is directed medially, forwards and downwards. The meatus can be straightened for examination by pulling the auricle *upwards, backwards and slightly laterally.*

The meatus or canal is about 24 mm long, of which the medial two-thirds or 16 mm is bony, and the lateral one-third or 8 mm is cartilaginous. Due to the obliquity of the tympanic membrane, the anterior wall and floor are longer than the posterior wall and roof (Figs 18.3a and b).

The canal is oval in section. The greatest diameter is vertical at the lateral end, and anteroposterior at the medial end. The bony part is narrower than the cartilaginous part. The narrowest point, the *isthmus*, lies about 5 mm from the tympanic membrane.

The *bony part* is formed by the tympanic plate of the temporal bone which is C-shaped in cross-section. The posterosuperior part of the plate is deficient. Here the wall of the meatus is formed by a part of the squamous temporal bone. The meatus is lined by thin skin, firmly adherent to the periosteum.

The *cartilaginous part* is also C-shaped in section; and the gap of the 'C' is filled with fibrous tissue. The lining skin is adherent to the perichondrium, and contains hairs, sebaceous glands, and ceruminous or wax glands. *Ceruminous glands* are modified sweat glands.

Blood Supply

The outer part of the canal is supplied by the superficial temporal and posterior auricular arteries, and the inner part, by the deep auricular branch of the maxillary artery.

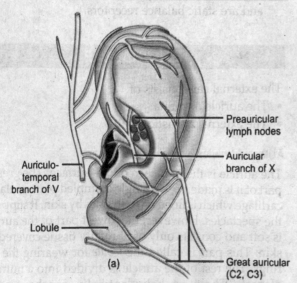

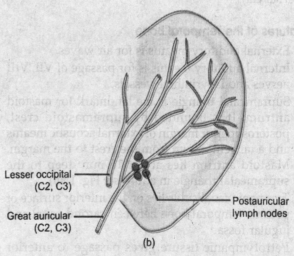

Figs 18.1a and b: Pinna of the ear: (a) Nerve supply and lymph nodes on the lateral surface, and (b) nerve supply on the medial surface

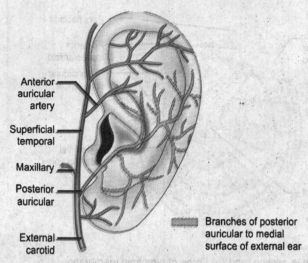

Fig. 18.2: Blood supply of the auricle

Lymphatics

The lymphatics pass to preauricular, postauricular and superficial cervical lymph nodes.

Nerve Supply

The skin lining the anterior half of the meatus is supplied by the auriculotemporal nerve, and that lining the posterior half, by the auricular branch of the vagus.

TYMPANIC MEMBRANE

This is a thin, translucent partition between the external acoustic meatus and the middle ear.

It is oval in shape, measuring 9 × 10 mm. It is placed obliquely at an angle of 55 degrees with the floor of the meatus. It faces downwards, forwards and laterally (Figs 18.4a and b).

The membrane has outer and inner surfaces.

The outer surface of the membrane is lined by thin skin. It is concave.

The inner surface provides attachment to the handle of the malleus which extends up to its centre. The inner surface is convex. The point of maximum convexity lies at the tip of the handle of the malleus and is called the *umbo*.

The membrane is thickened at its circumference which is fixed to the tympanic sulcus of the temporal bone on the tympanic plate. Superiorly, the sulcus is deficient. Here the membrane is attached to the tympanic notch. From the ends of the notch, two bands, the anterior and posterior malleolar folds, are prolonged to the lateral process of the malleus.

While the greater part of the tympanic membrane is tightly stretched, and is therefore, called the *pars tensa*, the part between the two malleolar folds is loose and is called the pars flaccida. The pars flaccida is crossed internally by the chorda tympani (Fig. 18.5). This part is more liable to rupture than the pars tensa.

The membrane is held tense by the inward pull of the tensor tympani muscle which is inserted into the upper end of the handle of the malleus.

Structure

The tympanic membrane is composed of the following three layers:

1 The *outer cuticular layer* of skin (Fig. 18.4a).
2 The *middle fibrous layer* made up of superficial radiating fibres and deep circular fibres. The circular fibres are minimal at the centre and maximal at the periphery (Fig. 18.4b). The fibrous layer is replaced by loose areolar tissue in the pars flaccida (Fig. 18.5).
3 The *inner mucous layer* (Fig. 18.4a) is lined by a low ciliated columnar epithelium.

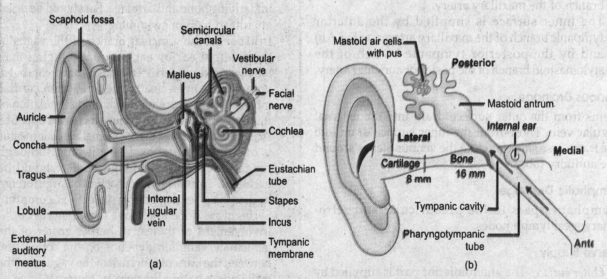

Figs 18.3a and b: (a) The normal ear, and (b) otitis media causing mastoid abscess

Head and Neck

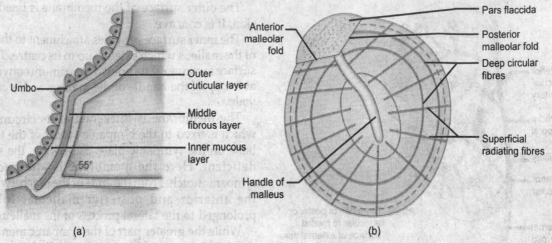

Figs 18.4a and b: (a) Tympanic membrane as seen in section, and (b) fibres of tympanic membrane

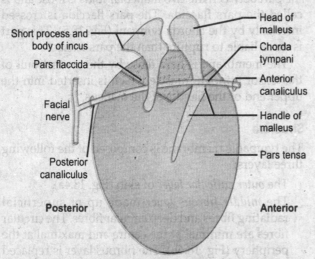

Fig. 18.5: Inner surface of the tympanic membrane

Blood Supply

1 The outer surface is supplied by the deep auricular branch of the maxillary artery.

2 The inner surface is supplied by the anterior tympanic branch of the maxillary artery (*see* Fig. 6.6) and by the posterior tympanic branch of the stylomastoid branch of the posterior auricular artery.

Venous Drainage

Veins from the outer surface drain into the external jugular vein. Those from the inner surface drain into the transverse sinus and into the venous plexus around the auditory tube.

Lymphatic Drainage

Lymphatics pass to the preauricular and retropharyngeal lymph nodes.

Nerve Supply

1 *Outer surface:* The anteroinferior part is supplied by the auriculotemporal nerve, and the posterosuperior part by the auricular branch of the vagus nerve with a communicating branch from facial nerve (Fig. 18.1).

2 *Inner surface:* This is supplied by the tympanic branch of the glossopharyngeal nerve through the tympanic plexus (Fig. 18.4a).

CLINICAL ANATOMY

• As already stated, for examination of the meatus and tympanic membrane, the auricle should be drawn upwards, backwards and slightly laterally. However, in infants, the auricle is drawn downwards and backwards because the canal is only cartilaginous and the outer surface of the tympanic membrane is directed mainly downwards (Fig. 18.6).

• Boils and other infections of the external auditory meatus cause a little swelling but are extremely painful, due to the fixity of the skin to the underlying bone and cartilage. Ear should be dried after head bath or swimming.

• Irritation of the auricular branch of the vagus in the external ear by ear wax or syringing may reflexly produce persistent cough called ear *cough*, vomiting or even death due to sudden cardiac inhibition. On the other hand, mild stimulation of this nerve may reflexly produce increased appetite.

• Accumulation of wax in the external acoustic meatus is often a source of excessive itching, although fungal infection and foreign bodies should be excluded. Troublesome impaction of large foreign bodies like seeds, grains, insects is common. Syringing is done to remove these (Fig. 18.7).

• Involvement of the ear in herpes zoster of the geniculate ganglion depends on the connection between the auricular branch of the vagus and the facial nerve within the petrous temporal bone.

- Small pieces of skin from the lobule of the pinna are commonly used for demonstration of lepra bacilli to confirm the diagnosis of leprosy.
- Pinna is used as grafting material.
- Hair on pinna in male represents Y-linked inheritance.
- A good number of ear traits follow mendelian inheritance.
- Infection of elastic cartilage may cause perichondritis.
- Bleeding within the auricle occurs between the perichondrium and auricular cartilage. If left untreated fibrosis occurs as haematoma compromises blood supply to cartilage. Fibrosis leads to "cauliflower ear". It is usually seen in wrestlers.
- Tympanic membrane is divided into an upper smaller sector, the pars flaccida bounded by anterior and posterior malleolar folds and a larger sector, the pars tensa. Behind pars flaccida lies the chorda tympani, so disease in pars flaccida should be treated carefully (Fig. 18.8).

- When the tympanic membrane is illuminated for examination, the concavity of the membrane produces a 'cone of light' over the *anteroinferior quadrant* which is the farthest or deepest quadrant with its apex at the umbo (Fig. 18.9). Through the membrane, one can see the underlying handle of the malleus and the long process of the incus.
- The membrane is sometimes incised to drain pus present in the middle ear. The procedure is called *myringotomy* (Fig. 18.9). The incision for myringotomy is usually made in the posteroinferior quadrant of the membrane where the bulge is most prominent. In giving an incision, it has to be remembered that the chorda tympani nerve runs downwards and forwards across the inner surface of the membrane, lateral to the long process of the incus, but medial to the neck of the malleus. If the nerve is injured taste from most of anterior two-thirds of tongue is not perceived. Also salivation from submandibular and sublingual glands gets affected.

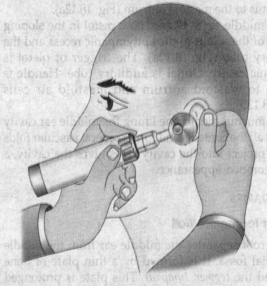

Fig. 18.6: Otoscopic examination

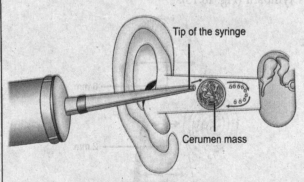

Fig. 18.7: Syringing of the ear

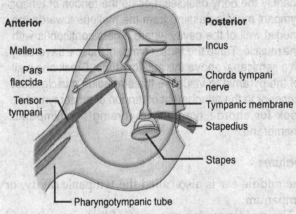

Fig. 18.8: Care to be taken in disease of pars flaccida

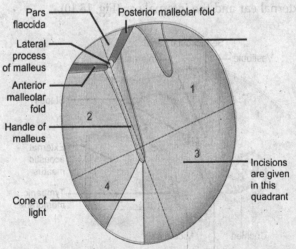

Fig. 18.9: The left tympanic membrane seen through the external acoustic meatus. (1) Posterosuperior quadrant, (2) anterosuperior quadrant, (3) posteroinferior quadrant, and (4) anteroinferior quadrant

Head and Neck

MIDDLE EAR

DISSECTION

Remove the dura mater and endosteum from the floor of the middle cranial fossa. Identify greater petrosal nerve emerging from a canaliculus on the anterior surface of petrous temporal bone. Trace it as it passes inferior to trigeminal ganglion to reach the carotid canal.

Carefully break the roof of the middle ear formed by tegmen tympani which is a thin plate of bone situated parallel and just lateral to the greater petrosal nerve. Cavity of the middle ear can be visualised. Try to put a probe in the anteromedial part of the cavity of middle ear till it appears at the opening in the lateral wall of nasopharynx. Identify the posterior wall of the middle ear which has an opening in its upper part. This is the aditus to mastoid antrum, which in turn, connects the cavity to the mastoid air cells.

Ear ossicles

Identify the bony ossicles. Locate the tendon of tensor tympani muscle passing from the malleus towards the medial wall of the cavity where it gets continuous with the muscle. Trace the tensor tympani muscle traversing in a semicanal above the auditory tube. Break one wall of the pyramid to visualise the stapedius muscle. Just superior to the attachment of tendon of tensor tympani, look for chorda tympani traversing the tympanic membrane.

Features

The middle ear is also called the tympanic cavity, or tympanum.

The middle ear is a narrow air filled space situated in the petrous part of the temporal bone between the external ear and the internal ear (Fig. 18.10).

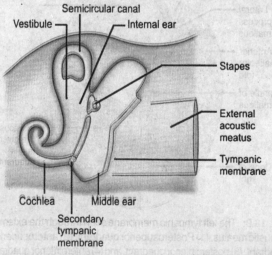

Fig. 18.10: Scheme to show the three parts of the ear

Shape and Size

The middle ear is shaped like a cube. Its lateral and medial walls are large, but the other walls are narrow, because the cube is compressed from side to side. Its vertical and anteroposterior diameters are both about 15 mm. When seen in coronal section the cavity of the middle ear is biconcave, as the medial and lateral walls are closest to each other in the centre. The distances separating them are 6 mm near the roof, 2 mm in the centre, and 4 mm near the floor (Fig. 18.11).

Parts

The cavity of the middle ear can be subdivided into the tympanic cavity proper which is opposite the tympanic membrane; and the epitympanic recess which lies above the level of the tympanic membrane.

Communications

The middle ear communicates anteriorly with the nasopharynx through the auditory tube, and posteriorly with the mastoid antrum and mastoid air cells through the aditus to the mastoid antrum (Fig. 18.12a).

The middle ear is likened to a pistol in the sloping course of the aditus to the epitympanic recess and the auditory tube (Fig. 18.12a). The trigger of pistol is tympanic cavity. Outlet is auditory tube. Handle is aditus to mastoid antrum and mastoid air cells (Fig. 18.12b).

The mucous membrane lining the middle ear cavity invests all the contents and forms several vascular folds which project into the cavity. This gives the cavity, a honeycombed appearance.

BOUNDARIES

Roof or Tegmental Wall

1. The roof separates the middle ear from the middle cranial fossa. It is formed by a thin plate of bone called the *tegmen tympani*. This plate is prolonged backwards as the roof of the canal for the tensor tympani (Fig. 18.13).

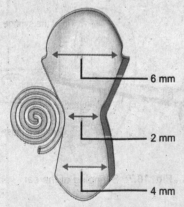

Fig. 18.11: Measurements

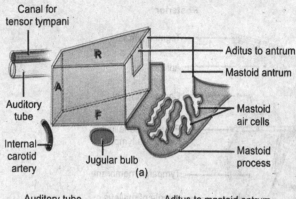

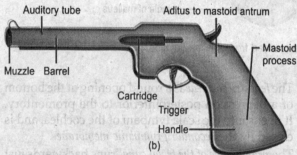

Figs 18.12a and b: (a) Scheme to show some relationships of the middle ear cavity, and (b) note that the cavity resembles a pistol

2 In young children, the roof presents a gap at the unossified petrosquamous suture where the middle ear is in direct contact with the meninges. In adults, the suture is ossified and transmits a vein from the middle ear to the superior petrosal sinus.

Floor or Jugular Wall

The floor is formed by a thin plate of bone which separates the middle ear from the superior bulb of the internal jugular vein. This plate is a part of the temporal bone (Fig. 18.13).

Near the medial wall, the floor presents the tympanic canaliculus which transmits the tympanic branch of the glossopharyngeal nerve to the medial wall of the middle ear.

Anterior or Carotid Wall

The anterior wall is narrow due to the approximation of the medial and lateral walls, and because of descent of the roof.

The uppermost part of the anterior wall bears the opening of the canal for the tensor tympani.

The middle part has the opening of the auditory tube.

The inferior part of the wall is formed by a thin plate of bone which forms the posterior wall of the carotid canal. The plate separates the middle ear from the internal carotid artery. This plate of bone is perforated by the superior and inferior sympathetic caroticotympanic nerves and the tympanic branch of the internal carotid artery (Fig. 18.14).

The bony septum between the canals for the tensor tympani and for the auditory tube is continued posteriorly on the medial wall as a curved lamina called the *processes cochleariformis*. Its posterior end forms a pulley around which the tendon of the tensor tympani turns laterally to reach the upper part of the handle of the malleus.

Posterior or Mastoid Wall

The posterior wall presents these features from above downwards.

1 Superiorly, there is an opening or *aditus* through which the epitympanic recess communicates with the mastoid or tympanic antrum (Figs 18.12a and 18.13).

2 The *fossa incudis* is a depression which lodges the short process of the incus.

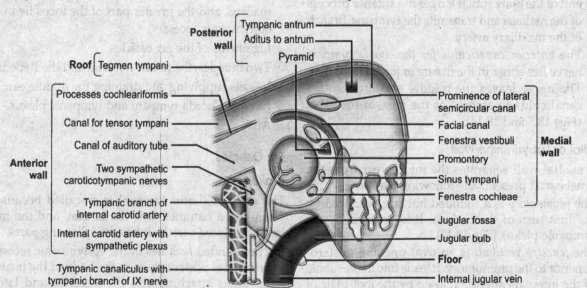

Fig. 18.13: Scheme to show the landmarks on the medial wall of the middle ear. Some related structures are also shown

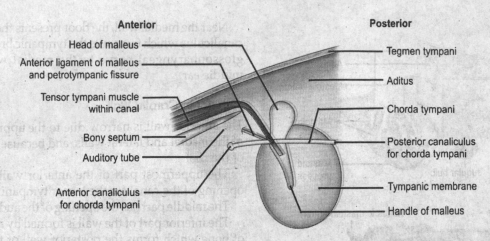

Anterior | Posterior

Head of malleus
Anterior ligament of malleus and petrotympanic fissure
Tensor tympani muscle within canal
Bony septum
Auditory tube
Anterior canaliculus for chorda tympani

Tegmen tympani
Aditus
Chorda tympani
Posterior canaliculus for chorda tympani
Tympanic membrane
Handle of malleus

Fig. 18.14: Lateral wall of the middle ear viewed from the medial side

3 A conical projection, called the *pyramid*, lies near the junction of the posterior and medial walls. It has an opening at its apex for passage of the tendon of the stapedius muscle.

4 Lateral to pyramid and near the posterior edge of the tympanic membrane, is the *posterior canaliculus for the chorda tympani* through which the nerve enters the middle ear cavity (Fig. 18.14).

Lateral or Membranous Wall

1 The lateral wall separates the middle ear from the external acoustic meatus. It is formed:
   a. Mainly by the tympanic membrane along with the tympanic ring and sulcus.
   b. Partly by the squamous temporal bone, in the region of the epitympanic recess (Figs 18.13 and 18.5).

2 Near the tympanic notch, there are two small apertures.
   a. The *petrotympanic fissure* lies in front of the upper end of the bony rim. It lodges the anterior process of the malleus and transmits the tympanic branch of the maxillary artery.
   b. The *anterior canaliculus for the chorda tympani* nerve lies either in the fissure or just in front of it. The nerve leaves the middle ear through this canaliculus to emerge at the base of the skull (Figs 18.5 and 18.14).

Medial or Labyrinthine Wall

The medial wall separates the middle ear from the internal ear. It presents the following features.

1 The *promontory* is a rounded bulging produced by the first turn of the cochlea. It is grooved by the tympanic plexus (Fig. 18.13).

2 The *fenestra vestibuli* is an oval opening postero-superior to the promontory. It leads into the vestibule of the internal ear and is closed by the foot-plate of the stapes.

3 The *fenestra cochleae* is a round opening at the bottom of a depression posteroinferior to the promontory. It opens into the scala tympani of the cochlea, and is closed by the *secondary tympanic membrane*.

4 The *prominence of the facial canal* runs backwards just above the fenestra vestibuli, to reach the lower margin of the aditus. The canal then descends behind the posterior wall to end at the stylomastoid foramen.

5 Prominence of lateral semicircular canal above the facial canal.

6 The *sinus tympani* is a depression behind the promontory, opposite the ampulla of the posterior semicircular canal.

CONTENTS

The middle ear contains the following.

1 Three small bones or ossicles, namely the malleus, the incus and the stapes. The upper half of the malleus, and the greater part of the incus lie in the epitympanic recess.

2 Ligaments of the ear ossicles.

3 Two muscles, the tensor tympani and the stapedius.

4 Vessels supplying and draining the middle ear.

5 Nerves: Chorda tympani and tympanic plexus.

6 Air.

Ear Ossicles

Malleus

The malleus (Latin *hammer*) is so-called because it resembles a hammer. It is the largest, and the most laterally placed ossicle. It has the following parts:

1 The rounded *head* lies in the epitympanic recess. It articulates posteriorly with the body of the incus. It provides attachment to the superior and lateral ligaments (Fig. 18.5).

2 The *neck* lies against the pars flaccida and is related medially to the chorda tympani nerve (Fig. 18.14).

3 The *anterior process* is connected to the petrotympanic fissure by the anterior ligament.

4 The *lateral process* projects from the upper end of the handle and provides attachment to the malleolar folds.

5 The *handle* extends downwards, backwards and medially, and is attached to the upper half of the tympanic membrane (Figs 18.4b and 18.14).

Incus or Anvil

It is so-called because it resembles an anvil, used by blacksmiths. It resembles a molar tooth and has the following parts:

1 The *body* is large and bears an articular surface that is directed forwards. It articulates with the head of the malleus.

2 The *long process* projects downwards just behind and parallel with the handle of the malleus. Its tip bears a lentiform nodule directed medially which articulates with the head of the stapes (Figs 18.9 and 18.15).

Stapes

This bone is so-called because it is shaped like a stirrup. It is the smallest, and the most medially placed ossicle of the ear (Fig. 18.15).

It has the following parts:

a. The small *head* has a concave facet which articulates with the lentiform nodule of the incus.

b. The narrow *neck* provides insertion, posteriorly, to the thin tendon of the stapedius.

c. *Two limbs* or crura; anterior, the shorter and less curved; and posterior, the longer which diverge from the neck and are attached to the footplate.

d. The *footplate*, a *footpiece* or *base*, is oval in shape, and fits into the fenestra vestibuli.

Joints of the Ossicles

1 The *incudomalleolar joint* is a saddle joint.

2 The *incudostapedial joint* is a ball and socket joint. Both of them are synovial joints. They are surrounded by

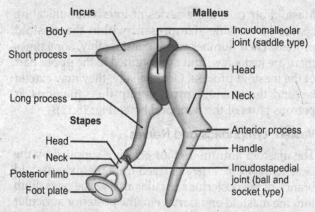

Fig. 18.15: Ossicles of the left ear, seen from the medial side

capsular ligaments. Accessory ligaments are three for the malleus, and one each for the incus and the stapes which stabilize the ossicles. All ligaments are extremely elastic (Fig. 18.15).

Muscles of the Middle Ear

There are two muscles, the tensor tympani and the stapedius. Both act simultaneously to damp down the intensity of high-pitched sound waves and thus protect the internal ear (Fig. 18.8).

The *tensor tympani* lies in a bony canal that opens at its lateral end on the anterior wall of the middle ear, and at the medial end on the base of the skull. The auditory tube lies just below this canal.

The muscle arises from the walls of the canal in which it lies. Some fibres arise from the cartilaginous part of the auditory tube and some from the base of the skull.

The muscle ends in a tendon which reaches the medial wall of the middle ear and bends sharply around the processus cochleariformis. It then passes laterally across the tympanic cavity to be inserted into the handle of the malleus.

The tensor tympani is supplied by the *mandibular nerve*. The fibres pass through the nerve to the medial pterygoid, and through the otic ganglion, without any relay. It develops from the *mesoderm of first branchial arch*.

The *stapedius* lies in a bony canal that is related to the posterior wall of the middle ear. Posteriorly, and below, this canal is continuous with the vertical part of the canal for the facial nerve. Anteriorly, the canal opens on the summit of the pyramid.

The muscle arises from the walls of this canal. Its tendon emerges through the pyramid and passes forwards to be inserted into the posterior surface of the neck of the stapes.

The stapedius is supplied by the *facial nerve*. It develops from the *mesoderm of the second branchial arch*.

Arterial Supply

The main arteries of the middle ear are as follows.

1 The anterior tympanic branch of the maxillary artery which enters the middle ear through the petrotympanic fissure.

2 The posterior tympanic branch of the stylomastoid branch of the posterior auricular artery which enters through the stylomastoid foramen.

3 Petrosal and superior tympanic branches of middle meningeal artery.

4 Branches of ascending pharyngeal artery.

5 Tympanic branches of internal carotid artery.

Venous Drainage

Veins from the middle ear drain into the superior petrosal sinus and the pterygoid plexus of the veins.

Lymphatic Drainage

Lymphatics pass to the preauricular and retro-pharyngeal lymph nodes.

Nerve Supply

The nerve supply is derived from the tympanic plexus which lies over the promontory. The plexus is formed by the following.

1 The tympanic branch of the glossopharyngeal nerve. Its fibres are distributed to the mucous membrane of the middle ear, the auditory tube, the mastoid antrum and air cells. It also gives off the lesser petrosal nerve.
2 The superior and inferior caroticotympanic nerves arise from the sympathetic plexus around the internal carotid artery. These fibres are vasomotor to the mucous membrane.

FUNCTIONS OF THE MIDDLE EAR

1 It transmits sound waves from the external ear to the internal ear through the chain of ear ossicles, and thus transforms the air-borne vibrations from the tympanic membrane to liquid-borne vibrations in the internal ear.
2 The intensity of the sound waves is increased ten times by the ossicles. It may be noted that the frequency of sound does not change.

TYMPANIC OR MASTOID ANTRUM

DISSECTION

Clean the mastoid temporal bone off all the muscles and identify suprameatal triangle and supramastoid crest. Use a fine chisel to remove the bone of the triangle till the mastoid antrum is reached. Examine the extent of mastoid air cells.

Remove the posterior and superior walls of external auditory meatus till the level of the roof of mastoid antrum. Identify the chorda tympani nerve at the posterosuperior margin of tympanic membrane.

Look for arcuate eminence on the anterior face of petrous temporal bone. Identify internal acoustic meatus on the posterior face of petrous temporal bone, with the nerves in it. Try to break off the superior part of petrous temporal bone above the internal acoustic meatus. Identify the facial nerve as it passes towards the aditus. Identify the sharp bend of the facial nerve with the geniculate ganglion.

Identify the facial nerve turning posteriorly into the medial wall. Trace it above the fenestra vestibuli till it turns inferiorly in the medial wall of aditus.

Identify facial nerve at the stylomastoid foramen. Try to break the bone vertically along the lateral edge of the foramen to expose the whole of facial nerve canal. Facial nerve is described in detail in Chapter 4, Voulme 4. Learn it from there.

Break off more of the superior surface of the petrous temporal bone. Remove the bone gently. Examine the holes in the bone produced by semicircular canals and look for the semicircular ducts lying within these canals. Note the branches of vestibulocochlear nerve entering the bone at the lateral end of the meatus. Study the internal ear from the models in the museum.

Features

Mastoid antrum is a small, circular, air filled space situated in the posterior part of the petrous temporal bone. It is of adult size at birth, size of a small pea, or 1 cm in diameter and has a capacity of about one milliliter (Fig. 18.13).

BOUNDARIES

1 *Superiorly:* Tegmen tympani, and beyond it the temporal lobe of the cerebrum.
2 *Inferiorly:* Mastoid process containing the mastoid air cells.
3 *Anteriorly:* It communicates with the epitympanic recess through the aditus. The aditus is related medially to the ampullae of the superior and lateral semicircular canals, and posterosuperiorly to the facial canal.
4 *Posteriorly:* It is separated by a thin plate of bone from the sigmoid sinus. Beyond the sinus there is the cerebellum.
5 *Medially:* Petrous temporal bone.
6 *Laterally:* It is bounded by part of the squamous temporal bone. This part corresponds to the *suprameatal triangle* seen on the surface of the bone. This wall is 2 mm thick at birth, but increases in thickness at the rate of about 1 mm per year up to a maximum of about 12 to 15 mm.

MASTOID AIR CELLS

Mastoid air cells are a series of intercommunicating spaces of variable size present within the mastoid process. Their number varies considerably. Sometimes there are just a few, and are confined to the upper part of the mastoid process. Occasionally, they may extend beyond the mastoid process into the squamous or petrous parts of the temporal bone (Fig. 18.12).

Vessels, Lymphatics and Nerves

The mastoid antrum and air cells are supplied by the *posterior tympanic artery* derived from the stylomastoid branch of the posterior auricular artery. The *veins* drain into the mastoid emissary vein, the posterior auricular vein and the sigmoid sinus.

Lymphatics pass to the postauricular and upper deep cervical lymph nodes.

Nerves are derived from the tympanic plexus formed by the glossopharyngeal nerve and from the meningeal branch of the mandibular nerve.

CLINICAL ANATOMY

- Fracture of the middle cranial fossa breaks the roof of the middle ear, rupture the tympanic membrane, and thus cause bleeding through the ear along with discharge of CSF.
- Throat infections commonly spread to the middle ear through the auditory tube and cause otitis media. The pus from the middle ear may take one of the following courses:
  a. It may be discharged into the external ear following rupture of the tympanic membrane.
  b. It may erode the roof and spread upwards, causing meningitis and brain abscess.
  c. It may erode the floor and spread downwards, causing thrombosis of the sigmoid sinus and the internal jugular vein (Fig. 18.16).
  d. It may spread backwards, causing mastoid abscess (Fig. 18.3).
  Chronic otitis media and mastoid abscess are responsible for persistent discharge of pus through the ear. Otitis media is more common in children than in adults.
- Inflammation of the auditory tube (eustachian catarrh) is often secondary to an attack of common cold. This causes pain in the ear which is aggravated by swallowing, due to blockage of the tube. Pain is relieved by installation of decongestant drops in the nose which helps to open the ostium.
- *Otosclerosis:* Sometimes bony fusion takes place between the foot plate of the stapes and the margins of the fenestra vestibuli. This leads to deafness. The condition may be surgically corrected by putting a prosthesis (Figs 18.17a and b).
- Mastoid abscess is secondary to otitis media. It is difficult to treat. A proper drainage of pus from the mastoid requires an operation through the supra-meatal triangle. The facial nerve should not be injured during this operation (Fig. 18.18).
- Infection from the mastoid antrum and air cells can spread to any of the structures related to them including the temporal lobe of the cerebrum, the cerebellum, and the sigmoid sinus.
- The ear on infected side is displaced laterally and can be appreciated from the back.
- *Hyperacusis:* Due to paralysis of stapedius muscle, movements of stapes are dampened; so sounds get distorted and get too high in volume. This is called hyperacusis.

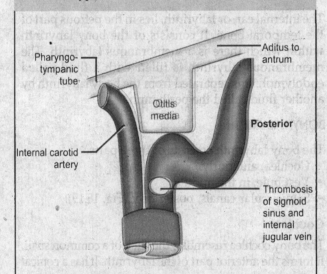

Fig. 18.16: Otitis media causing thrombosis of the sigmoid sinus and the internal jugular vein

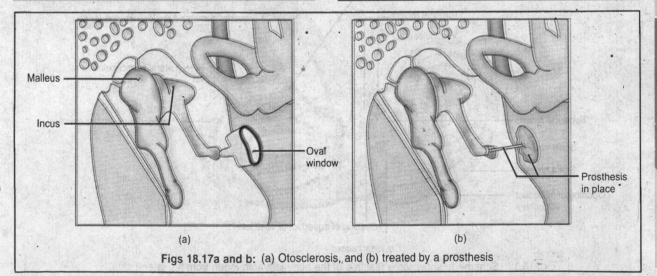

Figs 18.17a and b: (a) Otosclerosis, and (b) treated by a prosthesis

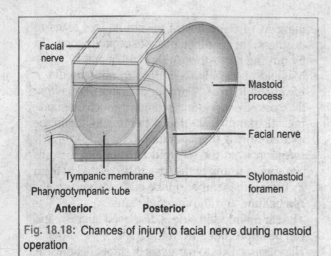

Fig. 18.18: Chances of injury to facial nerve during mastoid operation

INTERNAL EAR

The internal ear, or labyrinth, lies in the petrous part of the temporal bone. It consists of the bony labyrinth within which there is a membranous labyrinth. The membranous labyrinth is filled with a fluid called endolymph. It is separated from the bony labyrinth by another fluid called the perilymph.

BONY LABYRINTH

The bony labyrinth consists of three parts:
- Cochlea, anteriorly.
- Vestibule, in the middle.
- Semicircular canals, posteriorly (Fig. 18.19).

Cochlea

The bony cochlea resembles the shell of a common snail. It forms the anterior part of the labyrinth. It has a conical central axis known as the *modiolus* around which the cochlear canal makes two and three quarter turns.

The modiolus is directed forwards and laterally. Its apex points towards the anterosuperior part of the medial wall of the middle ear and the base towards the fundus of the internal acoustic meatus.

A spiral ridge of the bone, the *spiral lamina*, projects from the modiolus and partially divides the cochlear canal into the scala vestibuli above, and the scala tympani below. These relationships apply to the lowest part or basal turn of the cochlea. The division between the two passages is completed by the basilar membrane. The scala vestibuli communicates with the scala tympani at the apex of the cochlea by a small opening, called the *helicotrema*.

Vestibule

This is the central part of the bony labyrinth. It lies medial to the middle ear cavity. Its lateral wall opens into the middle ear at the fenestra vestibuli which is closed by the footplate of the stapes.

Three semicircular canals open into its posterior wall. The medial wall is related to the internal acoustic meatus, and presents the *spherical recess* in front, and the *elliptical recess* behind. The two recesses are separated by a *vestibular crest* which splits inferiorly to enclose the *cochlear recess* (Fig. 18.19).

Just below the elliptical recess, there is the opening of a diverticulum, the aqueduct of the vestibule which opens at a narrow fissure on the posterior aspect of the petrous temporal bone, posterolateral to the internal acoustic meatus. It is plugged in life by the ductus endolymphaticus and a vein; no perilymph escapes through it.

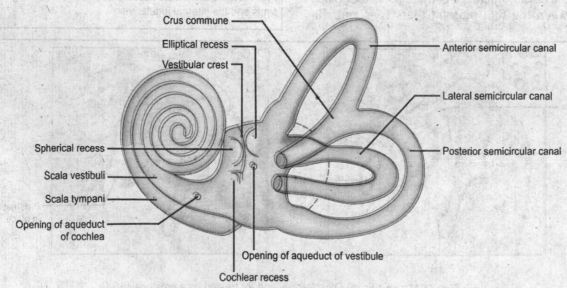

Fig. 18.19: Scheme to show some features of the bony labyrinth (seen from the lateral side)

Semicircular Canals

There are three bony semicircular canals: (1) An anterior or superior, (2) posterior, and (3) lateral; each has two ends. They lie posterosuperior to the vestibule, and are set at right angles to each other. Each canal describes two-thirds of a circle, and is dilated at one end to form the *ampulla. These three* canals open into the vestibule by *five* openings.

The *anterior or superior semicircular canal* lies in a vertical plane at right angles to the long axis of the petrous temporal bone. It is convex upwards. Its position is indicated by the arcuate eminence seen on the anterior surface of the petrous temporal bone. Its ampulla is situated anterolaterally. Its posterior end unites with the upper end of the posterior canal to form the *crus commune* which opens into the medial wall of the vestibule.

The *posterior semicircular canal* also lies in a vertical plane parallel to the long axis of the petrous temporal bone. It is convex backwards. Its ampulla lies at its lower end. The upper end joins the anterior canal to form the crus commune.

The *lateral semicircular canal* lies in the horizontal plane with its convexity directed posterolaterally. The ampulla lies anteriorly, close to the ampulla of the anterior canal.

Note that the lateral semicircular canals of the two sides lie in the same plane. The anterior canal of one side lies in the plane of the posterior canal of the other side (Figs 18.19 and 18.20).

MEMBRANOUS LABYRINTH

It is in the form of a complicated, but continuous closed cavity filled with endolymph. The epithelium of the membranous labyrinth is specialized to form receptors for sound, i.e. organ of Corti; for static balance, the maculae; and for kinetic balance, the cristae.

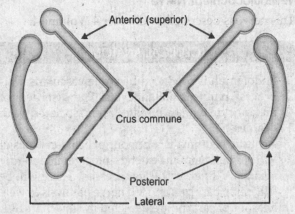

Fig. 18.20: The semicircular canals

Like the bony labyrinth, the membranous labyrinth also consists of three main parts:

a. The spiral duct of the cochlea or organ of Corti, anteriorly.
b. The utricle and saccule with maculae, the organs of static balance, within the vestibule.
c. The semicircular ducts with cristae, the organs of kinetic balance, posteriorly (Fig. 18.21).

Duct of the Cochlea or the Scala Media

The spiral duct occupies the middle part of the cochlear canal between the scala vestibuli and the scala tympani. It is triangular in cross-section. The floor is formed by the *basilar membrane;* the roof by the *vestibular* or *Reissner's membrane;* and the outer wall by the bony wall of the cochlea. The basilar membrane supports the spiral *organ of Corti* which is the end organ for hearing (Fig. 18.22). It comprises rods of Corti and hair cells. Hair is embedded in a gelatinous membrane called the membrana tectoria. The organ of Corti is innervated by peripheral processes of bipolar cells located in the *spiral ganglion.* This ganglion is located in the spiral canal present within the modiolus at the base of the spiral lamina. The central processes of the ganglion cells form the cochlear nerve.

Posteriorly, the duct of the cochlea is connected to the saccule by a narrow *ductus reunions.*

The sound waves reaching the endolymph through the vestibular membrane make appropriate parts of the basilar membrane vibrate, so that different parts of the organ of Corti are stimulated by different frequencies of sound. The loudness of the sound depends on the amplitude of vibration.

Saccule and Utricle

The *saccule* lies in the anteroinferior part of the vestibule, and is connected to the basal turn of the cochlear duct by the ductus reunions.

The *utricle* is larger than the saccule and lies in the posterosuperior part of the vestibule. It receives *the end of three* semicircular ducts through *five openings.* The duct of the saccule unites with the duct of the utricle to form the *ductus endolymphaticus.* The ductus endo-

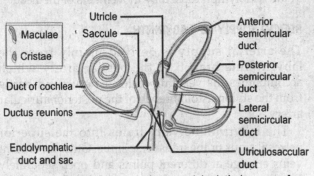

Fig. 18.21: Parts of the membranous labyrinth (as seen from the lateral side)

Head and Neck

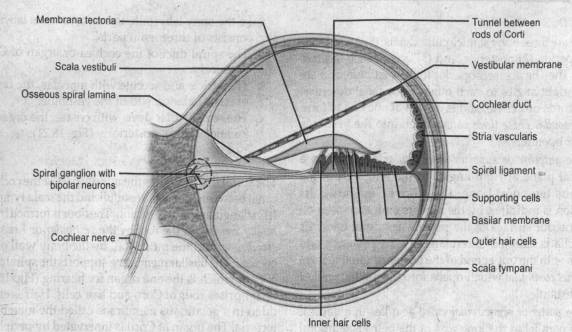

Fig. 18.22: Schematic section through one turn of the cochlea

lymphaticus ends in a dilatation, the saccus endolymphaticus. The ductus and saccus occupy the aqueduct of the vestibule.

The medial walls of the saccule and utricle are thickened to form a *macula* in each chamber. The maculae are end organs that give information about the position of the head. They are static balance receptors. They are supplied by peripheral processes of neurons in the vestibular ganglion (*see* Fig. 4.42, Volume 4).

Saccule gets stimulated by linear motions, e.g. going in "lift". Utricle gets stimulated by horizontal linear motion, e.g. going in car.

Semicircular Ducts

The three semicircular ducts lie within the corresponding bony canals. Each duct has an ampulla corresponding to that of the bony canal. In each ampulla, there is an end organ called the ampullary crest or *crista* or cupola (*see* Fig. 4.43, Volume 4). Cristae respond to pressure changes in the endolymph caused by movements of the head.

BLOOD SUPPLY OF LABYRINTH

The arterial supply is derived mainly from the labyrinthine branch of the basilar artery which accompanies the vestibulocochlear nerve; and partly from the stylomastoid branch of the posterior auricular artery.

The labyrinthine vein drains into the superior petrosal sinus or the transverse sinus. Other inconstant veins emerge at different points and open separately into the superior and inferior petrosal sinuses and the internal jugular vein.

DEVELOPMENT

1 *External auditory meatus:* Dorsal part of 1st ectodermal cleft.
2 *Auricle:* Tubercles appearing on 1st and 2nd branchial arches around the opening of external auditory meatus.
3 *Middle ear cavity and auditory tube:* Tubotympanic recess (*see* Tables A.6 and A.7 in Appendix).
4 *Ossicles*
   a. *Malleus and incus:* From *1st arch cartilage.*
   b. *Stapes:* From *2nd arch cartilage* (*see* Table A.5 in Appendix).
5 *Muscles*
   a. *Tensor tympani:* From *1st pharyngeal arch mesoderm.*
   b. *Stapedius:* From *2nd pharyngeal arch mesoderm.*
6 Membranous labyrinth from ectodermal vesicle on each side of hindbrain vesicle. Organ of Corti—ectodermal.

Vestibulocochlear Nerve

This nerve is described in Chapter 4, Volume 4.

CLINICAL ANATOMY

- Endolymph is produced by striae vascularis. This process requires melanocytes. The disorders of melanocytes, i.e. albinism, are associated with deafness.
- Acoustic neuroma is a tumour of Schwann cells of VIII nerve. If neuroma extends into internal auditory meatus, VII nerve will get pressed. There will be VIII nerve paralysis and VII nerve paralysis as well.
- Reasons of earache are depicted in Flowchart 18.1.

Flowchart 18.1: Reasons of earache

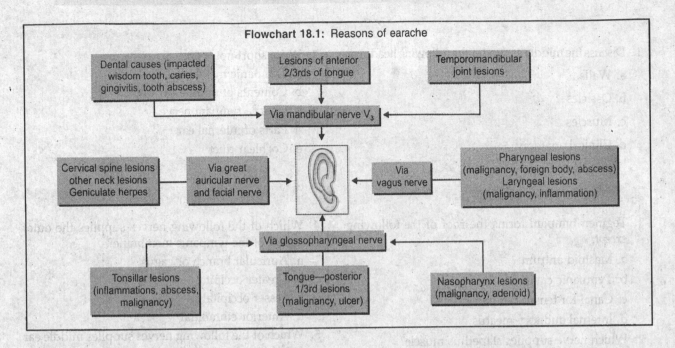

Mnemonics

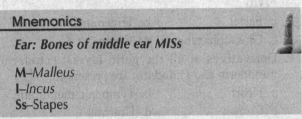

Ear: Bones of middle ear MISs

M–*Malleus*
I–*Incus*
Ss–*Stapes*

- There are 2 synovial joints between these three bony ossicles, which are fully developed at birth.
- Ear is an engineering marvel
- One may slowly become deaf to soft sounds, if one is continuously exposed to lot of loud sounds.

✍ FACTS TO REMEMBER

- Tympanic membrane develops from ectoderm, mesoderm and endoderm
- Outer aspect of tympanic membrane is supplied by part of V and X nerves
- Syringing the ear may cause slowing of the heart rate and feeling of nausea.
- Malleus and incus develop from 1st pharyngeal arch, while stapedius develops from second pharyngeal arch.
- Tensor tympani develops from 1st arch and is supplied by V3, while stapedius develops from 2nd arch and is supplied by VII nerve
- Suprameatal triangle (Macewen's triangle) demarcates the position of mastoid antrum at a depth of 12–13 mm in adult.
- Eustachian tube equalizes the pressure on both sides of the tympanic membrane. This tube connects the nasopharynx to the anterior wall of middle ear.
- Malleus, incus and stapes are *bone within bone*, as these 3 bony ossicles lie within the petrous temporal bone.

CLINICOANATOMICAL PROBLEM

A young boy has only deformity of the auricle/pinna. No treatment is done and he is fine in studies, games, etc.
- What are the uses of the auricle?
- Name its nerve supply.

Ans: There is hardly any medical use of the pinna in human. It is mainly cosmetic. However, there are other uses. These are:
- Lobule, the lowest part of auricle is used for wearing ear rings of different shape, size, colour and quality.
- It is used for supporting glasses. Nature knew million of years ago that human would need glasses, and the auricles were not removed.
- A small bit of skin is taken to examine lepra bacilli
- Hairy pinna is the only symptom of Y chromosome
- Pinna used to be pulled as a part of punishment for disobedience.

Nerve supply: Medial surface in its upper two-thirds part is supplied by lesser occipital and in its lower one-third part by great auricular. Lateral surface in its upper two-thirds part is supplied by auriculo-temporal nerve and in its lower one-third part by great auricular again.

1. Discuss the middle ear under the following headings.
   a. Walls
   b. Ossicles
   c. Muscles
   d. Clinical anatomy

2. Write short notes on:
   a. Tympanic membrane
   b. Contents of middle ear
   c. Chorda tympani nerve
   d. Parts of internal ear
   e. Cochlear duct

---

1. Tegmen tympani forms the roof of the following *except:*
   a. Mastoid antrum
   b. Tympanic cavity
   c. Canal for tensor tympani
   d. Internal auditory meatus

2. Which nerve supplies stapedius muscle?
   a. Oculomotor   b. Trochlear
   c. Trigeminal   d. Facial

3. By how many openings do the semicircular canals open in the vestibule?
   a. 3   b. 5
   c. 4   d. 2

4. Which of the following nerves supplies the outer aspect of the tympanic membrane?
   a. Auricular branch of vagus
   b. Greater occipital
   c. Lesser occipital
   d. Anterior ethmoidal

5. Which of the following nerves supplies middle ear cavity?
   a. Facial   b. Trigeminal
   c. Glossopharyngeal d. Vagus

6. Derivatives of all the germ layers; ectoderm, mesoderm and endoderm are present in:
   a. Heart   b. Tympanic membrane
   c. Cornea   d. Urachus

NOISE POLLUTION

"Noise pollution leads to mind body suffering
Plug the ears, decrease volume, seek policing

Sweet soft "lecture" induces happy sleeping
Loud prolonged noise causes auditory crippling

One should not even mind job changing
But do not, at any cost lose your hearing

Lest one's very dear cell phone
One would not be hearing"

Head and Neck

19

Eyeball

Our eyes are placed in front because it is more important to look ahead than look back

INTRODUCTION

Sense of sight perceived through retina of the eyeball is one of the five special senses. Its importance is obvious in the varied ways of natural protection. Bony orbit, projecting nose and various coats protect the precious retina. Each and every component of its three coats is assisting the retina to focus the light properly. Lots of advances have been made in correcting the defects of the eye. Eyes can be donated at the time of death, and a "will" can be prepared accordingly.

About 75% of afferents reach the brain through the eyes. Adequate rest to eye muscles is important. A good place for rest could be the "classroom" where palpebral part of orbicularis oculi closes the eyes gently. The eyeball is the organ of sight. The camera closely resembles the eyeball in its structure. It is almost spherical in shape and has a diameter of about 2.5 cm. It is made up of three concentric coats. The outer or *fibrous coat* comprises the sclera and cornea. The middle or *vascular coat* also called the uveal tract consists of choroid, the ciliary body and the iris. The inner or *nervous coat* is the retina (Fig. 19.1).

Light entering the eyeball passes through several *refracting media*. From before backwards these are the cornea, the aqueous humour, the lens and the vitreous body.

OUTER COAT

DISSECTION

Use the fresh eyeball of the goats for this dissection. Clean the eyeball by removing all the tissues from its surface. Cut through the fascial sheath around the margin of the cornea. Clean and identify the nerve with posterior ciliary arteries and ciliary nerves close to the posterior pole of the eyeball. Identify venae vorticosae piercing the sclera just behind the equator.

Incise only the sclera at the equator and then cut through it all around and carefully strip it off from the choroid. Anteriorly, the ciliary muscles are attached to the sclera, offering some resistance. As the sclera is steadily separated, the aqueous humour will escape from the anterior chamber of the eye. On dividing the optic nerve fibres, the posterior part of sclera can be removed.

SCLERA

The sclera (*skleros* = hard) is opaque and forms the posterior five-sixths of the eyeball. It is composed of dense fibrous tissue which is firm and maintains the shape of the eyeball. It is thickest behind, near the entrance of the optic nerve, and thinnest about 6 mm behind the sclerocorneal junction where the recti muscles are inserted. However, it is weakest at the entrance of the optic nerve. Here the sclera shows numerous perforations for passage of fibres of the optic nerve. Because of its sieve-like appearance, this region is called the *lamina cribrosa* (*crib* = sieve).

The *outer surface* of the sclera is white and smooth, it is covered by Tenon's capsule (*see* Fig. 13.3). Its anterior part is covered by conjunctiva through which it can be seen as the white of the eye. The *inner surface* is brown and grooved for the ciliary nerves and vessels. It is separated from the choroid by the *perichoroidal space* which contains a delicate cellular tissue, termed the *suprachoroidal lamina* or *lamina fusca of the sclera*.

The sclera is continuous anteriorly with the cornea at the *sclerocorneal junction or limbus* (Fig. 19.1). The deep part of the limbus contains a circular canal, known as the *sinus venosus sclerae or the canal of Schlemm*. The aqueous humour drains into the anterior scleral or ciliary veins through this sinus.

The sclera is fused posteriorly with the *dural sheath of the optic nerve*. It provides insertion to the extrinsic

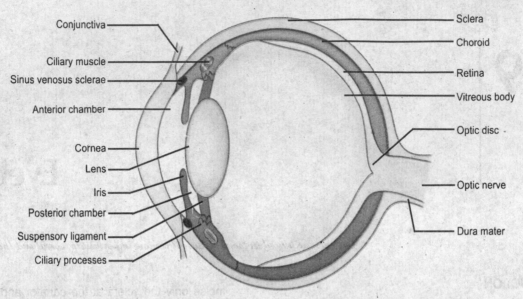

Fig. 19.1: Sagittal section through the eyeball

muscles of the eyeball: The recti in front of the equator, and the oblique muscles behind the equator.

The sclera is pierced by a number of structures:

a. The *optic nerve* pierces it a little inferomedial to the posterior pole of the eyeball.

b. The *ciliary nerves and arteries* pierce it around the entrance of the optic nerve.

c. The *anterior ciliary arteries* derived from muscular arteries to the recti pierce it near the limbus.

d. Four *venae vorticosae* or the choroid veins pass out through the sclera just behind the equator (Figs 19.2 and 19.3).

The sclera is almost avascular. However, the loose connective tissue between the conjunctiva and sclera called as the *episclera* is vascular.

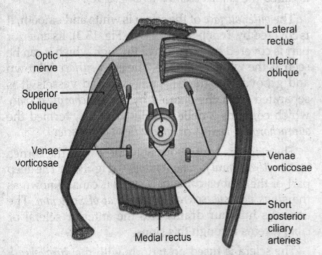

Fig. 19.2: Structures piercing the posterior aspect of the eyeball

CORNEA

DISSECTION

Identify the cornea. Make an incision around the corneoscleral junction and remove the cornea so that the iris is exposed for examination. Identify the middle coat comprising choroid, ciliary body and iris deep to the sclera. Lateral to iris is the ciliary body with ciliary muscles and ciliary processes.

Strip off the iris, ciliary processes, anterior part of choroid. Remove the lens and put it in water. As the lens is removed, the vitreous body also escapes. Only the posterior part of choroid and subjacent retina is left.

Features

The cornea is transparent. It replaces the sclera over the anterior one-sixth of the eyeball. Its junction with the sclera is called the *sclerocorneal junction or limbus.*

The cornea is more convex than the sclera, but the curvature diminishes with age. It is separated from the iris by a space called the *anterior chamber of the eye.*

The cornea is avascular and is nourished by lymph which circulates in the numerous corneal spaces and by the lacrimal fluid.

It is supplied by branches of the ophthalmic nerve (through the ciliary ganglion) and the short ciliary nerves. Pain is the only sensation aroused from the cornea.

Histology

Structurally, the cornea consists of these layers, from before backwards:

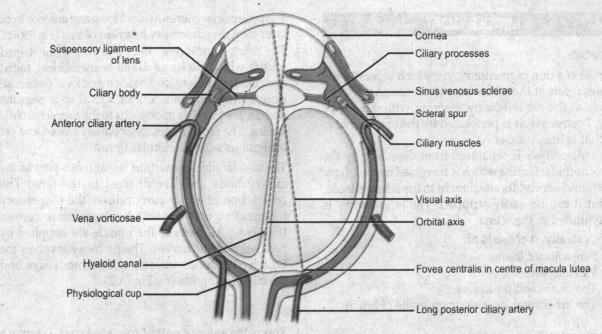

Fig. 19.3: Structures piercing the eyeball seen in a sagittal section

1 *Corneal epithelium* (stratified squamous non-keratinized type) (Fig. 19.4).
2 *Bowman's membrane* or anterior elastic lamina.
3 The *substantia propria*.
4 *Descemet's membrane* or posterior elastic lamina.
5 Simple squamous *mesothelium*.

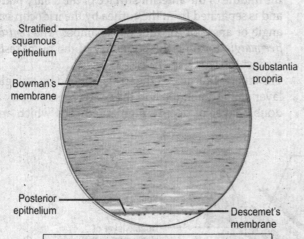

Fig. 19.4: Histology of cornea

- Stratified squamous epithelium
- Substantia propria is thick
- Descemet's membrane next to posterior epithelium

- Cornea can be grafted from one person to the other, as it is avascular.

- Injury to cornea may cause opacities. These opacities may interfere with vision.
- Eye is a very sensitive organ and even a dust particle gives rise to pain.
- Bulbar conjunctiva is vascular. Inflammation of the conjunctiva leads to conjunctivitis. The look of palpebral conjunctiva is used to judge haemoglobin level.
- The anteroposterior diameter of the eyeball and shape and curvature of the cornea determine the focal point. Changes in these result in myopia or short-sightedness, hypermetropia or long-sightedness (Fig. 19.5).

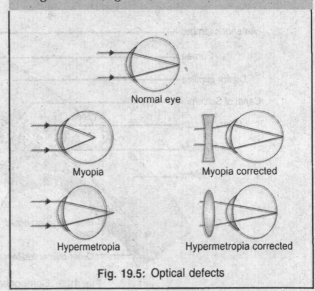

Fig. 19.5: Optical defects

MIDDLE COAT

CHOROID

Choroid is a thin pigmented layer which separates the posterior part of the sclera from the retina. Anteriorly, it ends at the *ora serrata* by merging with the ciliary body. Posteriorly, it is perforated by the optic nerve to which it is firmly attached.

Its *outer surface* is separated from the sclera by the suprachoroidal lamina which is traversed by the ciliary vessels and nerves. Its attachment to the sclera is loose, so that it can be easily stripped. The *inner surface* is firmly united to the retina.

Structurally, it consists of:
a. *Suprachoroid lamina.*
b. *Vascular lamina.*
c. The *choriocapillary lamina.*
d. The inner *basal lamina* or membrane of Bruch.

CILIARY BODY

Ciliary body is a thickened part of the uveal tract lying just posterior to the corneal limbus. It is continuous anteriorly with the iris and posteriorly with the choroid. It suspends the lens and helps it in accommodation for near vision.

1 The ciliary body is triangular in cross-section. It is thick in front and thin behind (Fig. 19.6). The scleral surface of this body contains the ciliary muscle. The posterior part of the vitreous surface is smooth and black (pars plana). The anterior part is ridged anteriorly (pars plicata) to form about 70 ciliary processes. The central ends of the processes are free and rounded.

2 Ciliary zonule is thickened vitreous membrane fitted to the posterior surfaces of ciliary processes (Fig. 19.7).

The posterior layer lines hyaloid fossa and anterior thick layer form the suspensory ligament of lens (Fig. 19.6).

3 The *ciliary muscle* (Fig. 19.6) is a ring of unstriped muscle which are longitudinal or meridional, radial and circular. The longitudinal or meridional *fibres* arise from a projection of sclera or scleral spur near the limbus. They radiate backwards to the suprachoroidal lamina. The radial fibres are obliquely placed and get continuous with the circular fibres.

The *circular fibres* lie within the anterior part of the ciliary body and are nearest to the lens. The contraction of *all the parts* relaxes the suspensory ligament so that the lens becomes more convex (Fig. 19.6). All parts of the muscle are supplied by parasympathetic nerves. The pathway involves the Edinger-Westphal nucleus, oculomotor nerve and the ciliary ganglion (*see* Fig. A.2).

IRIS

1 This is the anterior part of the uveal tract. It forms a circular curtain with an opening in the centre, called the *pupil*. By adjusting the size of the pupil, it controls the amount of light entering the eye, and thus behaves like an adjustable diaphragm (Fig. 19.3).

2 It is placed vertically between the cornea and the lens, thus divides the anterior segment of the eye into anterior and posterior chambers, *both containing aqueous humour.* Its *peripheral margin* is attached to the middle of the anterior surface of the ciliary body and is separated from the cornea by the iridocorneal angle or angle of the anterior chamber. The *central free margin* forming the boundary of the pupil rests against the lens (Fig. 19.1).

3 The anterior surface of the iris is covered by a single layer of mesothelium, and the posterior surface by a double layer of deeply pigmented cells which are

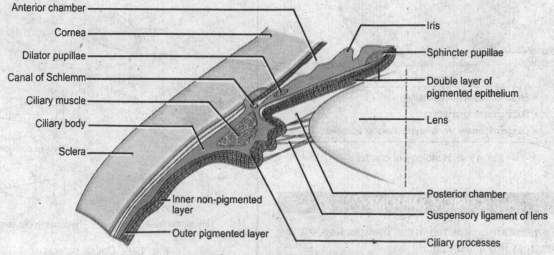

Fig. 19.6: Components of ciliary body and iris

Anterior chamber

Cornea

Dilator pupillae

Canal of Schlemm

Ciliary muscle

Ciliary body

Sclera

Inner non-pigmented layer

Outer pigmented layer

Iris

Sphincter pupillae

Double layer of pigmented epithelium

Lens

Posterior chamber

Suspensory ligament of lens

Ciliary processes

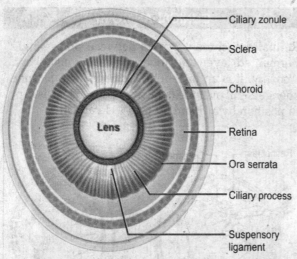

Fig. 19.7: Anterior part of the inner aspect of the eyeball seen after vitreous has been removed

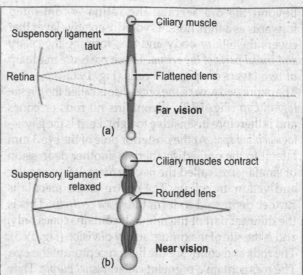

Figs 19.8a and b: (a) Relaxed ciliary muscles with flattened lens, and (b) contracted ciliary muscles with round lens

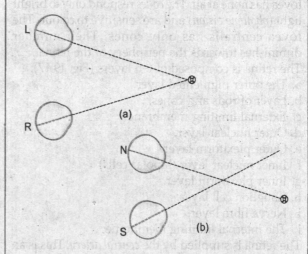

Figs 19.9a and b: (a) Normal eyes, and (b) in squinting eyes

continuous with those of the ciliary body (Fig. 19.6). The main bulk of the iris is formed by stroma made up of blood vessels and loose connective tissue in which there are pigment cells. The long posterior and the anterior ciliary arteries join to form the *major arterial circle* at the periphery of the iris. From this circle vessels converge towards the free margin of the iris and join together to form the *minor arterial circle* of the iris (*see* Fig. 13.10).

The colour of the iris is determined by the number of pigment cells in its connective tissue. If the pigment cells are absent, the iris is blue in colour due to the diffusion of light in front of the black posterior surface.

4 The iris contains a well-developed ring of muscle called the *sphincter pupillae* which lies near the margin of the pupil. Its nerve supply (parasympathetic) is similar to that of the ciliary muscle. The *dilator pupillae* is an ill-defined sheet of radial muscle fibres placed near the posterior surface of the iris. It is supplied by sympathetic nerves (Fig. 19.6).

CLINICAL ANATOMY

• While looking at infinite far the light rays run parallel; ciliary muscle is relaxed, suspensory ligament is tense and lens is flat (Fig. 19.8a).
• While reading a book, the ciliary muscles contract and suspensory ligament is relaxed making the lens more convex (Fig. 19.8b).
• Human vision is coloured, binocular and three-dimensional. Normally, right and left eyes are focused on one object (Fig. 19.9a). In squinting, fixing eye (F) focuses on the object, but the squinting eye (S) is "turned inwards" resulting in a convergent squint (Fig. 19.9b).

INNER COAT/RETINA

1 This is the thin, delicate inner layer of the eyeball. It is continuous posteriorly with the optic nerve. The outer surface of the retina (formed by pigment cells) is attached to the choroid, while the inner surface is in contact with the hyaloid membrane (of the vitreous). Opposite the entrance of the optic nerve (infero-medial to the posterior pole) there is a circular area known as the *optic disc*. It is 1.5 mm in diameter.

2 The retina diminishes in thickness from behind forwards and is divided into optic, ciliary and iridial parts. The *optic part of the retina* contains nervous tissue and is sensitive to light. It extends from the optic disc to the posterior end of the ciliary body. The anterior margin of the optic part of the retina forms a wavy line called the ora serrata (Fig. 19.1).

Beyond the ora serrata, the retina is continued forwards as a thin, non-nervous insensitive layer that covers the ciliary body and iris, forming the *ciliary and iridial parts of the retina*. These parts are made up of two layers of epithelial cells (Fig. 19.6).

3 The depressed area of the optic disc is called the *physiological cup* (Fig. 19.3). It contains no rods or cones and is therefore insensitive to light, i.e. it is the *physiological blind spot*. At the posterior pole of the eye 3 mm lateral to the optic disc, there is another depression of similar size, called the *macula lutea*. It is avascular and yellow in colour. The centre of the macula is further depressed to form the *fovea centralis*. This is the thinnest part of the retina. It contains cones only, and is the site of maximum acuity of vision (Fig. 19.3).

4 The rods and cones are the light receptors of the eye. The *rods* contain a pigment called *visual purple*. They can respond to dim light (*scotopic vision*). The periphery of the retina contains only rods, but the fovea has none at all. The *cones* respond only to bright light (*photopic vision*) and are sensitive to colour. The fovea centralis has only cones. Their number diminishes towards the periphery of the retina.

5 The retina is composed of ten layers (Fig. 19.17):
   a. The outer pigmented layer.
   b. Layer of rods and cones.
   c. External limiting membrane.
   d. Outer nuclear layer.
   e. Outer plexiform layer.
   f. Inner nuclear layer (bipolar cells)
   g. Inner plexiform layer.
   h. Ganglion cell layer.
   i. Nerve fibre layer.
   j. The internal limiting membrane.

6 The retina is supplied by the *central artery*. This is an end artery. In the optic disc, it divides into an upper and a lower branch, each giving off nasal and temporal branches. The artery supplies the deeper layers of the retina up to the bipolar cells. The rods and cones are supplied by diffusion from the capillaries of the choroid. The retinal veins run with the arteries (Fig. 19.10, also *see* Figs 13.10 and 13.11).

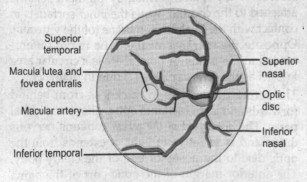

Fig. 19.10: Distribution of central artery of the retina

Superior temporal
Macula lutea and fovea centralis
Macular artery
Inferior temporal
Superior nasal
Optic disc
Inferior nasal

Retinal detachment occurs between outer single pigmented layer and inner nine nervous layers. Actually, it is an inter-retinal detachment. Silicone sponge is put over the detached retina, which is kept in position by a "band" (Figs 19.11a and b).

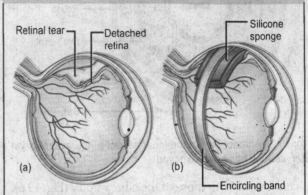

Retinal tear
Detached retina
Silicone sponge
Encircling band
(a)   (b)

Figs 19.11a and b: (a) Detached retina, and (b) banding of the retina

AQUEOUS HUMOUR

This is a clear fluid which fills the space between the cornea in front and the lens behind the anterior segment. This space is divided by the iris into anterior and posterior chambers which freely communicate with each other through the pupil.

The aqueous humour is secreted into the posterior chamber from the capillaries in the ciliary processes. It passes into the anterior chamber through the pupil. From the anterior chamber, it is drained into the anterior ciliary veins through the spaces of the iridocorneal angle or angle of anterior chamber (located between the fibres of the ligamentum pectinatum) and the canal of Schlemm (Fig. 19.5).

Interference with the drainage of the aqueous humour into the canal of Schlemm results in an increase of intraocular pressure (glaucoma). This produces cupping of the optic disc and pressure atrophy of the retina causing blindness.

The intraocular pressure is due chiefly to the aqueous humour which maintains the constancy of the optical dimensions of the eyeball. The aqueous is rich in ascorbic acid, glucose and amino acids, and nourishes the avascular tissues of the cornea and lens.

CLINICAL ANATOMY

Over production of aqueous humour or lack of its drainage or combination of both raise the intraocular pressure. The condition is called glaucoma. It must be treated urgently.

LENS

DISSECTION

Give an incision in the anterior surface of lens and with a little pressure of fingers and thumb press the body of lens outside from the capsule.

Features

The lens is a transparent biconvex structure which is placed between the anterior and posterior segments of the eye. It is circular in outline and has a diameter of 1 cm. The central points of the anterior and posterior surfaces are called the anterior and posterior *poles* (Fig. 19.12). The line connecting the poles constitutes the *axis* of the lens, while the marginal circumference is termed the *equator*. The chief advantage of the lens is that it can vary its dioptric power. It contributes about 15 dioptres to the total of 58 dioptric power of the eye. A dioptre is the inverse of the focal length in meters. A lens having a focal length of half meter has a power of two dioptres.

The posterior surface of the lens is more convex than the anterior. The anterior surface is kept flattened by the tension of the suspensory ligament. When the ligament is relaxed by contraction of the ciliary muscle, the anterior surface becomes more convex due to elasticity of the lens substance.

The lens is enclosed in a transparent, structureless elastic *capsule* which is thickest anteriorly near the circumference. Deep to capsule, the anterior surface of the lens is covered by a *capsular epithelium*. At the centre of the anterior surface, the epithelium is made up of a single layer of cubical cells, but at the periphery, the cells elongate to produce the *fibres* of the lens. The fibres are concentrically arranged to form the lens substance. The centre (nucleus) of the lens is firm (and consists of the oldest fibres), whereas the periphery (cortex) is soft and is made up of more recently formed fibres (Fig. 19.12).

The *suspensory ligament of the lens* (or the zonule of Zinn) retains the lens in position and its tension keeps the anterior surface of the lens flattened. The ligament is made up of a series of fibres which are attached peripherally to the ciliary processes, to the furrows between the ciliary processes, and to the ora serrata. Centrally, the fibres are attached to the lens, mostly in front, and a few behind the equator (Fig. 19.5).

CLINICAL ANATOMY

- Lens becomes opaque with increasing age (cataract). Since the opacities cause difficulty in vision, lens has to be replaced.
- The central artery of retina is an end-artery. Blockage of the artery leads to sudden blindness.
- Left third nerve paralysis causes partial ptosis and dilated pupil. The cornea is turned downwards and outwards (Fig. 19.13).
- Horner's syndrome results in partial ptosis and miosis (Fig. 19.14).
- In brainstem death, both the pupils are dilated and fixed (Fig. 19.15).
- Eye sees everyone. One can see the interior of the eye by ophthalmoscope. Through the ophthalmoscope, one can see the small vessels in the retina and judge the changes in diabetes and hypertension (Figs 19.16a and b). In addition, one can also examine the optic disc for evidence of papilloedema, caused by raised intracranial pressure.

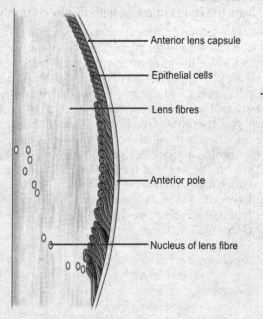

Fig. 19.12: The lens

Labels:
- Anterior lens capsule
- Epithelial cells
- Lens fibres
- Anterior pole
- Nucleus of lens fibre

VITREOUS BODY

It is a colourless, jelly-like transparent mass which fills the posterior segment (posterior four-fifths) of the eyeball. It is enclosed in a delicate homogeneous *hyaloid membrane*. Behind it is attached to the optic disc, and in front to the ora serrata; in between it is free and lies in contact with the retina. The anterior surface of the vitreous body is indented by the lens and ciliary processes (Fig. 19.1).

DEVELOPMENT

Optic vesicle forms optic cup. It is an outpouching from the *forebrain* vesicle.

Lens from *lens placode (ectodermal)*

Retina—pigment layer from the *outer layer of optic cup*; nervous layers from the *inner layer of optic cup*.

Choroid, sclera—*mesoderm*

Cornea—*surface ectoderm forms the epithelium, other layers develop from mesoderm.*

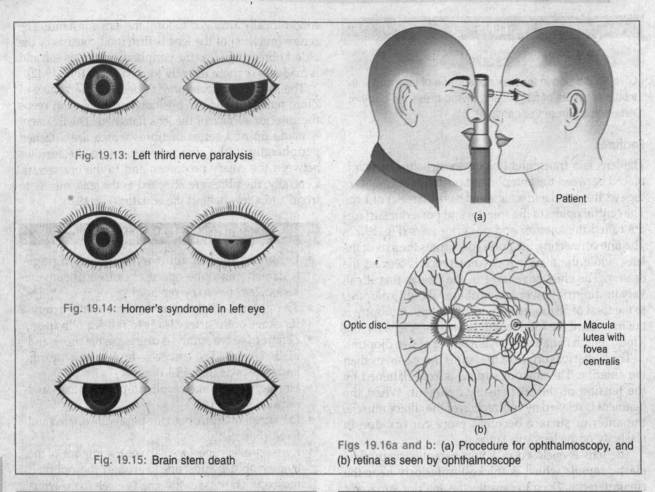

Fig. 19.13: Left third nerve paralysis

Fig. 19.14: Horner's syndrome in left eye

Fig. 19.15: Brain stem death

Patient

(a)

Optic disc

Macula lutea with fovea centralis

(b)

Figs 19.16a and b: (a) Procedure for ophthalmoscopy, and (b) retina as seen by ophthalmoscope

FACTS TO REMEMBER

- Cornea is used for grafting or transplantation.

- Sclera is pierced by number of structures including the optic nerve.

- Choroid contains big capillaries. These nourish the layer of rods and cones of retina by diffusion.

- Ciliary body contains ciliary muscles supplied by short ciliary nerves. These contract to relax the suspensory ligament of lens, so that the anterior surface of lens can become more convex for accommodation.

- Iris contains a weak dilator pupillae at the periphery, supplied by sympathetic fibres. It also contains a strong constrictor or sphincter pupillae near the pupillary margin. This is supplied by parasympathetic fibres relayed through ciliary ganglion.

- Central artery of retina is an "end artery"

- Through dilated pupil one can see the state of blood vessels of the retina.

CLINICOANATOMICAL PROBLEM

A patient was diagnosed as a case of "retinal detachment"

- Is retinal detachment, detachment of retina from the choroid?
- Name the layers of retina with its blood supply.

Ans: The retinal detachment is actually an inter-retinal detachment. The outer pigmented layer stays with choroid, while the inner nine layers get detached and cause the problem. The outer layer is developed from the outer layer of optic cup whereas the inner layers arise from the inner layer of optic cup. The blood supply of the outer five layers is from choroidal arteries whereas those of the inner nervous layers is by the "central artery of retina", which is an absolute end artery. The layers of retina (Fig. 19.17) are:

1. Outer pigmented layer
2. Layer of rods and cones
3. External limiting membrane
4. Outer nuclear layer
5. Outer plexiform layer
6. Bipolar cell layer
7. Inner plexiform layer
8. Ganglionic cell layer
9. Layer of optic nerve fibres
10. Inner limiting membrane

Head and Neck

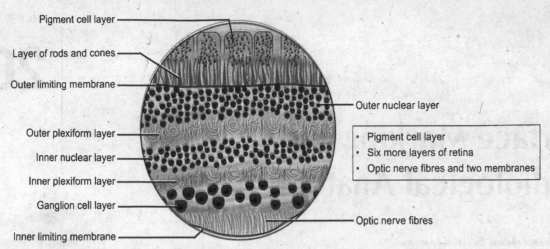

Pigment cell layer

Layer of rods and cones

Outer limiting membrane

Outer plexiform layer

Inner nuclear layer

Inner plexiform layer

Ganglion cell layer

Inner limiting membrane

Outer nuclear layer

- Pigment cell layer
- Six more layers of retina
- Optic nerve fibres and two membranes

Optic nerve fibres

Fig. 19.17: Histological layers of the retina

FREQUENTLY ASKED QUESTION

1. Write short notes/enumerate:
   a. Cornea
   b. Choroid
   c. Structures piercing the sclera
   d. Layers of retina
   e. Ciliary muscles
   f. Lens
   g. Aqueous humour

MULTIPLE CHOICE QUESTIONS

1. Which of the following muscles does not develop from mesoderm?
   a. Muscles of heart   b. Muscles of iris
   c. Deltoid   d. Superior rectus

2. Which of the following nerves supplies the cornea?
   a. Supraorbital   b. Nasociliary
   c. Lacrimal   d. Infraorbital

3. Parasympathetic fibres supply all the following muscles *except:*
   a. Constrictor pupillae
   b. Dilator pupillae

   c. Radial fibres of ciliaris muscle
   d. Circular fibres of ciliaris muscle

4. Retina consists of the following number of layers:
   a. Eight
   b. Ten
   c. Nine
   d. Eleven

5. One of the following symptoms is not seen in Horner's syndrome:
   a. Partial ptosis   b. Miosis
   c. Anhydrosis   d. Exophthalmos

ANSWERS

1. b   2. b   3. b   4. b   5. d

Surface Marking and Radiological Anatomy

Prayer does not change God, it changes us
—B. Graham

INTRODUCTION

The bony and soft tissue landmarks on the head, face and neck help in surface marking of various structures. These landmarks are of immense value to the clinician for locating the part to be examined or to be operated.

SURFACE LANDMARKS

LANDMARKS ON THE FACE

Some important named features to be identified on the living face have been described in Chapter 2. Other landmarks are as follows.

1 The *supraorbital margin* lies beneath the upper margin of the eyebrow. The *supraorbital notch* is palpable at the junction of the medial one-third with the lateral two-thirds of the supraorbital margin (except in those cases in which the notch is converted into a foramen). A vertical line drawn from the supraorbital notch to the base of the mandible, passing midway between the lower two premolar teeth, crosses the infraorbital foramen 5 mm below the infraorbital margin, and the mental foramen midway between the upper and lower borders of the mandible (Fig. 20.1).

2 The *superciliary arch* is a curved bony ridge situated immediately above the medial part of each supraorbital margin. The *glabella* is the median elevation connecting the two superciliary arches and corresponds to the elevation between the two eyebrows.

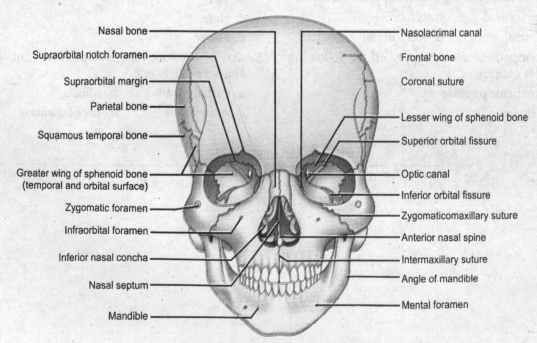

Nasal bone	Nasolacrimal canal
Supraorbital notch foramen	Frontal bone
Supraorbital margin	Coronal suture
Parietal bone	
Squamous temporal bone	Lesser wing of sphenoid bone
	Superior orbital fissure
Greater wing of sphenoid bone (temporal and orbital surface)	Optic canal
Zygomatic foramen	Inferior orbital fissure
Infraorbital foramen	Zygomaticomaxillary suture
Inferior nasal concha	Anterior nasal spine
Nasal septum	Intermaxillary suture
Mandible	Angle of mandible
	Mental foramen

Fig. 20.1: Foramina in norma frontalis

3 The *nasion* is the point where the internasal and frontonasal sutures meet. It lies a little above the floor of the depression at the root of the nose, below the glabella (Fig. 20.1).

LANDMARKS ON THE LATERAL SIDE OF THE HEAD

The external ear or pinna is a prominent feature on the lateral aspect of the head. The named features on the pinna are shown in Fig. 20.2. Other landmarks on the lateral side of the head are as follows.

1 The *zygomatic bone* forms the prominence of the cheek at the inferolateral corner of the orbit. The *zygomatic arch* bridges the gap between the eye and the ear. It is formed anteriorly by the temporal process of the zygomatic bone, and posteriorly by the zygomatic process (zygoma) of the temporal bone. The *preauricular point* lies on the posterior root of the zygoma immediately in front of the upper part of the tragus (Fig. 20.3).

2 The head of the mandible lies in front of the tragus. It is felt best during movements of the lower jaw. The *coronoid process* of the mandible can be felt below the lowest part of the zygomatic bone when the mouth is opened. The process can be traced downwards into the anterior border of the *ramus* of the mandible. The posterior border of the ramus, though masked by parotid gland, can be felt through the skin. The outer surface of the ramus is covered by the masseter which can be felt when the teeth are clenched. The lower border of the mandible can be traced posteriorly into the *angle* of the mandible (Fig. 20.3).

3 The *parietal eminence* is the most prominent part of the parietal bone, situated far above and a little behind the auricle.

4 The *mastoid process* is a large bony prominence situated behind the lower part of the auricle. The *supramastoid crest*, about 2.5 cm long, begins immediately above the external acoustic meatus and soon curves upwards and backwards. The crest is continuous anteriorly with the posterior root of the zygoma, and posterosuperiorly with the temporal line (Fig. 20.3).

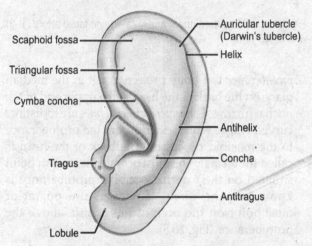

Fig. 20.2: Named features on the pinna

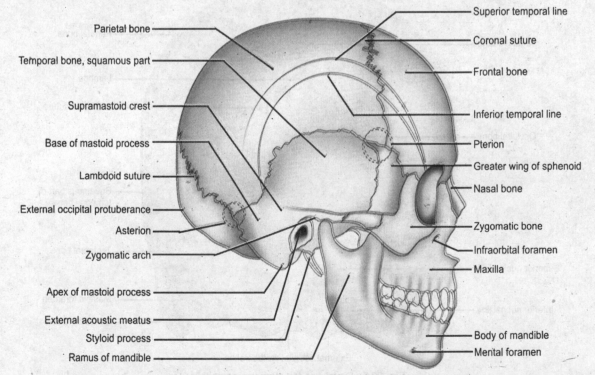

Fig. 20.3: Parts of mandible seen in norma lateralis

5 The *temporal line* forms the upper boundary of the temporal fossa which is filled up by the temporalis muscle. The upper margin of the contracting temporalis helps in defining this line which begins at the zygomatic process of the frontal bone, arches posterosuperiorly across the coronal suture, passes a little below the parietal eminence, and turns downwards to become continuous with the supramastoid crest. The area of the temporal fossa on the side of the head, above the zygomatic arch, is called the *temple* or temporal region.

6 The *pterion* is the area in the temporal fossa where four bones (frontal, parietal, temporal and sphenoid) adjoin each other across an H-shaped suture. The centre of the pterion is marked by a point 4 cm above the midpoint of the zygomatic arch, falling 3.5 cm behind the frontozygomatic suture. Deep to the pterion lie the anterior branch of the middle meningeal artery, the middle meningeal vein, and deeper still the stem of the lateral sulcus of the cerebral hemisphere (at the *Sylvian point*) dividing into three rami. The pterion is a common site for trephining (making a hole in the skull) during operation (Fig. 20.4). Surface marking of middle meningeal artery is given later.

7 The junction of the back of the head with the neck is indicated by the external occipital protuberance and the superior nuchal lines. The *external occipital*

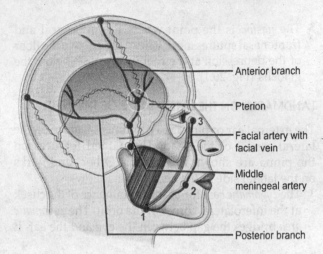

Fig. 20.4: Middle meningeal artery (a–e) and facial artery (1–3) with facial vein

protuberance is a bony projection felt in the median plane on the back of the head at the upper end of the nuchal furrow. The *superior nuchal lines* are indistinct curved ridges which extend from the protuberance to the mastoid processes. The back of the head is called the *occiput*. The most prominent median point situated on the external occipital protuberance is known as the *inion*. However, the posterior most point on the occiput lies a little above the protuberance (Fig. 20.5).

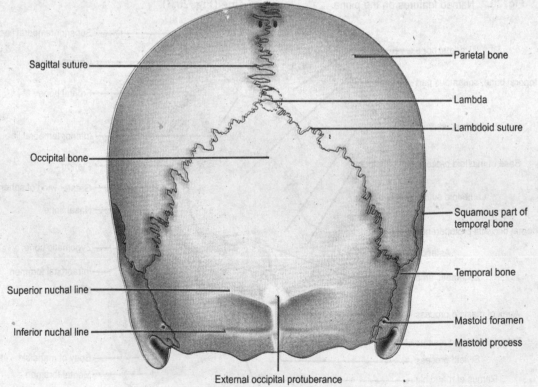

Fig. 20.5: Structures felt in norma occipitalis

LANDMARKS ON THE SIDE OF THE NECK

1 The *sternocleidomastoid* muscle is seen prominently when the face is turned to the opposite side. The ridge raised by the muscle extends from the sternum to the mastoid process (Fig. 20.6).

2 The *external jugular vein* crosses the sternocleidomastoid obliquely, running downwards and backwards from near the auricle to the clavicle. It is better seen in old age (Fig. 20.7).

3 The *greater supraclavicular fossa* lies above and behind the middle one-third of the clavicle. It overlies the cervical part of the brachial plexus and the third part of the subclavian artery (Fig. 20.6).

4 The *lesser supraclavicular fossa* is a small depression between the sternal and clavicular parts of the sternocleidomastoid. It overlies the internal jugular vein.

5 The *mastoid process* is a large bony projection behind the auricle (concha) (Fig. 20.6).

6 The *transverse process of the atlas vertebra* can be felt on deep pressure midway between the angle of the mandible and the mastoid process, immediately anteroinferior to the tip of the mastoid process. The *fourth cervical transverse process* is just palpable at the level of the upper border of the thyroid cartilage; and the *sixth cervical transverse process* at the level of the cricoid cartilage. The anterior tubercle of the *transverse process of the sixth cervical vertebra* is the largest of all such processes and is called the *carotid tubercle* (of Chassaignac). The common carotid artery can be best pressed against this tubercle, deep to the anterior border of the sternocleidomastoid muscle.

7 The *anterior border of the trapezius muscle* becomes prominent on elevation of the shoulder against resistance (Fig. 20.6).

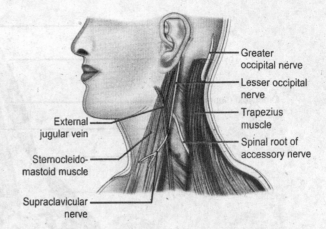

Fig. 20.7: External jugular vein and cutaneous nerves

LANDMARKS ON THE ANTERIOR ASPECT OF THE NECK

1 The *mandible* forms the lower jaw. The lower border of its horseshoe-shaped body is known as the *base of the mandible* (Fig. 20.8). Anteriorly, this base forms the *chin*, and posteriorly it can be traced to the *angle of the mandible*. Numerous structures are attached to mandible.

2 The body of the U-shaped *hyoid bone* can be felt in the median plane just below and behind the chin, at the junction of the neck with the floor of the mouth. On each side, the body of hyoid bone is continuous posteriorly with the *greater cornua* which is overlapped in its posterior part by the sternocleidomastoid muscle (Fig. 20.9).

3 The *thyroid cartilage* of the larynx forms a sharp protuberance in the median plane just below the hyoid bone. This protuberance is called the *laryngeal*

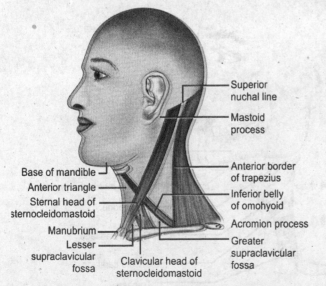

Fig. 20.6: Sternocleidomastoid, trapezius and inferior belly of omohyoid

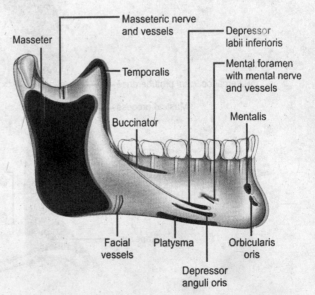

Fig. 20.8: Attachments on the mandible

Head and Neck

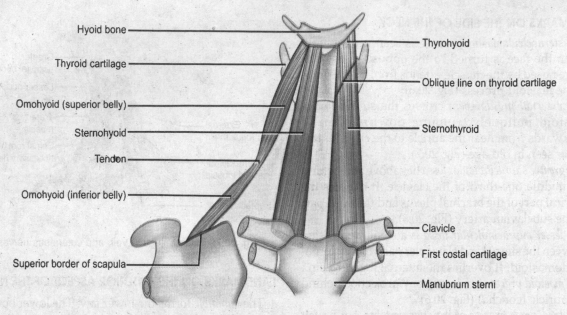

Fig. 20.9: Attachments on hyoid bone and thyroid cartilage

prominence or Adam's apple. It is more prominent in males than in females (Fig. 20.10).

4 The rounded arch of the *cricoid cartilage* lies below the thyroid cartilage at the upper end of the trachea (Fig. 20.10).

5 The trachea runs downwards and backwards from the cricoid cartilage. It is identified by its cartilaginous rings. However, it is partially masked by the *isthmus of the thyroid gland* which lies against the second to fourth tracheal rings. The trachea is commonly palpated in the *suprasternal notch* which lies between the tendinous heads of origin of the right and left sternocleidomastoid muscles. In certain diseases, the trachea may shift to one side from the median plane. This indicates a shift in the mediastinum (Fig. 20.10).

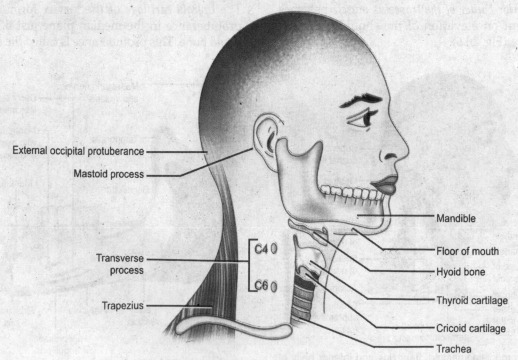

Fig. 20.10: Landmarks on anterior aspect of neck

OTHER IMPORTANT LANDMARKS

1 The *frontozygomatic suture* can be felt as a slight depression in the upper part of the lateral orbital margin.
2 The *marginal tubercle* lies a short distance below the frontozygomatic suture along the posterior border of the frontal process of the zygomatic bone.
3 The *Frankfurt's plane* is represented by a horizontal line joining the infraorbital margin to the centre of the external acoustic meatus. Posteriorly, the line passes through a point just below the external occipital protuberance (*see* Fig. 1.1).
4 The *jugal point* is the anterior end of the upper border of the zygomatic arch where it meets the frontal process of the zygomatic bone.
5 The *mandibular notch* is represented by a curved line concave upwards, extending from the head of the mandible to the anterior end of the zygomatic arch. The notch is 1–2 cm deep (Fig. 20.8).

SURFACE MARKING OF VARIOUS STRUCTURES

ARTERIES

Facial Artery

It is marked on the face by joining these three points.
• Point 1 on the base of the mandible at the anterior border of the masseter muscle.
• Point 2 1.2 cm lateral to the angle of the mouth.
• Point 3 at the medial angle of the eye.
The artery is tortuous in its course and is more so between the first two points (Fig. 20.4).

Common Carotid Artery

It is marked by a broad line along the anterior border of the sternocleidomastoid muscle by joining the following two points.
• Point 1 on the sternoclavicular joint.
• Point 2 on the anterior border of the sternocleidomastoid muscle at the level of upper border of the thyroid cartilage (Fig. 20.11).
The thoracic part of the left common carotid artery is marked by a broadline extending from a point a little to the left of the centre of the manubrium to the left sternoclavicular joint.

Internal Carotid Artery

It is marked by a broadline joining these two points.
• Point 2 on the anterior border of the sternocleidomastoid muscle at the level of the upper border of the thyroid cartilage.
• Point 3 on the posterior border of the condyle of the mandible (Fig. 20.11).

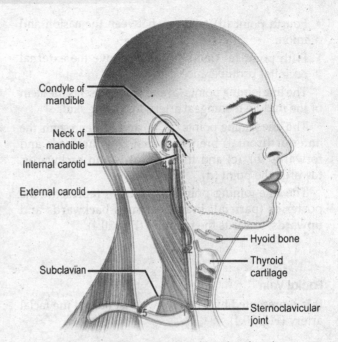

Fig. 20.11: Some arteries of head and neck

External Carotid Artery

The artery is marked by joining these two points.
• Point 2 on the anterior border of the sternocleidomastoid muscle at the level of the upper border of the thyroid cartilage.
• Point 4 on the posterior border of the neck of the mandible.
The artery is slightly convex forwards in its lower half and slightly concave forwards in its upper half (Fig. 20.11).

Subclavian Artery

It is marked by a broad curved line, convex upwards, by joining these two points.
• Point 1 on the sternoclavicular joint.
• Point 5 at the middle of the lower border of the clavicle (Fig. 20.11).
The artery rises about 2 cm above the clavicle.
The thoracic part of the left subclavian artery is marked by a broad vertical line along the left border of the manubrium a little to the left of the left common carotid artery.

Middle Meningeal Artery

It is marked by joining these points.
• First point (a) immediately above the middle of the zygoma. The artery enters the skull opposite this point (Fig. 20.4).
• Second point (b) 2 cm above the first point. The artery divides deep to this point.
• Third point (c) (centre of pterion) 3.5 cm behind and 1.5 cm above the frontozygomatic suture.

- Fourth point (d), midway between the nasion and inion.
- Fifth point (e) (lambda) 6 cm above the external occipital protuberance.

The line joining points (a) and (b) represents the stem of the middle meningeal artery inside the skull.

The line joining points (b), (c) and (d) represents the anterior (frontal) branch. It first runs upwards and forwards (b), (c) and then upwards and backwards, towards the point (d).

The line joining points (b) and (e) represents the posterior (parietal) branch. It runs backwards and upwards, towards the point (e) (Fig. 20.4).

VEINS/SINUSES

Facial Vein

It is represented by a line drawn just behind the facial artery (Fig. 20.4).

External Jugular Vein

The vein is usually visible through the skin and can be made more prominent by blowing with the mouth and nostrils closed (Fig. 20.12).

It can be marked, if not visible, by joining these points.

- Point $_1$ a little below and behind the angle of the mandible.
- Point $_2$ on the clavicle just lateral to the posterior border of the sternocleidomastoid (Fig. 20.12).

Internal Jugular Vein

Internal jugular vein is marked by a broadline by joining these two points.

- Point $_3$ on the neck medial to the lobule of the ear.
- Point $_4$ at the medial end of the clavicle (Fig. 20.12).

The lower bulb of the vein lies beneath the lesser supraclavicular fossa between the sternal and clavicular heads of the sternocleidomastoid muscle.

Subclavian Vein

Subclavian vein is represented by a broadline along the clavicle extending from a little medial to its midpoint to the medial end of the bone.

Superior Sagittal Sinus

Superior sagittal sinus is marked by two lines (diverging posteriorly) joining these two points.

- One point $_{(1)}$ at the glabella.
- Two points $_{(2)}$ at the inion, situated side by side, 1.2 cm apart (Fig. 20.13).

Transverse Sinus

Transverse sinus is marked by two parallel lines, 1.2 cm apart extending between the following points.

- Two points $_{(2)}$ at the inion, situated one above the other and 1.2 cm apart (Fig. 20.13).
- Two points $_{(3)}$ at asterion 3.75 cm behind external auditory meatus and 1.25 cm above this point (Fig. 20.13).
- Two points $_{(4)}$ at the base of the mastoid process, situated one in front of the other and 1.2 cm apart.

Sigmoid Sinus

Sigmoid sinus is marked by two parallel lines situated 1.2 cm apart and extending between the following two points:

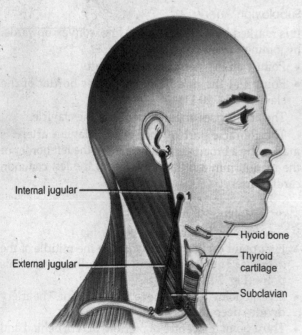

Fig. 20.12: Internal and external jugular veins

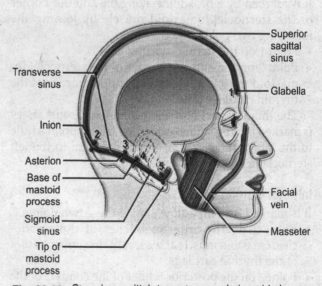

Fig. 20.13: Superior sagittal, transverse and sigmoid sinuses

- Two points (4) at the base of the mastoid process, situated one in front of the other and 1.2 cm apart (Fig. 20.13).
- Two similar points (5) near the posterior border and 1.2 cm above the tip of mastoid process.

NERVES

Facial Nerve

Facial nerve is marked by a short horizontal line joining the following two points.

- Point 1 at the middle of the anterior border of the mastoid process. The stylomastoid foramen lies 2 cm deep to this point.
- Point 2 behind the neck of mandible. Here the nerve divides into its five branches to the facial muscles (Fig. 20.14, also see Fig. 5.3).

Auriculotemporal Nerve

Auriculotemporal nerve is marked by a line drawn first backwards from the posterior part of the mandibular notch (point 3) (site of mandibular nerve) across the neck of the mandible, and then upwards across the preauricular point 4 (Fig. 20.14).

Mandibular Nerve

Mandibular nerve is marked by a short vertical line in the posterior part of the mandibular notch just in front of the head of the mandible.

Lingual and Inferior Alveolar Nerves

Lingual nerve is marked by a curved line running downwards and forwards by joining these points (Fig. 20.14).

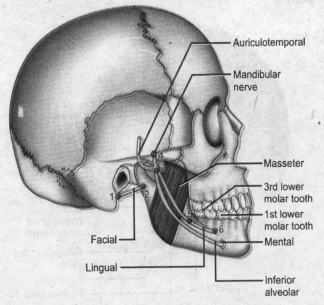

Fig. 20.14: Position of facial and some branches of mandibular nerves

- Point 3 on the posterior part of the mandibular notch, in line with the mandibular nerve.
- Point 5 a little below and behind the last lower molar tooth.
- Point 6, opposite the first lower molar tooth.

The concavity in the course of the nerve is more marked between the 5 and 6 points and is directed upwards.

Inferior alveolar nerve lies a little below and parallel to the lingual nerve.

Glossopharyngeal Nerve

Glossopharyngeal nerve is marked by joining the following points.

- Point 1 on the anteroinferior part of the tragus.
- Point 2, anterosuperior to the angle of the mandible.

From 2nd point, the nerve runs forwards for a short distance above the lower border of the mandible. The nerve describes a gentle curve in its course (Fig. 20.15).

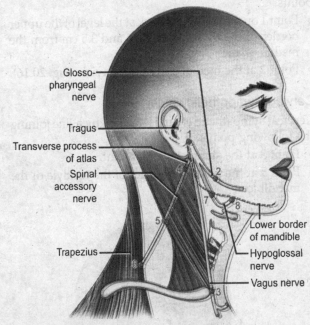

Fig. 20.15: Position of last four cranial nerves

Vagus Nerve

The nerve runs along the medial side of the internal jugular vagus vein. It is marked by joining these two points.

- Point 1 at the anteroinferior part of the tragus.
- Point 3 at the medial end of the clavicle (Fig. 20.15).

Accessory Nerve (Spinal Part)

Accessory nerve (spinal part) is marked by joining the following four points.

Head and Neck

- Point 1 at the anteroinferior part of the tragus (Fig. 20.15).
- Point 4 at the tip of the transverse process of the atlas.
- Point 5 at the middle of the posterior border of the sternocleidomastoid muscle.
- Point 6 on the anterior border of the trapezius 6 cm above the clavicle (Fig. 20.15).

Hypoglossal Nerve

Hypoglossal nerve is marked by joining these points.

- Point 1 at the anteroinferior part of the tragus.
- Point 7, posterosuperior to the tip of the greater cornua of the hyoid bone.
- Point 8, midway between the angle of the mandible and the symphysis menti.

The nerve describes a gentle curve in its course (Fig. 20.15).

Phrenic Nerve

Phrenic nerve is marked by a line joining the following points.

- Point 1 on the side of the neck at the level of the upper border of the thyroid cartilage and 3.5 cm from the median plane.
- Point 2 at the medial end of the clavicle (Fig. 20.16).

Cervical Sympathetic Chain

Cervical sympathetic chain is marked by a line joining the following points.

- Point 3 at the sternoclavicular joint.
- Point 5 at the posterior border of the condyle of the mandible.

The *superior cervical ganglion* extends from the transverse process of the atlas (point 4) to the tip of the greater cornua of the hyoid bone. The *middle cervical ganglion* lies at the level of the cricoid cartilage, and the *inferior cervical ganglion,* at a point 3 cm above the sterno-clavicular joint (Fig. 20.16).

Trigeminal Ganglion

Trigeminal ganglion lies a little in front of the preauri-cular point at a depth of about 4.5 cm.

GLANDS

Parotid Gland

Parotid gland is marked by joining these four points with each other (Fig. 20.17).

- The first point (a) at the upper border of the head of the mandible.
- The second point (b), just above the centre of the masseter muscle.
- The third point (c), posteroinferior to the angle of the mandible.
- The fourth point (d) on the upper part of the anterior border of the mastoid process.

The anterior border of the gland is obtained by joining the points (a), (b), (c); the posterior border, by joining the points (c), (d); and the superior curved border with its concavity directed upwards and backwards, by joining the points (a), (d) across the lobule of the ear (Fig. 20.17).

Parotid Duct

To mark this duct first draw a line joining these two points.

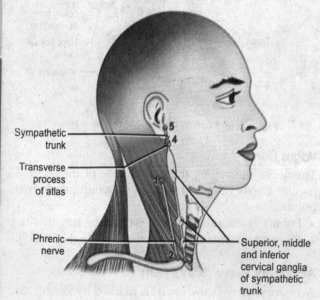

Fig. 20.16: Position of phrenic nerve and sympathetic trunk

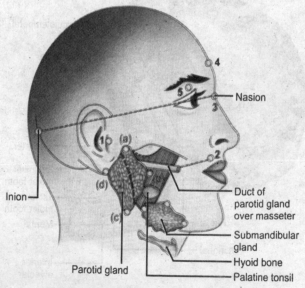

Fig. 20.17: Position of parotid gland with its duct, submandibular gland and palatine tonsil

- First point 1 at the lower border of the tragus.
- Second point 2, midway between the ala of the nose and the red margin of the upper lip.

The middle-third of this line represents the parotid duct (Fig. 20.17).

Submandibular Gland

The submandibular salivary gland is marked by an oval area over the posterior half of the base of the mandible, including the lower border of the ramus. The area extends 1.5 cm above the base of the mandible, and below to the greater cornua of the hyoid bone (Fig. 20.17).

Thyroid Gland

The isthmus of thyroid gland is marked by two transverse parallel lines (each 1.2 cm long) on the trachea, the upper 1.2 cm and the lower 2.5 cm below the arch of the cricoid cartilage.

Each lobe extends up to the middle of the thyroid cartilage, below to the clavicle, and laterally to be overlapped by the anterior border of sternocleido-mastoid muscle. The upper pole of the lobe is pointed, and the lower pole is broad and rounded (Fig. 20.18).

Palatine Tonsil

Palatine tonsil is marked by an oval (almond-shaped) area over the masseter just anterosuperior to the angle of the mandible (Fig. 20.17).

PARANASAL SINUSES

Frontal Sinus

Frontal sinus is marked by a triangular area formed by joining these three points.
- The point 3 at the nasion.
- The point 4, 2.5 cm above the nasion.
- The point 5 at the junction of medial one-third and lateral two-thirds of the supraorbital margin, i.e. at the supraorbital notch.

Maxillary Sinus

The roof of maxillary sinus is represented by the inferior orbital margin; the floor, by the alveolus of the maxilla; the base, by the lateral wall of the nose. The apex lies on the zygomatic process of the maxilla.

RADIOLOGICAL ANATOMY

In routine clinical practice, the following X-ray pictures of the skull are commonly used.
1 Lateral view for general survey of the skull.
2 A special posteroanterior view (in Water's position) to study the paranasal sinuses.
3 Anteroposterior and oblique views for the study of cervical vertebrae.

LATERAL VIEW OF SKULL (PLAIN SKIAGRAM)

The radiogram is studied systematically as described here.

Cranial Vault

1 *Shape and size:* It is important to be familiar with the normal shape and size of the skull so that abnormalities, like oxycephaly (a type of cranio-stenosis), hydrocephalus, microcephaly, etc. may be diagnosed.
2 *Structure of cranial bones:* The bones are unilamellar during the first three years of life. Two tables separated by diploe appear during the fourth year, and the differentiation reaches its maximum by about 35 years when diploic veins produce characteristic markings in radiograms. The sites of the external occipital protuberance and frontal bone are normally thicker than the rest of the skull. The squamous temporal and the upper part of the occipital bone are thin.

Generalized thickened bones are found in Paget's disease. Thalassaemia, a congenital haemolytic

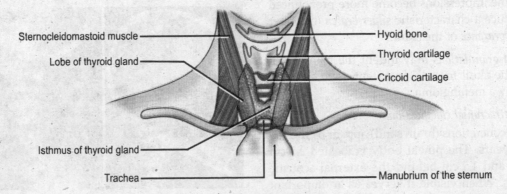

Fig. 20.18: Thyroid gland

Sternocleidomastoid muscle
Lobe of thyroid gland
Isthmus of thyroid gland
Trachea
Hyoid bone
Thyroid cartilage
Cricoid cartilage
Manubrium of the sternum

Head and Neck

anaemia, is associated with thickening and a characteristic sunray appearance of the skull bones. A localised hyperostosis may be seen over a meningioma. In multiple myeloma and secondary carcinomatous deposits, the skull presents large punched out areas. Fractures are more extensive in the inner table than in the outer table.

3 *Sutures:* The coronal and lambdoid sutures are usually visible clearly. The coronal suture runs downwards and forwards in front of the central sulcus of the brain. The lambdoid suture traverses the posteriormost part of the skull.

Obliteration of sutures begins first on the inner surface (between 30 and 40 years) and then on the outer surface (between 40 and 50 years). Usually the lower part of the coronal suture is obliterated first, followed by the posterior part of the sagittal suture. Premature closure of sutures occurs in craniostenosis, a hereditary disease. Sutures are opened up in children by an increase in intracranial pressure.

4 *Vascular markings:*
  a. *Middle meningeal vessels:* The anterior branch runs about 1 cm behind the coronal suture. The posterior branch runs backwards and upwards at a lower level across the upper part of the shadow of the auricle.
  b. The *transverse sinus* may be seen as a curved dark shadow, convex upwards, extending from the internal occipital protuberance to the petrous temporal.
  c. The *diploic venous markings* are seen as irregularly anastomosing, worm-like shadows produced by the frontal, anterior temporal, posterior temporal and occipital diploic veins. These markings become more prominent in raised intracranial pressure.

5 *Cerebral moulding*, indicating normal impressions of cerebral gyri, can be seen. In raised intracranial tension, the impressions become more pronounced and produce a characteristic *silver beaten* (or *copper beaten*) *appearance* of the skull.

6 *Arachnoid granulations* may indent the parasagittal area of the skull to such an extent as to simulate erosion by a meningioma.

7 *Normal intracranial calcifications*
  a. Pineal concretions (brain sand) appear by the age of 17 years. The pineal body is located 2.5 cm above and 1.2 cm behind the external acoustic meatus. When visible it serves as an important radiological landmark.

b. Other structures which may become calcified include the choroid plexuses, arachnoid granulations, falx cerebri, and other dural folds.

8 *The auricle:* The curved margin of the auricle is seen above the petrous temporal.

9 The *frontal sinus* produces a dark shadow in the anteroinferior part of the skull vault.

Base of Skull

1 The *floor of the anterior cranial fossa* slopes backwards and downwards. The shadows of the two sides are often seen situated one above the other. The surface is irregular due to gyral markings. It also forms the roof of the orbit (Fig. 20.19).

2 The *hypophyseal fossa* represents the middle cranial fossa in this view. It is overhung anteriorly by the anterior clinoid process (directed posteriorly), and posteriorly by the posterior clinoid process. It measures 8 mm vertically and 14 mm anteroposteriorly. The interclinoid distance is not more than 4 mm. The fossa is enlarged in cases of pituitary tumours, arising particularly from acidophil or chromophobe cells.

3 The *sphenoidal air sinus* lies anteroinferior to the hypophyseal fossa. The shadows of the orbit, the nasal cavities, and the ethmoidal and maxillary sinuses lie superimposed on one another, below the anterior cranial fossa.

4 The *petrous part of the temporal bone* produces a dense irregular shadow posteroinferior to the hypophyseal fossa. Within this shadow there are two dark areas representing the external acoustic meatuses of the two sides; each shadow lies immediately behind the head of the mandible of that side. Similar dark shadows of the internal acoustic meatuses may also be seen. The posterior part of the dense shadow merges with the mastoid air cells producing a honeycomb appearance.

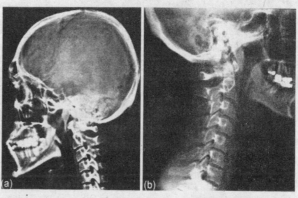

Figs 20.19a and b: Lateral view of the skull and cervical vertebrae

5 In addition to the features mentioned above, the *mandible* lies anteriorly forming the lower part of the facial skeleton. The *upper cervical vertebrae* lie posteriorly and are seen as a pillar supporting the skull.

SPECIAL PA VIEW OF SKULL FOR PARANASAL SINUSES

This picture is taken with the head extended in such a way that the chin rests against the film and the nose is raised from it (Water's position). This view shows the frontal and maxillary sinuses clearly (Fig. 20.20).

The frontal sinuses are seen immediately above the nose and medial parts of the orbits. The nasal cavities are flanked on each side by the orbits above, and the maxillary sinuses below. The normal sinuses are clear and radiolucent, i.e. they appear dark. If a sinus is infected, the shadow is either hazy or radio-opaque.

CERVICAL VERTEBRAE

The cervical vertebrae can be visualised in anteroposterior view of the neck and in oblique view of the neck. In the anteroposterior view, the body of cervical vertebrae, intervertebral discs, pedicles and

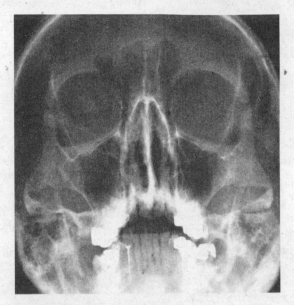

Fig. 20.20: X-ray of skull showing paranasal sinuses

spines are seen. In the oblique view, the adjacent inferior articular and superior articular processes and intervertebral foramen are visualised.

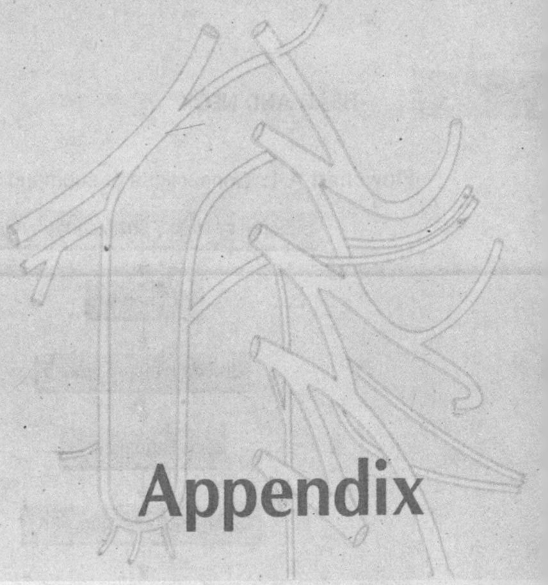

Appendix

What matters is not to add years to your life but life to your years

—Alexis Carrel

INTRODUCTION

The appendix contains upper cervical nerves, and sympathetic trunk of the neck in Table A.1.

The four parasympathetic ganglia are shown in Flowcharts A.1 to A.4 and Table A.2.

Summary of the arteries is depicted in Tables A.2 to A.4.

The pharyngeal arches, pouches and clefts are shown in Tables A.5 to A.7. It also includes the Clinical Terms.

CERVICAL PLEXUS

Ventral rami of C1, C2, C3, C4 form the cervical plexus. C1 runs along hypoglossal and supplies geniohyoid and thyrohyoid. It also gives superior limb of ansa cervicalis, which supplies superior belly of omohyoid and joins with inferior limb to form ansa. Inferior limb of ansa cervicalis is formed by ventral rami of C2, C3 Branches from ansa supply sternohyoid, sternothyroid, inferior belly of omohyoid. Cervical plexus also gives four cutaneous branches lesser occipital (C2), great auricular (C2, C3), supraclavicular (C3, C4) and transverse or anterior nerve of neck (C2, C3) (*see* Figs 3.6 and 9.8).

PHRENIC NERVE

Phrenic nerve arises primarily from ventral rami of C4 with small contributions from C3 and C5 nerve roots or through nerve to subclavius. It is the only motor supply to its own half of diaphragm and sensory to mediastinal pleura, peritoneum and fibrous pericardium. Inflammation of peritoneum under diaphragm causes referred pain in the area of supraclavicular nerves supply, especially tip of the shoulders as their root value is also ventral rami of C3 and C4 (*see* Fig. 9. 9).

SYMPATHETIC TRUNK

Branches of cervical sympathetic ganglia of sympathetic trunk are given in Table A.1.

PARASYMPATHETIC GANGLIA (TABLE A.2)

SUBMANDIBULAR GANGLION

Situation (Fig. A.1)

The submandibular ganglion lies superficial to hyoglossus muscle in the submandibular region.

Table A.1: Branches of cervical sympathetic ganglia

	Superior cervical ganglion	*Middle cervical ganglion*	*Inferior cervical ganglion*
Arterial branches	i. Along internal carotid artery as internal carotid nerve ii. Along common carotid and external carotid arteries	Along inferior thyroid artery	Along subclavian and vertebral arteries
Grey rami communicans	Along 1–4 cervical nerves	Along 5 and 6 cervical nerves	Along 7 and 8 cervical nerves
Along cranial nerves	Along cranial nerves IX, X, XI and XII	–	–
Visceral branches	Pharynx, cardiac	Thyroid, cardiac	Cardiac

Flowchart A.1: Connections of submandibular ganglion

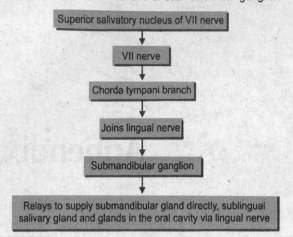

Superior salivatory nucleus of VII nerve
↓
VII nerve
↓
Chorda tympani branch
↓
Joins lingual nerve
↓
Submandibular ganglion
↓
Relays to supply submandibular gland directly, sublingual salivary gland and glands in the oral cavity via lingual nerve

Flowchart A.2: Connections of pterygopalatine ganglion

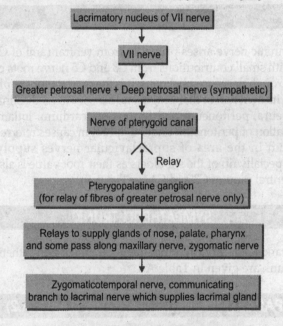

Lacrimatory nucleus of VII nerve
↓
VII nerve
↓
Greater petrosal nerve + Deep petrosal nerve (sympathetic)
↓
Nerve of pterygoid canal
↓ Relay
Pterygopalatine ganglion
(for relay of fibres of greater petrosal nerve only)
↓
Relays to supply glands of nose, palate, pharynx and some pass along maxillary nerve, zygomatic nerve
↓
Zygomaticotemporal nerve, communicating branch to lacrimal nerve which supplies lacrimal gland

Flowchart A.3: Connections of otic ganglion

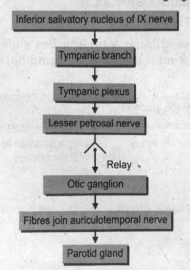

Inferior salivatory nucleus of IX nerve
↓
Tympanic branch
↓
Tympanic plexus
↓
Lesser petrosal nerve
↓ Relay
Otic ganglion
↓
Fibres join auriculotemporal nerve
↓
Parotid gland

Flowchart A.4: Connections of ciliary ganglion

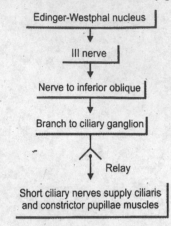

Edinger-Westphal nucleus
↓
III nerve
↓
Nerve to inferior oblique
↓
Branch to ciliary ganglion
↓ Relay
Short ciliary nerves supply ciliaris and constrictor pupillae muscles

Functionally, submandibular ganglion is connected to facial nerve, while topographically it is connected to lingual branch of mandibular nerve (*see* Fig. 7.10).

Roots

The ganglion has sensory, sympathetic and secretomotor or parasympathetic roots.

1 Sensory root is from the lingual nerve. It is suspended by two roots of lingual nerve.
2 Sympathetic root is from the sympathetic plexus around the facial artery. This plexus contains postganglionic fibres from the superior cervical ganglion of sympathetic trunk. These fibres pass express through the ganglion and are vasomotor to the gland.
3 Secretomotor root is from superior salivatory nucleus through nervus intermedius via chorda tympani which is a branch of cranial nerve VII. Chorda tympani joins lingual nerve. The parasympathetic fibres get relayed in the submandibular ganglion (Flowchart A.1).

Branches

The ganglion gives direct branches to the submandibular salivary gland.

Some postganglionic fibres reach the lingual nerve to be distributed to sublingual salivary gland and glands in the oral cavity.

PTERYGOPALATINE GANGLION

Situation

Pterygopalatine or sphenopalatine is the largest parasympathetic ganglion, suspended by two roots of maxillary nerve. Functionally, it is related to cranial nerve VII. It is called the ganglion of "hay fever."

Roots

The ganglion has sensory, sympathetic and secretomotor or parasympathetic roots.

Table A.2: Connections of parasympathetic ganglia (Fig. A.1)

Ganglia	Sensory root	Sympathetic root	Secretomotor root/ parasympathetic root	Motor root	Distribution
Submandibular (Fig. A.1)	2 branches from lingual nerve	Branch from plexus around facial artery	Superior salivatory nucleus → facial nerve → chorda tympani (joins the lingual nerve)	— —	a. Submandibular b. Sublingual c. Anterior lingual glands
Pterygopalatine (Fig. A.1)	2 branches from maxillary nerve	Deep petrosal from plexus around internal carotid artery	Superior salivatory nucleus, and lacrimatory nucleus → nervus intermedius → facial nerve → geniculate ganglion → greater petrosal nerve + deep petrosal nerve = nerve of pterygoid canal	—	a. Mucous glands of nose, paranasal sinuses, palate, nasopharynx b. Some fibres pass through zygomatic nerve → zygomatico-temporal nerve → communicating branch to lacrimal nerve → lacrimal gland
Otic (Fig. A.1)	Branch from auriculotemporal nerve	Plexus along middle meningeal artery	Inferior salivatory nucleus → glosso-pharyngeal nerve → tympanic branch → tympanic plexus → lesser petrosal nerve.	Branch from nerve to medial pterygoid	a. Secretomotor to parotid gland via auriculotemporal nerve b. Tensor veli palatini and tensor tympani via nerve to med. pterygoid (unrelayed)
Ciliary (Fig. A.1)	From nasociliary nerve	Plexus along ophthalmic artery	Edinger-Westphal nucleus → oculomotor nerve → nerve to inferior oblique	—	a. Ciliaris muscles b. Sphincter pupillae

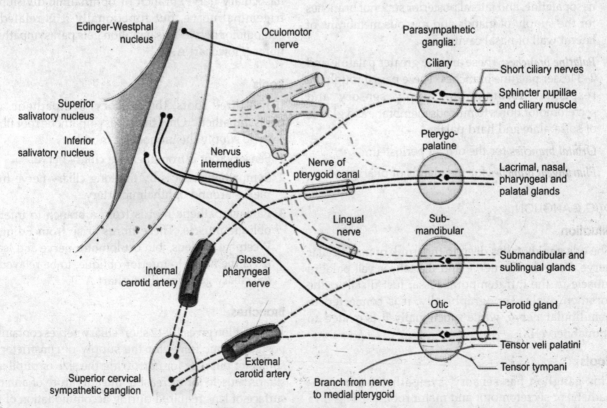

Fig. A.1: Parasympathetic ganglia

Head and Neck

1 Sensory root is from maxillary nerve. The ganglion is suspended by 2 roots of maxillary nerve.

2 Sympathetic root is from postganglionic plexus around internal carotid artery. The nerve is called deep petrosal. It unites with greater petrosal to form the nerve of pterygoid canal. The fibres of deep petrosal do not relay in the ganglion.

3 Secretomotor or parasympathetic root is from greater petrosal nerve which arises from geniculate ganglion of cranial nerve VII. These fibres relay in the ganglion (Flowchart A.2).

Branches

The ganglion gives number of branches. These are:

1 *For lacrimal gland:* The postganglionic fibres pass through zygomatic branch of maxillary nerve. These fibres hitch hike through zygomaticotemporal nerve into the communicating branch between zygomaticotemporal and lacrimal nerve, then to the lacrimal nerve for supplying the lacrimal gland.

2 *Nasopalatine nerve:* This nerve runs on the nasal septum and ends in the anterior part of hard palate. It supplies secretomotor fibres to both nasal and palatal glands.

3 *Nasal branches:* These are medial, posterior, superior branches for the supply of glands and mucous membrane of nasal septum; the largest is named nasopalatine; and lateral posterior superior branches for the supply of glands and mucous membrane of lateral wall of nasal cavity.

4 *Palatine branches:* These are one greater palatine and 2–3 lesser palatine branches. These pass through the respective foramina to supply sensory and secretomotor fibres to mucous membrane and glands of soft palate and hard palate.

5 *Orbital branches* for the orbital periosteum.

6 *Pharyngeal branches* for the glands of pharynx.

OTIC GANGLION

Situation

The otic ganglion lies deep to the trunk of mandibular nerve, between the nerve and the tensor veli palatini muscle in the infratemporal fossa, just distal to the foramen ovale. Topographically, it is connected to mandibular nerve, while functionally it is related to cranial nerve IX.

Roots

This ganglion has sensory, sympathetic, parasympathetic or secretomotor and motor roots (*see* Figs 6.15 and 6.16).

1 Sensory root is by the auriculotemporal nerve.

2 Sympathetic root is by the sympathetic plexus around middle meningeal artery.

3 Secretomotor root is by the lesser petrosal nerve from the tympanic plexus formed by tympanic branch of cranial nerve IX. Fibres of lesser petrosal nerve relay in the otic ganglion. Postganglionic fibres reach the parotid gland through auriculotemporal nerve (Flowchart A.3).

4 Motor root is by a branch from nerve to medial pterygoid. This branch passes unrelayed through the ganglion and divides into two branches to supply tensor veli palatini and tensor tympani.

Branches

The postganglionic branches of the ganglion pass through auriculotemporal nerve to supply the parotid gland.

The motor branches supply the two muscles tensor veli palatini and tensor tympani.

CILIARY GANGLION

Situation

The ciliary ganglion is very small ganglion present in the orbit. Topographically, the ganglion is related to nasociliary nerve, branch of ophthalmic division of trigeminal nerve, but functionally it is related to oculomotor nerve. This ganglion gets parasympathetic fibres (Flowchart A.4).

Roots

It has three roots, the sensory, sympathetic and parasympathetic. Only the parasympathetic root fibres relay to supply the intraocular muscles.

1 Sensory root is from the long ciliary nerve.

2 Sympathetic root is by the long ciliary nerve from plexus around ophthalmic artery.

3 Parasympathetic root is from a branch to inferior oblique muscle. These fibres arise from Edinger-Westphal nucleus, join oculomotor nerve and leave it via the nerve to inferior oblique, to be relayed in the ciliary ganglion (Flowchart A.5).

Branches

The ganglion gives 10–12 short ciliary nerves containing postganglionic fibres for the supply of constrictor or sphincter pupillae for narrowing the size of pupil and ciliaris muscle for increasing the curvature of anterior surface of lens required during accommodation of the eye.

Table A.3: Arteries of head and neck

Artery	Beginning, course and termination	Area of distribution
Common carotid	It is a branch of brachiocephalic trunk on right side and a direct branch of arch of aorta on the left side. The artery runs upwards along medial border of sternocleidomastoid muscle enclosed within the carotid sheath. The artery ends by dividing into internal carotid and external carotid at the upper border of thyroid cartilage (*see* Fig. 4.14)	This artery has only two terminal branches. These are internal carotid and external carotid. Their area of distribution is described below.
Internal carotid	It is a terminal branch of common carotid artery. It first runs through the neck (cervical part), then passes through the petrous bone (petrous part), then courses through the sinus (cavernous part) and lastly lies in relation to the brain (cerebral part)	Cervical part of the artery does not give any branch. Petrous part gives branches for the middle ear; cavernous part supplies hypophysis cerebri. The cerebral part gives ophthalmic artery for orbit, anterior cerebral, middle cerebral, anterior choroidal and posterior communicating for the brain
External carotid	It is the one of the terminal branches of common carotid artery and lies anterior to internal carotid artery. External carotid artery starts at the level of upper border of thyroid cartilage, runs upwards and laterally to terminate behind the neck of mandible by dividing into larger maxillary and smaller superficial temporal branches (*see* Fig. 4.13)	It supplies structures in the front of neck, i.e. thyroid gland, larynx, muscles of tongue, face, scalp, ear
Superior thyroid	It arises from anterior aspect of external carotid artery close to its origin. It runs downwards and forwards deep to the infrahyoid muscles to the upper pole of thyroid gland (*see* Fig. 8.6)	Superior laryngeal branch which pierces thyroid membrane to supply larynx. Sternocleidomastoid and cricothyroid branches are to the muscles. Terminal branches supply the thyroid gland
Lingual	It arises from anterior aspect of external carotid artery forms a typical loop which is crossed by XII nerve. Its 2nd part lies deep to the hyoglossus. The 3rd part runs along the anterior border of hyoglossus and 4th part runs forwards on the under surface of tongue (*see* Fig. 4.15)	As the name indicates, it is the chief artery of the muscular tongue. It supplies various muscles, papillae and taste buds of the tongue. It also gives branches to the tonsil
Facial	This tortuous artery from anterior side also arises a little higher than lingual artery. It runs in the neck as cervical part and in the face as facial artery (*see* Fig. 2.17)	Cervical part gives off ascending palatine, tonsillar, glandular branches for the submandibular and sublingual salivary glands. The facial part lies on the face giving branches to muscles of face and its skin
Occipital	It arises form the posterior aspect of external carotid artery and runs upwards along the lower border of posterior belly of digastric muscle. Then it runs deep to mastoid process and the muscles attached to it. The artery then crosses the apex of suboccipital triangle and then it pierces trapezius 2.5 cm from midline to supply the layers of scalp (*see* Fig. 4.14)	It gives two branches to sternocleidomastoid muscle, and branches to neighbouring muscles. It also gives a meningeal and mastoid branch
Posterior auricular	It arises from posterior aspect of external carotid artery, it runs along the upper border of posterior belly of digastric muscle to reach the back of auricle	It gives branches to scalp. Its stylomastoid branch enters the foramen of the same name to supply mastoid antrum, nerve air cells and the facial
Ascending pharyngeal	It arises from the medial side of external carotid artery, close to its origin. It runs upwards and between pharynx and tonsil on medial side and medial wall of middle ear on the lateral side (*see* Fig. 4.13)	It gives branches to tonsil, pharynx and a few meningeal branches
Superficial temporal	It is the smaller terminal branch of external carotid artery. It begins behind the neck of the mandible, runs upwards and crosses the preauricular point, where its pulsations can be felt. 5 cm above the preauricular point it ends by dividing into anterior and posterior branches (*see* Fig. 2.5)	Its two terminal branches supply layers of scalp and superficial temporal region. It also supplies parotid gland, facial muscles and temporalis muscle
Maxillary	It is the larger terminal branch of external carotid artery. It is given off behind the neck of the mandible. Its course is divided into 1st, 2nd and 3rd parts according to its relations with lateral pterygoid muscle. 1st part lies below the lateral pterygoid, 2nd part lies on the lower head of lateral pterygoid and 3rd part lies between the two heads	Branches of—1st part: Deep auricular, anterior tympanic, middle meningeal and inferior alveolar. 2nd part: Muscular branches to medial pterygoid, masseter, temporalis and lateral pterygoid 3rd part: Posterior superior alveolar, infraorbital, greater palatine and sphenopalatine branches, pharyngeal and artery of pterygoid canal

Table A.4: Branches of maxillary artery

Branches	Foramina transmitting	Distribution
A. Of first part (*see* Fig. 6.6)		
1. Deep auricular	Foramen in the floor (cartilage or bone) of external acoustic meatus	Skin of external acoustic meatus, and outer surface of tympanic membrane
2. Anterior tympanic	Petrotympanic fissure	Inner surface of tympanic membrane
3. Middle meningeal	Foramen spinosum	Supplies more of bone and less of meninges; also V and VII nerves, middle ear and tensor tympani
4. Accessory meningeal	Foramen ovale	Main distribution is extracranial to pterygoids
5. Inferior alveolar	Mandibular foramen	Lower teeth and mylohyoid muscle
B. Of second part		
1. Masseteric	—	Masseter
2. Deep temporal (anterior)	—	Temporalis
3. Deep temporal (posterior)	—	Temporalis
4. Pterygoid	—	Lateral and medial pterygoids
5. Buccal	—	Skin of cheek
C. Of third part (*see* Fig. 6.7)		
1. Posterior superior alveolar	Alveolar canals in body of maxilla	Upper molar and premolar teeth and gums; maxillary sinus
2. Infraorbital	Inferior orbital fissure	Lower orbital muscles, lacrimal sac, maxillary sinus, upper incisor and canine teeth
3. Greater palatine	Greater palatine canal	Soft palate, tonsil, palatine glands and mucosa; upper gums
4. Pharyngeal	Pharyngeal (palatinovaginal) canal	Roof of nose and pharynx, auditory tube, sphenoidal sinus
5. Artery of pterygoid canal	Pterygoid canal	Auditory tube, upper pharynx, and middle ear
6. Sphenopalatine (terminal part)	Sphenopalatine foramen	Lateral and medial walls of nose and various air sinuses

Table A.5: Subclavian artery

Course

It is the chief artery of the upper limb. It also supplies part of neck and brain. On the right side, subclavian artery is a branch of the brachiocephalic trunk. On the left side, it is a direct branch of arch of aorta. The artery on either side ascends and enters the neck posterior to the sternoclavicular joint. The arteries of two sides have similar course.

The artery arches from the sternoclavicular joint to the outer border of the first rib where it continues as the axillary artery. It is divided into three parts by the crossing of scalenus anterior muscle (*see* Figs 8.19 and 8.20)

Branches and area of distribution

Branches of 1st part:

- Vertebral artery is the largest branch. It supplies the brain. The artery passes through foramina transversaria of C6–C1 vertebrae, then it courses through suboccipital triangle to enter cranial cavity

- Internal thoracic artery runs downwards and medially to enter thorax by passing behind first costal cartilage. It runs vertically 2 cm, on lateral side of sternum till 6th intercostal space to divide into musculophrenic and superior epigastric branches

- Thyrocervical trunk is a short wide vessel which gives suprascapular, transverse cervical and important inferior thyroid branch. Inferior thyroid artery gives glandular branches to thyroid and parathyroid glands. In addition, this artery gives inferior laryngeal branch for the supply of mucous membrane of larynx

- Costocervical trunk arises from 2nd part of subclavian artery on right side and from 1st part on left side. It ends by dividing into superior intercostal and deep cervical branches

- 3rd part may give dorsal scapular branch

Table A.6: Structures derived from skeletal and muscular components of pharyngeal arches

Pharyngeal arch	Nerve of the arch	Muscles derived	Skeletal and ligamentous structures derived
First (mandibular) arch (I) Meckel's cartilages	Trigeminal and mandibular divisions of trigeminal (V cranial nerve)	Muscles of mastication (temporalis, masseter, medial and lateral pterygoids) Mylohyoid Anterior belly of digastric tensor tympani Tensor veli palatini	Mandible ⎤ Malleus ⎬ Quadrate cartilage Incus ⎦ Anterior ligament of malleus Sphenomandibular ligament Spine of sphenoid Most of the mandible Genial tubercles
Second (hyoid) arch (II) Reichert's cartilage	Facial (VII cranial nerve)	Muscles of facial expression (buccinator, auricularis, frontalis, platysma, orbicularis oris, and orbicularis oculi) Posterior belly of digastric Stylohyoid, stapedius	Stapes Styloid process Lesser cornua of hyoid Upper part of body of hyoid Stylohyoid ligament
Third (III)	Glossopharyngeal (IX cranial nerve)	Stylopharyngeus	Greater cornua of hyoid Lower part of body of hyoid bone
Fourth (IV)	Superior laryngeal branch of vagus	Cricothyroid Levator veli palatini Striated muscles of oesophagus Constrictors of pharynx	Thyroid cartilage Corniculate cartilage Cuneiform cartilage
Sixth (VI)	Recurrent laryngeal branch of vagus (X cranial) nerve).	Intrinsic muscles of larynx	Cricoid cartilage Arytenoid cartilage

By intramembranous ossification of mesenchyme of I arch, maxilla, zygomatic, squamous part of temporal are developed.

Table A.7: Derivatives of endodermal pouches

Pharyngeal pouch	Derivatives
Dorsal ends of I and II pouches form tubotympanic recess	Proximal part of tubotympanic recess gives rise to auditory tube. Distal part gives rise to tympanic cavity and mastoid antrum. Mastoid cells develop at about 2 years of age
Ventral part of II pharyngeal pouch	Epithelium covering the palatine tonsil and tonsillar crypts. lymphoid tissue is mesodermal in origin
III pharyngeal pouch	Thymus and inferior parathyroid gland or parathyroid III. Thymic epithelial reticular cells and Hassall's corpuscles are endodermal. Lymphocytes are derived from haemopoietic stem cells during 12th week
IV pharyngeal pouch	Superior parathyroid or parathyroid IV
V pharyngeal pouch (ultimobranchial body)	Parafollicular or 'C' cells of the thyroid gland

Table A.8: Derivatives of ectodermal clefts

Dorsal part of I ectodermal cleft	Epithelium of external auditory meatus.
Auricle	Six auricular hillocks; three from I arch and three from II arch
Rest of ectodermal clefts	Obliterated by the overgrowth of II pharyngeal arch. The closing membrane of the first cleft is the tympanic membrane.

Head and Neck

CLINICAL TERMS

Anaesthetist's arteries: These are the arteries used by the anaesthetists who are sitting at the head end of the patient being operated:
- The superficial temporal artery as it crosses the root of zygoma in front of ear (*see* Fig. 5.3).
- Facial artery at the anteroinferior angle of masseter muscle (*see* Fig. 2.17).
- Common carotid at the anterior border of sternocleidomastoid.

Hilton's method of draining parotid gland abscess: The incision given to drain parotid abscess is the horizontal incision or by making many holes. This incision does not endanger the various branches of facial nerve, coursing through the gland (*see* Fig. 5.8).

Frey's syndrome: The sign of Frey's syndrome is the appearance of perspiration on the face while the patient eats food. In certain healing of wounds, the auriculotemporal nerve and great auricular nerves may join with each other. When the person eats food, instead of saliva, sweat appears on the face.

Waldeyer's ring: It is the ring of lymphoid tissue present at the oropharyngeal junction. Its components are lingual tonsils anteriorly, palatine tonsils laterally, tubal tonsils above and laterally and pharyngeal tonsils posteriorly (*see* Fig. 14.13).

Killian's dehiscence: It is a potential gap between upper thyropharyngeus and lower cricopharyngeus parts of inferior constrictor muscle. Thyropharyngeus is the propulsive part of the muscle, supplied by recurrent laryngeal nerve, while cricopharyngeus is the sphincteric part, supplied by external laryngeal nerve. If there is incoordination between these two parts, bolus of food is pushed backwards in region of Killian's dehiscence, producing pharyngeal pouch or diverticula (*see* Fig. 14.22).

Safety muscle of larynx: Posterior cricoarytenoid muscles are the only abductors of vocal cords. The paralysis of both these muscles causes unopposed adduction of vocal cords, with severe dyspnoea. So posterior cricoarytenoid is the life-saving muscle (*see* Fig. 16.10).

Singer's nodules: These are little swellings on the vocal cords at the junction of anterior one-third and posterior two-thirds of vocal cords. During phonation, the cords come close together, and there is slight friction as well. If friction is more and continuous, there is some inflammation with thickening of vocal cords, leading to Singer's or Teacher's nodules (*see* Fig. 16.8).

Tongue is pulled out during anaesthesia: Genioglossus muscles are responsible for protrusion of tongue. If these muscles are paralysed, the tongue falls back upon itself and blocks the airway. So tongue is pulled out during anaesthesia to keep there air passage clean (*see* Fig. 17.5).

Passavant's ridge: The horizontal fibres of right and left palatopharyngeus muscles form a Passavant's fold at the junction of nasopharynx and oropharynx. During swallowing, palatopharyngeus muscles form a ridge, which closes nasopharynx from oropharynx, so that bolus of food passes, through oropharynx only. In paralysis of these muscles, there is nasal regurgitation.

Ludwig's angina: When there is cellulitis of floor of the mouth, due to infected teeth, the condition is known as Ludwig's angina. The tongue is pushed upwards and mylohyoid is pushed downwards. This cellulitis may spread backwards to cause oedema of larynx and asphyxia.

Little's area of nose: This is the area in the anteroinferior part of nasal septum. Four arteries take part in Kiesselbach's plexus formed by:

Septal branch of superior labial from facial artery, terminal part of sphenopalatine artery:
- Anterior ethmoidal artery,
- Greater palatine artery. Picking of the nose may give rise to nasal bleeding or epistaxis (*see* Fig. 15.5).

Syringing of ear causes decreased heart rate: The external auditory meatus is supplied by auricular branch of vagus. Vagus also supplies the heart with cardio-inhibitory fibres. During syringing of the ear, vagus nerve is stimulated which causes bradycardia (*see* Fig. 18.7).

Nerve of near vision: Oculomotor nerve is the nerve of close vision. It supplies medial rectus, superior and inferior recti. The sphincter pupillae and ciliaris muscles are supplied by parasympathetic fibres via III nerve. It also supplies levator palpebrae superioris which opens the eye.

Injury to spine of sphenoid: Chorda tympani nerve is related on the medial side of spine of sphenoid, while auriculotemporal nerve is related on the lateral side. Chorda tympani gives secretomotor fibres to submandibular and sublingual salivary glands, whereas auriculotemporal gives secretomotor fibres to the parotid gland. So injury to spine of sphenoid may injure both these nerves affecting the secretion from all three salivary glands (*see* Fig. 6.10).

Extradural haemorrhage: There is collection of blood due to rupture of middle meningeal vessels in the space between skull and the endosteum. It may press upon the motor area of brain. Blood has to be drained out from the point called 'pterion' (*see* Fig. 1.11).

Loss of corneal blink reflex: In case of injury to ophthalmic nerve, there is loss of corneal blink reflex as the afferent part of reflex arc is damaged.

Loss of sneeze reflex: In injury to maxillary nerve, the sneeze reflex is lost, as afferent loop of the reflex arc formed by the maxillary nerve is damaged.

Loss of jaw jerk reflex: The afferent and efferent limbs of the reflex arc are by V nerve. Damage to mandibular nerve causes loss of jaw jerk reflex.

FURTHER READING

1 Anderson SD. The intratympanic muscles. In: Hinchcliffe R (ed). Scientific Foundations of Otolaryngology Heinemann, London, 1976; pp 257–80.

2 Ashmare J. The mechanics of hearing. In Roberts D (ed). Signals and Perception: The Fundamentals of Human Sensation. Basingstoke and New York: Palgrave Macmillan, 2002; 3–16.

3 Barker BCW, Davies PL. The applied anatomy of the pterygomandibular space. Br J Surg 1972; 10:43–55.

4 Bennett AG, Rabbets RB. Clinical Visual Optics, 2nd edn London; Butterworth-Heinemann, 1989.

5 Berkovitz BKB, Moxham BJ, H Flickey S. The anatomy of the larynx. In: Ferlito A (ed). Diseases of the Larynx, London: Chapman and Hall, 2000; 25–44.

6 Berkovitz, BKB, Moxham, BJ. Colour Atlas of the Skull. London: Mosby-Wolfe, 1989.

7 Broadbent CR, Maxwell WE, Ferrie R, Wilson DJ, Gawne-Cain M, Russell R. Ability of anaesthetists to identify a marked lumbar interspace. Anaesthesia, 2000; 55:1122–26.

8 Cady B, Rossi RL (eds). Surgery of the Thyroid and Parathyroid Glands. Philadelphia, Saunders 1991.

9 Cagan RN (ed). Neural Mechanisms in Taste Boca Raton, Fl: CRC Press 1989.

10 Davis RA, Anson BJ, Budinger JM, Kurth LE. Surgical anatomy of the facial nerve and parotid gland based upon a study of 350 cervicofacial halves. Surg Gynecol Obstet, 1956; 102:385–412.

11 Doig TN, McDonald SW, McGregor OA. Possible routes of spread of carcinoma of the maxillary sinus to the oral cavity. Clin Anat, 1998; 11:149–56.

12 Ger R, Evans JT. Tracheostomy, an anatomio-clinical review. Clin Anat, 1993; 6:337–41.

13 Grey P. The clinical significance of the communicating branches of the somatic sensory supply of the middle and external ear. J Laryngol Otol, 1995; 109:1141–45.

14 Jones LT. The anatomy of the upper eyelid and its relation to ptosis surgery. Am J Ophthalmol, 1964; 57:943–59.

15 Knop E, Knop N. A functional unit for ocular surface immune defence formed by the lacrimal gland, conjunctiva and lacrimal drainage system. Adv Exp Med Biol, 2002; 506B:635–44.

16 Lahr, MM. The Evolution of Modern Human Diversity A Study of Cranial Variation, Cambridge: Cambridge University Press, 1996.

17 Lang J. Clinical Anatomy of the Nose, Nasal Cavity and Paranasal Sinuses. Stuttgart Thieme 1989.

18 MacLaughlin SM, Oldale KNM. Vertebral body diameters and sex prediction. Ann Hum Biol, 1992; 19:285–93.

19 Mc Gowan DA, Baxter PN, James J. The Maxillary Sinus, Oxford Wright 1993.

20 Munir Turk L, Hogg DA. Age changes in the human laryngeal cartilages.Clin Anat, 1993; 6:154–62.

21 Myint K, Azian AL, Khairual FA. The clinical significance of the branching pattern of facial nerve in Malaysian Subjects. Med J Malaysia, 1992; 47:114–21.

22 Pracy R. The infant larynx. J Laryngol Otol, 1983; 97:933–47.

23 Reidenbach MM. Normal topography of the conus elasticus. Anatomical basis for the spread of laryngeal cancer. Surg Radiol Anat, 1995; 17:107–11.

24 Sade J (ed). Basic Aspects of the Eustachian Tube and Middle Ear Disease. Geneva: Kugler and Ghedini, 1989.

25 Sato I, Shinada, K. Arborization of the inferior laryngeal nerve and internal nerve on the posterior surface of larynx. Clin Anat, 1995; 8:379–87.

26 Turker KS. Reflex control of human jaw muscles. Crit Rev Oral Biol Med 2002; 13:85–104.

27 Vidarsdottir US, O'Higgins P, Stringer C. A geometric morphometric study of regional differences in the ontogeny of the modern human facial skeleton. J Anat, 2002; 201:211–29.

28 Wassle H, Boycott BB. Functional architecture of the mammalian retina. Physiol Rev, 1991; 71:447–80.

29 Wilson-Pauwels I, Akesson EJ, Stewart PA. Cranial Nerves. Anatomy and Clinical Comments, Toronto, Decker, 1998.

30 Wood Jones I. The nature of soft palate. J Anat,1940; 77:147.

1. a. Identify the foramen.
   b. Name the structures passing through it.

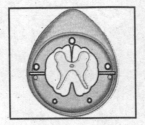

6. a. Identify the structure.
   b. Name its branches in order.

2. a. Identify the foramen.
   b. Name the structures passing through it.

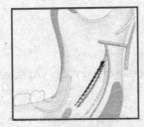

7. a. Identify the marked area.
   b. Name the vessels present here.

3. a. Identify the muscle.
   b. Name its parts.

8. a. Identify the structure.
   b. Name its extrinsic muscles with their nerve supply.

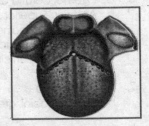

4. a. Identify the arrow marked circled structure.
   b. What type of fibres are carried by it?

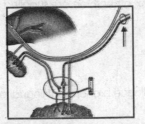

9. a. Identify the highlighted muscle.
   b. What is its action?

5. a. Identify the highlighted structure.
   b. Trace its secretomotor fibres.

10. a. Identify the organ.
    b. Name the arteries supplying it.

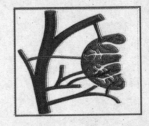

1. a. Foramen magnum
   b. Lowest part of medulla oblongata
      Three meninges
      One anterior spinal artery
      Two posterior spinal arteries
      Two vertebral arteries
      Spinal root of XI

2. a. Mandibular canal
   b. Inferior alveolar artery and nerve

3. a. Orbicularis oculi
   b. Orbital part, palpebral part and lacrimal part

4. a. Chorda tympani nerve
   b. General visceral efferent (GVE) fibres and special visceral afferent (Sp. VA) fibres

5. a. Parotid gland
   b. Inferior salivatory nucleus → IX nerve → tympanic plexus → lesser petrosal nerve → otic ganglion → postganglionic fibres join auriculotemporal nerve → parotid gland

6. a. External carotid artery.
   b. Anterior: Superior thyroid, lingual and facial
      Medial: Ascending pharyngeal
      Posterior: Occipital and posterior auricular
      Terminal: Superficial temporal and maxillary

7. a. Little's area
   b. Superior labial, greater palatine, anterior ethmoidal and sphenopalatine veins and capillaries.

8. a. Tongue
   b. Palatoglossus, hyoglossus, styloglossus, genioglossus
      Palatoglossus is supplied by vagoaccessory complex, other three are supplied by hypoglossal nerve.

9. a. Posterior cricoarytenoid muscle
   b. Only abductor of the vocal cords

10. a. Palatine tonsil
    b. Ascending palatine, ascending pharyngeal, dorsal lingue branches of lingual and greater palatine branch of maxillary artery.

Index